D1484136

THE PHYSICS AND CHEMISTRY OF SURFACES

THE PHYSICS AND CHEMISTRY OF SURFACES

BY

NEIL KENSINGTON ADAM

Sc.D., F.R.S.

PROFESSOR OF CHEMISTRY AT UNIVERSITY COLLEGE, SOUTHAMPTON
FORMERLY FELLOW OF TRINITY COLLEGE, CAMBRIDGE
ROYAL SOCIETY SORBY RESEARCH FELLOW AT
THE UNIVERSITY OF SHEFFIELD
HON. RESEARCH ASSOCIATE AND LECTURER AT
UNIVERSITY COLLEGE, LONDON

THIRD EDITION

OXFORD UNIVERSITY PRESS
LONDON : GEOFFREY CUMBERLEGE

OXFORD UNIVERSITY PRESS
AMEN HOUSE, E.C. 4
London Edinburgh Glasgow New York
Toronto Melbourne Cape Town Bombay
Calcutta Madras
GEOFFREY CUMBERLEGE
PUBLISHER TO THE UNIVERSITY

FIRST EDITION 1930
SECOND EDITION 1938
THIRD EDITION 1941
Reprinted photographically in Great Britain
in 1944, 1948, 1949
by LOWE & BRYDONE, PRINTERS, LTD., LONDON,
from sheets of the third edition

PREFACE TO THE THIRD EDITION

In view of the short interval which has elapsed since the appearance of the second edition, and also of the war, much of the text of the second edition is reproduced here. A few sections, in which recent work has necessitated considerable correction, have been rewritten. Those important advances in the subject which could not conveniently be incorporated in the space of the earlier text are given in an appendix. My best thanks are due to Dr. A. E. Alexander, Dr. D. H. Bangham, and Dr. E. A. Guggenheim for their kind advice and help in this revision.

N. K. A.

PREFACE TO THE SECOND EDITION

ALTHOUGH the book has been largely rewritten, and a considerable enlargement has seemed unavoidable, its plan remains unchanged: namely, to provide a text-book of Surface Chemistry and Physics, and also to give an account of our knowledge of Surface Films in some little detail. The chapter on the properties of molecules, deduced from methods other than those of Surface Chemistry, has been omitted, partly because it is irrelevant to the main plan of the book, but also because information on this subject is now much more readily accessible than it was in 1929. An account of electrical phenomena at surfaces has been added.

Publication in the field of Surface Chemistry continues at a pace which renders the task of its historians extremely laborious. I have tried, frequently, to assist the reader by giving references not only to original papers, but also to other text-books and articles reviewing a subject; without carefully digested writings of this kind, it would scarcely be possible for much of the contents of research papers to find its way into common knowledge. As far as possible, I have kept the main argument in larger type, leaving details, and discussions of doubtful points, in smaller type, so that these can be skipped without interfering with the development of the subject. It is scarcely possible, however, to suit every reader's requirements in this way, and I hope that the arrangement of the book in sections, with some cross-references, will enable any subject dealt with to be quickly found.

My thanks are due to many friends and colleagues, particularly Dr. F. P. Bowden, Dr. R. J. G. Fraser, Professor H. Freundlich, Dr. E. A. Guggenheim, Dr. G. S. Hartley, Dr. F. O. Koenig, Professor J. E. Lennard-Jones, Professor H. S. Taylor, Dr. Ian W. Wark, and Dr. A. T. Williamson, for friendly advice and criticism of various parts of the book.

To Professor F. G. Donnan I owe much gratitude for continual personal encouragement during many years. My debt to him extends, however, farther than this, for it has been my privilege to be very closely associated with the great school of Chemistry working under his far-sighted guidance at University College, London, during the past seven years. From this happy association, and the many friendships arising from it, I have gained more than can be put into words.

I am indebted to the American Chemical Society, the Biochemical Society, the Chemical Society, the Faraday Society, the Royal Society, the *Zeitschrift für physikalische Chemie*, and the proprietors of *Reviews of Modern Physics*, for permission to reproduce various diagrams not found in the first edition.

Journal references are made in conformity with the practice of the Chemical Society, except that the *Journal of the American Chemical Society* has been shortened to *J.A.C.S.*

N. K. A.

The Sir William Ramsay Laboratories of
Physical and Inorganic Chemistry,
University College, London;
and University College,
Southampton.

CONTENTS

CHAPTER I

LIQUID SURFACES: CAPILLARITY

1. Spontaneous contraction of a liquid surface. The fundamental property of liquid surfaces is that they tend to contract to the smallest possible area. This tendency is shown in the spherical form of small drops of liquid, in the tension exerted by soap films as they tend to become less extended, and in many other properties of liquid surfaces. Plateau[1] has undertaken a prolonged study of the forms assumed by liquid surfaces, under conditions when the disturbing effect of gravity is absent; he showed that the surfaces always assume a curvature such that, if R_1 and R_2 are the principal radii of curvature at any point,

$$\frac{1}{R_1}+\frac{1}{R_2} = \text{constant}. \tag{1}$$

It is a geometrical fact that surfaces for which the relation (1) holds are surfaces of minimum area.

The methods of eliminating the effect of gravity on the form of the surfaces were two: Plateau used soap films, which are practically weightless; and he suspended masses of olive oil in a mixture of alcohol and water of practically the same density. By the latter device, spheres many centimetres in diameter were obtained.

Under conditions where the weight of the liquid cannot be neglected, the shapes are more complicated. The effect of gravity can, however, be allowed for (see equation (4) below). Plateau's experiments give a very complete experimental proof of the tendency of liquid surfaces to contract; the various forms assumed with different supports are of more interest to the mathematician than the physicist, and reference should be made to Plateau's book, Boys's *Soap Bubbles,*[2] or Maxwell's article[3] for further details of them.

2. Molecular explanation of the tendency to contract. The simplest properties of molecules in liquids suffice to account for this tendency of the surfaces to contract. Molecules are small objects, possessing definite size and shape, in all states of matter; in all fluids they are free to move relative to one another, and in liquids they are kept close to each other, by the cohesional forces between them. Liquids are thus distinguished from solids by their fluidity, that is, the freedom of the molecules to move; and from gases by the fact that the attraction between the molecules restrains the motions sufficiently to prevent more than a small

[1] *Statique expérimentale et théorique des Liquides soumis aux seules Forces moléculaires* (1873).

[2] *Soap Bubbles and the Forces which mould them,* 2nd ed., 1920.

[3] *Works,* **2,** 541; *Ency. Brit.,* art. 'Capillarity', 9th ed. (1876), revised for later editions by Rayleigh.

proportion of the molecules escaping into vapour. Translatory and rotatory motions go on within the liquids with considerable freedom.

In the interior each molecule is surrounded by others on every side; it is therefore subject to attraction in all directions. On the average, over periods of time long compared with molecular vibrations, the attraction on any molecule is uniform in all directions. At the surface, however, conditions are entirely different. The molecules at the surface are attracted inwards, and to each side, by their neighbours; but there is no outward attraction to balance the inward pull, because there are very few molecules outside. Hence *every surface molecule is subject to a strong inward attraction, perpendicular to the surface.*

This inward attraction causes the surface to diminish in area, because the surface molecules are continually moving inwards more rapidly than others move outwards to take their places; the number of molecules in the surface is therefore continually diminishing, and the contraction of the surface continues until the maximum possible number of molecules are in the interior, i.e. until the surface is the smallest possible for a given volume, subject to the external conditions or forces acting on the drop.

3. Free energy of the surface: 'surface tension'. The fact that a liquid surface contracts spontaneously shows that there is free energy associated with it, that work must be done to extend the surface. The origin of this work, in terms of the molecules, is that when the surface is extended molecules must be brought from the interior to the surface against the inward attractive forces; work must be done against these inward attractive forces for each molecule which is brought to the surface. Since the molecules have definite size there will always be a definite number of them in the surface (we need not at the moment discuss whether the surface is one or more molecules in depth); provided the surface is of the same nature and structure everywhere, the work done in extending it will be definite.

This free energy in the surface is of fundamental importance; a vast number of problems relating to the equilibrium of surfaces can be solved without knowing more than the magnitude of this free energy. In the solution of such problems a mathematical device is almost invariably employed to simplify the calculations; it is to substitute for the surface free energy a hypothetical tension, acting in all directions parallel to the surface, equal to the free surface energy. This is what is generally known as the *surface tension.* It is always possible, mathematically, to replace a free energy per unit area of surface by a tension acting parallel to the surface. Such a surface tension has, of course, the same dimensions as a a surface energy $\left(\frac{\text{mass}}{\text{time}^2}\right)$; and it must have the same numerical magnitude. The work done in extending a surface which is pulling with a tension γ dynes per cm., by one square cm., will be γ ergs per sq. cm.: hence the free surface energy of such a surface will be γ ergs per sq. cm.

This substitution of a hypothetical tension for a free energy per unit area is the converse of the mathematical method of 'virtual work' often used in statics. There the calculations are often simplified by considering the energy changes involved in a slight displacement of the system, adding all together, and finally equating the sum of the energy changes to zero, to obtain the condition of equilibrium. In systems involving liquid surfaces the equilibrium could be obtained by adding up the changes in surface energy in the various surfaces whose area is altered during a displacement; it is, however, simpler to pay no attention to these changes in area directly, but to consider the surfaces as each pulling with the appropriate 'surface tension' upon their boundaries, for the equilibrium of the tensions is usually obvious. The conception of surface tension can always be used in considering the properties of surfaces which depend solely on the existence of this free surface energy. Surface free energy, due to the inward pull on the molecules at the surface, is the fundamental property of surfaces; surface tension will be taken simply as its mathematical equivalent.

4. Absence of any special 'contractile skin' or physical tension, parallel to the surface of liquids. The great convenience of the hypothesis of surface tension, as the equivalent of free surface energy, combined with the fact that it was in use nearly a century before the conception of energy became definite, has given the words 'surface tension' a predominance in the literature of surfaces, which does not rightly or logically belong to them. The term 'surface tension' has often been strained to imply that liquids have in their surfaces some mechanism like a stretched membrane pulling parallel to the surface. The surface is said to be in a 'state of tension'. This view must not be pushed too far. Any mechanism possessing free energy in the surface will undergo the spontaneous contraction which has led to the idea of surface tension; hence we can gain practically no idea of the actual nature of the mechanisms in the surface from this fact of spontaneous contraction alone. The view that there is some skin in the surface, pulling parallel to it, leads to great difficulties when the structure of the supposed skin is considered in terms of molecules. Some of these will now be mentioned; others will appear later in the book.

The interface between liquids normally possesses a positive free energy; conditions may however arise in which this may become negative. If the spontaneous contraction of the interface with positive surface tension is due to a contractile skin at the interface, then the interface with negative surface tension ought to have an expanding skin at the interface, and spontaneously extend itself. This will cause puckering and folding of the interface as it expands. Liquids which mix, however, do not do so by a process of puckering and folding of the interface initially present between them, but by diffusion of the molecules across the interface. Clerk Maxwell[1] made a remark which has been interpreted as suggesting such a mechanism for the mixing of liquids, although he clearly did not believe that it ever occurred. Kelvin[2] took him to task for this suggestion. Recently the subject has again arisen, through the reporting of a case of supposed 'intertraction', or mixing by means of a great extension, with folding, of the original boundary between the liquids;[3] it has

[1] *Works*, **2**, 553. [2] *Popular Lectures and Addresses*, **1**, 53.

[3] Sir A. Wright, *Proc. Roy. Soc.* B, **92**, 118 (1921); Schoneboom, *ibid.*, A, **101**, 531 (1922).

been proved, however, that this so-called intertraction, or 'barophoresis', is merely the result of currents set up in the two liquids, caused by alterations in specific gravity due to unequal rates of diffusion in the two solutions employed,[1] and has no connexion with capillary forces.

On molecular theory, positive surface free energy, or surface tension, is due to an inward attractive force, exerted on the surface molecules by the underlying molecules. There is no special force between the surface molecules, pulling parallel to the surface. If surface tension became negative, it would mean that the inward attractive force was replaced by some force tending to push the molecules outwards, away from the liquid. The surface tension of a liquid could only be negative above its critical point, where the liquid cannot exist; and the interfacial tension between two *miscible* liquids is also negative. The vanishing of interfacial tension between two liquids is the condition of complete miscibility.

Attempts to explain the surface phenomena of pure liquids in terms of a pull parallel to the surface are still rather frequent; and two other aspects of these attempts may be noticed. Some writers suggest that the surface molecules have their force-fields so deflected as to form a kind of linked skin in the surface, the attractions of the surface molecules being directed along the surface instead of equally in all directions. Apart from the fact that such a deflexion of the force-fields would be difficult to account for unless the molecules were capable of a very special orientation in the surface, it would seem that this closely knit skin would be a hindrance, rather than a help, to the contraction of the surface; for the essential occurrence when a surface contracts is that molecules are expelled from it, and a particularly strong linkage between the surface molecules would tend to keep them in the surface. This is a fair specimen of the contradictory nature of theories which are based on a desire to ascribe a physical reality to the purely mathematical device of surface tension.

Another form of the theory is mathematically correct, but is somewhat difficult to develop as a molecular theory. The classical theory of Capillarity considers matter as infinitely divisible, or at any rate as so finely divisible, that the methods of a continuous calculus may be applied to the surface layers. According to this theory, the pressure in the liquids diminishes gradually on passing through the surface layer, from the liquid to the vapour. The total deficiency of pressure, measured parallel to the surface, and summed through the thickness of the surface layer, is numerically equal to the surface free energy, and is regarded by some as the real mechanism of 'surface tension'. This point of view has been thoroughly developed by Bakker,[2] whose book should be consulted for a very complete account of theories of Capillarity based on the conception of liquids as continuous media. It is now certain, however, that the surface layer is ordinarily only a very few molecules thick, so that the conception of pressure and its variation parallel to the surface becomes rather intangible in terms of molecules. The essential mechanism, even on Laplace's theory (which subdivides the liquid indefinitely) of the production of the free surface energy, is the perpendicular inward attraction, exerted on the surface molecules

[1] Peskov, *Kolloid-Z.*, **33**, 215; Szegvari, *ibid.*, **33**, 324 (1923). Adam and Jessop, *Proc. Roy. Soc.* A, **108**, 324, and B, **98**, 206 (1925). Further discussion, *ibid.*, A, **112**, 213; **113**, 478; **114**, 576; **118**, 262; *Kolloid-Z.*, **56**, 138 (1931).

[2] *Kapillarität u. Oberflächenspannung; Wien-Harms' Handb. d. Experimentalphysik*, vol. 6 (1928); cf. also *Z. physikal. Chem.* A, **171**, 49 (1934).

by the underlying ones; there is no need to speculate how this can be transformed into a surface tension parallel to the surface, for the surface tension does not exist as a physical reality, and is only the mathematical equivalent of the free surface energy. The mathematical device will always be available as a substitute for this free energy, whatever the mechanism by which this energy is produced molecularly; it can therefore never tell us anything about the mechanisms at the surface.

5. Sharpness of a liquid surface. There is very strong evidence that the change of density from liquid to vapour is exceedingly abrupt, the transitional layers being generally only one or two molecules thick. Perhaps the clearest evidence is that derived from the nature of the light reflected from the surfaces. According to Fresnel's law of reflection, if the transition between air and a medium of refractive index n is absolutely abrupt, the light is completely plane polarized, when the angle of incidence is the Brewsterian angle, that is $\tan^{-1} n$. But if the transition is gradual, the light is elliptically polarized.

This happens to be a test of such sensitiveness that it will detect layers of the order one molecule thick. Jamin and others had found that the light reflected from most solid and liquid surfaces usually deviates considerably from this law, but Rayleigh[1] showed that when the accidental layer of grease was carefully cleaned away from a water surface practically no trace of ellipticity remains. It is known now that the layer of grease on water is only one molecule thick (see Chap. II); hence the practical absence of ellipticity indicates that a water surface is a definite transition, within the thickness of about one molecule.

Raman and Ramdas[2] found that there is still some small amount of residual ellipticity in their cleanest surfaces of water, and also that these scatter light to some extent. There appears to be a slight discrepancy between these results and Rayleigh's, but both agree that the transitional layer is about one molecule thick; the slight residual ellipticity is ascribed to the thermal agitation of the water molecules at the surface.

Further evidence is given by the very dense nature of the films of fatty substances which can be supported on the surface of water. These have practically the same density as the substances in bulk, and are very strongly attached to the surface of the water (Chap. II). This could scarcely occur unless the surface layers of water were of nearly the normal density.

Edser[3] has worked out a theory of the internal cohesion and surface tension of liquids, based on the assumption that the molecules may be regarded as occupying a space spherical in shape (not because the molecules themselves are spherical, but because they will probably sweep out a space more or less spherical during any considerable period of time), and concludes that about 94 per cent. of the free energy of the surface resides

[1] *Phil. Mag.*, **33**, 1 (1892).
[2] *Phil. Mag.*, **3**, 220 (1927). Cf. *Proc. Roy. Soc.* **A, 108**, 561; **109**, 150, 272 (1925).
[3] *4th Colloid Report*, 58 (1922).

in the top layer of molecules. The assumptions underlying the investigation probably render this only approximate, but it is clear that by far the greatest part of the transition between liquid and vapour is confined to the top layer of molecules.

Theories of Capillarity have been proposed, in which a gradual transition between liquid and vapour is assumed. These cannot now be considered as resting on a basis of fact.

6. Violent molecular agitation of liquid surfaces. There are few things in nature presenting an appearance of more complete repose than a liquid surface at rest; yet the kinetic theory of matter shows that a water surface would be seen to be in most violent agitation, by a being capable of seeing molecules. The extent of this agitation may be calculated by considering the number of molecules which must evaporate each second from the surface, in order to maintain the vapour pressure of water. When a liquid is in contact with its saturated vapour the rate of evaporation of molecules is equal to the rate of condensation. Langmuir and others considered[1] that, as a general rule, the majority of the molecules which hit a surface condense, so that the number evaporating should be of the same order of magnitude as the number which hit a given area of surface from the vapour.[2] This number can be calculated by the methods of the kinetic theory of gases; the mass which strikes one sq. cm. per second, when the density of the gas is ρ, and the vapour pressure p mm. of mercury, is

$$\rho\sqrt{\frac{RT}{2\pi m}} = 0{\cdot}0583p\sqrt{\frac{M}{T}};$$

R is the gas constant, $1{\cdot}372\times10^{-16}$, m the mass of a molecule, M the molecular weight, T the absolute temperature.[3]

At 20° the vapour pressure of water is 17·5 mm., therefore the real rate of evaporation of water should be about 0·25 gm. per second from each sq. cm., which is $8{\cdot}5\times10^{21}$ molecules. The size of the water molecules permits only about 10^{15} to be present, closely packed, in each sq. cm. of the surface layer at any moment; so that we have the startling conclusion

[1] *Physical Rev.*, **2**, 331 (1913); cf. *J.A.C.S.* (1916), 2250.

[2] Alty (*Proc. Roy. Soc.* **A**, **131**, 554 (1931); **149**, 104 (1935); *Phil. Mag.*, **15**, 82 (1933)) finds that the rate of evaporation of water into a vacuum is only about one-thirtieth of that suggested above, indicating that the 'condensation coefficient', i.e. the fraction of the molecules hitting the surface which condense, is small. On the other hand, he finds that the 'accommodation coefficient' is unity, i.e. that practically all the molecules reach thermal equilibrium with the surface. The meaning of the result, that the great majority of the molecules reach thermal equilibrium with the surface without really becoming part of the water, and 'condensing', is a little obscure, but it may be that the rate of interchange between surface and interior is considerably less than that between surface layers and gas. If these results are correct, then the speed with which molecules leave the surface for the two adjacent phases, i.e. liquid and gas, is only about one-thirtieth of that suggested in the text; but it still remains true that the agitation in the liquid surface is very great.

[3] Jeans, *Dynamical Theory of Gases*, 121 (1921). *International Critical Tables*, **1**, 91.

that the average life of each molecule in the surface is only about one eight-millionth of a second. This tremendous interchange between liquid and vapour is no doubt accompanied by a similar interchange between the interior of the liquid and its surface. It is evident that there is an extremely violent agitation in the liquid surface.

This result may seem, at first sight, to be erroneous, since of course pools of water do not ordinarily dry up at anything approaching the above rate. This is, however, because the evaporation into air is very much slower than that into a vacuum, which is that given by the formula. Nearly all the molecules evaporating hit other molecules and return to the water; so that it is not the real rate of evaporation which is measured, but rather the rate of diffusion through a layer of air just above the surface. Knudsen[1] has verified the formula as giving the correct rate of evaporation for mercury into a vacuum; it cannot be verified directly for water, since this liquid boils long before a high vacuum is reached.

The last two paragraphs show that, although the thermal agitation of water molecules is so violent that they jump in and out of the surface very rapidly, yet the attractive forces between them are able to maintain the surface definite within one or two molecules thickness. This is a most remarkable result of molecular theory.

7. Surfaces between two liquids. When two liquids which do not mix completely are in contact, the dividing surface possesses free surface energy or surface tension, and contracts spontaneously. Interfacial tensions between two liquids are less than the surface tension of the liquid with the higher tension, because the molecules of each liquid attract those of the other across the interface, thus diminishing the inward pull exerted by that liquid on its own molecules at the surface. The precise relation between the surface tensions of the two liquids separately against their vapour, and the interfacial tension between the liquids, depends on the chemical constitution and orientation of the molecules at the surfaces. In many cases, a rule proposed by Antonow[2] holds good with considerable exactness, that the interfacial tension of two *mutually saturated* liquids is equal to the difference between their surface tensions, measured when each liquid is thoroughly saturated with the other. In other cases the interfacial tension may be greater than given by Antonow's rule; it appears never to be less than this. A discussion of the validity of this rule is given in Chap. VI, § 3.

8. Adhesion between two liquids. The attraction exerted by one liquid across the interface on the other requires that work must be done to separate them. It may easily be shown that this work, called the 'adhesional work' between the liquids, is equal to the sum of the surface tensions of the liquids singly, less the interfacial tension of the liquid-liquid interface. Suppose A and B (Fig. 1) are the liquids in a column one square centimetre in cross-section; then when they are in contact the energy of the interface is γ_{AB}; when they have been separated by a direct

[1] *Ann. Physik*, **47**, 697 (1915).

[2] *J. Chim. Phys.*, **5**, 372 (1907).

pull the energy is $\gamma_A+\gamma_B$. The work required to effect the separation must be the difference between these energies, i.e. work of adhesion

$$=W_{AB}=\gamma_A+\gamma_B-\gamma_{AB}. \qquad (2)$$

This important relation is due to Dupré.[1] It is so much easier to visualize the attraction W_{AB}, which one liquid has for another, than the surface tension, or inward pull on the surface molecules, that an insight into the nature of a phenomenon may often be obtained simply by transforming the observed surface tensions into adhesions by this equation. For given values of the single liquid surface tensions, the greater the work of adhesion, the smaller the interfacial tension.

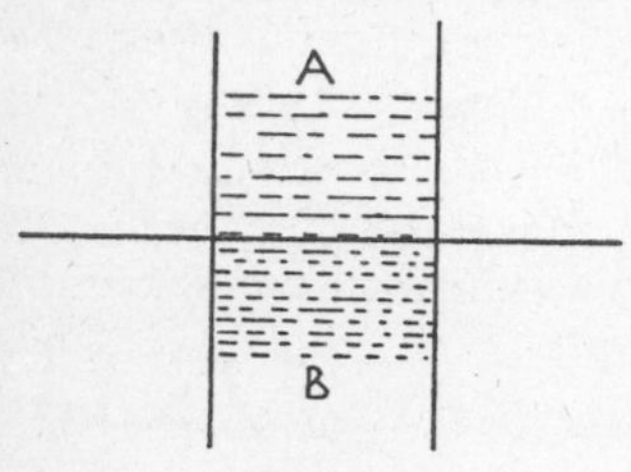

FIG. 1.

The work of adhesion cannot be measured directly, but must at present be deduced from equation (2) for liquids. The work of adhesion between a liquid and a solid can be deduced from the contact angle, as will be shown in Chapter V.

The condition for complete miscibility of two liquids is simply that the interfacial tension between them should be zero or negative. If this is so, then the molecular forces no longer operate to keep the liquids apart, for each liquid attracts the molecules of the other as much as, or more than, they are attracted by their own liquid. W_{AB} becomes equal to, or greater than, $\gamma_A+\gamma_B$; and therefore molecules move across from one liquid to the other quite freely.

9. Cohesional work. Harkins[2] has introduced the term 'cohesional work', to denote the work required to separate a column of a liquid, one square centimetre in cross-section, into two; since the result of this operation is to produce two square centimetres of liquid surface where no interface was before, the cohesional work of a liquid is 2γ. Comparison of the cohesional work with the adhesional work to another liquid gives a fair comparison of the relative intensities with which the molecules of a liquid attract the molecules of the same and of another liquid.

10. Relation between surface tension and the pressure differences across a curved liquid surface. We must now return to a most important consequence of the existence of free surface energy, which was known to Young and Laplace, and is the foundation of the classical theory of Capillarity, and of most of the methods of measuring surface tension. If a liquid surface be curved the pressure is greater on the concave side than on the convex, by an amount which depends on the surface tension and on the curvature. This is because the displacement of a curved surface, parallel to itself, results in an increase in area as the surface moves towards the convex side, and work has to be done to increase the area. This work is supplied by the pressure difference moving the surface.

The calculation may be made by considering the energy changes

[1] *Théorie Mécanique de la Chaleur*, pp. 369 ff. (1869). [2] *J.A.C.S.* (1921), 35.

involved in a displacement of the surface. In Fig. 2, $ABCD$ is a small part of the surface with sides at right angles; let this area be displaced parallel to itself, away from the concave side, by a distance δn, with the normals to the boundaries in the displaced position $A'B'C'D'$ the same as the normals in the original position. The normals at A and B meet at O_1, those at B and C at O_2. Let the radius of curvature of the arc AB be R_1 and that of BC be R_2. The angle AO_1B is AB/R_1 radians and BO_2C is BC/R_2. The area of the element of surface after the displacement is

$$\left(AB+\frac{AB}{R_1}\delta n\right)\left(BC+\frac{BC}{R_2}\delta n\right),$$

or, neglecting second-order quantities,

$$ABCD\left(1+\frac{\delta n}{R_1}+\frac{\delta n}{R_2}\right).$$

The work done against the free energy or surface tension γ of the surface is therefore

$$\gamma ABCD\,\delta n\left(\frac{1}{R_1}+\frac{1}{R_2}\right).$$

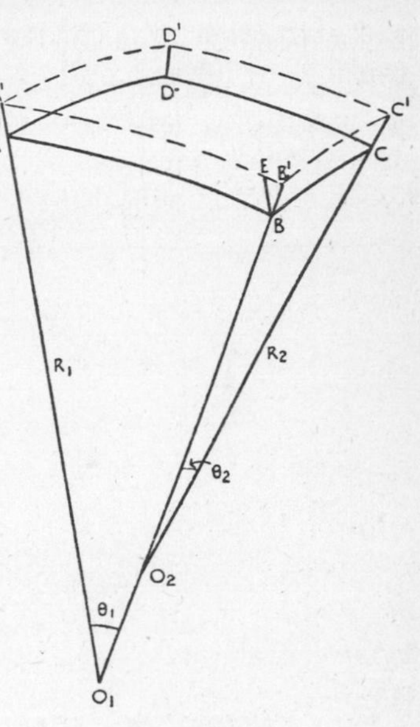

FIG. 2.

If the pressure on the concave side is p_1 and on the convex p_2, the work done by this pressure difference is

$$(p_1-p_2)\,\delta n\,ABCD.$$

No work is done by any other forces, hence these quantities are equal and

$$p_1-p_2=\gamma\left(\frac{1}{R_1}+\frac{1}{R_2}\right). \qquad (3)$$

Equation (3) is the fundamental equation of Capillarity. It permits the calculation of the forms of liquid surfaces when the weight of the liquid is not negligible, for the pressures can be expressed in terms of the height above a fixed point in the fluids, and their densities.

11. Form of the surface dividing two fluids of unequal density. Fig. 3, a and b, represents the surface of separation between two fluids. At a point A, in case a, the surface is concave upwards; in case b, it is concave downwards. Take another point P on the curve, at a level z above or below A, z being positive on the concave side of the curve at A (positive values of z are up in case a and down in case b). Let p_1 be the pressure on the *concave* side at A, and p_2 that on the *convex* side; let D_1 be the density on the *lower* side and D_2 that on the *upper*. Let $p_1-p_2 = C$, C being determined by the curvature at A according to (3). The pressures at P will be p_1-gD_2z and p_2-gD_1z in case a, and p_1+gD_1z and p_2+gD_2z in case b;

in both cases the pressure difference across the curved surface at P will be $p_1-p_2+gz(D_1-D_2)$, so that, by (3),

$$\gamma\left(\frac{1}{R_1}+\frac{1}{R_2}\right) = C+gz(D_1-D_2) \tag{4}$$

is the general equation of a curved surface under surface tension and gravity. It provides a means of measuring surface tension by comparing its magnitude with gravity. Unfortunately radii of curvature of fluid surfaces are not easily measured, and when quantities which can be measured are substituted in (4) the equation becomes impossible of

FIG. 3.

solution in finite terms. Numerous approximate solutions have been given, however, for special cases; the most general is one by Bashforth and Adams[1] for the case of figures of revolution about a vertical axis. A brief account of their transformation of this equation will be given in Chapter IX, in connexion with the methods of measuring surface tension.

12. Elementary theory of the capillary rise and maximum bubble-pressure methods of measuring surface tension. It is not easy to measure radii of curvature directly, but definite curvatures can be imposed on liquid surfaces, and the pressure difference across the surface recorded by various devices. The well-known rise of a liquid in a capillary tube is simply an automatic recording of the pressure difference across the meniscus of the liquid in the tube, the curvature of the meniscus being determined by the radius of the tube and the angle of contact between the solid and the liquid. Let r (Fig. 4) be the radius of a cylindrical tube, so small that the liquid meniscus does not depart sensibly from the spherical form, and θ the contact angle between the liquid and the glass (this is generally zero). Then the radius of curvature of the meniscus is $r/\cos\theta$, and the pressure under the meniscus becomes less than that at the same height, in a liquid with a plane surface, by $(2\gamma\cos\theta)/r$. This produces a driving pressure, tending to force the liquid up the tube, and the meniscus will rise to a height h, such that the weight of the column of liquid elevated above the plane surface outside the tube just balances the pressure deficiency under the curved meniscus. If D_1-D_2 is the difference between the densities of the liquid rising in the tube and the surrounding fluid, h must be given by

$$\frac{2\gamma\cos\theta}{r} = gh(D_1-D_2)$$

or

$$\gamma\cos\theta = \tfrac{1}{2}grh(D_1-D_2). \tag{5}$$

[1] *An Attempt to test the Theories of Capillary Action* (Cambridge), 1883.

The liquid is not pulled up the tube by a hypothetical surface tension pulling on the walls, as is suggested by the explanation found in so many elementary text-books—it has never been made clear what is the hook on the wall to which this 'surface tension' attaches itself, nor how the hook contrives to move up the tube in advance of the rising meniscus. The energy relations determine what is the stable contact angle (cf. Chap. V,

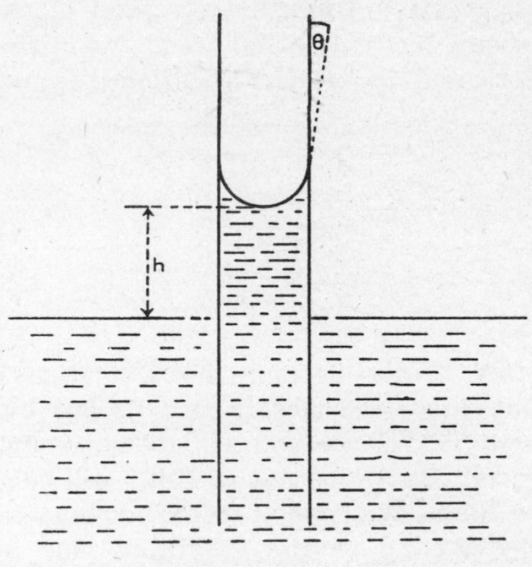

Fig. 4.

§ 6 ff.); the fluidity of the liquid permits the molecules to move about till they rest at this stable contact angle; the contact angle and the curvature of the tube curve the liquid surface; the pressure difference follows from the free energy resident in the surface, and the liquid then flows up the tube under the hydrostatic pressure.

When the contact angle is greater than 90°, $\cos\theta$ is negative, and the liquid falls in the tube. This occurs with mercury in glass, as a general rule, and with water in tubes coated with paraffin wax internally.

Fig. 5 shows a vertical tube of internal radius r dipping into a liquid. If a bubble is blown at the end of this tube it will have the form of a segment of a sphere, if the radius of the tube is small. The radius of this sphere will first decrease, until the bubble becomes hemispherical. Further growth of the bubble will increase the radius. By equation (3) the pressure in the bubble will be a maximum when the radius is a minimum, that is, when the radius of the bubble is equal to that of the tube. The bubble will be unstable when it has grown beyond the hemispherical shape, because the pressure decreases as more air passes into it. Hence the maximum pressure attainable in a bubble blown on a *small* tube is

$$gh_1(D-d)+\frac{2\gamma}{r}, \tag{6}$$

where h_1 is the distance below the surface of the liquid of the end of the tube.

The measurement of the maximum pressure in bubbles is one of the most convenient for measuring surface tensions. The exact theory of this method, and of the capillary height method, requires allowance to be made for the deviation from the spherical form of the meniscus in tubes of finite size.

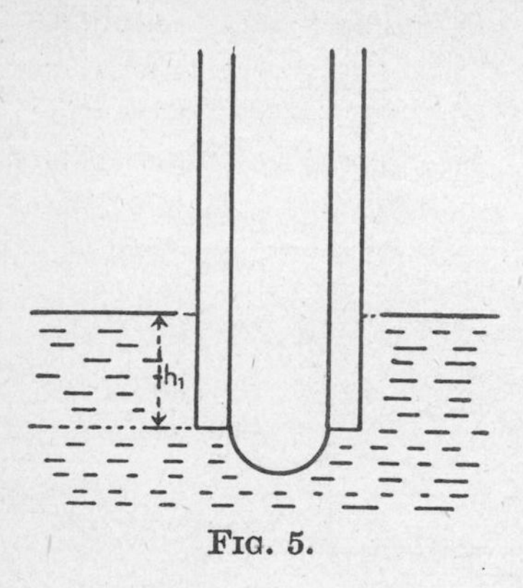

FIG. 5.

There are many other methods of measuring surface tension; as no new physical principles are involved in them they will be left to Chapter IX. It will be more interesting now to proceed with other phenomena which throw light on the molecular constitution of liquids and the nature of the forces between the molecules.

13. Thermal effects of increasing the surface. Total surface energy. The results of measurements of surface tension show that, almost invariably,[1] surface tension decreases with rising temperature. Kelvin[2] showed that it follows that there is an absorption of heat when the surface of a liquid is extended. Let q_s be the heat absorbed during an extension of one square centimetre.

Consider a cycle consisting of a reversible extension of the surface by unit area at a temperature $T+dT$ and a contraction at T. At $T+dT$ the quantity of heat put into the system is q_s+dq_s, and the surroundings do work on it $\gamma+d\gamma$. At T the system does work on its surroundings γ, and gives up the heat q_s. The net work done by the system on its surroundings is $-d\gamma$, and a quantity of heat q_s has fallen from $T+dT$ to T. Therefore, by Carnot's theorem,

$$-d\gamma = q_s\frac{dT}{T},$$

$$q_s = -T\frac{d\gamma}{dT},$$

and the total energy of formation of the surface is

$$\epsilon_s = \gamma+q_s = \gamma-T\frac{d\gamma}{dT}; \tag{7}$$

$d\gamma/dT$ being negative, q_s is positive.

q_s, or $-T\,d\gamma/dT$, is often called the latent heat of the surface, as it is the amount of heat which has to be added to the surface to maintain its temperature constant during an isothermal extension. It is clear that the total energy, ϵ_s, of the surface is made up of two parts: the free surface energy, γ, and the latent heat, $-T\,d\gamma/dT$.

[1] Certain metals appear to be an exception (see Chap. IV).
[2] *Phil. Mag.*, **17**, 61 (1859).

The reason why heat is absorbed on extending a surface is that molecules must be dragged from the interior against the inward attractive force, to form the new surface. As they leave the interior for the surface their motion is retarded by this inward attraction, so that the temperature of the surface layers is lower than that of the interior, unless heat is supplied from outside.

14. The 'specific heat' of the surface. From the variation of the total surface energy with temperature we can calculate how much the specific heat of a given amount of matter varies with the extent of its surface. Let c be the specific heat of a mass of fluid with surface area A, and let dc/dA be the variation of specific heat with surface. Suppose that the mass is warmed by dT degrees, and that its surface is increased by dA sq. cm.; the amount of energy which must be supplied will be the same whether the area is extended first or the temperature raised first. If the area is extended first, the energy absorbed is $\epsilon_s dA$; the specific heat being now $c+\frac{dc}{dA}dA$, the heat absorbed in subsequent warming is $\left(c+\frac{dc}{dA}dA\right)dT$. If, however, the temperature were raised first, the heat absorbed would be $c\,dT$, and the energy required to extend the surface at the higher temperature would be $\left(\epsilon_s+\frac{d\epsilon_s}{dT}dT\right)dA$. The sum of the energies absorbed must be the same; hence

$$\epsilon_s dA+\left(c+\frac{dc}{dA}dA\right)dT = c\,dT+\left(\epsilon_s+\frac{d\epsilon_s}{dT}dT\right)dA$$

or

$$\frac{dc}{dA}=\frac{d\epsilon_s}{dT}.$$

The quantity $d\epsilon_s/dT$ may be called the specific heat of the surface; it must be understood that it means the difference between the specific heat of matter in the interior and in the surface, just as ϵ_s itself means the difference between the total energy of matter in the interior and in the surface. Just as dU/dT is the specific heat of matter in bulk, where U is the total energy, so $d\epsilon_s/dT$ is the specific heat peculiar to the surface, where ϵ_s is the total energy peculiar to the surface.

Very many liquids have a nearly linear diminution of surface tension with temperature. With these the total surface energy is nearly constant, i.e. $d\epsilon_s/dT = 0$, as is seen by differentiating (7) when $d\gamma/dT$ is constant. Thus the specific heat of the surface is often practically zero, showing that the surface does not usually differ much in constitution from the interior of the liquid. If there were, in the surface, a differentiated membrane of any kind, we should expect to find that it had a specific heat different from the rest of the liquid.

15. Vapour pressure over a curved surface of liquid. The vapour pressure over a convex surface is greater than that over a plane; and over a concave surface it is less. The difference depends on the fact that condensation of vapour on a small convex drop of a liquid increases its surface area, so that the surface tension tends to oppose the condensation and to increase the vapour pressure. On a plane surface condensation does not alter the surface area, and on a concave surface the surface area is diminished by condensation of more vapour, so that the surface tension aids condensation in this case. The amount of the alteration may be calculated thermodynamically, for spherical surfaces, as follows.

Consider the isothermal and reversible distillation of dn gramme molecules from the plane surface, at the vapour pressure p, to the spherical drop at p'; let the molecular weight of the vapour be M, the radius of the drop r, the density of the liquid D. The distillation consists of four stages: the evaporation at p (work gained pV); compression to p' (work gained $-dn\,RT\log_e p'/p$), assuming the gas laws; condensation on the drop $(-p'V')$; and increase of the surface energy of the drop $(-8\pi r\gamma\,dr)$. The first and third terms cancel, as always in the isothermal distillation of liquids whose vapours obey the gas laws. The fourth term may be transformed thus: the volume of the liquid condensed is Mdn/D; it is also, since the increase of the radius of the drop is dr, $4\pi r^2\,dr$. Hence

$$8\pi r\gamma\,dr = \frac{Mdn}{D}\frac{2\gamma}{r}.$$

The total work gained is zero, therefore

$$dn\,RT\log_e\frac{p'}{p} = 8\pi r\gamma\,dr = dn\frac{2\gamma M}{rD},$$

$$2{\cdot}303RT\log_{10}\frac{p'}{p} = \frac{2\gamma M}{rD}. \tag{8}$$

This increase in vapour pressure amounts, with water at 20°, to the following ($p = 17{\cdot}5$ mm.).

TABLE I

Effect of radius of drop of water on its vapour pressure

Radius. *cm.*	p'/p
10^{-4}	1·001
10^{-5}	1·011
10^{-6}	1·114
10^{-7}	2·95

A direct experimental verification of equation (8) has been carried out by Thomä,[1] by comparing the vapour pressures of various liquids over plane surfaces and over the curved surfaces in capillary tubes of a few tenths of a millimetre diameter. The very small differences of vapour pressure were measured by recording, with an interferometer, the movements of a membrane separating the vapour spaces over the two liquid surfaces. Verification of equation (8) was achieved within an accuracy of

[1] *Z. Physik*, **64**, 224 (1930).

about 10 per cent., which is probably the experimental error of the very delicate measurements employed.

One consequence of this raising of vapour pressure is the well-known fact that water vapour will not condense in a dust-free (and ion-free) atmosphere, unless its vapour pressure considerably exceeds the saturation point. An 11 per cent. increase of vapour pressure would be required for condensation to drops of 10^{-6} cm. diameter; when it is considered that a sphere this size contains about 140,000 water molecules, it is clear that the chance of so many coming together as to start drops of this size, or larger, is small; some nucleus providing a less curved surface must be present if condensation is to occur anywhere near the usual saturated vapour pressure.

This theory assumes that the surface tension is unaffected by the curvature. At radii much smaller than 10^{-6} the number of molecules becomes so small that variations may well take place. The surface tension will not be constant if the molecules cannot be dragged from a place where they are entirely free from surface influences; so the final figure in the above table has not much meaning.

With still smaller particles the thermodynamical method of investigation probably breaks down, as the number of molecules is insufficient to treat the liquid without reference to individual molecules. Consideration of the chemical properties of the molecules, and perhaps of the different parts of individual molecules, will be necessary to develop a complete theory.

16. Independence of the fundamental equations from the nature of molecular attraction. All the results of this chapter have been deduced from the existence of a constant free energy in the surface; a constant amount of work must be done to form each fresh unit of area. The work comes from the inward pull exerted by the underlying molecules on the surface layer; its constancy from the mobility of the molecules and the assumption that the molecular attractions do not extend with sensible intensity to distances comparable with the mass of liquid considered, so that some part of the liquid is free from surface influences. This assumption excludes the hypothesis that the molecular attractions are gravitational, which is still sometimes suggested; if the attractions diminished as the inverse square of the distance, the surface tension of the oceans would be far greater than that of a cupful of water, because the distant parts would act with sensible effect. Any theory of molecular attraction, in which the forces practically vanish at small distances, will harmonize with the results of this chapter.

The classical theories of Young,[1] Laplace,[2] Gauss,[3] and Poisson[4] all led to the fundamental equation (3) and to some others. It is not proposed

[1] *Phil. Trans.* (1805), 65; and *Works* (ed. Peacock, 1855), **1**, 418.
[2] *Mécanique Céleste*, Suppl. to Book 10 (1806).
[3] *Principia Generalia Theoriae Figurae Fluidorum* (1830).
[4] *Nouvelle Théorie de l'Action Capillaire* (1831).

to deal with these theories here, as they are based on the assumption of indefinite subdivisibility of the liquid, and give little hope of being developed into a molecular theory; their most important results have been deduced from considerations of energy much more simply. The reader desiring further knowledge of them cannot do better than read Bakker's[1] recent account; Poincaré[2] also gives the mathematical theory clearly. Maxwell's article[3] and Rayleigh's papers[4] develop the theory; their perusal will be of much interest to the mathematician.

The forces round the molecules, which give rise to the phenomena of Capillarity, are identical with those which cause chemical reaction and solution, as well as all the phenomena of adhesion and cohesion. Most frequently, in liquids, the attractive forces between molecules are of the type now known as van der Waals' forces; pure electrostatic attractions or repulsions are, however, often superposed on these, particularly when electrolytically dissociated groups are present in the molecules. In the case of solid surfaces, forces of the covalent type are often the predominant factors in determining the nature and amount of cohesion. The intensity and distribution of all these forces round the molecules depends not only on the shape of the molecules but also on the nature and arrangement of the different chemical groupings within the molecules; and since the 'shape' of the molecules may be considered as only a convenient abbreviation for the contour of the repulsive forces associated with the atoms within the molecules, every type of attractive or repulsive force field round the molecule must ultimately be taken into account in a complete theory of Surface Chemistry. At the present time the theory of Organic Chemistry provides an extremely valuable body of information on these points, for it is now clear that the constitutional formulae used for the past three-quarters of a century represent the actual shapes and mechanical properties of the molecules with great fidelity, besides describing their chemical behaviour. The phenomena dealt with in the next chapter show the connexion between certain capillary properties and chemical constitution particularly clearly.

[1] *Loc. cit.*, p. 4. [2] *Capillarité* (1895). [3] *Loc. cit.*, p. 4.
[4] *Phil. Mag.*, **30**, 285, 456 (1890); **33**, 209, 468 (1892). *Works*, vol. iii.

CHAPTER II

SURFACE FILMS OF INSOLUBLE SUBSTANCES ON LIQUIDS

1. General considerations. A small quantity of a practically insoluble and non-volatile substance, placed on the surface of a liquid such as water, which has a high surface tension, may behave in one of two ways: it may either remain as a compact drop (or solid mass), leaving the rest of the surface clean, or it may spread out over the surface. It will be shown in Chapter VI that the necessary and sufficient condition for the substance to spread is that its molecules must attract the water more than they attract each other; quantitatively, that the work of adhesion between the substance and the water must be greater than the work of cohesion of the substance itself. Provided that these energy requirements for spreading are fulfilled, as many as possible of the molecules of the spreading substance move into direct contact with the underlying liquid (often called the 'substrate'),[1] forming a surface film one molecule thick. If space on the surface permits, the whole of the substance spreads into such a monomolecular layer. If there is not room for all the substance to spread fully, it is found that the final state of the surface is one in which the greater part is covered by a monomolecular film, any excess for which there is not room in this film being collected into visible droplets of very much greater thickness.[2]

These monomolecular films are a most interesting state of matter. In them the molecules are often arranged in a simple manner, so that from a study of the films much can be learned as to the size, shape, and other properties of the individual molecules. It is largely because they offer a simple way of studying the properties of molecules that so much attention has been devoted to these films during recent years.

Monomolecular films may exist in many different forms, which correspond, in the two dimensions of the surface, to the three principal states of matter in three dimensions, solid, liquid, and gaseous. The principal factor determining whether or not the films are stable is the strength of the anchorage of the molecules to the surface, an attraction perpendicular to the surface; the principal factors deciding the *state* of the surface films

[1] As the name substrate has been in regular use for the substance on which an enzyme acts, and confusion might arise, perhaps 'substratum' would be better, if the longer expressions 'underlying liquid', or 'underlying solid' are thought too clumsy.

[2] A detailed account of the mechanism of spreading will be given in Chapter VI; the final state of a monomolecular film with the excess collected locally in small drops seems always to be found with *pure* substances. Complex mixtures may, however, form much thicker films of considerable durability, e.g. kerosene on water.

are the amount and distribution of the adhesive forces between the molecules laterally. If the perpendicular attraction between the film molecules and the water is weak, the films tend to crumple up under small lateral compression, or perhaps cannot be formed at all. If there is a reasonably strong anchorage to the water, but the lateral adhesion is small, the film molecules move about independently on the surface, partaking in the translatory motions of the underlying water molecules; such a film resembles a gas or dilute solution on the surface and is called a 'gaseous' or 'vapour' film. If the lateral adhesion is strong, the molecules adhere together into large coherent islands of film, in which the thermal motions of translation of the molecules along the surface are restrained. A few molecules may escape from the boundaries of such coherent films along the surface, filling the vacant spaces in the surface with a dilute vapour film. This tendency to escape along the surface is analogous to the vapour pressure of a solid or liquid substance in three dimensions; it has a definite value, and is often large enough to be measurable.

Coherent films are sometimes solid, the molecules not being free to move about in the film, so that the film cannot flow on the surface unless sufficient force is applied to break it; films are more frequently liquid and can flow in the surface, even under considerable compression, fairly freely. Whether films are solid or liquid is often decided by small details of distribution of the adhesive forces between adjacent molecules; it is the total amount of the lateral adhesion which determines whether the molecules form coherent, or gaseous, films.

Monomolecular surface films[1] have measurable effects on the mechanical, electrical, and optical properties of the surface; the first two of these have yielded valuable information as to the molecular structure of these films. The simplest, and up to the present the most fruitful, method of studying the films is to measure the outward force exerted on a boundary confining them within a definite area of the surface. A great deal of information has also been obtained by measurement of the effect which these films have on the electrical potential difference between the liquid and the air. The principal optical effect is that the degree of ellipticity of polarization of the light reflected from the surface depends very much on the nature of the film covering the surface. In the next paragraphs an outline of the history of our knowledge of these films will be given; a description of modern methods of investigation and of the principal results obtained, with deductions concerning the structure of the films, will follow.

2. Historical. One at least of the properties of surface films of oil on water was known in ancient times: their power of protecting ships in a rough sea by hindering the breaking of waves. This calming action will be described in § 37. The surface currents set up by substances spreading along a surface of water were early noticed: Benjamin Franklin[2] described how dead flies, soaked in oil, move about vigorously (as if they had come

[1] Very conveniently called 'monofilms', or 'monolayers', nowadays.

[2] *The Ingenious Dr. Franklin*, 188 (ed. Goodman, 1931).

to life!) on a surface of water; the dancing motions of camphor, spreading on a water surface, have also been familiar for a long time.

As soon as the idea of surface tension became established, it was noted that oily contamination lowers the surface tension of water. Rayleigh[1] appears to have been the first to measure accurately the amount of this lowering of surface tension. In 1890 he found that 0·81 mg. of olive-oil was required, on an area of 555 sq. cm., to reduce the surface tension by the amount (about 16 dynes per cm.) required to stop the movements of camphor on water; the average thickness of this film was about 16 A.[2]

Rayleigh next showed that certain properties of water surfaces are really due to accidental films of grease, and disappear when the surfaces are cleaned. One of these was the elliptical polarization of the light reflected at the Brewsterian angle ($\tan^{-1}\mu$; μ being the refractive index of the water: see Chap. I, § 5); another was that the viscosity of water is apparently much higher in the surface than in the interior. The second phenomenon was described for water surfaces by Plateau,[3] but was shown by Rayleigh[4] to be due to the surface film, as it is destroyed when the surface of the water is really clean, the viscosity of a clean surface being normal.

A most important contribution came from Fräulein Pockels,[5] who modestly described herself as 'not a professional physicist', although in this, as in other branches of the theory of surfaces, she has shown an exceptionally clear understanding of the phenomena. She found, first, that surface films can be handled by pushing them in front of strips or 'barriers' extending the whole width of a trough of water filled to the brim, the barriers resting on the water surface and touching everywhere. The area available for the film on the surface can be very easily varied by moving these barriers, and since the surface left behind them is clean, being renewed by water molecules from the interior, the barriers provide a very effective method of cleaning a surface. Good 'barriers' are the foundation of accurate methods of experimenting with surface films.

The manner in which the surface tension fell with variation of the area was investigated. Provided the area exceeded a certain critical amount for a given quantity of oil, the surface tension was not perceptibly different

[1] *Proc. Roy. Soc.* **47**, 364 (1890).

[2] The Angstrom system of units, 1 A. = 10^{-8} cm., 1 sq. A. = 10^{-16} sq. cm., &c., will be used. This figure of Rayleigh's, assuming his olive-oil to be triolein, gives 100 sq. A. per molecule of oil in the film, and agrees very well with Adam and Jessop's value of 97 sq. A., determined with modern apparatus, at the same lowering of surface tension.

The reader interested in the development of the theory of the structure of monomolecular surface films will find excellent accounts in the following, to all of which the author is indebted. Rideal, *Surface Chemistry*, 2nd. ed., chap. iii (1930); Marcelin, *Solutions Superficielles* (1931); Freundlich, *Kapillarchemie*, 3rd. ed., pp. 438 ff. (1930); Heymann, *Kolloid-Z.*, **57**, 81 (1931); other reviews by the author may be found in *Chemical Reviews*, **3**, 163 (1926); *Science Progress*, **21**, 621 (1927); *Kolloid-Z.*, **57**, 125 (1931); **61**, 168 (1932).

[3] *Statique des Liquides, etc.*, **2**, 47 (1873).

[4] *Proc. Roy. Soc.*, **48**, 127 (1890).

[5] *Nature*, **43**, 437 (1891).

from that of clean water, and movement of the barrier had no effect. As the area was diminished below this critical amount, the surface tension fell very rapidly. Other facts of importance were also described; the damping of wave motion was found to begin at areas greater than the critical area at which the first fall of surface tension occurred, and reached its maximum at this area. Solid substances tended to spread along a clean surface of water, their spreading being made visible on a dusty surface by 'solution currents' outwards from the solid; this spreading increased with rise of temperature. She compared the outward pressure which causes these solution currents to osmotic pressure, and evidently regarded the surface films as a kind of surface solution, and the spreading as a surface diffusion. These ideas are the foundation of the modern theories of surface films.

In 1899 Rayleigh[1] contributed a most important idea to the theory of these films. He confirmed Pockels's observation that the surface tension is that of clean water, when the area exceeds a certain critical value, and that it falls fairly rapidly when the area is diminished below this value. He suggested that, at this critical point, the molecules are just crowded together into a layer one molecule thick, touching each other over the whole surface. He wrote: '. . . at what point will an opposition to contraction arise? The answer must depend upon the forces supposed to be operative between the molecules of oil. If they behave like the smooth rigid spheres of gaseous theory, no forces will be called into play until they are closely packed. . . . If we accept this view . . . the first drop in tension corresponds to a complete layer one molecule thick, and the diameter of a molecule of oil is about 1 $\mu\mu$. . . . An essentially different result would seem to require a repulsive force between the molecules, resisting concentration long before the first layer is complete.'[2]

3. Monomolecular character of surface films. Surface pressure. This passage contains two points of great importance: that the molecules

[1] *Phil. Mag.*, **48**, 337 (1899).

[2] The thermal motions of the molecules are neglected in this argument. It happened that all the oils used in the earlier researches formed films in which the thermal motions could be neglected, as the molecules had such a large attraction for one another laterally in the films that they were united into compact masses much too large to show independent thermal motion. For such coherent films Pockels's law that the surface tension does not drop appreciably till the critical point is reached, and then drops suddenly, is true.

In the case of 'gaseous' films, in which the molecules move independently, Pockels's law does not hold good; the surface tension diminishes gradually from the largest areas. This is the 'essentially different result' referred to by Rayleigh above. This gradual diminution in surface tension will be seen later to be precisely analogous to the gradual increase in gaseous pressure, as the volume of a gas is diminished; it is due to the thermal motions of the molecules causing a bombardment pressure when far apart from one another. Rayleigh's suggestion that this result, if it were found, would indicate a *repulsive force* between the molecules when separated is a misapprehension of the same kind as was made before the kinetic theory of gases was introduced, when it was often thought that the particles of gases repelled one another at great distances.

are floating objects, repelling one another when in a single layer in contact, so that the first point at which the surface tension is reduced is when the film is one molecule thick; and that the diminution in surface tension is simply the repulsion between the film molecules, i.e. the resistance which the film opposes to lateral compression. This resistance to compression of an insoluble surface film can be measured by enclosing the film with boundaries which it cannot pass. Fig. 6 illustrates the manner in which the outward pressure of a film on its boundaries may be measured. A light

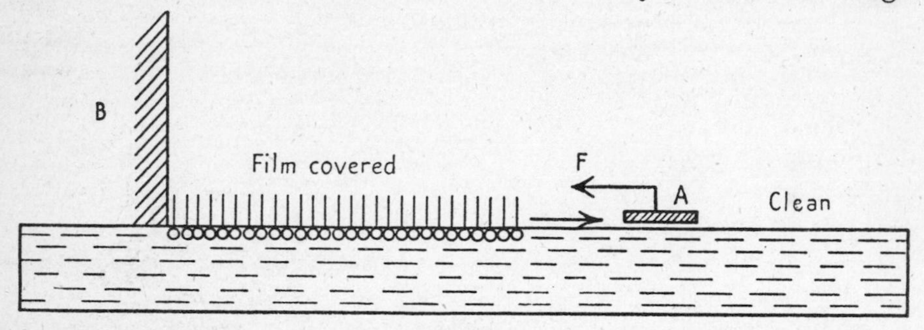

Fig. 6.

floating strip A bounds the film at one end; there is an area of clean water surface to the right of A. The area available for the film can be varied by moving the heavy barrier B at the other end of the film. The light float A is connected with some instrument for measuring the outward force F exerted by the film on it. This force is nowadays usually called the 'surface pressure'.

Provided that the thermal motions of the molecules in the film can be neglected, as will be the case if they are collected together by lateral adhesion into large coherent islands, it is clear that the first point at which a resistance to contraction of area of the film will arise is that at which the film is one molecule in thickness. If the surface were covered by floating corks instead of molecules, it is obvious that no resistance to compression would arise, and therefore no surface pressure would be observed, until the corks were packed in contact with one another in a layer one thick. Rayleigh's argument that the sudden resistance to contraction observed by Pockels, at a definite area of these films, indicates a layer one molecule thick, is thus equivalent to treating the molecules simply as small floating objects.

The connexion between the 'surface pressure' of the film and the 'surface tension' of the film-covered surface is also very simple. Surface tension is the free energy per unit area of the surface, or the work which must be done to increase the area of the surface by one square centimetre. If the floating barrier A is displaced a small distance dx to the right, then the work done on it by the surface pressure F is $Fl\,dx$, where l is the length of the float. But if γ is the surface tension of the clean water surface, and γ' that of the film-covered surface, an area $l\,dx$ of free energy γ has been replaced by one of free energy γ', and the work done must be $(\gamma-\gamma')l\,dx$. These two expressions for the work must be equal, hence $F = \gamma-\gamma'$. The surface pressure is therefore *equal to the diminution of the surface tension of the water by the film.*

This surface pressure F, exerted outwards by a film on a floating barrier separating it from a clean surface, is a very convenient and definite conception in terms of the molecules. It is exactly analogous, in the two dimensions of the surface, to osmotic pressure in three dimensions. The float is here the semipermeable membrane which renders the osmotic pressure measurable; it is indeed, for an insoluble and non-volatile film, the most perfect semipermeable membrane obtainable, for the film molecules cannot pass it at all, while the water molecules can pass it almost instantaneously below, and to some extent also above, through the vapour. Osmotic equilibrium between the film-covered surface and the clean surface beyond the barrier, in the presence of a given force on the float, is established practically instantaneously, a desirable state of affairs never reached in measurements of osmotic pressure in three dimensions. The comparison between surface pressure and osmotic pressure is a strict analogy between two and three dimensions. Surface films are often called 'surface solutions', and the analogy between surface films considered as two-dimensional solutions and three-dimensional solutions is of great value.

With less strictness the surface pressure can be compared with the three-dimensional pressure on isolated matter; and, with due consideration of the effects of the underlying water molecules on the behaviour of the molecules in the film, the conception of surface pressure as the effect of the repulsive forces between the film molecules and the boundary A of the film has yielded a very large part of our present information as to the molecular structure of these films.[1]

[1] The term 'surface pressure' has been criticized, on two grounds principally. The first is physical; the objection being that a surface must be regarded as in tension, and that the action of the film is to reduce this tension. In Chap. I, § 3, it was pointed out that 'surface tension' is only the mathematical equivalent of the free surface energy of the water, and some aspects of the fallacy that there exists, in the surface, a skin in tension were considered there. Perhaps nowhere is the futility of this belief in a tensile surface skin more obvious than with these surface films. It is practically impossible to explain how a surface film diminishes the pulling power of any supposed surface skin; attempts to do so have been very few, and those that have been made have been obliged to postulate quite special properties of molecules. Thus Ramsden (*Trans. Faraday Soc.*, **22**, 492 (1926)) postulated 'haloes of disturbance' round each molecule in the film interfering with the tensile properties of the surface. The much more tangible conception of a repulsion between the floating molecules producing an outward force on the boundary of the film avoids any necessity for ascribing special properties to the molecules, and has shed a flood of light on the structure of the films and on the properties of molecules. It is not surprising that the theory of a tensile skin leads to difficulties. How far should we have progressed in the theory of gases if the pressure had been regarded as the difference between the tension of the clean vacuum outside the containing vessel, and the diminished tension of the contaminated vacuum inside?

The other criticism is one of propriety in nomenclature, rather than of physics;

With *pure* chemical substances no case appears yet to have been found of uniform films of thickness greater than one molecule. If a monomolecular film is compressed until it buckles, or if spreading is incomplete through the anchorage of the molecules to the surface by their water-soluble groups being small, the excess material for which there is not room in the film accumulates in aggregates, solid or liquid, of enormously greater thickness. A proved case of a stable, uniform second layer of molecules above the first, on a liquid, does not appear to have been found.[1] With complex mixtures, however, quite thick and reasonably uniform films of long duration are sometimes obtained; it is uncertain whether or not these are permanently stable. They are of great practical importance in the killing of mosquito larvae, where it is necessary to cover the surface of pools where the larvae breed with a thick film of oil, as nearly complete as possible.

Devaux[2] made numerous experiments between 1903 and 1914. Using a light powder sprinkled on the surface, which is a convenient way of rendering the movements of the oil visible, he confirmed most of the results of Pockels and Rayleigh. He found that the oils spread to a definite maximum extension, which is of course the same as that at which the first fall in surface tension appears. Calculating the thickness of the films, he found it of the same order as the then approximately known dimensions of molecules.[3] He was the first to notice that the films may be solid,

the objection is that the word 'pressure' is properly applicable only to three dimensions, having the dimensions of force divided by area. This does not seem justified even in physical, still less in common usage; dictionaries indicate clearly that the primary meaning of the word 'pressure' is a squeeze or a push, irrespective of the dimensions in which this squeeze takes place. We are certainly more familiar with the idea of a squeeze expressible as force per unit area, than with other types; yet 'electric pressure' is a commonly used term in physics, and elsewhere 'moral' or 'political' pressure, which presumably have no physical dimensions, are common enough. There is precedent also for the use of physical terms in more than one dimension, even in the terminology of those who oppose the use of 'surface pressure'. Tension most commonly means a pull, a force pure and simple, in one dimension; yet they regard 'surface tension', a pull divided by a line, as legitimate. Hence the words *surface pressure* seem to the author exactly right for describing the phenomenon of an outward push exerted along a line in a surface.

[1] Such cases have been occasionally reported, but appear to the author to be not established. The 'polymolecular' films of Harkins and Morgan (*Proc. Nat. Acad. Sci.*, **11**, 637 (1925)) were with substances which spread very badly and are almost certainly largely present as aggregates precipitated on the surface, not spread at all; Lyons and Rideal, and Schulman and Rideal (*Proc. Roy. Soc.* A, **124**, 344 (1929); **130**, 284 (1931)) described bimolecular films of fatty acids on alkaline solutions, but Adam and Miller (*ibid.*, **142**, 401 (1933)) found these to consist of mixtures of collapsed small aggregates, very thick, and monomolecular films.

[2] *Proc.-verb. Soc. Phys. Nat. Bordeaux*, 19 Nov., 3 Dec., 1903; 7 Jan., 14 Apr., 1904; 28 Mar., 1912. *J. Phys. Radium*, **3**, 450 (1904); **2**, 699, 891 (1912). *Ann. Rep. Smithsonian Inst.* (1913), 261.

[3] It has been stated that the monomolecular theory arose through Rayleigh noticing that the thickness of the films is about the known dimensions of a molecule. The passage quoted above from his paper shows that the theory rests not on a mere

possessing tangential rigidity in the surface, so that they cannot be blown about. Marcelin[1] studied the equilibrium between spread films and droplets of oil.

4. Langmuir's work in 1917: molecular orientation and detailed structure of the films. Langmuir[2] introduced new conceptions and new experimental methods of great importance into the study of these films. He measured the outward surface pressure F directly, by arranging a floating barrier with a device to measure the force on it, on a trough filled to the brim with water, and provided with paper barriers for cleaning the surface and handling the films, on the principle introduced by Pockels. Though his apparatus has been extensively modified, his principle of *directly* measuring the outward force on a floating barrier is nearly always used now. He employed, instead of 'oils', pure substances of known constitution, and observed the effect of varying this constitution; solid substances as well as liquid were used, spreading them by first dissolving in a volatile solvent such as benzene, which evaporates a few seconds after spreading. The results were expressed as areas *per molecule*, in sq. A., for each surface pressure.

The clearest results were obtained with the normal, saturated fatty acids and alcohols. These formed stable films, which would stand considerable compression laterally, and (at room temperature on distilled water) gave a very clearly marked critical area at which the surface pressure first appeared, this point being of course Pockels's critical point of the first diminution of surface tension. As the area was reduced from large initial areas no surface pressure could be detected until the area had reached about 22 sq. A. per molecule; and at 20·5 sq. A. the pressure increased very rapidly indeed with further increase of pressure. The curve I of Fig. 15 shows the relation between surface pressure and area per molecule, which is obtained with accurate apparatus for the fatty acids on water; curve III is that obtained with the alcohols.[3]

The most striking fact found by Langmuir was that the length of the hydrocarbon chains made no difference whatever to the shape of the curve, provided there were more than 14 carbons in all in the molecule. The length of the molecules has been varied from 14 to 34 carbons without showing any change, although when the chains in the molecule become very long, the finer details of the curves are apt to be obliterated, since the films are extremely rigid and do not yield readily to small lateral pressures.

The fact that the areas do not change as the length of the hydrocarbon chains is varied in the fatty acids

$$CH_3.CH_2.CH_2 \quad . \; . \; . \; . \; . \; . \; . \; . \; . \; . \; . \; . \; . \; . \; . \quad CH_2COOH$$

numerical coincidence but on the far firmer foundation of the idea of tangible, floating molecules. The films provide an independent means of measuring molecules.

[1] *Ann. de Physique*, **1**, 19 (1914). [2] *J.A.C.S.* (1917), 1848.

[3] Langmuir's curves now have only historical interest; they seem to be complicated by the effects of leaks past the barriers. His value for the area of the film at small pressures was 21 sq. A., very close to the above.

proves that the molecules are oriented steeply to the surface, and all at the same angle in all the films. The presumption is that the orientation of the molecules is vertical, from the evidence on the films alone, but we shall see later that this is not certain.

From simple considerations of the dimensions of the molecules, it can be seen at once that they are greatly elongated in the direction perpendicular to the surface. Palmitic acid, with sixteen carbons in the molecule, has a molecular volume of 300 c.c., and therefore the molecule has a volume of 495 cub. A.;[1] its cross-section as measured is 20·5 sq. A., so that its length (measured perpendicular to the surface) must be some 24·2 A., if the density in the films is the same as that in bulk. It must therefore be four or five times as long as thick.

All the acids, of whatever length, showed the same area; hence the length of the molecules must be proportional to the number of carbons. The molecular volume of a CH_2 group is 17·8 c.c., and the volume of one CH_2 therefore 29·4 cub. A.; the cross-section being measured as 20·5 sq. A., the length of each CH_2 group perpendicular to the surface, or the vertical height of one carbon above another, is about 1·43 A. Such estimates are only rough, as they assume the density in the film to be the same as in the substance in bulk. X-ray measurements on long chain compounds show that the carbon atoms are probably 1·54 A. apart in the chain; they are not arranged in a straight line, but in a zigzag in accordance with stereochemical theory, the lines joining successive atoms being inclined at the tetrahedral angle of 109° 28′. If the chains are oriented perpendicular to the surface, the height of one carbon above another should be 1·26 A. The difference from the value 1·43 calculated above is very likely due to error in the assumption that the density is the same in the films and in the bulk substance. The fact that there is this measure of agreement confirms, however, the view that the long chains are either vertically or very steeply oriented in the surface.

These results, that the molecules are elongated and oriented steeply to the surface, gave at once a great deal of information as to the forces round the molecules themselves. The alcohols and acids, which form such stable films, have an OH or a COOH group at each end. In shorter chain compounds, such as ethyl alcohol or acetic or butyric acids, these groups confer solubility on the whole molecule; they may be called 'water-soluble' groups. In the long chain compounds they cannot pull the whole molecule into the water owing to the resistance of the long chains to immersion; instead, they spread the substance out as a monomolecular film on the surface. The long chain paraffins do not even form a surface film,[2] for

[1] The number of molecules, and certain dimensions such as the volume of the molecule, are found from the corresponding quantities for the gramme-molecule by multiplication or division by the Avogadro number $6{\cdot}06 \times 10^{23}$.

[2] The lateral adhesion between the molecules also affects the spreading. It is not an invariable rule that purely hydrocarbon substances never spread—the shortest chain liquid paraffins do spread; and when the chains become too long, spreading of compounds which contain a water-soluble group may be prevented.

there is no water-soluble group present in them. The formation of the stable, monomolecular surface films may be regarded as a solution of the end group of the molecule in the water, the rest refusing to be dragged in.

The lateral adhesion between the long chains probably assists to keep the molecules out of the water by causing them to pack side by side. This adhesion is certainly the main factor in keeping the molecules together as a coherent film, which shows no appreciable surface pressure beyond 22 sq. A. Langmuir studied, besides the insoluble surface films of the long chain acids, adsorbed surface films of shorter chain, slightly soluble acids, by methods which will be given in detail in Chapter III. These were found to be 'gaseous' films, the molecules moving about separately and lying flat in the surface instead of being oriented steeply.

Langmuir predicted that, as the chains were lengthened, transitional phenomena would be found between the coherent films which, up to that time, were the only type of films observed with long chain *insoluble* fatty substances, and the gaseous adsorbed films of the soluble fatty substances; these phenomena should be analogous to the evaporation and critical phenomena of liquids and vapours in three dimensions.

5. Outline of recent developments. In 1926 Schofield and Rideal showed (Chap. III, § 4) that as the length of the hydrocarbon chains in the soluble fatty acids increases, the lateral adhesion between the molecules in the gaseous films adsorbed at the surface increases, until with the twelve carbon acid there is nearly enough lateral adhesion to form a coherent film. In the same year Adam and Jessop, using a new sensitive instrument for measuring surface pressures, were able to trace in detail the transition between gaseous and coherent films, finding that there is an extremely close resemblance between these transitions and the condensation of three-dimensional gases to liquids (§ 13).

Indications of further complexities in the coherent type of surface films were found by Langmuir, and have been further investigated by Labrouste,[1] Adam, and others. It is now well established that there frequently exists a coherent, 'expanded' state in insoluble surface films of fatty substances, intermediate in area between the very closely packed 'condensed' films, and the gaseous films in which the molecules move about independently on the surface. This most interesting type of film will be discussed in §§ 18 and 19.

Although the fact that surface films affect the contact potential between the liquid and the air has been known for some time, Guyot (1924)[2] was the first to make systematic measurements of the effect of surface films of insoluble fatty substances on this potential. Frumkin (1925)[3] continued this and Schulman and Rideal (1931)[4] undertook a detailed study of several types of insoluble film, comparing the measurements of surface potential[5]

[1] *Ann. Physique*, **14**, 164 (1920). [2] *Ibid.*, **2**, 506 (1924).
[3] *Z. physikal. Chem.*, **116**, 485 (1925). [4] *Proc. Roy. Soc.* A, **130**, 259 (1931).
[5] The term 'surface potential' is now used to denote the change in the contact potential between the liquid and air, caused by the presence of a surface film.

with those of surface pressure, over a large range of areas. The work has been continued by Rideal, Schulman, Hughes, and by Adam, Harding, and others; the simultaneous measurement of surface pressure and surface potential is now easily carried out and is a necessary part of any thorough investigation of a surface film. It has not, as yet, been possible to interpret the meaning of surface-potential measurements in terms of the molecular structure of the films with the same precision as surface pressure; but surface potential has been most useful, especially in giving information as to the homogeneity, or otherwise, of a film, and in tracing the course of chemical reactions in films. It also affords qualitative information as to the orientation of the polar end groups in the molecules to the surface of the water (§ 10).

The work of Bouhet and Tronstad (§ 9), in developing technique for measuring the ellipticity of the light reflected from the surface, has provided yet another method of investigating surface films, but owing to the difficulties in interpreting the optical effect of the films in terms of the effect of individual molecules in the films, this method has not as yet contributed much to our knowledge of their structure.

Zocher and Stiebel (1930) showed how dark ground ultramicroscopic examination of a surface film yields invaluable information as to the extent to which the material is spread on the surface (§ 8).

Finally, electron diffraction is now available as a method for examining surface films of non-volatile substances on liquids which can be placed in a high vacuum, such as mercury; it does not, however, appear to have been much used on liquids, though on solids it is now one of the most important experimental methods.

6. Exact experimental methods. Surface-pressure measurements. Nearly all the methods in use at present are modifications of Langmuir's method, of directly measuring the outward force exerted on a light floating barrier which divides the film-covered surface from a clean surface; and for the manipulation of the films, and adjustment of the area available for them, modifications of Pockels's barriers are almost always used. Ths essential points requiring attention for accuracy are as follows:

(1) the barriers used to confine the film must be proof against leakage of the film, under any surface pressure, and must be heavy enough not to move under the surface pressure;

(2) leakage of the film past the ends of the light floating barrier, on which the pressure is measured, must be prevented in such a way as to interfere as little as possible with the sensitivity of the measuring instrument;

(3) sufficiently sensitive means of measuring the force on the float must be provided;

(4) all the apparatus must be as clean as possible and means must be provided of measuring the amount of contamination of the surface which is always present, accidentally, to some extent;

(5) an accurate means of measuring the amount of film-forming sub-

stance put on the surface must be available; and the solvents used for dissolving the substance must be carefully purified until no appreciable trace of film-forming impurity is present in them.

One satisfactory type of apparatus is illustrated diagrammatically in Fig. 7. There is a trough on three levelling screws (not shown), filled to the brim with water; an instrument with two torsion wires for measuring

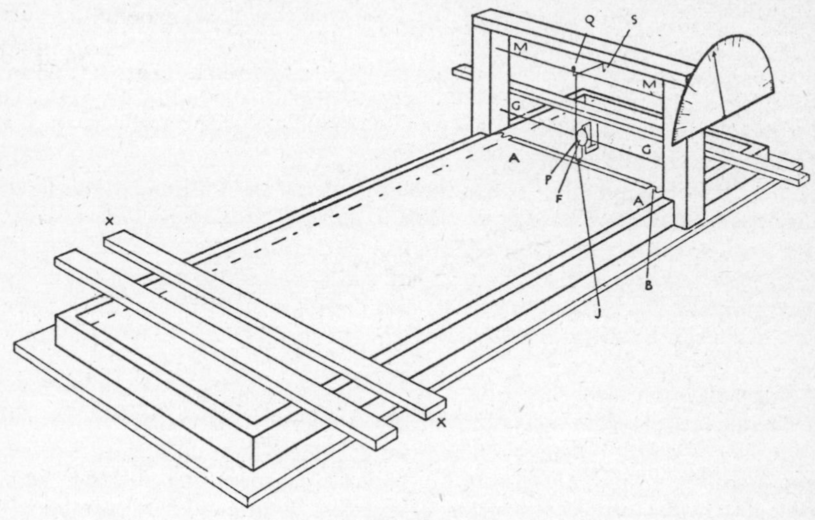

FIG. 7.

the surface pressure, placed towards one end of the trough but with at least 15 cm. length of water surface behind it, so as to permit of the operation of the two barriers needed for efficient cleaning, and a considerable length of water surface in front of the instrument, on which the film is spread, also provided with two barriers. Some details of construction and use of this and some other instruments are given below.

(1) Barriers can conveniently be made of strips of plate glass, not less than 1 cm. wide and a few mm. thick, so as to be heavy. They must be coated, after cleaning, with a good hard paraffin wax.

Troughs may be made of brass, or other non-rusting metals, or of glass or silica.[1] For surface-potential work a trough of non-conducting material is very desirable. Recent work has shown that traces of divalent metals may affect the films (§ 30), so that silica is probably to be preferred. Harkins recommends a trough made entirely of paraffin wax, but details of its use are not yet available. Troughs should be *large*: $60 \times 14 \times 1{\cdot}5$ cm. deep is convenient.

The tops of the sides of the trough should be several millimetres wide at least, and ground flat, so that the barriers fit them. Both the tops of the sides of the trough, and if desired the whole surface of the trough, must be covered with hard paraffin wax. This is easily painted on from benzene solution, and adheres best if the trough is heated sufficiently for the wax to be molten. The function of the wax is to provide a non-wetting layer, over which the water

[1] Opaque silica troughs may be obtained from the Thermal Syndicate, Ltd.

cannot spread; if the barriers, or the tops of the sides of the trough become wet, channels of water may extend under and round the barriers, permitting the film to leak past.

Under favourable conditions troughs require cleaning only every few days, the residual material from each experiment being collected behind barriers out of the way, at the end of the trough.

(2) In Langmuir's original instrument, and Adam's first modification of it, leakage of the film past the ends of the float was prevented by leaving narrow gaps, closed by jets of air. These are effective if carefully adjusted, but disturb the float slightly so that delicate surface-pressure measurements are not possible.

Nowadays the float is generally ended a centimetre or more from the sides of the trough and the gaps blocked by flexible material. Adam and Jessop used gold, or platinum, strips; the former are very difficult to solder without dissolving them completely. Guastalla[1] introduced light threads, vaselined so that they do not wet. These have been found satisfactory by many workers, but the author still uses platinum ribbons.

Leaks past barriers or float can be tested for by sprinkling talc on the surface; this travels with the film leaking past, and can be seen at once. With metallic ribbons leaks can be stopped by leading the water surface up, by stroking with a thin wire, preferably heated just previously so as to agitate the water surface. Once stopped, leaks rarely recur.

(3) The surface pressure was balanced and measured, in the earlier instruments, by a simple bell crank balance in which weights were hung in a pan. Nowadays torsion wires are nearly always used. These instruments have either vertical or horizontal wires, and the position of the float is indicated by a mirror. As a rule the instruments are used as 'null' instruments, i.e. the twist that must be applied to the torsion wire, to bring the float back to the zero position it had before any film was put on, is measured.

Adam and Jessop's instrument[2] is shown in detail in Fig. 8. It will measure surface pressures down to about 0·01 dynes per cm. It has two horizontal torsion wires; the lower, *GG*, about 13 mm. from the surface, carries the mirror *F*, in a light holder of copper foil, which has a light tail projecting down to about 2 mm. from the surface of the water. The float is usually of thin metal foil, with a lug *J* projecting up, about the centre. The upper wire *MM* has a light rigid framework *PQRS* soldered to its middle point; the lower end is a stirrup, coming about 2 mm. from the surface. A silver wire 0·04 mm. diameter is soldered to the lug on the float, the stirrup, and the tail projecting down from the mirror holder, so that the three move together when there is tension on the wire; this is secured by twisting the torsion head on the lower wire *GG*. The tension on the horizontal torsion wires can be adjusted by the heads *N* and *H*. The upper wire *MM* has a large divided torsion head. The ribbons at the end of the float are now made in the simple form of Fig. 9. If these ribbons are *lightly* waxed they give little trouble. There are screws to clamp the float when not in use, and the whole instrument has a strong brass frame, easily slipped off the trough for cleaning.[3] The vibrations of the mirror are damped by a light plunger *L*, part of the mirror holder, which dips into a small bath full of *non-spreading*, viscous oil.

[1] *Compt. rend.*, **189**, 241 (1929). [2] *Proc. Roy. Soc.* A, **110**, 423 (1926).

[3] A vital point in the design of surface-pressure instruments is easy dismounting for cleaning.

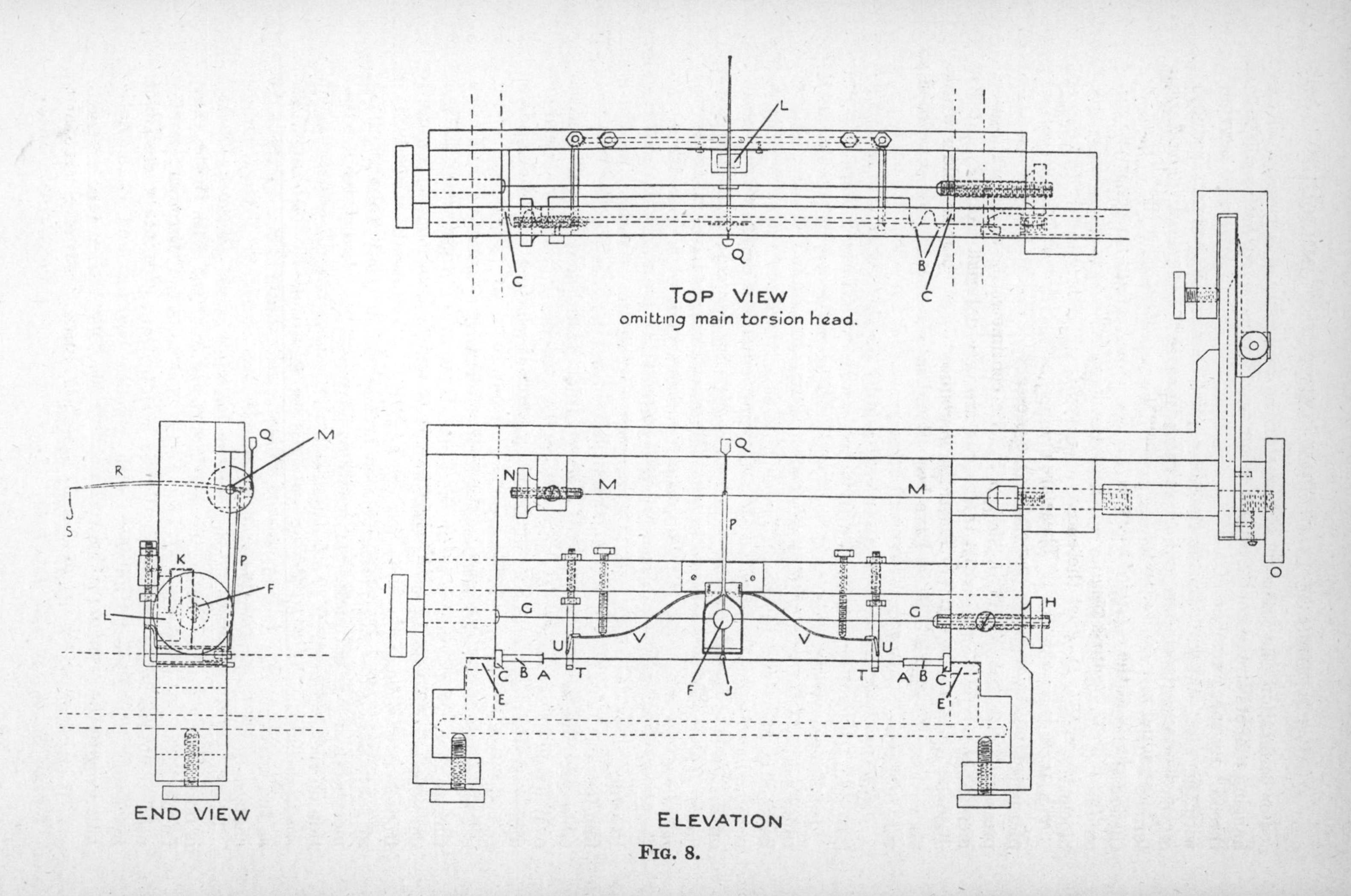
TOP VIEW
omitting main torsion head.
L
Q
C
B
C
END VIEW
Q
M
R
S
K
P
F
L
ELEVATION
Q
N
M
M
P
O
I
G
G
H
U
V
V
U
C
B
A
T
F
J
T
A
B
C
E
E
Fig. 8.

For calibration, the value of a degree of the torsion head is ascertained by hanging weights on the hook S, which hangs from the end of $PQRS$ by a flexible thread. By measurement of the distance from the end of R to the junction with the wire, and from this to the bottom of the stirrup, the force in dynes on the centre of the float is found, for a known weight on the hook. The angle formed by the end of the horizontal arm R, the wire MM, and the bottom of the stirrup, should be a right angle. The force is converted into dynes per cm. on the float, allowing half the width of the gaps blocked by the ribbons as belonging to the float.

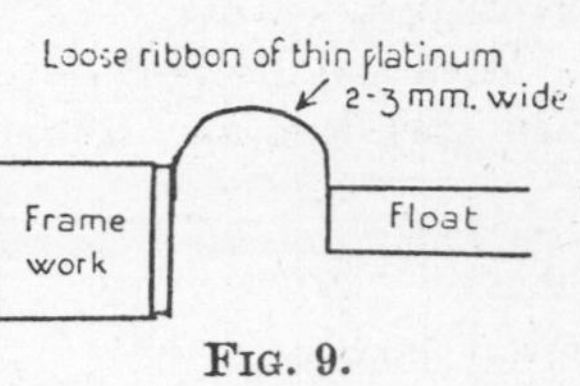

FIG. 9.

The thickness required in the torsion wires, of phosphorbronze preferably, depends on the range of pressures to be measured. The author uses two instruments, one with an upper wire of 0·18 or 0·20 mm. diameter, giving about 4° per dyne,[1] for pressures above 0·3 dyne; and a more sensitive one, the upper wire 0·12 mm., for pressures from 0·01 to 4 dynes. This has about 35° per dyne. The lower wire is simply a frictionless bearing for the mirror; it should be 0·07 mm. for sensitive work but may be larger for the higher pressures.

In taking measurements the surface is first cleaned by sweeping three or four times with the barriers, on both sides of the float. In a minute the oscillations have died down, and the main torsion head is set to zero; the spot of light is brought to a zero position on the scale, first by adjusting the torsion head on the lower wire GG, then by racking the scale for the spot of light up and down. This rack is a most useful device, and permits the setting of the spot to zero in a very few seconds. The greatest possible rapidity is desirable in all work with these films, since accidental contamination is always accumulating to some extent, but much less rapidly when there is a film on the surface. The film-forming substance is now put on, dissolved preferably in a solvent immiscible with water and very clean and volatile. It is generally completely evaporated in less than a minute, and readings of surface pressure are taken at different areas, by setting the barrier to any desired area and turning the torsion head till the spot of light returns to zero.

The cleanliness of the surface as left after cleaning should be tested from time to time, by moving up the barrier towards the float. A very clean surface develops a surface pressure of less than 0·03 dyne, when its length is reduced from 35 to 8·75 cm., i.e. to one-quarter. The trough may often be used for days in succession before the contamination becomes twice this amount, and for most work that is harmless. Salt solutions often give trouble with contamination on their surfaces. It is most desirable, *particularly in studies of the rate of reactions in films*, to keep a very watchful eye for accidental contamination, as the arrival of this at a surface may very easily be confused with chemical changes in the films themselves.

The principal advantage of using two torsion wires is that greater sensitivity is obtained by placing the mirror near the surface and the main torsion wire farther away. For pressures above 0·3 dyne one horizontal wire only can be used, the mirror being attached to it. One such instrument has been described by Lyons and Rideal;[2] another, with jewelled bearings and chainomatic balancing of the pressure, is due to Langmuir and Schaefer.[3]

[1] 'Dynes' will often be used for dynes per cm.

[2] *Proc. Roy. Soc.* A, **124**, 344 (1929).

[3] *J.A.C.S.* (1937), 2404.

Gorter[1] describes an instrument with a light horizontal beam working on jewelled bearings; a spiral spring is twisted through a measured angle to balance the rotation of this beam by the surface pressure acting on a float below the beam. Platinum strips blocked the gaps.

Two very sensitive instruments have been constructed with vertical torsion wires. Marcelin's instrument[2] has a vertical wire placed to one side of the trough; if it is combined with Guastalla's vaselined threads to block the gaps at the ends of the float, it gives good results.

Moss and Rideal[3] have used, for the investigation of gaseous films at very low pressures, an ingenious instrument shown in Fig. 10. The trough is made

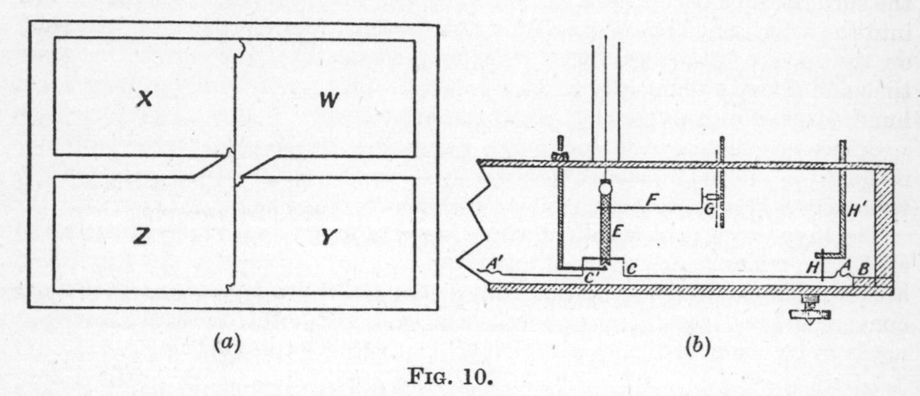

FIG. 10.

in four compartments, the diagonally opposite areas X and Y being clean, the film covering W and Z. The film exerts a surface pressure in the form of a couple on the float, which traverses the middle of the trough; the float is supported by a vertical torsion wire; its position and movements are recorded by an optical lever and a micrometer screw working against a post at the ends of the float. The apparatus is very sensitive but is at present much more laborious in use than most other instruments.

Finally, Marcelin[4] has also used an instrument, which may be called a two-dimensional aneroid. It has a hollow framework enclosing an area of clean water in the surface; one side of the framework consists of a long, flexible strip of mica, which is deflected by the surface pressure of a film on the water surface outside. The deflexions are magnified by a suitable lever, and the instrument is said to be sensitive to about 2 dynes per cm.

An important point in the design of apparatus for work with surface films is that it should be capable of easy dismantling and reassembling, so that the operations of cleaning can be easily conducted, and observations made with no unnecessary delay. At low surface pressures contamination accumulates rapidly, but at higher pressures than about 5 dynes delay is less serious.

(4) Metal troughs should be cleaned with emery cloth under a stream of water till they wet all over, then thoroughly washed with *hot* water, dried, and waxed with a benzene solution of wax when hot. Silica troughs can be thoroughly cleaned with soap and much hot water, and waxed. The surface-pressure instruments are usually cleaned with re-distilled hot benzene, and lightly waxed

[1] *J. Gen. Physiol.*, **18**, 427 (1935).
[2] *Ann. Physique*, **4**, 481, 503 (1925).
[3] *J.C.S.* (1933), 1525.
[4] *Ann. Physique*, **4**, 505 (1925).

where they touch the water. The vaseline used on the silk threads, if these are employed, should be the cleanest obtainable and be used sparingly.

(5) The solvents used should be as little miscible with water as possible, and must be thoroughly purified from traces of grease. Distillation in apparatus free from cork or rubber is desirable for the final purification. Light petroleum, b.p. 60–70°, is probably the best solvent to use; if the substance will not dissolve in that, benzene, mixtures of benzene with up to two-fifths of its volume of alcohol, ethyl acetate, and other solvents may be used. High volatility is desirable in order that the solvent shall disappear from the surface very rapidly; also the more miscible with water the solvent is, the deeper it penetrates below the surface; such penetration has two effects: it may carry the substance down into the interior and cause some of it to be precipitated there instead of spread on the surface; also the solvent itself may remain near the surface for some time and set up a temporary surface pressure. This is not, however, over a few hundredths of a dyne per cm., with ordinary solvents.

Gorter has succeeded in employing water itself as the solvent, for proteins; if the drops are small and very carefully put on the surface, practically perfect spreading takes place, though it may take time.

The measurement of the amount put on is probably best made by means of an 'Agla' micrometer syringe;[1] this measures down to one ten-thousandth of a c.c. A simple dropping pipette with a teat and a fine tip is somewhat more convenient, and accurate to about 2 per cent.; with this a slight correction needs to be made for the evaporation of the more volatile solvents.[2]

7. Surface-potential measurements. The arrangement now generally used for measuring the surface potential, i.e. the effect of the surface film on the potential difference between the water and the air, is shown diagrammatically in Fig. 11. An insulated metal wire or plate A (the 'air electrode') is held a short distance above the surface of the liquid in the trough. A reversible electrode, consisting of a silver wire B coated with silver chloride, usually a small concentration of chloride being present in the water in the trough, or a calomel half cell, dips into the solution in the trough. The air electrode is connected with an electrometer, and the reversible electrode in the solution, with a potentiometer P. The main difficulty in the measurement of the air-liquid potentials, a difficulty not present in most solid-liquid or liquid-liquid potential measurements, is that the air is normally non-conducting; this is usually overcome by coating the tip of the air electrode with a small amount of a radioactive material, preferably giving off α rays only. Polonium is very suitable. These ionize the air within a short distance of the electrode, and render the gap between the air electrode and the water conducting. A source of γ rays, carefully shielded so that the ionizing radiation can travel only straight from the air electrode to the liquid surface, can also be used.[3] The arrangement thus constitutes a rather complex electrolytic cell, with two electrolytes, the liquid in the trough and the ionized air, and three sur-

[1] (From Messrs. Burroughs, Wellcome & Co., Ltd. Cf. Trevan, *Biochem. J.*, **19**, 1111 (1925).)

[2] Cf. Adam and Jessop, *Proc. Roy. Soc.* A, **112**, 363 footnote (1926).

[3] Gee and Rideal, *ibid.*, A, **153**, 118 (1935).

faces, the reversible electrode in the liquid, the air-liquid surface, and the surface of the air electrode. Only one of these, the air-liquid surface, can have its potential difference affected by the presence of an insoluble and non-volatile film on the liquid; measurements of the surface potential of the films are therefore taken by first noting the e.m.f. of the cell with the liquid surface clean; then putting on the film and noting the e.m.f. at

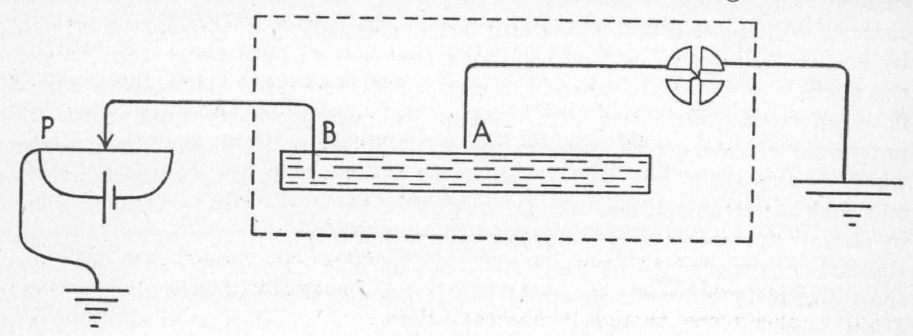

Fig. 11.

various areas per molecule. *The difference between the e.m.f. of the cell with a film-covered surface and the e.m.f. with a clean surface of liquid is defined as the surface potential of the film.*

In order to avoid electrical disturbances the trough, air electrode, and electrometer must be enclosed in an earthed metallic cage (dotted in Fig. 11), and experiments should be conducted at as great a distance as possible from high-tension discharges and other electrical disturbances. The electrometer used should be rapid in action; the ordinary Dolezalek type is rather too slow, but the Lindemann form is quite suitable.[1] Very often a high-resistance valve is used instead of the electrometer, the air electrode being connected to the grid and the anode current recorded by a galvanometer, which need not be particularly sensitive.[2] Any form of 'valve potentiometer' capable of being used with a high-resistance arrangement (such as a glass electrode) should give satisfactory results with the ionized air gaps.

The air electrode should be capable of being moved over the surface, parallel to it, so as to explore the whole surface for variations in surface potential; this may be accomplished by mounting the air electrode on a carriage running on steel rods or rails adjusted parallel to the water surface. It is very desirable, and not difficult, to measure the surface pressure simultaneously with the surface potential.

Detailed descriptions of apparatus for measurement of surface potential by this method, with or without simultaneous measurement of surface pressure, have been given by Schulman and Rideal,[1] Adam and Harding[2] (this instrument now has a silica trough and a valve electrometer), Harkins and others,[3] Andauer and Lange,[4] Dervichian and others.[5]

[1] Cf. Schulman and Rideal, *Proc. Roy. Soc.* **A, 130**, 259 (1931).
[2] Cf. Harding and Adam, *Trans. Faraday Soc.*, **29**, 837 (1933).
[3] *J. Chem. Physics*, **1**, 852 (1933); **3**, 693 (1935).
[4] *Wien-Harms' Handb. d. Experimentalphysik*, **12**, pt. 2, p. 310.
[5] *J. phys. rad.*, **6**, 427 (1935).

Hughes, Rideal, and others[1] constructed an instrument on a very small scale for measuring surface potentials on 0·1 c.c. of heavy water; this has no means of cleaning the surface.

The surface potential can be measured without the use of an ionized air gap by some modification of Volta's original 'condenser' method (Chap. VIII, § 3). An insulated plate, connected with an electrometer, is held above the water surface; the plate and the water surface form a condenser, whose capacity changes if the plate is moved towards or from the water. If the plate is brought, by an outside source, to the same potential as the water, no current flows to the surface of the plate when it is moved; at any other potential a current flows on moving the plate so as to alter the capacity of the condenser. The potentials which must be given to the plate, in order that no current may flow when the plate is moved, are measured for clean and for film-covered surfaces, and their difference is the surface potential of the film. This method was used by Guyot[2] as a check on the results of the ionization method; also by Garrison.[3] Recently Yamins and Zisman,[4] and E. F. Porter,[5] have successfully amplified the alternating currents developed when the plate is rapidly moved up and down, thus rendering contact potential measurements possible within a few tenths of a millivolt.

8. Ultramicroscopic examination of surface films. A valuable piece of accessory technique was introduced by Zocher and Stiebel in 1930;[6] they fixed a powerful dark-ground illuminator of the cardioid type in the bottom of the trough, and focused it sharply on the surface of the water. Using a powerful source of light, it is usually easy to detect at once whether or not any part of the material is unspread. A monomolecular film scatters no light under these conditions, and appears dark; unspread material, or aggregates formed by collapse of a monomolecular film under pressure, show up as more or less brilliantly illuminated regions. Dust particles, which are always present, are bright, but quite different in appearance from unspread material. As a partially spread or partially collapsed film is sometimes reasonably stable under pressure, and simulates the behaviour of a fully spread film when examined by surface pressure or surface potential alone, there is a risk that the measured areas may be too small, part of the material being rendered ineffective through being in large aggregates not affecting the properties of the film. By passing a considerable area of the film over the dark-ground illuminator, it can be ascertained in a few minutes whether or no there is any considerable amount of unspread material. The arrangement for focusing the condenser used by Zocher and Stiebel was somewhat elaborate; a very simple alternative[7] is to have the cardioid in a sliding sleeve, to adjust it roughly by hand, and finely by altering the level of the liquid in the trough, adding or subtracting liquid from a large pipette standing in one corner of the trough, until the focus is exactly right. Any good high-power dark-ground illuminator will serve the purpose.

9. Examination of light reflected from surface films. Apparatus for measuring the ellipticity of polarization of the light reflected from surfaces covered by films is described by Freundlich and others,[8] Bouhet,[9] and

[1] *J.C.S.* (1934), 1106.
[2] *Ann. Physique*, **2**, 506 (1924).
[3] *J. Physical Chem.*, **29**, 1517 (1925).
[4] *J. Chem. Physics*, **1**, 656 (1933).
[5] *J.A.C.S.* (1937), 1884.
[6] *Z. physikal. Chem.*, **147** A, 401.
[7] Adam, *Trans. Faraday Soc.*, **29**, 90 (1933).
[8] *Z. physikal. Chem.*, **128**, 321; **130**, 289 (1927).
[9] *Ann. Physique*, **15**, 5 (1931).

Tronstad,[1] besides the references given in Chap. I, § 5. The nature of the light reflected depends on the structure of the films, but the interpretation is so difficult in terms of molecules that most writers merely give an 'optical thickness' for the film, which has an unknown relation even to the actual thickness. Strachan[2] has attempted to treat the film as a two-dimensional assembly of oriented molecules, each of which scatters light, but his expressions for the optical constants are of such mathematical complexity that the connexion between the optical properties and the molecules is not easy to understand. This optical method does, however, at once indicate heterogeneity in a film, different types of film giving different constants, as Bouhet has shown.

10. The interpretation of surface-pressure and surface-potential measurements.[3] Surface pressure F is best plotted against area A, as this shows up the resemblance between the films and three-dimensional PV isothermals. For gaseous films, however, curves with FA as ordinates and F as abscissae are very useful.

If the F–A curve is asymptotic to the axis of A, never reaching a definite limiting area, the film is probably gaseous. A sensitive pressure-measuring device is needed to decide this, as some films approach the area axis fairly gently, but at a definite angle nevertheless (liquid-expanded films). An ideal gaseous film should obey equation (1) below and have a pressure of 4 dynes at 100 sq. A., 1 dyne at 400 sq. A., 0·1 dyne at 4,000 sq. A. per molecule. Most gaseous films, however, depart considerably from this (§ 12), and from the departures the amount of lateral adhesion, and the space occupied on the surface by the molecules, can be roughly estimated. Adhesion predominates if the areas are smaller than those just given.

Gaseous films are homogeneous in surface potential; if the air electrode is moved over the surface there should be no large fluctuations of potential.

If the film reaches a definite limiting area, the pressure falling steeply until this area is reached, and becoming constant, or nearly so, at larger areas, the film is a coherent one. Confirmation of this may usually be obtained by moving the air electrode over the surface; at areas greater than the limiting area there are always violent fluctuations of potential as the air electrode moves from patches of coherent liquid or solid film over regions covered only by dilute-vapour film. The surface vapour pressure may be too small to measure, and in practice there is often a certain amount of rounding off of the discontinuity between the curve of the coherent film and the region of constant surface vapour pressure. A sensitive pressure-measuring instrument is necessary for deciding whether or not a film is coherent, as measurements ought to be reliable down to 0·05 dyne or less. With a movable air electrode there is now little difficulty in deciding when the limiting area of a film is reached. There are, however, some cases when a coherent film, at moderate pressures,

[1] *Trans. Faraday Soc.*, **29**, 502 (1933); **31**, 1151 (1935). *J. Sci. Instr.*, **11**, 144 (1934).

[2] *Proc. Camb. Phil. Soc.*, **29**, 116 (1933).

[3] This section is intended as a guide to those commencing work on the films, and may be more easily understood after later sections have been read. The curves found are often puzzling at first.

shows fluctuations of potential; but these are not usually as large as those in a two-phase region covered by islands of coherent film in equilibrium with vapour film.

The molecular orientation in a coherent film can generally be ascertained in considerable detail by considering (*a*) the compressibility, and (*b*) the absolute values of the area per molecule, comparing with the areas to be expected from models of the molecules. Very convenient models can be made, approximately to a scale of 1 inch to the A., out of spheres of hard-wood, bored tetrahedrally for carbon, oxygen, and nitrogen, whose dimensions may be taken as 1·5 A. diameter; hydrogen is represented by spheres of 1 A. *Short* pegs are used so that the spheres touch. Rotation is possible round the pegs, but not bending of the pegs, so that the models imitate not only the size but the flexibility of the molecules. It is found that the horizontal cross-section of the rectangular parallelepiped just enclosing these molecular models is usually a close approximation to the area actually occupied by the molecules in the film; the area occupied in the films is practically never less than this. If it is much greater, the cause is usually to be found in a tilt of the molecules.

If there is more than a quite small degree of compressibility, there is a rearrangement of the molecules going on during compression. This is often an alteration of the angle of tilt to the vertical, but the tilt need not necessarily be a simple tilting over of the whole molecule (see § 19, on liquid expanded films, below). Deformation of complex molecules, or rearrangement by vertical motion allowing packing of local, not too large projections on the side of the molecules into the hollows of the zig-zags, or even squeezing away of loosely attached water molecules, may also account for a certain amount of compressibility.

Bearing in mind the rules that the molecules never occupy less space than the molecular models, and that the water-soluble groups always try to approach the water as closely as possible, a detailed study of the pressure-area curves will usually reveal the main features of the structure of the films. Care must be taken that the areas measured are real areas per molecule, i.e. that the whole of the material is spread out as a mono-molecular film. There is especial danger of incomplete spreading if the polar groups in the molecule have a not very large attraction for water, e.g. if they belong to the classes (*a*) and (*b*) of § 29. If the water-attractive powers of any group are unknown, a sound guide is to compare the solubility in water of simple aliphatic compounds containing two or three carbon atoms and this group, with that of a compound with an equal number of carbon atoms and a polar group such as OH, $COOCH_3$, ether, etc., whose anchoring powers for films of long-chain compounds are known and given in § 29. Obstruction of a water-soluble group by projecting hydrocarbon parts of the molecule may also endanger the strength of the anchorage to the water and the completeness of spreading of the films. The films should always be examined by dark-ground illumination if there is any doubt as to the completeness of spreading.

Surface-potential measurements are more difficult to interpret quantitatively in terms of molecules, but there is now little doubt about certain important points. The contribution of each molecule to the potential is found by dividing the surface potential (the change in the air-liquid contact potential caused by the presence of the film) by the number of molecules. It is customary to draw the analogy between the electrical double layer at the surface and a plane parallel condenser in this evaluation, and most writers[1] express the results in terms of μ, where ΔV, the surface potential, is given by

$$\Delta V = 4\pi n\mu,$$

n being the number of molecules in the film. μ would be the vertical component of the dipole moment of one film molecule if all the surface potential were due to the dipole moments of the film molecules arranged in a plane, and if the dielectric constant of the film could be treated as unity. The presence of the film molecules unquestionably causes a rearrangement of ions in the solution, and the dielectric constant cannot be unity, as there are plenty of water molecules near enough to have their normal orientation changed when the film molecules are put on.[2] The values of μ are rarely greater than a quarter of the dipole moments of molecules containing the same end groups measured by the ordinary methods.[3]

In spite of the deficiencies of this analogy with a simple plane condenser, there is some little evidence that μ does not change much, as the film is compressed and the molecules crowded, unless there is a re-orientation of the molecules of the film.[4] If θ is the angle of tilt of the dipole of the molecule to the vertical, $\bar{\mu}$ the dipole moment, and D the dielectric constant of the equivalent plane parallel condenser which would give the same potential, then

$$\mu = \frac{\bar{\mu}\cos\theta}{D}.$$

It appears that, to a first approximation, D, which includes all the effects of re-orientation and redistribution of water molecules and ions, is often independent of the closeness of packing of the molecules. Then if μ varies with the area of the film, there is a probability that the tilt of the dipole to the surface is changing. And, comparing the values of μ for two compounds of related constitution, containing the same polar group, the one with the larger value of μ probably has the axis of the dipole tilted more steeply to the surface. This has been found useful in the sterols in distinguishing between stereoisomers in which the hydroxyl group is differently oriented to the ring structure.

It must be remembered that the resultant dipole of most kinds of mole-

[1] Harkins prefers to state the results simply as $\Delta V/n$ (*J. Chem. Physics*, **1**, 860 (1933)).

[2] Cf. Schulman and Rideal, *Proc. Roy. Soc.* A, **130**, 270; Schulman and Hughes, *ibid.*, **138**, 430.

[3] Cf. Frumkin and Williams, *Proc. Nat. Acad. Sci.*, **15**, 400 (1929).

[4] Cf. Adam and others, *Proc. Roy. Soc.* A, **138**, 411; **143**, 104; **147**, 491.

cule contains several components, some of which are capable of alteration of direction relatively to each other. The forces between the film molecules and the underlying water, and the interactions of neighbouring molecules in the film, may greatly alter the normal arrangements of these component dipoles and hence the magnitude and direction of the resultant dipoles.

To sum up, a surface potential fluctuating violently from point to point indicates a film consisting of two or more surface phases. With compounds of similar end groups and similar constitution, a rise in the value of μ probably indicates an increasing tilt of the dipole to the surface. Further, chemical changes, especially those leading to ionization of the end group, may lead to large changes in the value of μ, which can usually be accounted for, qualitatively, by considering the change in distribution of ions under each molecule of the film (see for instance § 21).

When surface potentials are negative, which does occasionally occur, it indicates that the negative end of the total dipole of the molecules in the film is uppermost. One or two instances of negative surface potentials among insoluble films have been found among sterol-like compounds, but the 'record' for a negative potential has recently been handsomely broken by Frumkin's measurements[1] on ω-bromohexadecanoic acid,

$$Br(CH_2)_{15}COOH,$$

which on neutral solutions (when the carboxyl group is probably ionized so that it makes little contribution to the potential) gives about -850 mv. The film is condensed, and there is no reasonable doubt that the bromine atom at the upper end of the molecule makes a large negative contribution to the resultant moment perpendicular to the surface.

11. The main types of film. Langmuir established the existence of one type of coherent film, with insoluble substances, and of the gaseous films, with the adsorbed layers of soluble substances at an air-liquid surface. It is now known that a number of different types of insoluble film can exist with long-chain aliphatic substances; these are best classified according to the lateral adhesion between the molecules. These are

(1) condensed films, in which the molecules are closely packed, and very steeply oriented to the surface, as with the acids and alcohols investigated by Langmuir;

(2) liquid-expanded films, which are still coherent, but occupy a much larger area than the gaseous films. These can form, on the surface, a separate phase from a vapour film, with which they are in equilibrium;

(3) vapour-expanded films, which are rather similar to liquid-expanded films but have less cohesion, and do not show a region of constant surface pressure, with two distinct types of film, between coherent and gaseous or vapour film on the surface; and

(4) gaseous or vapour films, in which the molecules are separate, moving about independently, the surface pressure being exerted on the barriers by a series of collisions.

[1] *J. Chem. Physics*, **4**, 624 (1936).

A single substance may, under appropriate conditions of temperature and surface pressure, be obtained as a condensed film, either a liquid- or a vapour-expanded film, but not both, and a gaseous film. The class of vapour-expanded film is rather ill defined, and shades into the gaseous films; but the properties of these films are often so different from those of the gaseous films, and so close to the liquid-expanded films, that a separate name seems desirable. The expanded films form a state without any close parallel in three-dimensional matter. So far as is known, they are only found with long-chain aliphatic substances.

These films will be described in order of decreasing simplicity of structure.

12. Gaseous films. Much the simplest type of film is the gaseous. An ideal gaseous film would consist of molecules of negligible size, quite insoluble in water, and without any lateral adhesion for each other, though with sufficient adhesion for the water to prevent their flying off as vapour. Such ideal gaseous films are not experimentally realizable, because, unless the molecules are large, they will dissolve in the water if the attraction is high, or evaporate if it is low. Nevertheless, the properties of an ideal gaseous film can be calculated, and in some cases films can be obtained, with insoluble substances, whose properties approach quite closely, at large areas and low pressures, to those of an ideal gaseous film. In Chapter III it will be shown that the adsorbed films of soluble, capillary active substances are nearly always gaseous.

The molecules will have the usual average kinetic energy appropriate to their temperature; this is $\frac{1}{2}kT$ for each degree of freedom, where k is the gas constant per molecule, $1{\cdot}372 \times 10^{-16}$ ergs per degree. The two degrees of freedom of translational kinetic energy in the two dimensions of the surface produce the surface pressure, which is due to successive collisions between the moving film molecules and the float. It is easy to show, by the ordinary mathematics of kinetic theory, that such an ideal film would have a surface pressure F, where

$$FA = kT. \tag{1}$$

If the unit of area is the sq. A., k becomes $1{\cdot}372$. The proof of this relation follows exactly, in two dimensions, the lines of the proof of the ordinary gas laws in three, and need not be repeated here.[1]

At room temperature the product kT is about 400, in terms of sq. A. per molecule. A perfect gaseous film would thus exert a pressure of 1 dyne at 400 sq. A. It will be seen later that the molecules in gaseous films nearly always lie flat, and since the area occupied by an aliphatic substance containing some sixteen carbon atoms in the chain will be of the order 120 sq. A., the instruments used for investigating the gaseous state of the films must be capable of measuring pressures down to a very small fraction of a dyne, in order that the films may be so 'dilute' that the mole-

[1] Adam and Jessop, *Proc. Roy. Soc.* A, **110**, 423 (1926); cf. also Mitchell, *Trans. Faraday Soc.*, **31**, 980 (1935).

cules in them shall not occupy more than a small fraction of the total surface.

Equation (1) assumes that the molecules move about singly in the surface. If the product of surface pressure and area is approximately constant, and about 400 at room temperature, when the area is sufficiently

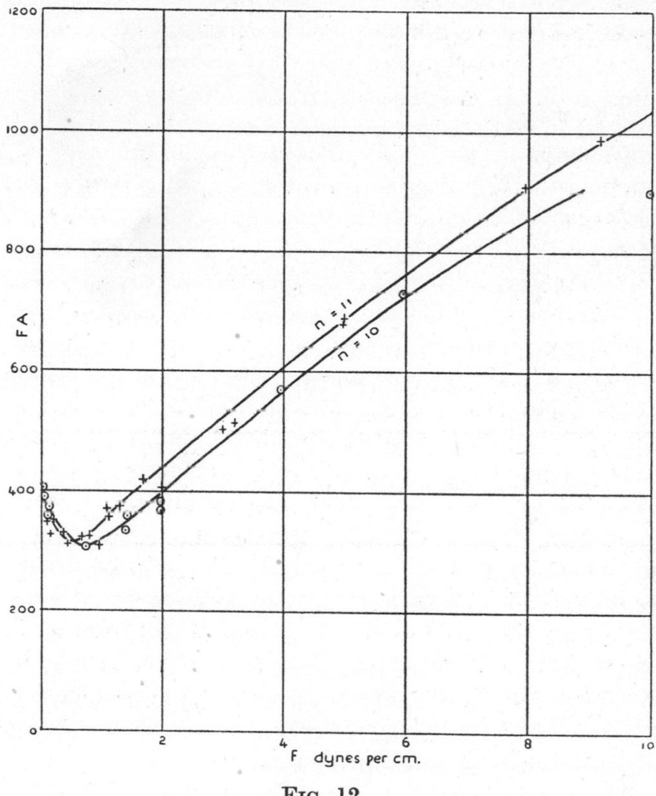

Fig. 12.

large, the film is gaseous, with *single* molecules moving in the surface. A smaller value of k in equation (1) would indicate some degree of association of the molecules into groups.

Several cases have been found in which insoluble films give nearly the theoretical value of k for single molecules. Fig. 12 shows the surface pressure-area relation found for two dibasic esters having a carboxyl group at each end,[1] plotted with the product FA against the surface pressure F. This method exhibits the deviations from the perfectly gaseous state, which would give a horizontal straight line at $FA = 400$, clearly, just as plotting PV against P shows the imperfections of actual gases.[2]

At low pressures the theoretical value of 400 for FA is attained with

[1] Adam and Jessop, *Proc. Roy. Soc.* A, **112**, 376 (1926).
[2] Cf. Preston, *Theory of Heat*, 2nd ed., ch. v, § 7 (1904).

an accuracy of about 10 per cent., showing that the value of the gas constant in surface films is not different from that in three-dimensional matter. The form of the curves at higher pressures closely resembles that of the PV–P curves for most gases under high pressure. Between 0 and 1 dyne per cm. there is a fall in the value of FA, the area being less than the theoretical for a perfect gaseous film; this is due to some lateral adhesion between the molecules. Above 1 dyne the pressure rises almost linearly, approximately according to the equation

$$FA = 85F + 0{\cdot}5kT. \tag{2}$$

Dividing (2) by F, it is clear that the area would tend to 85 sq. A. at high surface pressures, if the physical conditions of this part of the curve were maintained (this is not actually the case, as the molecules tilt, and occupy much less space in gaseous films at high compressions). The value of the first constant on the right of (2) is an indication of the area of the molecules lying flat, but it usually gives results which are rather too small.

A gaseous film can always be recognized by the surface pressure approaching the zero value asymptotically, the theoretical value of FA being approached at very low pressures. The extent of the corrections to the perfect gas law (1) is usually a good deal larger than in the cases shown in Fig. 12. There is, however, little difficulty in distinguishing between a gaseous film and any of the known coherent types. A surface-pressure curve which gives a continuously descending value of the pressure with increasing area, from a few dynes at 100 sq. A. to a few tenths at 1,000 or more, with a series of values of FA varying qualitatively in the same way as the curves of Fig. 12, is always a gaseous film. Gaseous films, moreover, are always homogeneous; their surface potential does not vary from point to point as the air electrode is moved over the surface or the film is *gently* blown about. A coherent film rarely gives surface pressures greater than its surface-vapour pressure, above 100 or 200 sq. A. per molecule, and these surface-vapour pressures are constant, rarely exceeding 0·3 dyne; and, in the two-phase region where there is a constant surface-vapour pressure, the surface is never homogeneous, violent fluctuations of surface potential being obtained as the air electrode is moved over the surface, passing over regions of coherent, or of vapour film.

The following gaseous films have been found to approach closely to the limiting value of $FA = 400$ at great dilution: the acetates of long-chain amines;[1] nonoyl trimethoxybenzene,[2]

OCH_3

$C_8H_{17}CO$—(benzene ring)—OCH_3;

OCH_3

[1] Adam, *Proc. Roy. Soc.* A, **126**, 533 (1930).
[2] *Ibid.*, **119**, 635 (1928).

the triacetate of oestriol,[1]

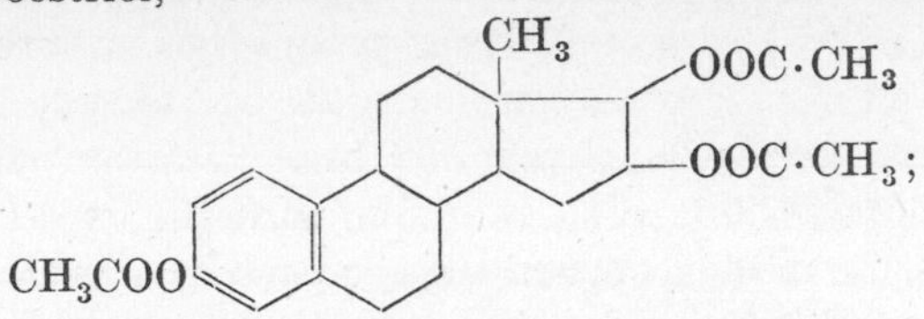

CH_3 $OOC \cdot CH_3$ $OOC \cdot CH_3$; CH_3COO

and the fatty acids on N/10 alkaline solutions[2] when first put on the surface.[3]

Adam and Jessop[4] considered that their observations on the vapour state of the fatty acids on dilute acid solutions, also of long-chain ethyl esters, nitriles, and alcohols, verified the theoretical value of k in (1) within 25 per cent. In these cases, especially in the gaseous films of the acids, there is sufficient lateral adhesion to cause very great deviations from the perfect gas law at pressures of a few tenths of a dyne, and these measurements were probably not accurate enough to decide whether the vapour films, at great dilution, consisted of single molecules moving about or whether there was association. Moss and Rideal,[5] using their sensitive instrument described above, found a nearly constant value of FA at 200, not 400, at pressures below 0·2 dyne, with myristic acid (14 carbons). Adam[6] also found that $\omega\omega'$-diresorcinyl decane,

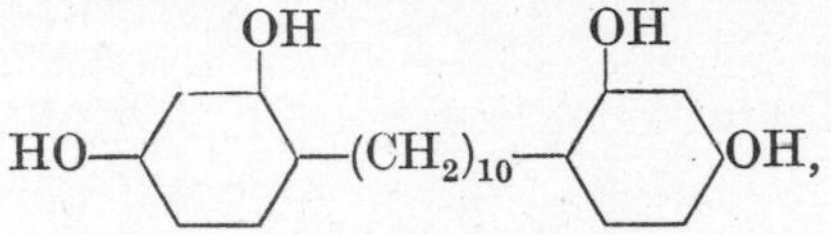

OH OH HO—$(CH_2)_{10}$—OH,

tended to a limiting value of about 200 in a film which was unquestionably gaseous, while its tetra-acetate tended to 400. It would seem that occasionally, especially when the polar groups in the molecules possess strong tendencies to association as with carboxyl or hydroxyl, the gaseous films consist mainly of double molecules moving about in the surface. On the other hand, Guastalla, using Marcelin's sensitive instrument, found that oleic acid tends at very high dilutions to a value of 400,[7] indicating single molecules. Further work on gaseous films, with very sensitive instruments at areas over 1,000 sq. A., is desirable.

It is practically certain that, in gaseous films, the molecules lie flat, with their whole length parallel to the surface. The evidence for this will, however, be left till §17.

13. Transition from gaseous to coherent films: condensation phenomena in two dimensions. With several series of long-chain fatty substances, transition phenomena have been found between the gaseous and coherent states of the films which show the most striking similarity to the condensation of vapours to liquids in three dimensions. A very sensitive means of measuring surface pressures is necessary for observing the transition from gaseous to coherent films.

[1] Adam, Danielli, and others, *Biochem. J.*, **26**, 1235 (1932).
[2] Adam and Miller, *Proc. Roy. Soc.* A, **142**, 403 (1933).
[3] These subsequently collapse to aggregates visible under dark-ground illumination.
[4] *Proc. Roy. Soc.* A, **110**, 423 (1926).
[5] *J.C.S.* (1933), 1525.
[6] *Proc. Roy. Soc.* A, **119**, 639 (1928).
[7] *Compt. rend.*, **189**, 241 (1929).

Fig. 13 shows the curves of surface pressure against area for the fatty acids with from 11 to 15 carbon atoms in the hydrocarbon chains.[1] The main diagram has the surface pressure as ordinates and the area as abscissae; inset are the *FA–F* curves. With the shorter chain acids, below about 0·1 dyne, the product *FA* is of the same order as, but somewhat below, the value for a perfect and unassociated gaseous film; Moss and

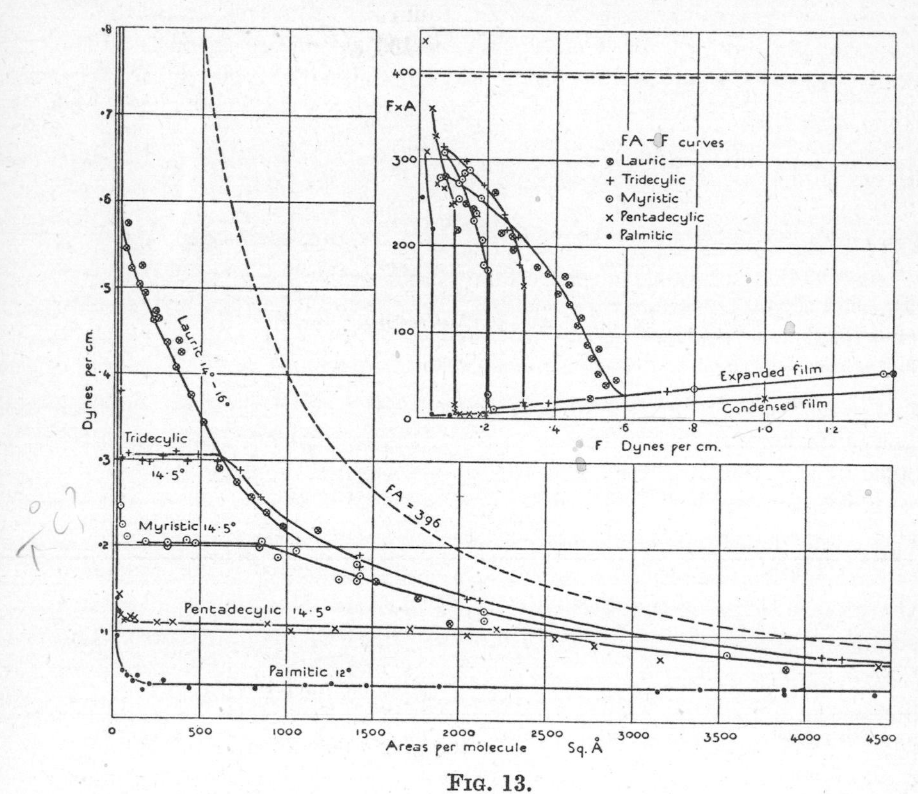

Fig. 13.

Rideal found, for one of these acids, that the vapour film was associated into double molecules.

As the area is diminished below some thousands of sq. A., where the molecules cover only a small fraction of the surface, the surface pressure rapidly becomes much smaller than that of a perfect gas, and in the four acids with the longest chains becomes constant over a considerable region. The curves are indeed a very faithful reproduction of Andrews's curves for the relation between pressure and volume, for carbon dioxide, at temperatures near the critical. The horizontal regions in the curves correspond to the vapour pressure of liquids, and indicate the presence of an equilibrium between two surface phases, the vapour film, and islands of liquid, coherent film.

It has now been shown unquestionably, by measurement of surface

[1] *Proc. Roy. Soc.* A, **110**, 423.

potential and by optical means, that the surface consists of two kinds of film in the region of constant surface-vapour pressure. The surface potential fluctuates violently,[1] at different points of the surface, at all areas between 48 and 800 sq. A. per molecule for myristic acid, that is, in the two-phase region, but is nearly constant below 48 and above 800 sq. A., i.e. where the surface consists entirely of either coherent or gaseous film. The value of the surface potential of the liquid film of myristic acid, under the surface-vapour pressure of 0·2 dyne, is 160 or 170 mv.; that of the vapour film at 800 sq. A. is 4 mv. At intermediate areas the average surface potential corresponds closely with that to be expected if the material on the surface were present only in the forms of islands of coherent film with an area of 48 sq. A. per molecule, and of vapour film at 800 sq. A. per molecule, covering the rest of the surface.

Bouhet[2] examined the degree of ellipticity of the light reflected from a water surface covered with myristic or palmitic acids, finding that the surface consisted of two kinds of patches, possessing different powers of producing elliptical polarization in the reflected light; these were the islands of coherent film, and the vapour film covering the rest of the surface.

Zocher and Stiebel,[3] examining surfaces covered by films in the two-phase region, by dark-ground illumination, considered that they could see the outlines of some of the islands of coherent film by the lines of dust particles which these collected round their boundaries as they floated about on the surface.

The value of the surface pressure in the two-phase region where it is constant is called the 'surface-vapour pressure'; it measures the tendency of the molecules to escape from the liquid film into the vapour film, and is smaller the greater the lateral adhesion between the molecules. The adhesion increases steadily the longer the hydrocarbon chains; in tridecylic acid it first becomes great enough to form a separate liquid phase; lauric acid, with twelve carbons, is at, or just above, its 'critical point'.

Table II shows the principal measurements of surface-vapour pressure recorded. While many coherent films show no measurable pressure at areas slightly greater than that at which the molecules are closely packed, owing to the lateral adhesion being very high, at least six different homologous series have been found to show surface-evaporation phenomena with a measurable constant pressure. The highest surface-vapour pressure yet recorded is 0·39 dyne; this may seem small, but considering the extreme thinness of the film, it is really fairly large. The molecules are lying flat, and therefore the thickness of the film perpendicular to the surface is about 4·5 A.; a surface pressure of 0·39 dyne per cm. is thus roughly $8{\cdot}7\times10^6$ dyne per sq. cm., or 8·5 atmospheres. This is smaller than the critical pressure of most liquids in three dimensions, but is not many times smaller.

The variation of surface-vapour pressure with temperature has not yet been measured; the difficulties of sufficiently accurate measurement except at room

[1] Adam and Harding, *Proc. Roy. Soc.* A, **138**, 419 (1932); Schulman and Hughes, *ibid.*, **138**, 430 (1932).

[2] *Ann. Physique*, **15**, 102 (1931).

[3] *Z. physikal. Chem.*, **147** A, 401 (1930).

TABLE II

Surface-vapour Pressures

Substance	Number of carbons in chain $C_n H_{2n+1}$	Vapour pressure, dynes per cm.	Reference[2]
Tridecylic acid	12	0·30	*g*
Myristic acid[1]	13	0·19	"
Pentadecylic acid[1]	14	0·11	"
Palmitic acid[1]	15	0·04	"
Myristic nitrile	13	0·39	*t*
Palmitic nitrile	15	0·15	*g*
Margaric nitrile	16	0·10	"
Stearic nitrile	17	0·04	"
Tetradecyl alcohol	13	0·11	"
Hexadecyl alcohol	15	0·02	"
α-monomyristin	13	0·17	*j*
α-monopalmitin	15	$<0·04$	"
Ethyl margarate	16	0·10	*g*
Ethyl stearate	17	0·03	"
p-nonyl phenol	9	0·03	*j*
Lauryl dimethoxybenzene	12	0·07	*k*
Cholesterol, and many derivatives, tripalmitin, pentaerythritol tetrapalmitate, and higher members of the preceding series	..	$<0·02$	..

[1] The acids were examined on very dilute (N/50) HCl, all the other compounds on water.

[2] References by letter are to papers listed below Table III.

temperature are too great. It may be roughly estimated by considering that, since one additional CH_2 group on a chain alters the other properties of a film which depend on lateral adhesion, to the same degree as a decrease of temperature of 8–10°, the differences shown in Fig. 13 between the surface-vapour pressures of the 13, 14, and 15 carbon acids correspond to this interval of temperature; i.e. that dF_p/dT is of the order 0·01 dyne per cm. per degree, F_p being the surface-vapour pressure.

14. Condensed films. These are the most commonly found films. In them the molecules adhere to each other laterally, very strongly, and if there is more space on the surface than can be covered by the adhering molecules, the surface becomes a two-phase system, at once detectable by the fluctuations of surface potential, when the electrode is moved, or the film blown along the surface. The form of the surface pressure-area curves for condensed films is always a nearly sudden development of pressure as the area is reduced to that at which the molecules are closely packed. Further reduction of area increases the pressure very rapidly. There are several distinguishable kinds of condensed films.

Three typical instances are shown in Fig. 14 which gives the surface pressure as ordinates and the area per molecule as abscissae. Curve I is that for the fatty acids on distilled water, curve III for the saturated acids on dilute (N/10 to N/100) hydrochloric acid, and curve IV for the $\alpha\beta$ unsaturated iso-oleic acid,

$$CH_3(CH_2)_{14}CH{=}CH \cdot COOH,$$

also on dilute acid.

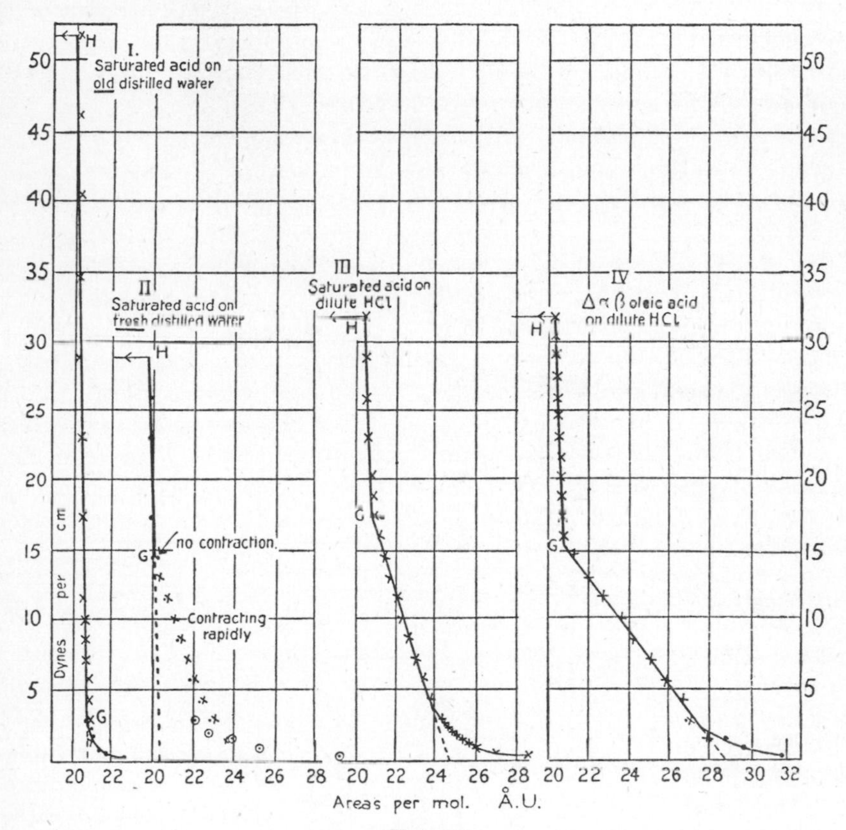

FIG. 14.

The upper part of all these curves is the same; curve I is steep for its whole length, and if produced cuts the abscissa at 20·5 sq. A.

With the fatty acids on distilled water the very steep curve I continues almost down to zero pressure. On dilute acid solutions, however, this steep curve only occurs above about 17 dynes per cm., and below this pressure there is a second, nearly straight portion of the curve (see curve III), cutting the abscissa at about 25 sq. A. Both the upper and lower parts of these curves are very little changed when the number of carbon atoms in the acid is altered from 14 to 22 carbon atoms: the steep curve always tends to an area within 1 sq. A. of 20·5; the lower part on acid solutions tends to 25 sq. A. for the medium-chain acids, about 16 carbons, and to very slightly smaller areas for longer chain acids (24 for the 22 carbon acid).[1] The lower part of curve IV, for an acid in which the end group is —CH:CH·COOH instead of the saturated —CH_2·CH_2·COOH, reaches 28·7, a decidedly larger area.[2] It is clear that the limiting areas of the films on dilute acid depend on the nature of the end groups.

Fig. 15 and Table III give the results of measurements on numerous other series of compounds. Curve I is identical with curve I of the preceding figure, and is obtained on over a dozen different homologous series at some surface pressure. With all these compounds the area is the same, within about 1 sq. A., i.e. 20·5 sq. A. at no compression. Curves to the left of curve I, i.e. with smaller areas, have never been obtained with fully spread films, which show no unspread patches when examined by Zocher and Stiebel's dark-ground illumination. Moreover, when areas as small as this are found, the films are always very incompressible, and the curves very steep.

What is the difference in structure in the films which gives rise to so many different curves for various substances in condensed films ? In every case the molecules appear to be in contact, and the films are coherent, so that the differences must be due to differences in the shape and size, or the mode of packing of the molecules. Curve I is, without doubt, that of a film composed of the long hydrocarbon chains closely packed. Obviously these long-chain compounds cannot pack more closely than with their long chains lying side by side and oriented vertically, although if their end groups were thicker than the chains, they might pack to larger areas. Films giving curve I will be referred to as those with '*close-packed chains*'.

A study of the compressibility confirms the conclusion that the chains are closely packed, and that there is practically no rearrangement in the films during compression. With chains of seventeen carbon atoms[3] the decrease in area for an additional 25 dynes per cm. compression is only 1 per cent. The thickness of the film is roughly 26 A., calculating from the density of the substance in bulk. Each dyne per cm. on the film must thus be a lateral compression of about $3{\cdot}85 \times 10^6$ dynes per sq. cm., or 3·8 atmospheres. This affords a means of comparing the compressibility of the film with long-chain substances in bulk; it is only about 25 per cent. more compressible than a long-chain paraffin, when the pressure is applied from all sides, and the molecules cannot escape from compression by rearrangement. This result has been reached by assuming that the whole length of the molecules resists compression in the films; had only a part of the length taken the pressure, the resistance to compression of the parts really in contact would have been much higher. It is scarcely possible that these compounds, in two dimensions, should resist compression more strongly than they do in three; so that the great incompressibility of curve I indicates that the molecules are closely packed over their whole length.

Though it is practically certain that the long chains are closely packed when curve I is obtained, it is not, however, certain that they are vertical. Reasoning

[1] Cf. Adam and Harding, *Proc. Roy. Soc.* A, **138**, 423 (1932).

[2] Hughes (*J.C.S.* (1933), 339) gives 26·4 sq. A. for the limiting area of this acid.

[3] *Proc. Roy. Soc.* A, **101**, 458 (1922).

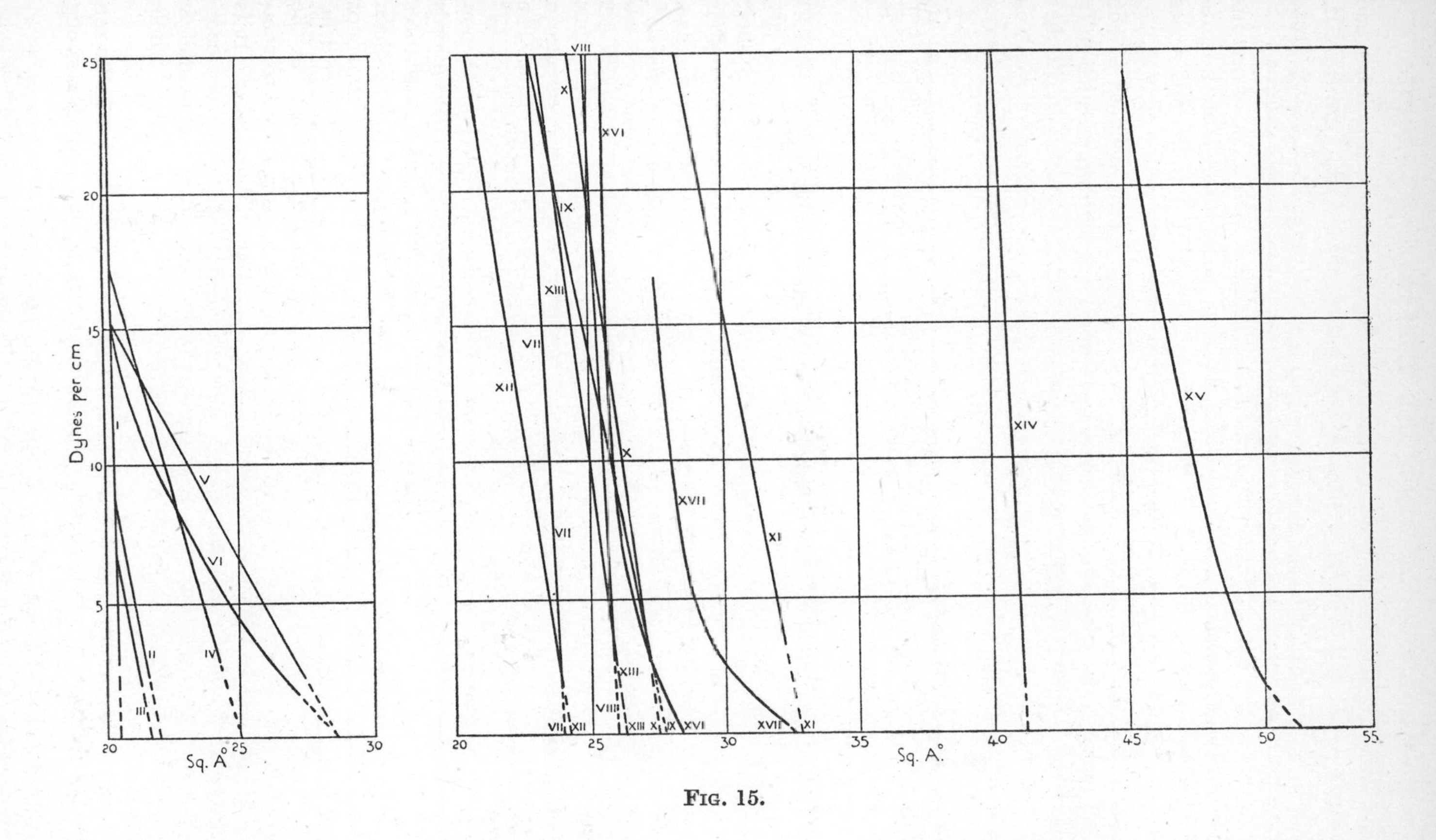

FIG. 15.

TABLE III

Condensed films of long-chain compounds $C_n H_{2n+1} X$

Curve	Series	End group X	Area at zero compression, sq. A. per molecule	Minimum number, n, of carbons in chain, to render film condensed at 15°	Reference
I	Acids on water.	—COOH	20·5	(< 13)	a, b
I	Dibasic esters.	—$COOC_2H_5$ (*each end*)	20·5	17	i
I	Amines (on alkaline solution).	—CH_2NH_2	20·5	13	o
I	Amides.	—$CONH_2$	20·5	13	b, e
I	Methyl ketones.	—$COCH_3$	20·5	14	h
I	Triglycerides (area per *chain*).	—$COOCH_2$	20·5	(10)	b, 1
I	Ureas (*above transition temperature*).	—$NH{\cdot}CO{\cdot}NH_2$	20·5	(13)	b, e, f
I	Acetamides (*below transition temp.*).	—$NH{\cdot}CO{\cdot}CH_3$	20·5	16	f
II	Esters of saturated acids.	—COOR	22·0	various	b, c, e, f
III	Alcohols.	—CH_2OH	21·6	11	b, c, f
IV	Acids on dilute HCl.	—COOH	25·1	14	a, b, c, f, n
V	Iso-oleic acid on HCl.	—CH:CH·COOH	28·7	15	b, c
VI	Ethyl iso-oleate.	—$CH{:}CH{\cdot}COOC_2H_5$	28·7	16	e
VII	Phenols, and other simple *p*-substituted benzene compounds.	—C_6H_4—OH	24·0	12	d, j
VII		—C_6H_4—OCH_3	24·0	—	d, j
VII		—C_6H_4—NH_2	24·0	—	d, j
VIII	Ureas (*below transition temperature*).	—$NH{\cdot}CO{\cdot}NH_2$	26·0	(13)	b, e, f
IX	Nitriles.	—C≡N	27·7	17	b, e, f, t
X	α-Bromo-acids on HCl. n = 16–19	—CHBr·COOH	27·2	16	e
XI	α-Bromo-acids on HCl. n = 15	—CHBr·COOH	32·8	16	e
XII	Acetamides (*above transition temp.*).	—$NH{\cdot}CO{\cdot}CH_3$	24·2	16	f

XIII	α-Monoglycerides.	$—COOCH_2\cdot CHOH\cdot CH_2OH$	26·3	16	*j*
XIV	Cholesterol.	..	40·8	—	*l, m*
XV	Hydrolecithin.	..	52·0	—	*h*
XVI	Acyl resorcinols.	—CO⟨ring⟩OH, OH	(28)	< 7	*k*
XVII	Acyl phloroglucinols.	—CO⟨ring⟩OH, OH, OH	(32)	< 7	*k*
..	Acetanilide.	—⟨ring⟩$NH\cdot CO\cdot CH_3$	28·2 or 25·8	—	*d*
..	Aldoximes.	—CH = NOH	24 to 25·4	14	*e, u*
..	Alkyl resorcinols.	—⟨ring⟩OH, OH	(28)	18	*k*
..	Acetates.	$—O\cdot CO\cdot CH_3$	23	16	*f*
..	*p*-Alkyl cyclohexanols.	$—HC<(CH_2—CH_2)(CH_2—CH_2)>CHOH$	30	*c.* 11	2
..	Lactones.	$—CH$ (—O—) CO, $CH_2\cdot CH_2$	29	—	*q*

(*a*) Adam, *Proc. Roy. Soc.* A, **99**, 336 (1921). (*b*) Adam, *ibid.*, **101**, 452 (1922). (*c*) Adam., *ibid.*, **101**, 516 (1922). (*d*) Adam, *ibid.*, **103**, 676 (1923). (*e*) Adam, *ibid.*, **103**, 687 (1923). (*f*) Adam and Dyer, *ibid.*, **106**, 694 (1924). (*g*) Adam and Jessop, *ibid.*, **110**, 423 (1926). (*h*) Adam and Jessop, *ibid.*, **112**, 362 (1926). (*i*) Adam and Jessop, *ibid.*, **112**, 376 (1926). (*j*) Adam, Berry, and Turner, *ibid.*, **117**, 532 (1928). (*k*) Adam, *ibid.*, **119**, 628 (1928). (*l*) Adam and Jessop, *ibid.*, **120**, 473 (1928). (*m*) Adam and Rosenheim, *ibid.*, **126**, 25 (1929). (*n*) Adam, *ibid.*, **126**, 366 (1930). (*o*) Adam, *ibid.*, **126**, 526 (1930). (*p*) Adam and Harding, *ibid.*, **138**, 411 (1932). (*q*) Adam, *ibid.*, **140**, 223 (1933). (*r*) Adam and Miller, *ibid.*, **142**, 401 (1933). (*s*) Adam and Miller, *ibid.*, **142**, 416 (1933). (*t*) Adam and Harding, *ibid.*, **143**, 104 (1933). (*u*) Adam, Danielli, and Harding, *ibid.*, **147**, 491 (1934).

(1) Gorter and Grendel, *Proc. K. Akad. Wetensch. Amsterdam*, **29**, 1268 (1926). (2) Adam, Danielli, *et. al.*, *Biochem. J.*, **26**, 1233 (1932).

from the evidence on the films alone, it would appear that they are vertical, for very nearly the same area is found with a large number of different end groups and with lengths of chain varying from 14 to 22 or more carbons. For the area to remain the same it is only necessary that the angle of tilt to the surface should be the same in every case; but it is difficult to see why a large variety of lengths of molecule, and of end groups, should give a distribution of force round the molecules such as to orient them all at the same angle, unless this is vertical. In crystals, however, the area of long chains parallel and closely packed is 18·4 sq. A.,[1] i.e. about 10 per cent. less than the area in the films of closely packed chains on water. Though the measurements on the films are less accurate than those on the crystals (the figure of 20·5 sq. A. can be relied on to 5 per cent. or slightly better), there is undoubtedly a difference in area. Either, then, the chains are packed more tightly in the crystal than in the films, or they are tilted to about 26½° to the vertical in the films, the packing being the same as in the crystals.

If the chains are vertical, the larger area required in the films is probably due to the molecules of water. The influence of the water molecules underlying the films will naturally be to increase their area; these molecules are in constant motion along the surface, and must exert a certain amount of disrupting force antagonistic to the lateral adhesions between the long chains. Again, it is probable that a certain number of water molecules are entrapped among the film molecules, and this also may cause a greater area than corresponds to the packing in the dry crystals.

Lyons and Rideal[2] considered that the chains of the molecules in the film are packed as closely as in crystals, and that the reason why they tilt over to the angle of 26½° to the vertical, at which the area is 20·5 sq. A. in the plane of the surface, is that at this angle the zigzag chains of carbon atoms interlock exactly. If the zigzag chains are vertical it is considered that they will interlock, through the points on one molecule coming at the same level as the hollows in the next; tilting first throws the zigzags out of step, but when the tilt reaches 26½° they again interlock, the next lower point coming into step. This would give the observed area of 20·5 sq. A. very closely. Further tilting throws the zigzags again out of step until a tilt of 45° is reached, giving an area of 26·1 sq. A. They considered that, for solid condensed films, these two areas are the most probable. The theory has been criticized[3] and there appears no valid evidence for the occurrence of the second interlocking position at 26·1 sq. A. The question is still open, however, whether the area of 20·5 sq. A. for the films with close-packed chains is due to the chains being packed exactly as in crystals, at a tilt of 26½°, or to the chains being vertical and packed less closely, owing to the influence of the water molecules.

The meaning of the larger areas found with the other curves of Figs. 14 and 15 now requires attention. They range all the way from 21·7 for the alcohols up to 40·8 for cholesterol and 52 for the lecithin group, and it is the nature of the end groups which determines these areas, for in practically all cases they are independent of the length of the chains, provided the films are condensed.[4]

[1] Cf. Müller, *Proc. Roy. Soc.* A, **114**, 542; **120**, 437 (1927–8).

[2] *Ibid.*, **124**, 333 (1929).

[3] Adam, *ibid.*, **126**, 536 (1930).

[4] In the bromo-acids there is a considerable effect on the curve when the chain

There is no doubt that, in many cases, the *size* of the end groups is responsible for the areas. In most cases the groups which would be expected to be large from the constitutional formulae give films with large areas at zero compression; thus the bromo-acids are decidedly larger than the simple acids; the cyclohexanols and the polyphenols XVI and XVII are larger than the simple benzene derivatives VII, and cholesterol is very bulky indeed. The nitriles give 27·7, an area which might appear large at first sight; but the volume of the C⋮N group, as indicated by the 'parachor',[1] is large, and the size is due to the triple bond between the carbon and the nitrogen. Perhaps, here, the area of the film is due to contact between the C⋮N groups, the area measured being really that of the exterior limits of the electron orbits of the six valency electrons which join the carbon to the nitrogen.

In other cases there is no obvious correlation between the size of the end group as expected from the constitutional formula, and the area in the films. Thus the esters II give smaller areas than the acids on dilute acid; the $\alpha\beta$ unsaturated iso-oleic acid and its ester give areas that are obviously determined in some way by the double bond (28·7). This might be due to the local swelling caused by the double bond, but since the volume of a double bond (as indicated by the parachor) is much smaller than that of the triple bond, and this area is greater than that of the nitriles, it seems more likely that the large area is due to a sudden bend in the molecule at the double bond, causing packing to be more difficult than with the simple zigzag of the saturated chains. Those acids such as erucic and brassidic, which have 22 carbons in the chain and a double bond near the middle, do not show this increase in area due to the double bond, probably because the flexibility of the chains allows the awkwardly shaped ethylenic linkage to be tucked away, provided it is not too close to the end groups.

The areas of the curves, when greater than those of close-packed chains (curve I), give a measure of the cross-section of the head groups of the molecules, as packed in the films. Since, however, we do not know the orientation of the end groups to the surface, these areas do not tell us much about the real size of these groups. The films in which the chains are prevented from packing closely by the end groups are in some cases easily rearranged by compression, in others not, the compressibility being either high or low. When the compressibility is high, as in the curves for the acids on dilute-acid solutions (lower part of curves IV and V), the nitriles, or the acetamides (curves IX and XII), the area is so much altered by compression that little importance can be ascribed to its numerical value. The packing of the heads of the molecules is changed by compression. This might occur in several ways: either the heads themselves are compressible, or they can be tucked away into recesses in the chains of

becomes longer than 15 carbons; in the aldoximes (*e*) and the alcohols (*f*), there appears to be a slight effect.

[1] *J.C.S.* (1924), 1179; cf. Chap. IV, § 11.

neighbouring molecules, by some vertical rearrangement of the molecules, under the lateral compression. There is no difficulty in this supposition of recesses in the chains, for the analysis of crystal structure has proved that the chains are zigzag structures, not straight. It is not possible to decide which of these two hypotheses is correct, but the second is perhaps the more probable, since those end groups which are very bulky and could not be tucked away into the chains always give films of the incompressible type. This type of condensed film has been called '*close-packed heads, rearranged by compression*'.

Instances of films with closely packed heads, in which there is no appreciable rearrangement by compression, are the phenols and resorcinols (curves VII and XVI), the ureas and the monoglycerides (VIII and XIII). In these cases the areas are again the cross-section of the end groups, as packed in the films; but until more is known about the orientation of these end groups, and the manner in which they fit into one another and into any parts of the chains with which they come into contact, interpretation of these areas is difficult.

Bragg's measurements on the crystals of certain aromatic compounds[1] gave about 21·5 sq. A. for the cross-section of naphthalene and anthracene molecules, as packed in the crystals, the section being taken perpendicular to the plane of the rings of the molecules. The area of cross-section of the benzene ring, as packed in the films shown by curve VII, is about 24 sq. A. The packing thus appears to be somewhat looser than that in the crystals, or there is some tilt in the benzene rings in the films. The packing in the crystals is a criss-cross arrangement and could probably be easily varied; also a tilt is quite possible.

The compressibility of the films in curve VII is about the same as that of benzene itself in bulk, if we assume that the whole of the compression on the films is taken by a layer 6 A. thick, which is about the width of the benzene ring (*d*). This is some confirmation of the view that the heads of the molecules alone are closely packed in these films. The compressibilities of the urea derivatives and of the monoglycerides (VIII and XIII) are also so small as to be consistent with the view that the molecules are held apart at this packing, mainly by the structure formed by the closely packed heads.

Films of this type have been called '*close-packed heads, not rearranged by compression*'.

The arrangement of the chains in the molecules, when the heads have packed closely, is a matter of speculation at present. There can, however, be little doubt that the chains do not remain vertical, but tilt over until the space above the heads is filled as completely as possible. The ordinary stereochemical theory of Organic Chemistry requires that the long chains should be flexible, with a joint at every carbon atom produced by the power of free rotation about the carbon-to-carbon linkage; and evidence as to the flexibility of the chains will appear at various points in this

[1] *Proc. Physical Soc.*, **34**, 33 (1921); **35**, 167 (1922). *X-Rays and Crystal Structure*, 4th ed., 233 (1924).

chapter. It is possible that the tilt will not be a regular one, for the chains can bend in a variety of ways.

15. Changes of state in condensed films: allotropy. In several cases one substance forms two different condensed films, with a temperature of transition between them. Thus the urea derivatives (*b*, *e*, *f*) give curve VIII, with an area 26 sq. A. at no compression, below 28° (for the octadecyl compound), but at a few degrees above this temperature curve I with close-packed chains is obtained. It appears that there is a stable structure of the $NH \cdot CO \cdot NH_2$ end groups formed below the transition temperature, which is strong enough to resist compression. When the temperature reaches 28° this structure becomes unstable, or melts, so that the chains are then free to come together. With the ureas the low-temperature curve is solid, and the temperature of transition is raised by about 2° for each additional carbon atom in the chain. Hexadecyl acetanilide (*d*) packs into two forms, in just the same manner as the ureas, the transition temperature being about 27°, and the areas at no compression being 28·2 and 25·8 sq. A.

A change of state in the opposite direction with temperature is given by the acetamide derivatives which have the end group $NH \cdot CO \cdot CH_3$ (*f*). These give curve I and close-packed chains below, and curve XII above the transition temperature. The low-temperature film is here solid, and the high-temperature liquid. This is one of the few cases where a definite, sharply marked melting-point has been found in the films. A possible mechanism for the change is as follows: the $NH \cdot CO \cdot CH_3$ heads may be slightly asymmetric, with a projection to one side. In the solid, low-temperature state the molecules may not be able to rotate freely about their long axis, and the projections on the heads may be tucked away into recesses on the zigzags of neighbouring molecules. At the temperature of transition the power of free rotation may suddenly be developed; then the films will become liquid, and the projection will rotate, sweeping out a larger area than that of the close-packed chains, and forcing the molecules slightly apart so that the film becomes suddenly and definitely liquid.

These changes of state appear to be in no way different from allotropic changes in matter in bulk, and it is interesting to see how the break-down or 'melting' of a fairly small detail of the structure, consolidated mainly by the cohesive forces between a few carbon atoms only, may be the cause of such allotropic changes.

Reference has frequently been made to the solid and liquid states of the films. The solidity may be detected, if present, by dusting the surface with talc or other light powder, and blowing gently; if the film is solid, the powder does not move appreciably. The solidity or otherwise of the films depends on the adhesive forces between both heads and chains. At about 16 carbons in the chain the alcohols are liquid and the acids solid, although the compression curve is practically the same and both appear to give the 'close-packed chain' type of structure.[1] When the chains are over

[1] Adam, *Proc. Roy. Soc.* A, **101**, 465 (1922).

24 carbons in length, practically all films are solid.[1] Langmuir and Schaefer[2] found that films of calcium and barium stearate were very rigid; the divalent ions help to bring two chains close together. Sometimes the rigidity is very great; films have been known to form a bridge across a trough 14 cm. wide, with a pressure of 2 or 3 dynes per cm. (say 10 atmospheres) on one side, and no support on the other, without moving. Supercooling is a common phenomenon in the films, and melting is rarely observed to be sharp. This is a natural result of the fact that the molecules are deposited on the surface at random, and the solid aggregates first formed may be rearranged very slowly to form larger solid patches.

The rigidity of some solid films has been measured by Mouquin and Rideal.[3] It diminishes rapidly with rising temperature, when approaching the melting-point. It is difficult to interpret the results of rigidity measurements on the films in terms of intermolecular forces, since the solid films are almost certainly, from the hasty manner in which they are formed, heterogeneous masses of very small and irregular two-dimensional crystals.

16. Hysteresis and elastic after-working in the condensed films. As a rule, if the compression on the films is reduced, they expand nearly along the original curve of compression, with but little time-lag. In the neighbourhood of the transition temperature of the urea derivatives, however, a decided difference between the curve of compression and of decompression was found (*f*).

Elastic after-working has been found to be pronounced with hydrolecithin (*h*, p. 368), and with dodecyl phenol. In both these films the heads of the molecules are in contact. On reducing the area the pressure rose suddenly and fell off slowly, reaching in about ten minutes a value much smaller than the initial pressure. On increasing the area the pressure first fell, and then slowly rose to a final value. In both these films the heads of the molecules are in contact. The aromatic rings in crystals are probably packed with the planes of the different rings not the same, so that there is an interlacing network in the layer of molecules which constitutes the unit of the crystal; the fairly close correspondence between the areas occupied by the molecules in the films and in the crystals indicates that the structure of the films is somewhat similar. Perhaps this slow response to changes in lateral compression in the simple substance, dodecyl phenol, is due to the rings altering their angle of packing with difficulty.

Signs of elastic afterworking have been observed in a number of cases, though never so pronounced as in the above two. There seems to be a slight delay in reaching equilibrium in the films of myristic acid, especially in the transition region between the expanded and condensed states. A closer investigation of this phenomenon is needed.

17. Orientation of molecules in the condensed and gaseous films. Summarizing the evidence given above as to the arrangement of the

[1] Adam and Dyer, *Proc. Roy. Soc.* A, **106**, 705 (1924). [2] *J.A.C.S.* (1936), 284.

[3] *Proc. Roy. Soc.* A, **114**, 690 (1927). Cf. also Talmud and others, *Z. physikal. Chem.* A, **151**, 401 (1930).

molecules of long-chain aliphatic compounds in the condensed films, it may be said that in the films with close-packed chains the general direction of the chains is probably upright, apart from the usual zigzags in the carbon-to-carbon linkage rendered necessary by the angle of $109\frac{1}{2}°$ between the valencies; if there is any tilt to the vertical it is not over $26\frac{1}{2}°$. If this type of film is formed the end groups must either be smaller in cross-section than the hydrocarbon chains (i.e. less than 20·5 sq. A.), or the amount by which they project must not be too great to be tucked away into the hollows in the zigzags of the hydrocarbon chains of adjacent molecules. When films *with close-packed heads, rearranged by compression*, occur the end groups are too large at low compressions for the area of 20·5 sq. A., but higher compressions may either deform the end groups in such a way that they occupy less space on the surface or, more probably, cause the end groups to tuck away more or less completely into the recesses of the chains of neighbouring molecules, adjacent molecules moving up and down perpendicular to the surface in order to permit this rearrangement. In the case of films *with close-packed heads, not rearranged by compression*, the end groups are too large to be tucked away, either laterally or perpendicularly to the surface, and often take the greater part of the compression themselves. Thus the chains may be permanently kept apart at distances larger than that of close-packed chains, sometimes a good deal larger; it is probable that the chains then fill up the extra space as completely as possible above the end groups, either by tilting uniformly, preserving the flat zigzag form which is the nearest approach to a straight chain ever obtained, or by tilting and bending irregularly, rotation about the valency linkages occurring at the carbon atoms.

In the gaseous films there are several lines of evidence that the molecules lie flat, when sufficient space is allowed. Two of these are due to Langmuir. The first really refers to the adsorbed films of slightly soluble, capillary active substances, and will be described in full in Chap. III, § 5. It can be shown that the work of adsorption is increased by a constant amount for each CH_2 group added to the chain, so that the relation of every CH_2 to the water surface is the same, whatever its position in the chain. This can only be the case if the groups lie flat in the surface. These adsorbed, gaseous films form a continuous series, as the chains are lengthened, with the gaseous films of insoluble substances, so that there is every reason to suppose that the orientation in the gaseous films of insoluble substances is the same.

The second line is that, when calculations are made of the energies of molecules in various positions, arising from the fields of attractive force round the molecule, it is found that, *for an isolated molecule* on a water surface, the flat position has the least energy.[1] In such calculations the magnitude of the work done in bringing the molecules into any assigned position relative to the water molecules is calculated on the assumption that the surface energy of the molecule is the same as that of an equal

[1] *3rd Colloid Symposium Monograph*, 75 (1925).

area of a macroscopic surface of similar constitution, e.g. hydrocarbon or water.

The third evidence is that it is often possible to change a coherent film, condensed or liquid-expanded, into a gaseous film simply by introducing into the molecule a second point of attraction to the water, some distance from the first. These two water-soluble groups would naturally make the molecules lie flat. Thus the following form good gaseous films:

(1) $C_2H_5OOC \cdot (CH_2)_{11} \cdot COOC_2H_5$;

(2) HO–C_6H_3(OH)–$(CH_2)_{10}$–C_6H_3(OH)–OH, and its tetra-acetate;

(3) various derivatives of oestrin or of sterols containing two widely separated water-soluble groups.[1]

The corresponding compounds with a hydrocarbon group or hydrogen atom instead of the water-soluble group are either coherent films or vapour-expanded with much more lateral adhesion between the molecules.

With certain substances, such as oleic acid, which have a double linkage in the middle of the chain, it is possible to transform a coherent into a gaseous film simply by introducing potassium permanganate into the underlying water.[2] This tends to oxidize the double bond by adding two hydroxyl groups, and so to make the molecules lie flat. All the compounds tried which had a double bond in the middle of the chain, formed gaseous films on adding a suitable amount of permanganate to the water; but compounds with the double bond in the $\alpha\beta$ position, or saturated compounds, remained coherent films in the presence of the oxidizing agent.

Under conditions of high lateral compression gaseous films may reach areas much less than that of the molecules lying flat. Thus oleic acid on permanganate occupies an area of about 48 sq. A. at 16 dynes; and the soluble gaseous film of caproic acid (Chap. III, § 4) 28·6 sq. A. at 40 dynes. It appears that high lateral pressures can cause the molecules of gaseous films to tilt, when the area available for them is less than the area of the molecules lying flat. Confirmation of this is given by some measurements of surface potential. Certain derivatives of oestrin[3] give a constant value of μ (a measure of the surface potential per molecule, § 10) in gaseous films at areas where there is room for the molecules to lie flat, but the value alters, indicating tilt of the molecules, at smaller areas; and the same has been observed with dibasic esters with a water-attracting group at each end.[4]

18. Expanded films. A very interesting state of the films, intermediate in area and other properties between the gaseous and the condensed states, is very often found with the long-chain aliphatic substances.

[1] See references, § 25.

[2] Adam and Jessop, *Proc. Roy. Soc.* A, **112**, 367, 371 (1926).

[3] Adam, Danielli, *et. al.*, *Biochem. J.*, **26**, 1236 (1932).

[4] Adam, Danielli, and Harding, *Proc. Roy. Soc.* A, **147**, 493 (1934).

This is the 'expanded' state. Some of Langmuir's original surface pressure-area curves, notably that of oleic acid, were of the expanded type; in 1920[1] Labrouste noted its occurrence in a number of cases and described the change from condensed to expanded films at low surface pressures; Adam and others (esp. *c*, *h*)[2] mapped the course of the change more thoroughly, and have shown that two types of expanded film may occur

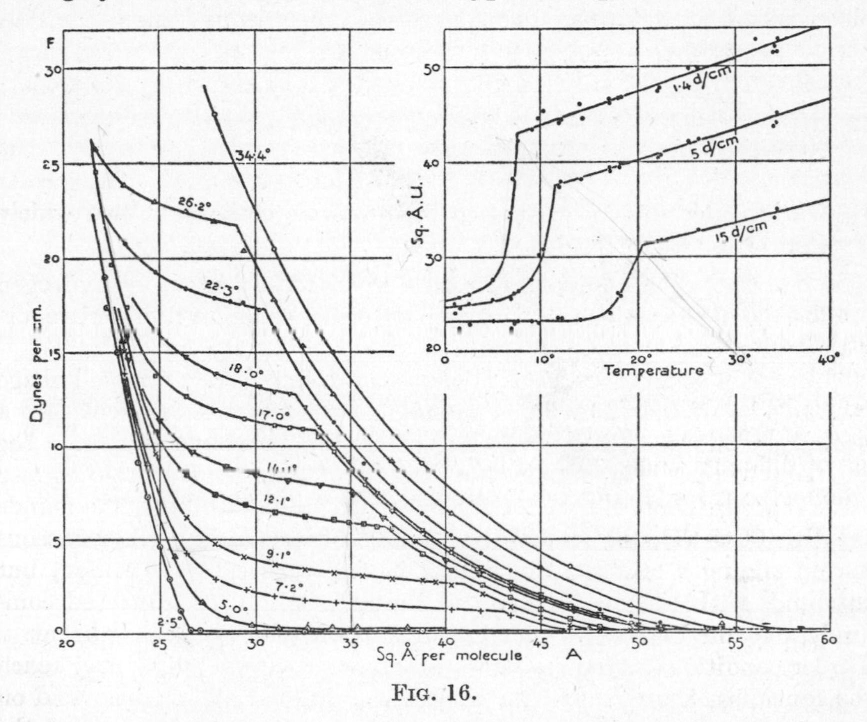

FIG. 16.

(one or the other, but never both, on the same substance), the coherent 'liquid-expanded' type and the non-coherent 'vapour-expanded' film, which is really continuous with the gaseous type of film, though it has so much residual cohesion between the molecules that it is convenient to treat it separately from the gaseous films.

Fig. 16 shows the effect of temperature on the pressure-area curves of myristic acid, on dilute acid solutions, between 2° and 35°; inset is the variation of area with temperature at three different surface pressures (*h*). This change is typical of the changes in area accompanying expansion in many other aliphatic compounds. At the lowest temperature the film is wholly condensed, the lower part being of the 'close-packed heads, re-arranged by compression' type; at the highest it is wholly expanded. At intermediate temperatures the films are expanded up to a certain pressure, which is higher the higher the temperature; once this pressure is exceeded a fairly sudden decrease of area commences, and the film begins to change

[1] *Ann. Physique*, **14**, 164 (1920).

[2] See foot of Table III; also Nutting and Harkins, *J.A.C.S.* (1939), 2040.

into the condensed film. It is always found that the curves of the transition region between expanded and condensed films are nearly, but not quite, horizontal at the right-hand end, forming an abrupt angle with the expanded curve; at the left-hand end, however, they slope upwards much more steeply and change almost imperceptibly into the condensed curves.

The expanded films tend to a definite area at low compressions, about 48 sq. A., at room temperature; they are coherent, and show a surface-vapour pressure of about 0·19 dyne (compare Fig. 13). At areas greater than this the surface is heterogeneous and can be shown by electrical or optical methods to consist of two types of film. As the temperature is increased there is no change of form in the expanded curves, but they move nearly parallel to themselves to somewhat larger areas. The pressure required to initiate the change from expanded to condensed films increases by approximately 1 dyne for every degree rise in temperature.

This type of expansion very frequently occurs among long-chain aliphatic compounds. All the fatty acids show it, and the expansion is very similar with the α-bromo-acids, the nitriles, alcohols, amides, ureas, oximes, amines, and acetamides. In all these series the expanded film is probably liquid, with a definite surface-vapour pressure, and the area is about 48 sq. A. at the lowest compression. Some other substances form similar films but of different areas; the *p*-alkyl phenols tend to 39 sq. A. (*j*), and the α-monoglycerides (*j*) and the α-glyceryl ethers[1] of long-chain alcohols,

$$C_nH_{2n+1}COO \cdot CH_2 \cdot CHOH \cdot CH_2OH \quad \text{and} \quad C_nH_{2n+1}OCH_2 \cdot CHOH \cdot CH_2OH,$$

occupy areas (in the expanded state) of 66 to 70 sq. A. at the lowest compression.

When there are two or three long chains in the molecule the area of the expanded films is slightly less than two or three times as much as that of a similar compound with but one chain in the molecule; e.g. glycol dilaurate (*n*) occupies about 83 sq. A., or some 85 per cent., of the area occupied by two separate chains; and so does octyl palmitate, whose acidic and alcoholic chains are both oriented away from the water. If three chains are present, as in the triglycerides, the area in the expanded state is 75 to 80 per cent. of the area of three separate single-chain molecules (*c*).

The change from condensed to expanded films resembles a change of phase, but not very exactly. Temperature has little effect on the condensed state up to a certain point; then the change into the expanded state takes place, but instead of being sudden, like a genuine change of phase, it requires several degrees rise of temperature for completion. At a given low pressure (the usual standard pressure for comparing temperatures of expansion among different compounds is 1·4 or more recently 1·5 dynes) it requires roughly 10° for completion. The isothermal pressure-area curves are similarly reminiscent of a phase change but are not horizontal, as a pure phase change would have to be.

[1] Knight, *Biochem. J.*, **24**, 258 (1930); Adam, *J.C.S.* (1933), 164.

In the transition region there is sometimes evidence of heterogeneity to an extent detectable by a moving air-electrode. Thus Schulman and Hughes[1] found that myristic acid films show small fluctuations of the order 20 mv. at 15° C. in the surface potential at areas lower than about 35 sq. A. Adam and Harding[2] found rather larger fluctuations, about 60 mv., with margaric nitrile in the transition region. Such fluctuations indicate a 'patchy' structure of the film in the transitional region, the patches being of the order millimetres across, at least.

The temperature at which the change from the condensed to the expanded state takes place depends both on the nature of the water-soluble end group and on the length of the hydrocarbon chain. In any single homologous series, as the chains are lengthened the temperature of expansion rises. This temperature is most conveniently chosen as that at which the area is half-way from that of the condensed to that of the expanded film, at a specified low pressure (usually 1·5 dynes per cm.). At this pressure the effect of adding one CH_2 group to a saturated chain is to raise the temperature of expansion by about 10°, if it is near to 0°, and by slightly less, 7 or 8°, if near 50° (*c*, *e*). Lengthening the chains does not alter the nature of the expansion, but only raises the temperature at which it takes place. This rule has been verified in over a dozen different homologous series of long-chain compounds.

A change from a saturated chain to one in which there is a double bond in the middle of the chain very considerably lowers the expansion temperature; e.g. oleic acid is fully expanded even at 0°, and may be estimated to have an expansion temperature somewhere about —30°, while the saturated acid, stearic, of equal chain-length, expands at 46°. The stereochemical configuration of the double bond in the chains is important; a 'trans' bond such as that in elaidic acid causes expansion to occur at a temperature only some 40° below that of the corresponding saturated acid.

The nature of the end group also affects the temperature of expansion. For equal lengths of saturated chain there may be differences of expansion temperature of over 35° between substances with different end groups; e.g. the nitrile with a sixteen-carbon chain in addition to the CN group expands at 17°, but the alcohol expands at 54°.

Some series of compounds do not form coherent 'liquid-expanded' films, but undergo a change which must be classed as expansion, since it is generally so similar to the above, to a film which has no definite limiting area or surface-vapour pressure, but passes without discontinuity into the gaseous type of film. These films, though continuous with the gaseous state, have so much cohesion that they resemble the liquid-expanded type of film more than the gaseous. These are called the 'vapour-expanded' films. Fig. 17 shows the pressure-area relation for ethyl palmitate up to 80 sq. A. (*h*), and Fig. 18 that for several esters of this series, continuing Fig. 17 up to large areas. These figures should be compared with Figs. 16 and 13. There is a strong resemblance between the change from the

[1] *Proc. Roy. Soc.* A, **138**, 443 (1932). [2] *Ibid.*, **143**, 107 (1933).

condensed to the expanded films in both liquid- and vapour-expanded films; and there is some resemblance between the 'evaporation' of myristic acid in Fig. 13 and the curves of ethyl palmitate at large areas in Fig. 18, but there is no constant vapour pressure for the ester. In Fig. 18 the two esters which do show a constant surface-vapour pressure are both condensed films.[1]

With ethyl palmitate there is a long region of fairly small slope, nearly straight, in the place of the constant vapour-pressure region of the liquid-expanded type of films. As the temperature is raised, or the length of the hydrocarbon chain shortened, the vapour-expanded films become less like the liquid-expanded and more like the gaseous films.

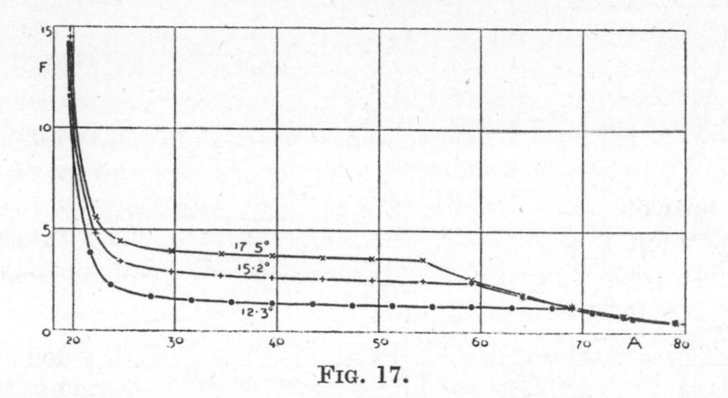

FIG. 17.

The nature of the end group appears to determine whether a given homologous series forms liquid- or vapour-expanded films on expansion from the condensed state. In particular, the amount of residual affinity in the end group seems important; if this is high, causing probably a considerable amount of lateral adhesion between the end groups of adjacent molecules in the films, the expanded film is 'liquid-expanded'; such are the acids, in the un-ionized or only slightly ionized state, the amides, nitriles, alcohols, &c. If the residual affinity is low, and the lateral adhesion between end groups low, the films are 'vapour-expanded'; among such are the esters and the methyl ketones. When the attraction between end groups is very much reduced, e.g. when the end group is ionized as with the fatty acids on alkaline solutions, so that there are electrostatic repulsive forces operating to counteract the van der Waals attractive forces between the end groups, the condensed films expand straight into gaseous films, no expanded state being formed (*c*, p. 522, *r*, *s*).

[1] The distinction between vapour- and liquid-expanded films may be difficult to make in practice. The most sensitive tests are to plot the FA–F curves as suggested by Schofield and Rideal (*Proc. Roy. Soc.* A, **110**, 170 (1926); cf. *h*, p. 370) and see whether, when produced, these pass through the origin; or to measure the surface pressure as accurately as possible between areas ranging from about 100 to 1,000 sq. A. For the distinction to be made with certainty the measurements must be made down to the second place of decimals.

Table IV summarizes the results of measurements on expanded films. Section I shows the effect of lengthening the chain in one series; section II the effect of the end group, the figures being given for a constant length of chain. In this section the figures have sometimes been obtained by interpolation from other members of the same series, using the rule for variation of expansion temperature stated above. It has been found in all cases that if one member

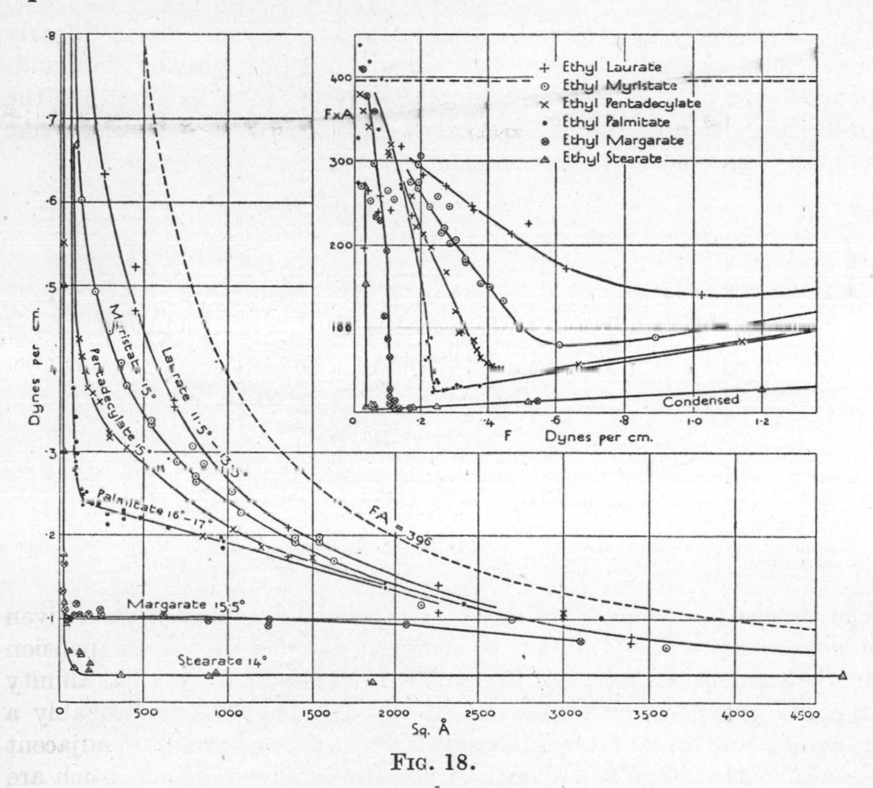

Fig. 18.

of a homologous series forms a liquid-expanded film, all the others do so also. Further warming of expanded films above the expansion temperature always makes them rather less coherent. No measurements have been possible below 0°, and those temperatures of expansion recorded below 0° have been estimated by extrapolation from measurements on other compounds with longer chains. As a rule, the error in the expansion temperatures in the table does not exceed 3°; bracketed figures are less certain. The 'expansion temperatures' are the temperatures at which the area, under 1·5 dynes pressure, is half-way from that of the condensed to that of the expanded film; these have also been called the 'half-expansion temperatures'.

19. Theory of the liquid-expanded films. The explanation of the curious properties of these films, particularly the fact that the limiting area does not correspond to any definite orientation of the molecules but is intermediate between that of the molecules standing upright and lying flat, has presented some little difficulty, but now, thanks to Langmuir, a theory which appears correct at least in its main outlines has been

TABLE IV

Expansion of Films

Series	*Chain length, n, in* C_nH_{2n+1}	*Head*	*Temperature of half-expansion, 1·4 dynes*	*State of expanded film**	*Limiting area of liquid-expanded films*	*Reference*
I.						
Saturated acids, on dilute HCl	11		below 0°			
	13		8			
	14		19·5	L		
	15		28·5			
	16	—COOH	37·5		48	*c, f, h*
	17		46			
	19		57·5	prob. L		
	20		65·6			
	21		72·5			
II.						
Acids, on N/10 NaOH	16	—COO′+Na˙	*c.* 2	G	..	*r*
Resorcinols	,,	—⬡—OH HO	15	L	58	*k*
Nitriles	,,	—CN	17	L	46	*c, e, t*
α-Bromo-acids	,,	—CHBr·COOH	22	L	50	*e*
Ethyl esters	,,	—$COOC_2H_5$	23	V	..	*c, e, f*
Mono-glycerides	,,	—$COOCH_2$·CHOH·CH_2OH	27	L	70	*j*
Methyl ketones	,,	—CO·CH_3	33	V	..	*h*
Methyl esters	,,	—$COOCH_3$	34	V	..	*c, e*
Acids on HCl	,,	—COOH	37·5	L	48	*c*
Aldoximes	,,	—C:NOH	42	prob. L	50	*e, u*
Amides	,,	—$CONH_2$	44	prob. L	50	*c, e*
Alcohols	,,	—CH_2OH	54	L	48	*f, u*
Amines (on p_H10 solutions)	,,	—CH_2NH_2	48	L	50	*o*
	,,					
Phenols	,,	—⬡—OH	55	L	39	*d, j*
γ-Hydroxy-acids	,,	—CHOH·CH_2·CH_2·COOH	28	L	60	1

* G = gaseous, V = vapour-expanded, L = liquid-expanded.

1. Fosbinder and Rideal, *Proc. Roy. Soc.* A, **143**, 63 (1933).

III.

Substance	*Chain*	*Head*	*Temperature*	*State*	*Limiting area*	*Ref.*
Methyl palmitate	$C_{15}H_{31}$	$—COOCH_3$	27·5	V		c, n
Allyl palmitate	,,	$—COOC_3H_5$	14	V		
Ethyl palmitate	,,	$—COOC_2H_5$	13	V		
n-Propyl palmitate	,,	$—COOC_3H_7$	below 5	prob. L	88	
n-Butyl palmitate	,,	$—COOC_4H_9$	,,	,,	88	
n-Octyl palmitate	,,	$—COOC_8H_{17}$	,,	,,	83	

IV.

Substance	*Formula*	*Temperature*	*State*	*Limiting area*	*Ref.*
Oleic acid on HCl	$C_8H_{15}CH:CH(CH_2)_7COOH$(*cis*)	(−30°)	L	55	c
Elaidic acid ,,	$C_8H_{15}CH:CH(CH_2)_7COOH$(*trans*)	−0·5	L	c. 50	
Erucic acid ,,	$C_8H_{15}CH:CH(CH_2)_{11}COOH$(*cis*)	4·5	L	,,	
Brassidic acid ,,	$C_8H_{15}CH:CH(CH_2)_{11}COOH$(*trans*)	31	L	,,	
Iso-oleic acid ,,	$C_{15}H_{31}CH:CHCOOH$	25	prob. L	,,	
Ethyl iso-oleate	$C_{15}H_{31}CH:CHCOOC_2H_5$	9	V	..	e
Dibasic ester	$C_2H_5OOC(CH_2)_{16}COOC_2H_5$	7	G	..	i

V.

Substance	*Temperature*	*State*	*Limiting area (per chain)*	*Reference*
Glycol dilaurate	below 0°	L	41	n
Tributyrin	,,	prob. G	..	2
Tricaprylin	,,	V		
Tricaproin	,,	V		
Trilaurin	8°±6	prob. L		
Tripalmitin	48	,,	..	c
Tristearin	57	,,		
Triolein	below 15	L	45	h
Lecithin	,,	L	55	
Hydrolecithin	28	L	55	

(2) Gorter and Grendel, *Proc. K. Akad. Wetensch. Amsterdam*, **29**, 1268 (1926). Grendel, *Thesis* (Utrecht, 1927).

developed. In 1925[1] Langmuir pointed out that there is a remarkable similarity between the pressure-area curves of the liquid-expanded films and the spreading force of a large, thin layer of a hydrocarbon oil resting on a water surface, with a monomolecular, gaseous film of some substance such as a long-chain fatty acid present at the interface between the oil and the water. This view was developed considerably in 1933[2] and the rather bold suggestion made that the upper portion of the monomolecular liquid-expanded film, consisting of the hydrocarbon-chain portion of the

[1] *3rd Colloid Symposium Monograph*, 71 (1925); Alexander's *Colloid Chemistry*, **1**, 525 (1926).
[2] *J. Chem. Physics*, **1**, 756 (1933).

molecules, should be regarded as a liquid 'phase', resting on the top of the water, with an upper hydrocarbon-air surface, and a lower interface against the water containing a number of water-soluble groups per sq. cm. equal to the number of molecules. The upper surface is assumed to have the same surface tension as a paraffin oil against air; the lower surface to be an oil-water interface containing a 'gaseous' film, the particles in this film being essentially the water-soluble heads of the molecules. Such films, with upper and lower interfaces and an intervening layer which may be considered as a liquid, are called 'duplex films'.

The spreading force (or 'spreading coefficient')[1] of an oil (A) on water (B) is

$$F_0 = \gamma_B - \gamma_A - \gamma_{AB}, \tag{3}$$

γ_A, γ_B, γ_{AB}, being the surface tensions of the oil-air, water-air, and oil-water interfaces respectively.

The surface pressure, or outward spreading force per centimetre, of the interfacial gaseous film at the lower interface of the duplex film would be ideally

$$F_{AB} = \frac{kT}{A} \tag{4}$$

for a perfect gaseous film composed of molecules whose size, as well as the lateral adhesive forces between them, could be neglected; k is the gas constant per molecule and A the area per molecule in the film. In actual cases the areas are not large enough for the area occupied by the molecules, or rather the water-soluble groups, to be neglected, and (4) is replaced by

$$F_{AB} = \frac{kT}{A - A_0}, \tag{5}$$

where A_0 is a constant related to the area actually covered by a water-soluble group.

In the case of a duplex film the total spreading force F is the sum of F_0 and F_{AB}, i.e.

$$(F - F_0)(A - A_0) = kT. \tag{6}$$

Equation (6) does not take account of any lateral adhesive forces which may be present between the water-soluble groups in the lower interface of the duplex film, but does allow, approximately, for the area occupied by these groups.

F_0 is, for a paraffin hydrocarbon of about 14 carbons in length, negative; for this length of chain no determination on a really pure compound exists, but an approximate determination by Langmuir gave about -6 dynes per cm., while some results by Harkins and Feldman[2] for various liquid 'medicinal paraffins' indicated a value about -13. Langmuir found that the curves for the liquid-expanded films of myristic acid, shown in Fig. 16 above, are accurately represented by equation (6), F_0 having a constant value for the whole temperature range of these measurements of $-11{\cdot}2$, and A_0 being $12 + 0{\cdot}178t$, t being the temperature in degrees C.

[1] See Chapter VI for further details.

[2] *J.A.C.S.* (1922), 2672.

This equation for the liquid-expanded films is a rectangular hyperbola having as asymptotes A_0, i.e. a constant closely related to the area actually occupied by the water-soluble groups in the lower, gaseous film, and F_0, the spreading force of the hydrocarbon portion of the film.

Considering now the molecular structure of the films, the only possible structure in which the hydrocarbon part of the films could be treated as a distinct *liquid* phase would have the long chains of the molecules in continuous, chaotic motion. Long hydrocarbon chains are undoubtedly flexible; rotation can occur about each of the valency bonds between successive carbon atoms, so that although probably each valency bond round a carbon cannot easily be bent or deflected from its normal angle of $109\frac{1}{2}°$ to the other three bonds, a chain of 14 or more carbons can undergo quite violent oscillations and contortions. It seems probable that the chains of the molecules in a liquid-expanded film are just as free to move as would be the chains of a hydrocarbon in the interior of a liquid, except that one end is constrained to lie in the lower face of the film because the water-soluble group must dip into the water. If the chains are long enough, this constraint would probably impose little restriction on the motions of the hydrocarbon chains at a distance more than three or four carbon atoms above the lower edge of the film.

Even apart from the quantitative correspondence with Langmuir's theory of the duplex films, showing the strong similarity with thin patches of oil on water with a film of a substance containing water-soluble groups at the interface, the view that the liquid-expanded films have the hydrocarbon chains of the molecules in chaotic oscillatory motion appears the only possible one. Adam (*j*, *l*) had tried to fit the properties of these films to various static arrangements of the molecules, including one with the long chains coiled into helices with axis vertical, but no structure possible on a molecular model would fit the facts established by measurements on numerous series of substances. A difficulty might seem to exist, why, if the orderly arrangement of the chains in the condensed films had been overcome by increased thermal agitation, the disruption of the films should not proceed until the molecules separated, and the film became gaseous. This difficulty is overcome by Langmuir's plan of regarding the hydrocarbon part of the film as a liquid with properties similar to those of a hydrocarbon oil in bulk. It is well known that the cohesion of liquids is not much less than that of solids, and therefore we should expect a very considerable amount of lateral adhesion between the long chains in contact, even though their arrangement is no longer orderly. We may regard the hydrocarbon portion of the monomolecular layer, in the liquid-expanded films, as having the lateral adhesion proper to a liquid layer of oil of equal thickness, and this lateral adhesion prevents the unlimited expansion of the film.

In the simple form given above the theory treats the lower face of the film as a gaseous film, neglecting the lateral adhesion between the water-soluble groups. This can scarcely be wholly true. The values for A_0 given above are rather unexpectedly small for a correction to the area due to the space on the surface actually covered by the end groups; they are less than the measured area even of chains when closely packed. Also, they increase rather rapidly with temperature. It is possible that these anomalies in the values of the area covered by the end groups are due to the neglect of the lateral adhesions between these end groups, and Langmuir says that too much significance should not be attached to the actual values of A_0.

For other substances the data for the calculation of F_0 and A_0 are not so complete, but for the fatty acids it is clear that $-F_0$ increases steadily with increasing length of chain from 10·4 for the 12-carbon acid to nearly 22 dynes per cm. for the 22-carbon. A_0 increases also with increasing length of chain, up to about 25 sq. A. for the 22-carbon acid. Introduction of unsaturated groups into the middle of the chain tends to increase A_0 but to decrease $-F_0$. The increase in A_0 caused by the double bond is possibly due to its attraction for water bringing a few of the double bonds into the water surface at any moment, and the decrease in $-F_0$ to the increase in surface pressure in the lower face of the film caused by the presence of a few double bonds there. The changes are not nearly large enough, however, to indicate that more than a very few of the double bonds in the middle of the chains have reached the water.

The transition between the expanded and condensed states now requires attention. The sharp break at the right-hand end of the transition curves in Fig. 16 suggests that a second type of film is appearing here. If this were a second phase, in the strict thermodynamic sense, the pressure in the transition region would be expected to be constant; in fact the pressure rises slowly near the expanded end, but sharply at the other end, passing almost imperceptibly into the condensed film. Langmuir suggests that the change which occurs at the right-hand end of the transition curve is a sudden beginning of aggregation of the molecules into micelles, which, though much larger than the single molecules, are not so large that they cannot move about separately in the surface. Assuming that the micelles move about independently, like the molecules in a gaseous film, in accordance with an equation similar to (6), and calculating the relative density on the surface of micelles, each containing β molecules, and of single molecules, at any point of the transition, he showed that the partial surface pressure of the micelles at any area a in the transition region would be

$$F_\beta = \frac{kT}{\beta a_J}\frac{a_J-a}{a-a_R}, \qquad (7)$$

a_J being the area at the right-hand (expanded) end of the transition curve and a_R that at the left-hand (condensed) end.

Assuming further that the equilibrium between the micelles and the single molecules is of such a nature that the contribution to the surface pressure made by the single molecules throughout the transition remains constant, at a value F_J, equal to the total pressure at the right-hand end of the transition region, so that the measured surface pressure of the film is given by

$$F = F_J+F_\beta, \qquad (8)$$

where F_β is given by (7), Langmuir found that for the fatty acids the value of the number of molecules in the micelles is of the order 13; for the p-alkyl phenols it is 5 and for the α-bromo-acids about 7. The size of the micelles is likely to be limited by the relative cross-sectional area of the chains and of the end groups. If the end groups occupy more space on the surface than the chain, it is not possible to pack an unlimited number of molecules together and still keep the chains lying closely packed and side by side, owing to the crowding apart of the heads caused by the bulky chains. This causes the size of the micelles to be smaller in those cases where the end groups are larger, as with phenols and α-bromo-acids.

The assumption that the partial surface pressure due to the single molecules is constant throughout the transition is equivalent to saying that the micelles have a constant surface-vapour pressure of dissociation F_J. The manner in which this varies with temperature is most interesting. Langmuir found that the difference $F_J - F_0$ obeys an equation of the Clapeyron type:

$$\log_{10}(F_J - F_0) = 8{\cdot}058 - B_n/T, \tag{9}$$

which indicates that the surface-vapour pressure of the micelles is exerted, as we should expect, at the lower interface of the duplex film, and that it behaves in a similar manner to an ordinary three-dimensional vapour pressure. B_n is the latent heat associated with the two-dimensional dissociation along the surface which occurs when the micelles break up into single molecules. For the series of fatty acids it is found to obey the equation

$$B_n = 1208 + 53n, \tag{10}$$

where n is the number of carbon atoms in the molecule; this corresponds to a latent heat of surface evaporation of $5{\cdot}52 + 0{\cdot}242n$ kg. calories per mole; i.e. this latent heat consists of a large constant term, presumably due mainly to the lateral adhesion between the carboxyl groups, and 0·242 kg. calories for each CH_2 group. According to Garner and others,[1] the latent heat of fusion of solid long-chain compounds, per CH_2 group, is approximately 1·0 kg. calories for the β modification and 0·61 for the α, the one stable at the melting-point. In an arrangement where about 13 single molecules are packed with the chains side by side in a micelle, about 40 per cent. of the surface area of the single molecules should still be free; i.e. if the work done in separating the micelles into single molecules were qualitatively the same as that required for melting a crystal, we should expect the heat of surface evaporation of the micelles to be about 60 per cent. of the latent heat of fusion, per CH_2 group. The actual heat of dissociation of the hydrocarbon part of the micelles is rather smaller than this, but of the same order.

The increase of the temperature of expansion with increasing length of chain is thus correlated both qualitatively and quantitatively with the work required to separate the long chains, closely packed side by side in the micelles.

The 'vapour-expanded' films have pressure-area curves with small values of $-F_0$. At low values of the pressure the area becomes so large that the molecules have to lie nearly flat on the surface; the thickness of the hydrocarbon part of the film thus becomes so small that there is much less opportunity for the chains to oscillate about the vertical direction than with the smaller areas of the liquid-expanded films. The hydrocarbon part of the film cannot therefore be considered as a liquid layer and the theory of duplex films tends to become inapplicable; owing to the molecules being nearly flat, the expanded state merges into the gaseous without abrupt change of slope.

From a comparison of the types of end group in Table IV which give vapour- or liquid-expanded films, it appears that those compounds whose end groups possess a considerable amount of residual affinity, such as undissociated fatty acids, amides, nitriles, &c., form liquid-expanded films; those which have less, such as esters or methyl ketones, form vapour-expanded. The lateral adhesion between the end groups therefore appears to have a controlling influence in

[1] *J.C.S.* (1926), 2491; (1931), 1533.

deciding the type of expanded film, and to affect $-F_0$. The most striking case is when the end group can be electrolytically dissociated: the fatty acids on neutral or acid solutions, i.e. with practically undissociated end groups, form typical liquid-expanded films; on alkaline solutions they form gaseous films; similarly, the amines on alkaline solutions form liquid-expanded films, and on acid solutions usually gaseous films. In its simple form above the theory of duplex films does not take into account the lateral adhesion between the end groups as a factor in preserving the lateral cohesion of the film, and is not wholly satisfactory. A complete theory will have to take this adhesion into account. At present a fairly satisfactory way of regarding the state of the duplex or liquid-expanded films is that a large part of the lateral cohesion is provided by the oscillating chains, this being of similar nature to the cohesion of a hydrocarbon liquid; the polar end groups in the water tend to disrupt the film except in so far as their thermal motions along the surface are restrained by lateral adhesion between them.

20. Influence of admixture of other molecules on expansion. Leathes[1] found that a film containing cholesterol and myristic, or other fatty acids, in a proportion of one molecule cholesterol to two or four of fatty acid, was often condensed at temperatures when the fatty acid alone would have been expanded. Adam and Jessop (*l*) found that not only cholesterol, but some other bulky molecules, such as tripalmitin or pentaerythritol tetrapalmitate (see p. 77), tend to make an expanded film condense. If the temperature is very far above the expansion temperature the condensation may not be complete, and also if the proportion of bulky molecules to the molecules which would normally form an expanded film were less than about one to four. This condensing effect might be due to one of three causes. There might be either a specific attraction between the fatty-acid chains and the cholesterol, or a mechanical interference with the oscillatory motions of the long chains, caused by the very bulky molecules, which are not themselves undergoing the oscillations, getting in the way of the chains oscillating. Langmuir,[2] more recently, suggests that the cholesterol molecules are so much taller than the myristic acid molecules that the upper surface of the film is very uneven, through the big molecules projecting, and so its area and surface energy are much increased, thus increasing the value of $-F_0$ and reducing the tendency of the film to expand. There is good evidence against the view that there is a specific attraction between the chains of the smaller molecules and the cholesterol, for the surface-vapour pressure of the mixtures is diminished only proportionately to the diminution in the number of smaller molecules (the cholesterol has a negligibly small surface-vapour pressure), i.e. a two-dimensional analogue of Raoult's law holds good. If there were a particularly large adhesion between the fatty-acid chains and the cholesterol, there ought to be a much larger lowering of surface-vapour pressure than corresponds to Raoult's law. There may be no essential conflict between the other two explanations. A film containing a number of long, rigid molecules, more or less uniformly intermingled with shorter ones which would otherwise be in chaotic oscillation, would probably have the oscillations much impeded, so that the hydrocarbon part of the film could no longer be regarded as a liquid. The rigidity of the large molecules would tend to make them project through the upper surface, provided

[1] *Proc. Physiol. Soc.*, Nov. 1923; *Lancet*, April 25, 1923.

[2] *J. Chem. Physics*, **1**, 773 (1933).

that they did not tilt over at a considerable angle to the vertical; and hence the smaller molecules would tend to cover up the bare surface of the projecting molecules, which they could only do by ceasing their oscillations about the vertical and standing upright, assuming the arrangement of a condensed film.

An interesting phenomenon was shown by *p*-nonyl phenol, normally a liquid-expanded film. This is not condensed at all by tripalmitin or bulky molecules containing several long chains, but it is completely condensed by cholesterol. This may be due to the fact that *p*-nonyl phenol is a rigid molecule in the aromatic portion, which forms the lower 6 A. or so of the thickness of the film; above this is a chain of 9 carbon atoms which can oscillate. Cholesterol is a rigid ring system whose rigid properties extend far above the rigid part of the nonyl phenol, probably right up to the upper end of the chain which might oscillate. Tripalmitin has three chains rigidly connected only at their bases; at a height of over 6 A. from the base of the film the three chains of tripalmitin are scarcely different from three chains belonging to separate molecules of, say, palmitic acid. Single chain compounds are not found to prevent expansion, even up to 22 carbon atoms in length. These facts incline the author to the view that mechanical obstruction of the oscillations of the chains is the cause of the condensing effect exerted by bulky molecules.

Vapour-expanded films are also found to be more or less condensed by admixture with cholesterol and tripalmitin, but the experimental data are much less complete.

The effect of increasing temperature on a film may be figuratively compared to a progressive intoxication of the molecules in the film. Starting with an orderly, condensed film, composed of molecules standing upright and having their long chains packed quietly side by side, at a certain point in the heating the thermal agitation becomes great enough to overcome the lateral adhesion between the chains, and these begin to oscillate violently. Nevertheless, some degree of coherence is still preserved; it requires a higher temperature, or a shortening of the chains, or a diminution in the lateral adhesion between the end groups, to cause the film to become gaseous. When this does occur the molecules fall down flat on the surface, and swim about independently. When the bulky molecules restrain expansion they may be regarded as policemen, who by mere bulk and inertia keep order; it is to be observed that one policeman of this rather inert type can only control about four chains wishing to oscillate. And it would appear that the policemen of the tripalmitin type are only sober at their bases, where family ties unite the single chains firmly together; higher up they are unable, or do not attempt, to control disorderly oscillations!

Schulman and Hughes[1] find that, in a mixture of 3 molecules of oleic acid to 1 of hexadecyl alcohol (a substance giving a condensed film ordinarily), the area is decidedly larger than the sum of the areas of the constituents measured separately, as if the chaotic oscillations of the oleic acid chains were communicated to the hexadecyl alcohol chains.

The principal types of film found with aliphatic substances have been described; the next paragraphs will deal with various effects of chemical constitution on film structure.

21. Influence of acidity in the water on substances with ionizable end groups. There is a very large diminution in the lateral adhesion

[1] *Biochem. J.*, **29**, 1249 (1935).

between the molecules in a film, when the end groups are ionized by an appropriate change in the acidity of the water. This was noticed by Adam (*c*, p. 522), who found that the temperature of expansion of fatty acids on alkaline solutions was much lower than on neutral or acid solutions. More detailed work with Miller (*r*) showed that the expansion temperatures are anything from 35° to 60° lower on p_H 12 than on p_H 4, the precise amount of lowering depending on the nature of the salts in the solution. On the acid side liquid-expanded films are formed; on the alkaline, gaseous films, indicating very much diminished adhesion between the molecules in the expanded state. This considerable loss of adhesion between the molecules is obviously due to the repulsion between the similar electric charges developed on adjacent end groups, when electrolytic dissociation takes place.

Similarly, the amines, with end group $—CH_2NH_2$, undergo a considerable lowering of expansion temperature on passing from the alkaline to the acid side (*o*), the weakly dissociated base passing into the strongly dissociated salt; and, usually, the expanded films are gaseous on the acid side. And when phenolic groups are present there is a similar decrease in lateral adhesion on strongly alkaline solutions, where salt formation occurs (*s*).

It may safely be said that the lateral adhesion in the films is very much diminished when the composition of the underlying solution is such that the end groups are ionized. There are, however, quite considerable variations in lateral adhesion on solutions of different salts with the same p_H, which are presumably due to the salts, or other complexes formed by interaction of the end groups of the film molecules with the substances in solution, having a greater or less lateral adhesion, this being probably of the van der Waals type. Thus, on borate buffers, of alkalinity greater than p_H 6, the expansion temperature of acids is some 30° higher than on phosphate and also a good deal higher than on caustic soda or carbonate of similar p_H (*r*, p. 407). Dissociation is probably nearly complete on all these solutions. With the amines, where ionization is probably complete not far on the acid side of the neutral point, there is very little lateral adhesion on acetate buffers of p_H 4, but a good deal on phthalate of the same p_H, also on benzene-sulphonic acid solutions which are more acid still (*o*, p. 532).

The surface potential is, naturally, very much changed when ionization takes place in the end groups, because the dipole moment at the end of the molecule is very much altered by the development of a pair of new electric charges. This was first observed by Frumkin with adsorbed films of soluble substances[1] (Chap. III, §10); for instance, solutions of the fatty acids give high *positive* surface potentials, while those of their salts give rather small *negative* potentials. The molecules are oriented in the adsorbed films with the positive carbon of the carboxyl above the negative oxygens, and if the hydroxyl group is not dissociated, the resultant dipole is large, with the positive end uppermost. If the hydroxyl is ionized, there is an additional dipole consisting of the positive ion below and the negative oxygen above; this rather more than neutralizes the dipole present in the

[1] *Z. physikal. Chem.*, **111**, 194 (1924).

fatty acid. A similar phenomenon was observed with insoluble films of oleic acid (positive) and potassium or sodium oleates (negative).[1] Schulman and Hughes[2] have followed the effects of ionization with various insoluble films in a much more thorough manner. Fig. 19 shows the changes in surface potential with p_H at a constant area of about 20 sq. A., the minimum obtainable without serious collapse of the films, of an acid, an

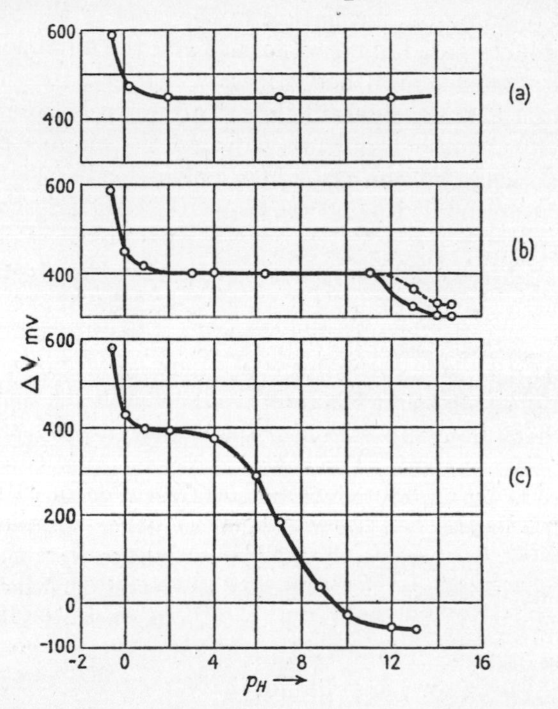

Fig. 19. Effect of p_H on surface potential of (*a*) octadecyl methyl ether, (*b*) tetradecyl alcohol, (*c*) myristic acid.

alcohol, and an ether. The acid (lowest curve) has a negative potential of —50 mv. at p_H 12 and beyond, which is clearly that of the fully dissociated salt; between 11 and 4 it rises to 400 mv., where it remains nearly constant till p_H 1. This is the potential of the undissociated acid. Between p_H 1 and quite strong acid, 4N hydrochloric acid, there is a further considerable rise of potential, due very probably to the formation of an oxonium salt, the oxygen tending to become positively charged and negative ions being attracted to the underside of the film from the solution. The alcohol shows a much longer region of constant potential (undissociated), but at the extreme alkaline end there is a slight fall, indicating probably a slight tendency towards salt formation with the alkali. The ether shows no salt formation with alkali, but both alcohol and ether show the same rise as the acid in very strongly acid solutions, and the explanation is probably the same, i.e. an oxonium salt is formed.

[1] *Ibid.*, **116**, 494 (1925). [2] *Proc. Roy. Soc.* A, **138**, 436 (1932).

The change in surface potential shown by amines, on passing from the alkaline to the acid side, is much smaller than that shown by the acids when salts are formed.[1] At about 20·5 sq. A. the potential on alkaline solutions is usually about 700 mv.; there are, however, considerable differences in potential between films on solutions containing different salts of similar p_H, and even on different concentrations of the same salt. The potential is slightly less, as a rule, for the films on acid solutions; and here also different salts give different results, the variations amounting to 100 to 150 mv.

22. Films of fatty substances with double bonds. Early work by Langmuir (1917) and Adam (*c*, *f*, *h*) showed that the presence of double linkages in the middle of a fatty chain causes the films to expand much more easily than films with saturated chains of similar length, and, usually, to occupy somewhat greater areas in the expanded state. Langmuir ascribed this to the double bonds attracting the water more than a saturated linkage; this must be the case since unsaturated hydrocarbons are more soluble in water than the saturated. The stereochemical configuration of the double bonds is of considerable importance; e.g. brassidic acid has an expansion temperature some 30° higher than erucic, where the double bond is in the same position but is probably *cis*, instead of *trans*.[2] This may be due to the double bond in the *cis* form approaching the water with less obstruction than that in the *trans*; or to differences in the packing rendering the stability of the closely packed chains in the condensed state greater with one form than with the other—probably to both causes.

A double bond in the $\alpha\beta$ position to the carboxyl group lowers the expansion temperature much less than in the middle of the chain (*c*). Hughes[3] has shown that it approximately doubles the surface potential, however, presumably through the displacement of electrons near the carboxyl head rendering the α carbon more negative and the β more positive than in the saturated chain. A double bond in the middle of the chain increases the surface potential of the molecule only slightly, but there is still a slight increase in dipole moment when a double bond is present in the middle of the chain.

Further very interesting studies of films of fatty acids and glycerides with from one to three double bonds in the chains come from Rideal's laboratory at Cambridge.[4] The fatty acids with from one to three double bonds, at points in the chain remote from the end group, form liquid-expanded films of which the limiting area increases with the number of double bonds in the molecule. One double bond gives about 55 sq. A.; three, in the elaeostearic acids

$$CH_3 \cdot (CH_2)_3CH:CH:CH:CH \cdot CH:CH \cdot (CH_2)_7 \cdot COOH,$$

give a limiting area of 100 sq. A. or slightly more; this probably means that the molecules are almost flat on the surface. These highly unsaturated acids[5] oxidize so fast that they must be examined on solutions of some substance

[1] Schulman, private communication (1935); cf. also E. F. Porter, *J.A.C.S.* (1937), 1888.

[2] Cf. Adam, *Nature*, **107**, 522 (1921).

[3] *J.C.S.* (1933), 338.

[4] Hughes and Rideal, *Proc. Roy. Soc.* A, **140**, 253 (1933); Gee and Rideal, *ibid.*, **153**, 116; Gee, *ibid.*, **153**, 129 (1935).

[5] For the chemistry of these important unsaturated acids see R. S. Morrell and others, *J.C.S.* (1932), 2251; *J.S.C.I.*, **52**, 130 T (1933).

which inhibits autoxidation, such as 0·1 per cent. hydroquinone. If allowed to oxidize, the films still remain coherent with a limiting area of 125 sq. A.

A triple bond, in stearolic acid, remote from the end group, gives such an increase in attraction for the water, combined with little increase in the lateral adhesion between the chains, that the films are vapour-expanded. This triple bond produces a considerable increase of surface potential.

Hughes obtained some very remarkable results with the compounds formed by adding maleic anhydride to the two elaeostearic acids (Fig. 20).[1] The

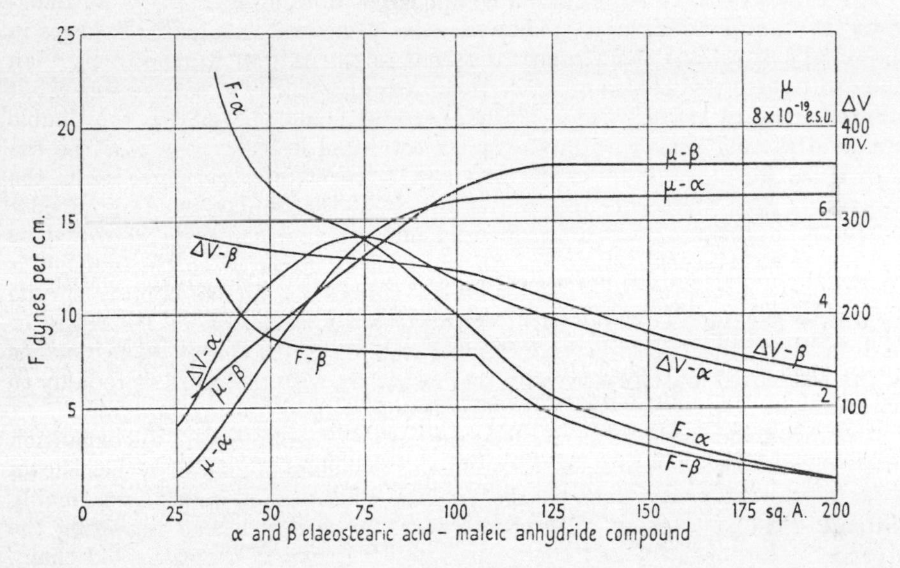

FIG. 20.

surface-pressure curves show that both the α and the β compounds are gaseous films at large areas; the molecules are therefore lying flat, and the values of μ are nearly the same, and constant, for the two acids in this orientation. As the area is diminished below about 120 sq. A. the molecules naturally become tilted, as there is not space for them to remain flat; but the behaviour of the α and β compounds is very different as the molecules become more nearly vertical. The β compound undergoes a transition, presumably to a condensed film (which, however, is somewhat unstable and readily collapses), commencing at 105 sq. A. and 7·6 dynes; as the molecule stands more nearly upright μ, and therefore the vertical component of the total dipole moment, diminish a good deal. The α compound does not undergo the transition to condensed film till a much higher pressure; the condensed film is much more stable, and the vertical component of the dipole moment falls to almost nothing when the molecule is nearly upright. There is nothing unusual about a decrease in μ when a molecule changes from a horizontal to a vertical position, but in this particular case the change is unprecedently great, and indeed is so large that the surface potential decreases to about one-third of its maximum value, while the number of molecules on unit area increases three times!

[1] Recalculated from original paper.

The changes in μ can be accounted for if the formulae are closely examined.

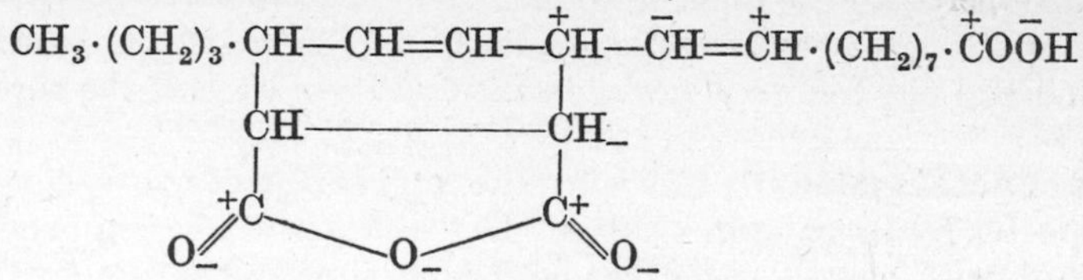

$$CH_3\cdot(CH_2)_3\cdot CH{-}CH{=}CH{-}\overset{+}{C}H{-}\overset{-}{C}H{=}\overset{+}{C}H\cdot(CH_2)_7\cdot\overset{+}{C}O\overset{-}{O}H$$

```
                 |                     |
                 CH--------------------CH_
                 |                     |
                +C                     C+
               //  \                 /  \\
             O_      ------O_------       O_
```

α compound.

$$CH_3\cdot(CH_2)_3\cdot\overset{+}{C}H{=}\overset{-}{C}H{-}\overset{+}{C}H\cdot CH{=}CH\cdot CH\cdot(CH_2)_7\overset{+}{C}O\overset{-}{O}H$$

```
                            |                     |
                           _CH--------------------CH
                            |                     |
                           +C                     C+
                          //  \                 /  \\
                        O_      ------O_------       O_
```

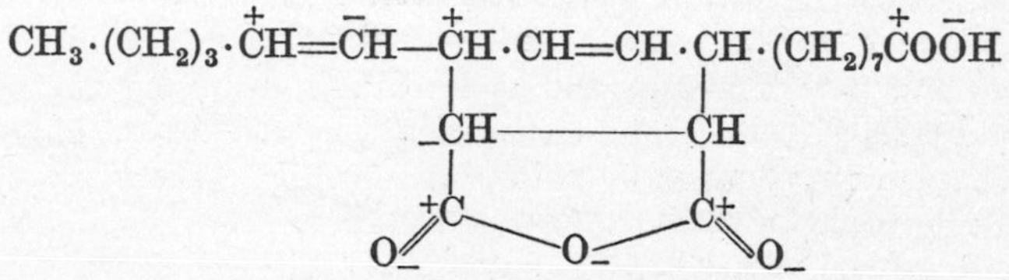

β compound.

When the molecules are horizontal all the principal dipoles of the maleic anhydride group make strong positive contributions to μ; but when tilting begins this contribution decreases till it becomes negligible. The reason for the very small final value of μ with the α acid is probably that the COO groups in the maleic anhydride induce dipoles in the neighbouring parts of the chains whose effects are particularly marked in the third double bond of the original three, which is not concerned with the addition of the maleic anhydride. The negative end of the induced dipole in this double bond is next to the maleic anhydride residue, the positive end farther away. In the α compound this double bond comes below the maleic anhydride residue when the molecule is upright; in the β acid, above; inspection of the formulae shows that it will make a negative contribution to the total dipole moment in the α compound, but a positive contribution in the β compound.

The β compound stands upright under less pressure than the α; it also collapses more easily. These differences may be due to the difference in distance of the large, water-attracting maleic anhydride residue from the main anchorage to the water at the terminal carboxyl group, but are perhaps more probably caused by stereochemical differences in the molecules affecting the accessibility of the water-attracting groups to the surface in the horizontal position, and the stability of packing of the complicated middle part of the molecule, in the condensed films and also perhaps in the crystalline solid state, to whose structure the collapsed material forced out of a film under pressure probably approaches.

Gee and Rideal find that the maleic anhydride compound of β-elaeostearin (the triglyceride corresponding to the above compound) gives very similar results, except that the films are coherent instead of gaseous, where the molecules lie flat. The limiting area agrees well with measurements on models lying flat; and the area at the sudden change in direction where the transition to the condensed film commences, with models in which the short hydrocarbon chain to the left of the unsaturated grouping (see formula above) has been forced upright.

Knight and Stamberger[1] find that addition of sulphur to double bonds in the

[1] *J.C.S.* (1928), 2791.

middle of a long chain (in the so-called 'vulcanized oils') does not noticeably affect the properties of the films on water.

For the surface pressure of castor oil, fairly pure triricinolein, which has one double bond and one hydroxyl group in the middle of each of the three chains, see Adam.[1]

23. The effect of gradually blocking the anchorage of the water-attracting groups by hydrocarbon chains. If the water-attracting group at the end of a molecule, such as palmitic acid, which already has one long chain, is substituted (e.g. by esterification) with a second chain, the effects depend on the length of the substituting chain. The attraction for the water of the end group is weakened, partly because its residual affinity is diminished by the esterification, and partly because the hydrocarbon group is reluctant to enter the water and tries to bend round either along the surface or, if long enough, upwards. This bending cannot be quite sharp owing to the angle between the valencies of the carbons in a chain, and consequently the access of water-attracting part of the end group to the water is partly blocked. Further, the lateral adhesion between adjacent molecules in the film may be much diminished, so that a gaseous, or vapour-expanded, film is formed where the unsubstituted molecule would have formed a condensed, or liquid-expanded, film; the temperature of expansion is usually lowered by this kind of substitution of the end group.

Adam found (*d*, p. 682) that the introduction of a sixteen-carbon chain, or a benzene or cyclohexane ring, into a sixteen-carbon acid or amine at the end group very much diminished the stability of the films. A study (*n*) of the effect of a progressive increase in the length of the alkyl chain esterifying palmitic acid showed that with chains of one to four carbons in length the expansion temperature is lowered, more the longer the esterifying chain, and the expanded films are vapour-, not liquid-expanded, showing diminished lateral adhesion between the end groups. It is still possible, even with butyl palmitate, at a sufficiently low temperature, to compress the films to the condensed state, when they occupy an area of about 20 sq. A.; here the alkyl chain must be dipping down into the water, continuing the line of the acidic chain of the palmitic acid. With octyl palmitate, eight carbons in the substituting chain, this can no longer happen; instead, the films are liquid-expanded with a limiting area of 83 sq. A. and are almost identical with films of glycol dilaurate; i.e. the two chains are directed mainly upwards and are oscillating in the usual manner for liquid-expanded films; the only difference between the films of octyl palmitate and glycol dilaurate was that the former were rather less stable, the anchorage afforded by the COO group between the acidic and alkyl chains being rather poor. Hexadecyl palmitate gave a very unstable film, but as far as could be observed its area was somewhere near to 41 sq. A., indicating a transient condensed film with two chains standing upright.

Pentaerythritol tetrapalmitate, an octopus-like molecule with four water-attracting groups, each esterified by a long chain and arranged symmetrically round a central carbon atom,

$$\begin{matrix} C_{15}H_{31}\cdot COO\cdot CH_2 & & CH_2\cdot OOC\cdot C_{15}H_{31} \\ & C & \\ C_{15}H_{31}\cdot COO\cdot CH_2 & & CH_2\cdot OOC\cdot C_{15}H_{31}, \end{matrix}$$

[1] *Trans. Faraday Soc.*, **29**, 104 (1933).

orients itself on the surface with all its four chains upwards (*f*). Two can start in an upward direction; the other two must start out from the central carbon downwards, but they bend round in the course of a few carbons length. The area at no pressure is about 100, decreasing to 80 at about 20 dynes. The end group is thus slightly fatter than the four chains, probably because of the space required on the surface for the bending of the two chains which have to start downwards. This film is only moderately stable, so that the measurements of area were only approximate.

24. Miscellaneous fatty substances. A hydroxyl group at the γ position in a long-chain fatty acid increases μ by about 30 per cent. over the usual value for a fatty acid in the liquid-expanded state when the molecule is considerably tilted for much of its time. Compression to the condensed state, when the hydroxyl group is forced away from the water as the molecules stand more nearly upright, decreases μ. Fosbinder and Rideal calculate[1] from the distribution of molecules between positions where the hydroxyl group is probably in the water and where it is not, at two temperatures, that the work of adhesion of the hydroxyl group in a γ-hydroxy acid is about 10×10^{-14} ergs per molecule, a value in good agreement with the work of adhesion to water of a terminal hydroxyl group in octyl alcohol. The lactone formed from hydroxystearic acid forms a condensed film with an area of 29, approximately that to be expected for an end group having the ring structure of a lactone (*q*).

The important complex fatty substances such as lecithin, kerasin, sphingomyelin form stable films[2]; if the two chains in the molecule are saturated, the films are usually condensed at room temperature, with limiting areas up to 70 sq. A. at low compressions, according to the complexity of the end group; compression results at a sufficiently high pressure in a fairly close approach of the area to that for two close-packed chains (41 sq. A.). Lecithin itself has an unsaturated chain and forms a liquid-expanded film of limiting area about 110 sq. A. Lysolecithin,[3] which is similar to lecithin in constitution but has only one long chain attached to the end group instead of two, occupies areas very nearly the same, per molecule, as lecithin, despite there being only one instead of two hydrocarbon chains, and this chain is saturated, whereas one of the chains in lecithin has an unsaturated group in the middle.

The cyclic ketones prepared by Ruzicka form fairly stable, incompressible films, whose area is a little over 40 sq. A. if there are about 30 carbons in the ring;[4] this indicates that the CO group anchors the ring to the water, and the ring is squeezed out to the longest possible extension vertically by the lateral adhesion between the molecules; the two sides of the ring rising from the CO group in the water lie side by side, probably in much the same manner as two chains of adjacent molecules in a condensed film of a long-chain acid or alcohol. With slightly smaller rings, of the order 20 carbons, the areas are 55–60 and the films are rather more compressible, indicating a less close packing of the two sides of the ring, possibly some oscillatory motion, though this is not certain.

Molecules with benzene rings and several hydroxyl groups in the ring, with one long chain, usually form condensed films with the benzene rings upright and closely packed side by side (*k*). In studying these compounds it had been

[1] *Proc. Roy. Soc* A, **143**, 65 (1933).

[2] Cf. Adam (*h*); Turner and Watson, *Biochem. J.*, **24**, 113 (1930).

[3] Hughes, *Biochem. J.*, **29**, 430 (1935).

[4] Buchner, Katz, and Samwel, *Z. physikal. Chem.* B, **5**, 327 (1929).

hoped to find the benzene ring lying flat on the surface, but this did not occur. There is, no doubt, a very strong attraction between the water and the hydroxyl groups in the ring; but there is also a very strong lateral adhesion between two oxygenated rings closely packed side by side and upright, and this arrangement can satisfy the attractive forces on both sides of the rings, whereas these forces could only be satisfied on one side if the rings had lain flat in the surface. If the hydroxyl groups are methylated the lateral adhesion between the closely packed rings is diminished, and films of much larger area are formed; these are, however, very compressible and it does not appear that the rings lie flat on the surface at all stably. The balance between cohesive forces tending to bring the oxygenated rings flat on the surface, or closely packed and upright, is very similar to the balance between the cohesional forces tending to keep cellulose chains together, and to spread them out on a water surface (§ 29). Methylation of the hydroxyl groups diminishes the cohesion of one group to another more than it diminishes the adhesion to water.

Humulone, the bitter principle of hops, does, however, spread with a ring apparently lying flat on the surface; it forms a very remarkable incompressible film, of area 90 sq. A. (*k*).

25. Surface films of sterols and other substances with complex ring systems. The sterols, and some of the recently discovered hormones which play an important part in the activity of the reproductive organs, form remarkably stable surface films, in which a great variety of orientations of the molecules are found. During the last few years the accepted views as to the constitution of these substances have undergone extensive changes; and the measurements of the size and shape of the molecules, by the X-ray investigations of Bernal on crystals and also by studies of surface films, have had a very important influence on the revision of these formulae.[1] The older formula for the sterol skeleton, and the formulae at present (1936) accepted for two sterols and for oestriol, are

```
                                        CH(CH3)2
                                        |
                                        CH2
                  CH3                   |
            CH2 |   CH2                 CH2
    H2C         C         CH2           |
     |          | C2H5 |                CH2
     CH         C ------- CH ---- CH
 H2C         C -------- CH2          |
  |          |          |            CH3
 H2C         CH         CH2
     CH         CH2
     |
     OH
```

Cholestanol (old formula).

[1] The chemical literature is voluminous, but is well summarized by Rosenheim and King (*Ann. Review Biochem.* (1934), 87) and by Kon (*Ann. Rep. Chem. Soc.* (1934), 206). Principal papers on sterols, &c., in surface films: Leathes, *J. Physiol., Proc.,*

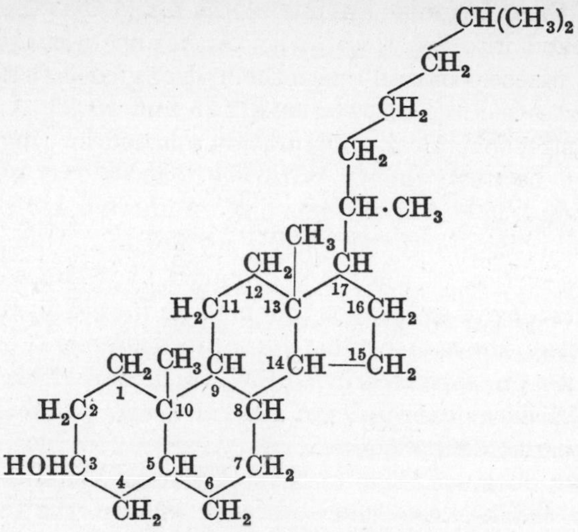

CH(CH3)2, CH2, CH2, CH2, CH·CH3, CH3, CH2, CH, H2C11, 12, 13C, 17, 16CH2, CH2, CH3, CH, 14CH, 15, CH2, 1, 9, H2C2, C10, 8CH, HOHC3, 5CH, 7CH2, 4, 6, CH2, CH2

Cholestanol (new formula).

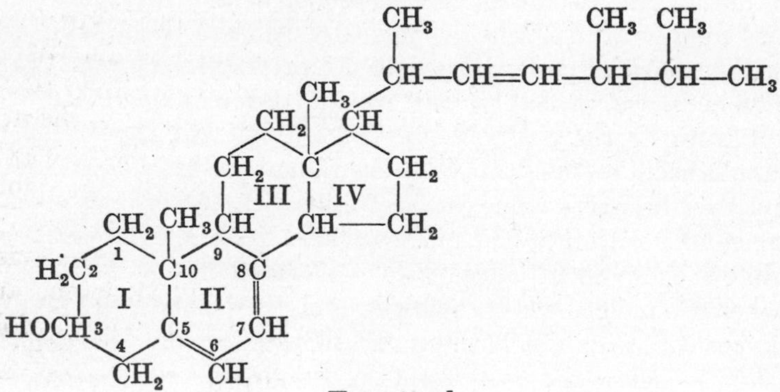

CH3, CH3, CH3, CH—CH=CH—CH—CH—CH3, CH3, CH2, CH, CH2, C, CH2, III, IV, CH2, CH3, CH, CH—CH2, 1, 9, H2C2, C10, 8C, I, II, HOCH3, C5, 7CH, 4, 6, CH2, CH

Ergosterol.

OH, CH3, CH2, CH, 12, 17, H2C11, 13C, 16CHOH, CH, CH, 14CH, 15, CH2, 1, 9, HC2, C10, 8CH, HOC3, 5C, 7CH2, 4, 6, CH, CH2

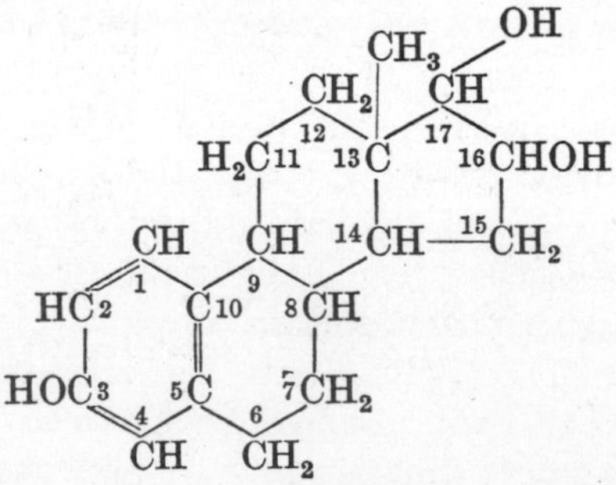

Oestriol.

Nov. 1923; Adam and Jessop, *Proc. Roy. Soc.* A, **120**, 473 (1928); Adam and Rosenheim, *ibid.*, A, **126**, 25 (1929); Rosenheim and Adam, *ibid.*, B, **105**, 422 (1929); Fosbinder, *ibid.*, A, **139**, 93 (1933); Danielli and Adam, *Biochem. J.*, **28**, 1583 (1934); Adam, Askew, and Danielli, *ibid.*, **29**, 1786 (1935); Adam, Danielli, Haslewood, and Marrian, *ibid.*, **26**, 1233 (1932); Danielli, Marrian, and Haslewood, *ibid.*, **27**, 311 (1933); Langmuir and others, *J.A.C.S.* (1937), 1406, 1751.

If models of these formulae are made, it is found that the older formula cannot be packed into less than 54 sq. A. in any orientation. The new formula, when placed vertically with the hydroxyl at 3 at the bottom, has a horizontal cross-section between about 35 and 40 sq. A., according to the particular stereochemical configuration selected for rings I and II and for the linkage between them. With the longest axis of the molecule vertical, position 3 is at the extreme end. A short but vitally important note[1] by Bernal pointed out that, in the crystals of sterols, not only is the measured cross-section of the space occupied by a single molecule, perpendicular to its longest axis, much too small for the old formula, but also its length is too great; the new formula fits the measurements on crystals well.

Measurements on surface films also are incompatible with the old formula; Fig. 21 shows the results on several sterols, all of which have their hydroxyl group at 3. All of these are very incompressible; the orientation of the molecules does not therefore change during compression; there can be little doubt that the molecules are vertically oriented. The measured areas vary from 37 to 44 sq. A., and it is probable that the differences in area are due to rings I and II having one or other of the possible 'boat' or 'chair' configurations, and the junction between them being either cis or trans. The surface potentials of these sterols are very remarkable, and the differences are probably due to the different inclinations of the hydroxyl group to the ring system. Cholestanol has about 400, but *epi*-cholestanol almost −100; this drop from a rather high value for a single hydroxyl to a negative value is most unusual; it is probably due to the interchange of position of the hydrogen and hydroxyl on carbon 3. It is likely that the dipole in cholestanol is directed nearly vertically downwards when the molecule is standing on end, the positive end being uppermost; in *epi*-cholestanol it is tilted and inverted so that the negative end comes slightly below the positive. Coprostanol and *epi*-coprostanol show a similar but smaller change when the hydrogen and hydroxyl change places; the dipole is probably a good deal tilted in both normal and *epi* isomers.

That the molecules in the preceding films are vertical is practically certain from their incompressibility and the smallness of the area; and since the carbon atom 3 is at the extreme end of the molecule it might be expected that all sterols and their derivatives with a single water-attracting group in this position would stand upright, giving the same type of incompressible film. This is not, however, the case; a number of substances in which it is scarcely possible for the polar group to be anywhere but at 3 form films whose area is much greater than this (Fig. 22). The most notable case is with coprostenone (formerly called cholestenone), the oxidation product of cholesterol which differs from the sterol in containing a keto group in place of the CHOH group; this simple change in constitution results in the film occupying 59 sq. A. at no compression, and being very compressible. Forming the oxime of this ketone reduces the

[1] *J.S.C.I.*, **51**, 466 (1932).

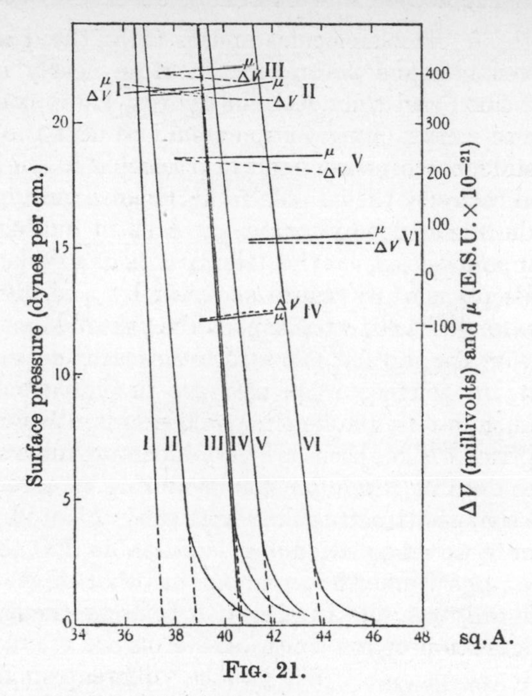

FIG. 21.

I. Ergosterol. II. Cholestane-3-ol. III. $\Delta^{5:6}$-Cholestene-3-ol (cholesterol). IV. *epi*-Cholestane-3-ol. V. Coprostane-3-ol (coprosterol). VI. *epi*-Coprostane-3-ol.

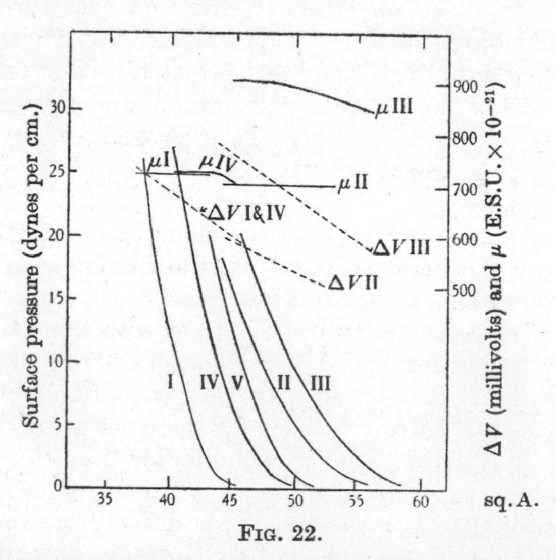

FIG. 22.

3-Keto compounds. I. Cholestane-3-one. II. Coprostane-3-one. III. $\Delta^{4:5}$-Coprostene-3-one ('cholestenone'). IV. Oxime of 'cholestenone'. V. 'Cholestenone' on 0·1 per cent. neutral $KMnO_4$ solution.

limiting area to 50. The molecules appear to be tilted at a considerable angle to the vertical, and to be brought more nearly upright by compression of the film; and the nature of the end group controls the degree of tilt. The most natural explanation would be that the CO group has a very strong tendency to orient itself at a particular angle to the surface and that the direction of its dipole forms a considerable angle with the long axis of the molecule, so that it succeeds in pulling the whole ring system over in opposition to the lateral adhesive forces which usually make the molecules occupy the least possible space and stand upright. Yet if that were so, one would expect the orientation of the dipole to change rapidly as the molecules are forced upright by external compression of the film; but μ does not change by more than a small fraction of its value when the film of coprostenone is compressed from 59 to 45 sq. A. This tilting over of the molecule when only one water-attracting group is present, at 3, is still a mystery; if it were due to unsaturated linkages elsewhere in the rings attracting the water, it would be naturally increased by permanganate in the solution, but curve V of Fig. 22 shows a much smaller area for coprostenone on permanganate than on water. The same tilt occurs with fully saturated ketones. Its amount depends on the stereochemical configuration of the rings.

In the case of coprostenone, admixture of cholesterol molecules, which stand upright, greatly decreases the area occupied by the coprostenone; if cholesterol and coprostenone molecules are present in equal numbers the area indicates that the coprostenone now stands nearly upright.

This peculiar orientation is not confined to substances with a CO group at 3; Danielli found that 3-hydroxy oestratriene[1] tends to a limit of 50 sq. A. and is intermediate in compressibility between cholesterol and coprostenone. Also the irradiation of ergosterol, which causes a complex series of changes culminating in the formation of calciferol or vitamin D, alters the tilt in the surface films very much. It is unlikely that the main water-attracting group moves from 3 during irradiation, but the double bonds in the molecule move about and stereochemical changes occur; also it is now thought that ring II is broken when the calciferol stage has been reached. Such ring breakage might be expected to straighten and lengthen the molecule, when anchored at 3 to the surface, causing it to occupy less space, not more, unless fresh points of attraction to the surface were introduced in ring II.

Derivatives of sterols with one water-attracting group at 6, with or without another at 3, usually occupy from 50 to 70 sq. A., and are very compressible; in ψ-cholesterol, where there is one hydroxyl, at 7, the limiting area is about 120, but little compression (0·5 dyne) is required to reduce the area to 80, and the film is not homogeneous in surface potential between 80 and 120. At 120 the molecule must be lying nearly flat. The minimum area obtainable on compression is 55 sq. A. Models show that the molecule could not be brought nearly upright without forcing the hydroxyl away from the water. The molecules are not, in this case, brought upright by mixing with cholesterol. There is a general

[1] For the systematic nomenclature of the oestrin group, see *Nature*, **132**, 205 (1933). This compound was originally described as the 'Clemmensen reduction product of keto-hydroxy oestrin', or 'oestrone' (3-hydroxy 17-keto oestratriene).

tendency for keto groups to produce a rather larger area than hydroxyl groups in the same position in the sterol ring, and at present there is no satisfactory explanation for this.

Harkins, Ries, and Carman[1] find that pimaric acid, which has a three-ring system with the carboxyl group in a position analogous to 4 in the four-ring system of the sterols, forms a rather compressible film of limiting area 54, resembling the sterols. Askew[2] finds that various resinols (amyrins) obtained from plant resins, &c.,[3] give films of limiting area 46 to 48, very slightly com-

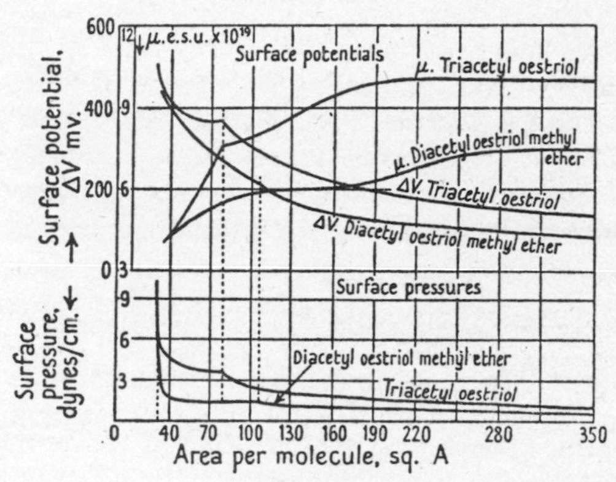

FIG. 23.

pressible, so that the molecules are very likely standing upright. These compounds probably have a ring system not unlike that of the sterols; the larger area may here be due to methyl groups in ring I.

Some results on the oestrin series are shown in Fig. 23. The compounds are the triacetate of the 3,16,17-trihydroxyoestratriene (triacetyl oestriol) and the diacetate of the 3-methyl ether of the same compound. They form gaseous films at low pressures, transition to condensed films occurring at a lower pressure with the diacetyl methyl ether than with the triacetate. The condensed films occupy an area 32·5 sq. A. In the gaseous films the molecules are lying flat, adhesion to the water being by the groups at both ends of the molecules; on compression, the necessity for the molecules occupying less space results in their standing upright, the polar group at 3 being forced away from the water. This group naturally leaves the water more easily if it is a methoxyl group than if it is an acetylated hydroxyl group; the latter has always been found to have a stronger attraction for the water. In the gaseous state of the films μ is much higher than in the condensed, indicating that the dipoles at 16 and 17 are inclined at a considerable angle to the plane of the ring system; the value is also so high when the molecules lie flat that there is little doubt that these dipoles reinforce one another, i.e. both the hydroxyls are on the same side of the ring.

In this group of compounds the molecules are found lying flat and standing upright; it is also possible, by eliminating the hydroxyls at 16 and 17, leaving only that at 3, to make the oestratriene skeleton stand upright on the other end, i.e. on the same end as the commoner sterols.

[1] *J.A.C.S.* (1935), 2224. [2] *J.C.S.* (1936), 1585.
[3] Cf. Meyer and Jacobson, *Org. Chem.*, II, **4**, 153.

If two water-attracting groups are present at a considerable distance apart in the molecules, say one in ring I and another in ring IV or in the side chain attached to ring IV, the films always seem to be gaseous, the molecules lying flat, unless the anchorage at one end of the molecules is so weak that compression of the film forces this end away from the surface. Two such cases of gaseous films with the sterol skeleton are apocholic acid, which has a carboxyl group at the end of the side chain, and pregnandiol, which is an oestrin derivative with two widely separated hydroxyl groups. No cases appear to have been examined of a compound with one polar group on ring I and one more in ring III, but it is likely that these also would give gaseous films.

26. Films of chlorophyll, haemin, &c. Gorter[1] found the area of chlorophyll to be about 100 sq. A., and Hughes[2] found a limiting area of about 135 sq. A. (with slight variations between the *a*- and *b*-chlorophylls); the films can be compressed to about 80 sq. A. At the higher compressions the films are solid, at lower they are liquid. On acid solutions the films are smaller in area (about 80 to 68 sq. A.) and less compressible, the magnesium being probably split off. Haemin gives a very incompressible, solid film of about 70 sq. A. It seems probable that the very complex ring structure of these substances[3] is orientated perpendicularly to the water at the area of 70 to 80 sq. A. At the larger areas found with chlorophyll films under low and moderate pressures they are probably tilted. The long chains attached to the ring structures may be tilted or possibly in chaotic motion, as in the liquid-expanded films.

27. Films of complex carbohydrates and synthetic polymers. Derivatives of cellulose have been investigated by Katz and Samwel,[4] Adam,[5] and Harding and Adam.[6] The ethers of cellulose with methyl, ethyl, and benzyl alcohols spread well. Esters spread less well, but the acetates are nearly completely spread on water, and the nitrates, though very incompletely spread on water, can be completely spread on strong (2N) caustic soda, on which solution they are so rapidly denitrated that the spread films probably consist of alkali cellulose. Highly nitrated celluloses (12·6 per cent. nitrogen and over) do not spread completely even on strong soda.

All cellulose derivatives show the same general types of pressure and potential curves. The pressure, above about 60 sq. A. per hexose group, is usually not over a dyne or two, except with considerably depolymerized derivatives such as the crystalline trimethyl and triethyl celluloses; this area is approximately that of the hexose ring lying flat on the surface. The films can be compressed without collapse to about 40 sq. A.; during this compression the value of μ falls considerably, indicating a re-orientation of the hexose groups, probably a tilting of the plane of the hexose rings to the water surface. It seems likely that the cellulose chains are stretched out fully on the surface when sufficient space is allowed. The benzyl ethers require rather more space, from 65 to 80 sq. A., according to the proportion of the bulky benzyl groups in the molecule.

The esters with fatty acids, and the benzyl ethers, have pressure-area curves which come down sharply to a definite limiting area. A rather curious pheno-

[1] Quoted by Hubert, *Rec. trav. bot. néerland.*, **32**, 370 (1935).
[2] *Proc. Roy. Soc.* A, **155**, 710 (1936).
[3] For the constitution cf. Stoll, *Naturwiss.*, **24**, 53 (1936).
[4] *Annalen*, **472**, 241; **474**, 296 (1929).
[5] *Trans. Faraday Soc.*, **29**, 90 (1933).
[6] *Ibid.*, **29**, 837 (1933).

menon is found, however, with the methyl and ethyl ethers on water and, to a less extent, with the esters on strong soda solutions. Below 1 or 2 dynes pressure the pressure-area curves approach the axis of no pressure very gradually. There is a limiting area beyond which no pressure greater than 0·02 dyne can be observed, but this is many hundreds of sq. A.

Films of trimethyl cellulose were found to be uniform in surface potential up to about 140 sq. A., above which area fluctuations, indicative of gaps in the film, occur. Miles suggested to the author that possibly the chains of methylated cellulose are vibrating in the surface, pushing each other apart, the adhesion between them being insufficient to keep them lying still side by side. Haller[1] had suggested that the vibration of very long molecules might be responsible for part of the osmotic (or swelling) pressures of certain colloidal solutions. Such oscillations might account for the existence of measurable surface pressure at areas much greater than that of closely packed hexose groups lying flat. The derivatives which show this phenomenon are, however, probably somewhat depolymerized and it is possible that they contain a certain proportion of molecules with chains short enough to form gaseous films. Values of μ do not begin to fall till the area is decreased to 62 sq. A., indicating that the molecules are flat at greater areas.

The fact that most cellulose derivatives can be spread to a film in which every chain of hexose groups is lying stretched out flat on the surface proves that, if there are any bundles of laterally adhering cellulose chains or 'micelles' in the solutions, the adhesion in such bundles is very weak, and can be disrupted by the adhesion to the water surface. The spreading experiments do, however, reveal differences in the cohesion of different derivatives of cellulose in their solutions. It is known that the anchoring power of ether groups for water is much less than that of acetate groups, yet the cellulose ethers spread completely on water, but cellulose acetates do not. This points to a higher lateral adhesion between cellulose-acetate chains in solution than between methyl- or ethyl-cellulose chains. As cellulose cannot be spread it probably has a much higher lateral adhesion between chains.

An interesting point was that a methylated starch derivative did not spread fully, in contrast to the methylated celluloses. If a model is made of the cellulose molecule, it can easily be stretched out on the table with every hexose group flat; the model of starch cannot be laid flat or completely stretched out, owing to the different arrangement of linkages in and between the rings. Haworth[2] suggests that this may be the reason why cellulose forms long fibrous structures, while starch does not.

Some, but not all, of the modern synthetic polymers with very large molecules, probably of long-chain structure, will spread on water. Moss[3] found that various polyethyl succinates spread; Harkins and others[4] that polymerized ω-hydroxydecanoic acid spreads until the molecules lie flat. Adam, however, found that polymerized methyl and ethyl α-methylacrylate would spread only partially on water, the dark-ground illuminator showing large amounts of unspread material and the area (per unit unpolymerized molecule) being only about half that of a fatty acid chain standing upright. The films are all coherent and moderately compressible, as if there was some possibility of tilting away parts of the chains from the surface.

[1] *Kolloid-Z.*, **49**, 74 (1929).
[2] *Ber.*, **65**, 62 (1932).
[3] *J.A.C.S.* (1934), 41.
[4] *J. Chem. Physics*, **3**, 692 (1935).

28. Surface films of proteins. Although most proteins are soluble in water they are usually sufficiently adsorbed to leave the interior of a solution almost completely for the surface, provided this is large enough. Also, if a protein is placed in a suitable manner at the surface of water, it will often spread out to a thin film, which is of the order one amino-acid in thickness; not only is the protein arranged in a monomolecular layer on the surface, but the complex protein molecules are themselves unfolded so that every amino-acid has its own place on the surface. Hence proteins can be studied by methods appropriate for insoluble films.

Two methods have been used for spreading proteins; the first, due to Gorter and Grendel in 1925, is to drop a fairly concentrated aqueous solution, very carefully from the least possible height, on to the clean surface of the water in the trough. If the drops are small, and the concentration of the solution dropped right, the protein spreads, in time, over the surface to a homogeneous layer showing no bright spots (except dust) and a uniform surface potential when compressed to a few dynes pressure. The composition of the underlying solution is very important, but under favourable conditions spreading is to a limiting area, at no compression, of about 1 sq. m. per mg., which is an average thickness of the film, assuming the density to be 1·33, of 7·5 A.

Rideal and his collaborators found that solid particles of protein spread very rapidly on a clean surface; their method of spreading is to coat a quartz fibre, first covered with paraffin wax, with a little protein; this is dipped into the water surface, and the amount of protein passing into the surface ascertained by weighing the fibre on a simple micro-balance.[1] By this method somewhat larger areas can sometimes be obtained, and films formed from proteins which cannot be made to form homogeneous films when spread by Gorter's technique; and in certain cases the average thickness of the fully spread film is only about 3 A.

The time allowed for spreading is important by both methods, and spreading occurs more rapidly at higher temperatures; in the case of a protein and a substratum on which spreading occurs slowly, it may be impossible to wait long enough to reach the final state of spreading. By Gorter's method the risk is that some of the protein dropped on the surface will penetrate into the interior of the solution and fail to reach the surface, or even if it does, fail to be properly unfolded as a surface film. By the other method there is some risk that small solid particles may become detached from the fibre and be embedded in the film, being prevented from spreading by the pressure of the film. This risk is much lessened, however, if not too much protein is put on the fibre. Dark-ground illumination gives a useful check on whether any considerable amount of protein is unspread, but owing to the probable closeness of the refractive index of a hydrated protein to that of water, small amounts of partially spread or partially unfolded protein may not be detected in this way.

Protein films are coherent; their molecules are much too large for gaseous films to be detectable. They are also very compressible; in all cases measured the area diminishes considerably between 2 and 12 dynes,

[1] Hughes, Schulman, and Rideal, *Nature*, **129**, 21 (1932); Hughes and Rideal, *Proc. Roy. Soc.* A, **137**, 62 (1932); Hughes, *Trans. Faraday Soc.*, **29**, 214 (1933); Fosbinder, *J. Franklin Inst.*, **215**, 583 (1933).

the contraction in this range of pressures being usually from 25 to 40 per cent. of the area at 2 dynes. At areas greater than about 1 sq. m. per mg. the films may be liquid, but on compression they become solid and elastic, a state called by Hughes and Rideal a 'gel'.

Fig. 24 shows the surface pressure, surface potential, and values of μ

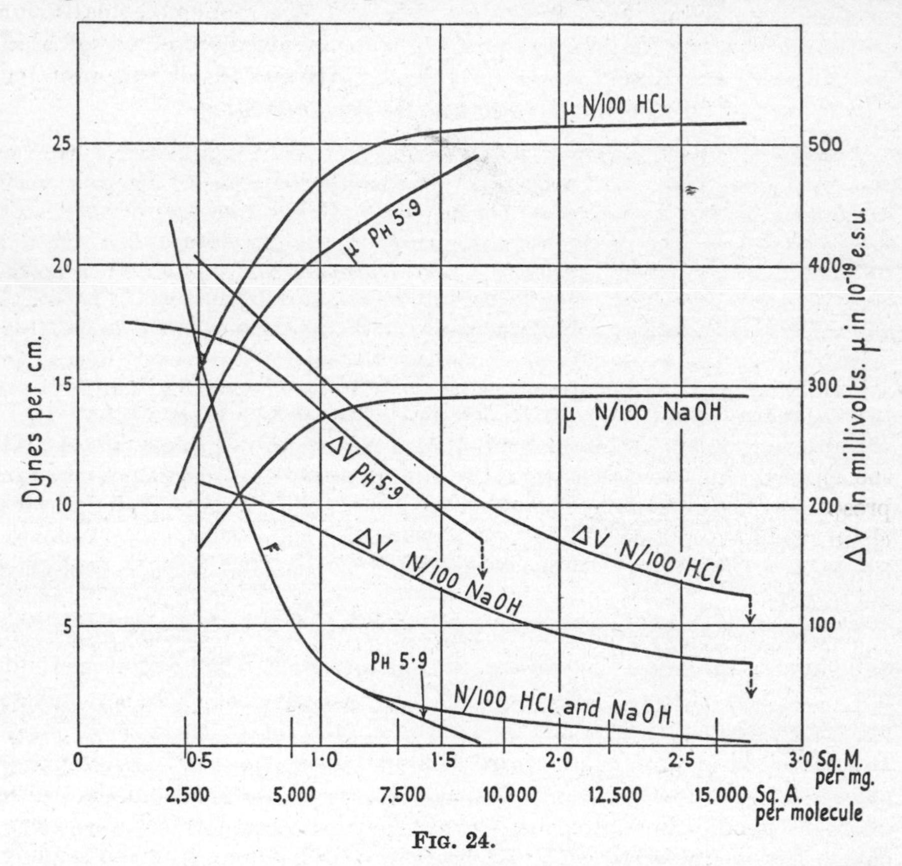

FIG. 24.

for gliadin films, recalculated from Hughes and Rideal's curves,[1] on N/100 acid and alkali, and on a phosphate buffer of p_H 5·9, which is slightly to the acid side of the iso-electric point. The areas per molecule and values of μ assume a molecular weight of 34,500. The limiting area on both acid and alkaline solutions is about 2·8 sq. m. per mg. (15,800 sq. A. per molecule), but this is decreased to only about 1·25 sq. m. per mg. at 2 dynes pressure. The limiting area on the buffer (p_H 5·9) is much smaller, but the pressure-area curves are practically identical, on all three solutions above 2 dynes. Surface potential is highest on the acid solution and lowest on the alkaline; μ falls rapidly at pressures of over 2 dynes, but is nearly constant at areas between 2·8 and 1·25 sq. m. per mg. The 'gel' state of the film appears when the pressure has reached about 15 dynes.

[1] *Proc. Roy. Soc.* A, **137**, 70 (1932).

The composition of a protein is, in general, a series of polypeptide linkages[1]

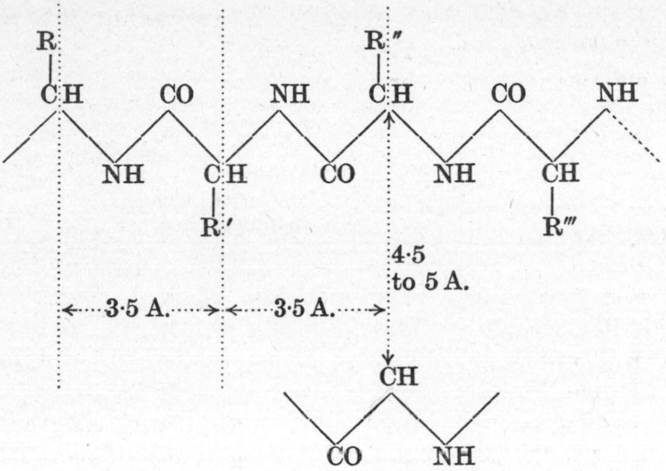

```
     R                           R″
     |                           |
     CH      CO        NH        CH       CO       NH
   /    \   /   \     /   \     /   \    /   \    /   \
         NH       CH        CO        NH       CH
                  |                            |
                  R′                           R‴
                                4·5
                                to 5 A.
     ←--3·5 A.--→←--3·5 A.--→
                                 ↓
                                 CH
                               /    \
                             CO      NH
```

in which R, R′, R″, R‴ either are hydrocarbon chains of from 1 to 6 carbons long (or hydrogen), or are chains with a COOH or NH_2 group at the end, in the cases where dibasic amino-acids or di-amino acids are present in the protein. This is the 'β-keratin' configuration of the protein chain, its most extended form. The length of one polypeptide group is 3·5 A., and the spacing apart of two chains, in the solid form, is probably 4·5 to 5 A.

In the most completely spread form of the protein, with the molecules still closely packed on the surface, the side chains R will be stretched out flat along the surface. This is most likely to occur if there are water-attracting groups at the ends of the side chains, such as COOH or NH_2. Rideal and Hughes calculate from Astbury's dimensions of protein molecules and the chemical composition of gliadin, that the side chains average about 3 carbon atoms long, and the area when completely spread with chains flat on the surface should be approximately the limiting area of 2·8 sq. m. per mg. given in Fig. 24. The area when the chains are forced, by compression, out of the surface, so that the molecules pack as indicated in the diagram above (the chains R being perpendicular to the paper), would be about 0·7 sq. m. per mg. It is suggested that the 'gel' state of the films occurs when the chains are forced out of the surface, so that the polypeptide chains are closely packed, side by side, in an arrangement resembling the β-keratin form of hair and silk.

Evidently very little force is required to remove the side chains nearly completely from the surface, since the compressibility above 1 sq. m. per mg. is so large. Gliadin contains a large proportion of the dibasic acid, glutamic, as well as smaller amounts of diamino acids, so that it is a

[1] Cf. Astbury, *Trans. Faraday Soc.*, **29**, 193 (1933); *Fundamentals of Fibre Structure*, V (Oxford, 1933).

particularly favourable case for the chains to spread out on the surface. Hughes found that glutenin and egg albumin do not spread to such large areas; they become gelatinous at much the same area as gliadin, but a much smaller pressure (only about 1 dyne) is required to reach this area and the gel state.

When the side chains are compressed away from the surface they may be forced upwards or downwards into the water. It is not improbable that they point upwards if purely hydrocarbon in nature, and down if they have COOH or NH_2 groups at their ends.

Prolonged compression of a protein film appears to render it incapable of re-expansion. It is possible that some change occurs causing combination, or some particularly close adhesion, between chains compressed side by side for some time. This may be a process similar to that which occurs when a protein is denatured, an increase in the internal cohesion of the protein particle preventing solution taking place. Ramsden,[1] many years ago, showed that adsorption at a surface, with shaking, often denatures a protein to the extent of making it insoluble; and Neurath, recently, finds that solutions of egg or serum albumin, if denatured by heat or ultra-violet light, fail to spread on solutions on which they spread quite well in the undenatured condition.[2] This points to a tightening of the internal linkages in a protein molecule as an essential part of the denaturation process.

These surface films of proteins are not infrequently formed on solutions in which the proteins are quite soluble, so that it may be argued that the protein has been altered or 'denatured' by its unfoldment in the surface film, in such a way as to render it less soluble or completely insoluble. Whether the unfoldment and spreading of the molecule always results in the loss of solubility is not proven; Gorter has been able to remove pepsin from a surface on which it has been spread by means of a fine net pulled up through the surface, and subsequently dissolved the material in water, finding that it retained its normal properties, including proteolytic activity.

It is possible that, although many proteins are soluble, their tendency to be adsorbed (when unrolled) is so great that a protein on the surface simulates complete insolubility, which may be changed into genuine and permanent insolubility if the spread protein is subjected to treatment which fixes it in the unfolded condition by strengthening or 'activating' the bonds between adjacent CO·NH, or other polar groups. One such treatment appears to consist in simply compressing the film, either by means of barriers or by shaking a protein solution so as to produce foam.

The values of surface potential and μ in Fig. 24 indicate that the number and the orientation of the dipoles in the film, at least on acid and alkaline solutions, does not change as the film is compressed to some 2 dynes; this may indicate that the earlier stages of the compression of the gliadin films only bring the ends of the chains R closer together, without removing the COOH or NH_2 groups at their ends from the water. Further compression, however, rapidly

[1] *Proc. Roy. Soc.*, **72**, 156 (1903); cf. also Metcalf, *Z. physikal. Chem.*, **52**, 1 (1905), and Ramsden, *Trans. Faraday Soc.*, **22**, 484 (1926).

[2] *J. Physical Chem.* (1936), 361 (see, however, Appendix).

lowers μ, indicating either removal of a number of dipoles from the surface or a drastic re-orientation of the dipoles. Of course, the very large values of μ per 'molecule' of 34,500 molecular weight are due to a large number of CO, NH, COOH, and NH_2 groups being present. The surface potential is very much diminished on alkaline solutions. This is to be expected, as in § 21 we saw that the contribution to the surface potential of a fully ionized COONa group is either very small or negative, and on alkaline solutions the COO groups will be in the form of metallic salts. The amines do not drop in surface potential much when they form salts, and therefore the potential of the protein on acid solutions, with the NH_2 groups present as salts, is high.

Spreading is very much more rapid on some solutions than on others. Gorter and others[1] have usually found the maximal spreading from solution (about 0·9 or 1·0 sq. m. per mg.) either on strongly acid or strongly alkaline solutions, or at the isoelectric point. All three maxima have been found with one and the same protein in some cases; maxima at one or more of these p_H values have been reported for egg albumin (θ, π), casein (β, p. 1273; γ, p. 480; δ, p. 404), with which the spreading has been traced on more alkaline solutions, the alkaline maximum occurring on solutions of higher p_H than 12. Zein (ι) and pepsin (ν) showed the same maximum on acid solutions and at the isoelectric point; some other proteins, e.g. oxyhaemoglobin and insulin, show a maximum on acid solutions and a rise at the isoelectric point, but not to the maximum. Gelatin, gliadin, and peptone could not be spread from aqueous solutions (γ); gelatin has not been spread by either method, being probably too soluble. Keratin will not spread from solid, no doubt on account of its high internal cohesion, which also renders it insoluble. It is as well that the scleroproteins will not dissolve or spread, otherwise hair, hoofs, &c., would rapidly disappear when continuously wetted.

In between the maxima the amount of spreading may drop to a small fraction

[1] Reference to the papers of Gorter and his colleagues on protein films will be made by Greek letter as below:

(α) Gorter and Grendel, *Proc. K. Akad. Wetensch. Amsterdam*, **29**, 371 (1925).
(β) Gorter and Grendel, *ibid.*, **29**, 1262 (1926).
(γ) Gorter and Grendel, *Trans. Faraday Soc.*, **22**, 477 (1926).
(δ) Gorter and Grendel, *Biochem. Z.*, **201**, 391 (1928).
(ϵ) Grendel, *Thesis* (Leiden, 1927).
(ζ) Gorter and Grendel, *Proc. K. Akad. Wetensch. Amsterdam*, **32**, 770 (1929).
(η) Gorter and Seeder, *Kolloid-Z.*, **61**, 246 (1932).
(θ) Gorter, van Ormondt, and Dom, *Proc. K. Akad. Wetensch. Amsterdam*, **35**, 838 (1932).
(ι) Gorter and van Ormondt, *ibid.*, **36**, 922 (1933).
(κ) Gorter, *ibid.*, **37**, 20 (1934).
(λ) Gorter, Meyer, and Philippi, *ibid.*, **37**, 355 (1934).
(μ) Gorter and Philippi, *ibid.*, **37**, 788 (1934).
(ν) Gorter, *J. Gen. Physiol.*, **18**, 421 (1935).
(ξ) Gorter, van Ormondt, and Meijer, *Biochem. J.*, **29**, 38 (1935).
(o) Gorter and van Ormondt, *ibid.*, **29**, 48 (1935).
(π) ter Horst, *Rec. Trav. Chim. Pays-Bas*, **55**, 1 (1936).
(ρ) Gorter and others, *Proc. K. Akad. Wetensch. Amsterdam*, **39**, 1187 (1936).
(σ) Gorter and Maaskant, *ibid.*, **40**, 71 (1937).
(τ) Gorter and Maaskant, *ibid.*, **40**, 73 (1937).
Cf. also Philippi, 'On the Nature of Proteins', *Thesis* (Amsterdam, 1936).

only of the maximum, e.g. at p_H 3 with egg albumin the spreading is to only about one-eighth of the area of spread at p_H 1 or 4·9. The amount of spreading by this method is really, however, a function of the time which elapses after the protein solution is placed on the surface. Recent work indicates that the main difference between solutions of different p_H is that some cause spreading to occur more rapidly than others.

If suitable concentrations of certain ions are introduced into the solutions, maximal spreading may be obtained even at a p_H close to those at which very little spreading usually occurs. Here the sign, and the degree of hydration of the ions are apparently of principal importance. On the acid side of the isoelectric point spreading may be accelerated by anions (θ, κ); the order of effectiveness of the monovalent anions follows the lyotropic series CNS > I > Br > Cl, i.e. those anions which are least hydrated are the most effective in aiding spreading. On the alkaline side it is the cations which aid spreading, in the order K > Na > Li, the least hydrated being again the most effective. Di- and tri-valent ions are more effective than monovalent. In these experiments the p_H could not be carefully controlled, owing to the necessity of keeping out ions other than those being studied.

Quite recently some doubt has been thrown on the rule that maximal spreading of proteins is always attained at the isoelectric point. Askew and Danielli, in preliminary measurements, found that, at an interface between bromobenzene and aqueous solutions, there was a minimum of spreading of ovalbumin at the isoelectric point, and Gorter and Philippi have observed some cases in which no maximum is obtained at this point.[1]

Certain rather complex proteins may be unable to spread on ordinary aqueous solutions, but their spreading may be achieved by slight proteolytic digestion; e.g. myosin spreads well on trypsin solutions but poorly on ordinary salts (o); the ferments pepsin and prothrombase aid the spreading of fibrinogen (ρ). Other organic solutes in the liquid may also aid spreading; e.g. Rideal, Moss, and Bate Smith[2] find that lactates aid the spreading of myosin, and Gorter and others find that tartrazine and glutathione aid the spreading of ovalbumin (ξ). These observations are suggestive, but much more systematic work is clearly necessary before any general theory of the action of these substances can be given. They presumably aid the spreading either by weakening the internal cohesion of the folded protein molecule, or by increasing the strength of adhesion of the unfolded molecule to the water surface.

Since, on the acid side, the protein contains free basic groups, and on the alkaline free acidic groups, the assistance to spreading is possibly due to salt formation between the ions in solution and the protein in the film; the reason why the least hydrated ions are the most effective may be that they come to the surface most easily, having less affinity for the water than the more hydrated.

29. Summary of the properties of molecules as learned from surface films. The study of condensed films has shown that the molecules of long-chain compounds are elongated objects, several times as long as thick; that they orient themselves very steeply to the surface, and that their end groups are often different in shape and size from the CH_2 groups in the chains, sometimes forming projections on the ends of the chains.

[1] Verbal communications, Royal Society discussion on Surface Films, 12 March 1936.

[2] *Nature*, **136**, 260 (1935).

Details of the shape and size of these end groups are of great importance in determining the packing of the molecules.

We learn that the chains are flexible from the configuration assumed by the pentaerythritol tetrapalmitate molecule, and from the behaviour of the esters when the carboxyl end group on an acid is blocked by a gradually increasing length of alcoholic chain (§ 23). The properties of the expanded films also require flexibility in the chains.

From the gaseous films it is learned that the molecules have the normal kinetic energy of translatory motion in the two dimensions of the surface, $\frac{1}{2}kT$, per degree of freedom.

Much information is also available as to the adhesional forces round the molecules.[1] Those groups which normally promote solution in water are found to attract the water strongly, providing a firm anchorage for the lower end of the molecules, without which a film cannot be stable. Partial obstruction of these groups diminishes or entirely destroys the stability of the film. The attraction for water can be roughly graded from the stability of films, and the length of chain required to prevent solution of the molecules, as follows.

(*a*) Very weak attraction, no film formed; hydrocarbon, CH_2I, CH_2Br, CH_2Cl, NO_3.

(*b*) Weak attraction, unstable and collapsing films (groups in increasing order of attraction for water): CH_2OCH_3 (*f*), $C_6H_4OCH_3$ (*d*, *j*), $COOCH_3$.

(*c*) Strong attraction, stable films, but inappreciable solution, with a 16-carbon chain: CH_2OH, $COOH$, CN, $CONH_2$, $CH{:}NOH$, C_6H_4OH, CH_2COCH_3, $NHCONH_2$, $NHCOCH_3$.

(*d*) Very strong attraction, substances dissolve with a 16-carbon chain: $C_6H_4SO_3'$, SO_3', OSO_3', $NR_3^{\cdot}$.

It will be seen in Chapter IV that these adhesions between different chemical groups are in good agreement with the values deduced from measurements of the adhesion between two liquids.

The side-by-side attraction between the long-chain molecules is of very great importance to the architecture of the films. In the condensed state this side-by-side attraction is the chief factor in retaining the molecules closely packed. This is shown by the influence of lengthening the chain on the expansion temperature; a given lengthening of the chain raises the expansion temperature by the same amount, whatever the nature of the end group. The end groups also contribute a substantial amount to the lateral attraction between the molecules, both in the condensed state and in the expanded; in the expanded state, we have seen that a high residual affinity or attraction between the end groups tends to make a liquid-expanded film, while a low attraction between the end groups gives a vapour-expanded or even a gaseous film.

In discussing the lateral adhesions between the molecules in the films, it must always be remembered that we are dealing with opposing sets of

[1] Cf. Adam, *Trans. Faraday Soc.*, **24**, 150 (1928).

forces. The study of cohesional forces, except at absolute zero, is always complicated by the effects of the thermal motions of the molecules, which tend to break up the structures formed by the packing of the molecules under their mutual adhesions. And in the surface films there is a further complication, because the adhesional forces between the upper parts of the molecules and the water may tend to antagonize the lateral adhesions between the film molecules, by making the molecules lie flat in the surface. There is nearly, if not quite, as much attraction between a given area of hydrocarbon and water, as between two hydrocarbon surfaces (see Chap. V, § 3). When the molecules are standing nearly upright, and are closely packed in the surface, the hydrocarbon chains have their affinity satisfied by contact with other hydrocarbon chains, over their whole surface except the ends. If the molecules are isolated, and lying flat as in the gaseous films, the affinity of the hydrocarbon chains is satisfied by contact with the water on one side only. The normal sequence of events, as the films are warmed from a temperature at which they are condensed, is for the side-by-side attraction between the chains to be overcome first, the film then becoming expanded; liquid-expanded if there is sufficient lateral adhesion between the heads, and vapour-expanded if there is not. Further rise of temperature diminishes the lateral adhesion in the expanded films and causes them to pass either continuously (as in the vapour-expanded films) or discontinuously (as in the liquid-expanded films) into the gaseous films, the molecules lying flat in the surface.

Conversely, if in a type of molecule which forms a gaseous film the chains are lengthened, other conditions remaining the same, first the cohesional corrections to the gaseous state of the films are increased; next the mutual attraction between the chains causes them to pack more closely and satisfy their mutual affinities all round the chains, by standing either upright, or tilted to the surface, cohering into masses of coherent film; finally the motions of the molecules disappear and the film solidifies in the condensed state.

The solidity of the films is conditioned both by the nature of the end groups and by the length of the chains. If the chains exceed 20 carbons in length, the films are usually solid, and sometimes so rigid that with a surface pressure of 2 dynes per cm. applied at one end of the film, the support at the other end may be removed altogether with a surface as wide as 14 cm. The size of the end groups has little to do with determining the solidity of the films, but their specific nature is important; thus the phenols, resorcinols, and phloroglucinol derivatives are solid, and the urea derivatives are so also; most of the sterols give liquid films, though ergosterol, with a molecule of the same size as most other sterols, is solid at 15°.

The antagonistic action of the cohesional forces tending to pull the molecules in different directions is shown in other ways besides the tendency of the chains to lie flat or stand upright. A similar effect is found with the benzene rings containing different substituents (*k*); it is impossible to make the benzene ring lie flat in the water surface by introducing oxygen-containing groups at various points in the ring, because although the attraction of the face of the ring to the water is no doubt increased by the presence of these groups, the lateral attraction between the rings, packed in a layer oriented steeply to the surface, is also increased, perhaps not so much as that for the water, but still sufficiently to make the molecule take advantage of the upright position, in which the affinities on both sides of the rings can be satisfied.

The good or bad spreading of proteins and carbohydrates, and of other very large molecules, is largely determined by the relative strengths of the adhesions of the water-attracting groups to the water, and to other similar groups in the molecule.

The equilibrium between the crystal, or material in bulk form, and the surface film is also determined by the relative intensities of the tendencies of the chains to lie side by side, and of the heads to reach the water. If the chains become very long, a mass on the surface becomes more stable than the spread film; the crystal will not spread spontaneously, and the film, if spread by the aid of a solvent, may become unstable and collapse readily. These facts will appear in § 35.

30. Chemical reactions in surface films. A principal point of interest in studies of the reactions undergone by substances in surface films is whether the reactivity of the substances is affected by reason of their presence at the surface. On solid surfaces, and on the surface of those complex colloidal particles known as enzymes, there is certainly an increase in reactivity of those substances whose reactions are catalysed by the surface or the enzyme. In general, it appears that the mere fact of their presence in a unimolecular layer at a liquid surface does not alter the intrinsic reactivity, most conveniently measured by the energy of activation, of molecules. Nevertheless, the work of Rideal and his colleagues has shown that quite frequently the *accessibility* of molecules in the surface film to the underlying molecules or ions with which they react is considerably modified by the orientation or crowding imposed in the film, and consequently the rate of reaction of a substance in a film may be greatly affected by the structure of the film. Up to the present, however, it appears that a liquid surface does not possess the rigidity necessary to impose the strains required to alter the state of activation of a molecule at its surface, unless the surface films are compressed. Solid surfaces and enzymes can, however, strain adsorbed molecules so as to alter their reactivity (Chap. VII).

The course of reactions in surface films may be followed either by surface pressure or by surface-potential measurements; the former detects any change accompanied by a marked re-orientation of the molecules, the latter any re-orientation of the dipoles or any change in the total amount of the dipole of the molecule. Usually surface potential reveals more than surface pressure of the course of any reactions proceeding in the films, but both measurements should be made.

Hughes and Rideal[1] found that oleic and petroselinic acids are very

[1] *Proc. Roy. Soc.* A, **140**, 253 (1933).

much more rapidly oxidized on dilute acid permanganate when the films are under low surface pressure than when compressed. Both these acids have a double bond in the middle of the chain, and form liquid-expanded films; when oxidized the double bond adds on hydroxyl groups and is more strongly attracted by the water, the molecule lying flat and the films becoming gaseous. The chance of the double bond coming into contact with the water is much greater if the molecules are much tilted to the vertical than if they are squeezed nearly upright by compression of the films. The rate of oxidation of the double bond can be reduced almost tenfold by crowding the molecules in the film, so that the accessibility of the molecules to the underlying solution is diminished. Gee and Rideal found a similar diminution in the rate of autoxidation of the maleic anhydride compound of β-elaeostearin on compressing films.

In the hydrolysis of simple esters,[1] also, there is a variation of the rate of hydrolysis by caustic soda, with the pressure on the film. This is probably due to the shorter of the two hydrocarbon chains dipping into the water downwards from the ester group, protecting this group from easy access by the hydroxyl ions and so retarding hydrolysis. Perhaps also the end group may be deformed, so that its reactivity is altered.

Both the oxidation and the subsequent polymerization of β-elaeostearin and its maleic anhydride addition compound give rise to an increase in area, and this rather complex reaction has been studied by Gee and Rideal,[2] starting from films under sufficient compression for the molecules to be steeply oriented to the surface. The rate of oxidation is decreased by increasing the pressure; polymerization begins slowly, the rate then increasing to a maximum and then falling off as the reaction is completed. A complicated kinetic treatment, for which the original papers must be consulted,[3] leads to the conclusion that there are two forms of oxidation product, one of which polymerizes very rapidly and the other more slowly. The mechanism of polymerization appears to be that the single molecules add on one by one to the chains of polymer, the velocity of polymerization being greatest at medium degrees of polymerization. A quite small amount of ethyl myristate in the film seriously retards polymerization. Under some circumstances an increase of surface pressure increases the rate of polymerization, which indicates that the activation of the molecules for the polymerization is increased by lateral compression of the film.

Hydrolysis of the lactone of γ-hydroxystearic acid, which is a condensed or liquid-expanded film according to temperature, to the free hydroxy-acid, occurs in films on solutions of caustic soda.[4] As the acid on the alkaline solution forms a gaseous film the area increases very much during the hydrolysis, and the course of the reaction may be followed by either pressure or potential measurements. The rate of reaction is proportional to the concentration of caustic soda; if this and the surface pressure are kept constant the reaction appears unimolecular, with an energy of activation of 12,500 calories per gm. molecule, which is within experimental error of the energy of activation of hydrolysis by the alcoholate ion in bulk solution.

[1] Alexander and Schulman, *Proc. Roy. Soc.* A, **161**, 115 (1937).
[2] *Ibid.*, **153**, 116, 129 (1935). [3] Cf. also *Trans. Faraday Soc.*, **31**, 969 (1935).
[4] Adam (*q*); Fosbinder and Rideal, *Proc. Roy. Soc.* A, **143**, 61 (1933).

Irradiation of films of proteins with ultra-violet light produces very complex changes in pressure and potential;[1] light of different wave-lengths produces different effects. The first effect is usually an increase of both pressure and potential; later the protein molecule appears to be broken down so far that some solution of the film takes place, so that pressure and potential fall. A remarkable fact is that very small traces of metallic ions in solution may cause some of these reactions to take place in visible light.

The digestion of proteins in the form of monomolecular films, by enzymes in the underlying solution, has been studied by Schulman and Rideal;[2] so far as the studies have gone there does not appear to be a very marked difference between digestion of a surface layer of protein and digestion of one dissolved in bulk solution.

Schulman has shown that tannic acid in the solution below a protein film greatly alters the surface potential, probably through combination with the protein film. Here apparently we have the phenomenon of 'tanning' a unimolecular film!

The effect of various snake venoms on surface films of lecithin is to remove one of the long-chain fatty-acid groups from the molecule, causing a considerable fall in surface potential;[3] this reaction is much slowed by compression of the film; as the result of compression is to remove the double bonds in the oleyl group (the one split off) of the lecithin from the surface, it is possible that the lecithinase, the enzyme which splits off the oleyl group, has a molecular structure which fits both the end group and the double bond in the lecithin.

There have recently come to light[4] some very remarkable effects of exceedingly small traces of ions in the water, on the properties and reactions of the films. The packing of condensed films of acids seems to depend on the ions; if divalent ions are present the tendency is for the chains to be close-packed at the usual area of 20·5 sq. A.; in the absence of such ions the curve may be that of close-packed heads, approximating, if great care is taken, using a quartz still for the water and a very heavily paraffined trough, to 25 sq. A., the area found on dilute acid solutions. Adam (*b*) had found in 1922 that distilled water put freshly into the brass trough gave (temporarily) a larger area than water which had been long in the trough (curve II of Fig. 14), and Myers now attributes this, probably correctly, to the absence of the divalent ions usually present. The surface potential is also often much altered by divalent ions.

Even more striking is the effect on chemical reactions in the films, particularly various photo-chemical reactions. The reactions of stearic anilide, α-hydroxystearic acid, and proteins, all appear to be affected by traces of metallic ions too small to be always identifiable. As yet, the results are preliminary, but they show promise of being well worth further investigation, particularly as traces of heavy metallic ions occasionally have a remarkable biological effect (the 'oligodynamic' action).

Some indication of the state of the material after spreading in a film can be obtained by causing the film to collapse, and then collecting the collapsed

[1] Rideal and Mitchell, *Proc. Roy. Soc.* A, **159**, 206 (1937).

[2] *Biochem. J.*, **27**, 1581 (1933).

[3] Hughes, *Biochem. J.*, **29**, 437 (1935).

[4] Harkins and Myers, *Nature*, **139**, 367 (1937); Rideal, Mitchell, and Schulman, *ibid.*, p. 625.

material. Adam[1] collected films of nitrocellulose which had been spread on strong caustic soda solutions, by means of a thin glass rod, which was pulled along the surface of the trough from end to end; the material was sufficiently adhesive and fibrous to stick to the rod; qualitative tests on the material removed showed that it had been de-nitrated. Langmuir and Schaefer[2] covered the surface of dilute barium and calcium hydroxide solutions with films of fatty acid; the area was then reduced and the collapsed material scooped up on platinum foil. Analysis showed, as might be expected, that it consisted of barium or calcium soap if the p_H of the liquid exceeded about 11. No soap was formed at p_H 3, and the film was about half soap in the neighbourhood of p_H 6.

31. Interaction between insoluble films and capillary active substances in solution. Penetration and displacement of insoluble films. A soluble substance may interact with an insoluble substance present as a monolayer on the surface of the solution in several different ways. Some effects so far observed include first, a non-specific penetration of dissolved molecules into the monolayer, with disruption of its cohesion and change of a normally coherent monolayer into a gaseous one; second, a more specific penetration, in which the dissolved molecules enter the monolayer and adhere to the molecules already there, forming molecular compounds or 'complexes'; third, adsorption of the soluble substance, often by rather specific forces, underneath the monolayer, probably without actual penetration; fourth, displacement of the insoluble monolayer from the surface altogether, by the soluble substance. The subject has been studied especially in Rideal's laboratory at Cambridge,[3] with some contributions from other workers.[4]

Quite small molecules with some tendency to be adsorbed may greatly reduce the cohesion of monolayers. The unusually small cohesion in films of long chain amines on solutions containing acetate buffers at about p_H 4 (p. 72) is due to acetic acid molecules penetrating the films. Acids or alcohols, with from 4 to 8 carbons, penetrate monolayers of aliphatic substances or sterols, forming gaseous films. Penetration occurs below a certain pressure, which is higher, the longer the hydrocarbon chain in the penetrating molecule, and lower, the greater the cohesion in the monolayer. This penetration is probably correlated with the work of adsorption at an *oil*-water interface.[5] Cetyl sodium sulphate penetrates a cholesterol film, rendering it gaseous, up to 50 dynes per cm.

When complexes are formed on penetration, the length and the stereochemical configuration of the hydrocarbon chains in the penetrating and the monolayer molecules are important; long chains penetrate more easily than short, and if double bonds are present, penetration into, or by, sub-

[1] *Trans. Faraday Soc.*, **29**, 96 (1933). [2] *J.A.C.S.* (1936), 284.

[3] Schulman and Hughes, *Biochem. J.*, **29**, 1236, 1243 (1935); Schulman and Rideal, *Proc. Roy. Soc.* B, **122**, 29, 46 (1937); Schulman and Stenhagen, *ibid.*, **126**, 356 (1938); Marsden and Schulman, *Trans. Faraday Soc.* (1938), 748; Cockbain and Schulman, *ibid.* (1939), 716; Schulman, *Ann. Rep. Chem. Soc.* (1939), 110; Rideal and Schulman, *Nature*, **144**, 100 (1939). [4] Bilham, *M.Sc. Thesis*, London (1938); Adam, Askew, and Pankhurst, *Proc. Roy. Soc.* A, **170**, 485 (1939); Pankhurst, *Ph.D. Thesis*, London (1940). [5] J. S. F. Gill, Unpublished Work (1939).

stances with saturated chains is better if the double bonds have the 'trans' than the 'cis' configuration, because they fit more closely beside saturated chains. Interaction between the polar groups is still more important; it may be very specific, e.g. digitonin penetrates cholesterol, forming a condensed film of exactly double the area of cholesterol, presumably with one molecule of each in the complex. Digitonin does not penetrate films of 'epimerised' sterols, i.e. those in which the hydroxyl group is at a considerable angle to the rings. Saponin penetrates cholesterol and ergosterol, but not cetyl alcohol, cholesteryl acetate, or calciferol. It is concluded, from the areas at which discontinuities occur in the pressure-area curves, that complexes with the molecules in a 1 : 1, 1 : 2, or 1 : 3 ratio often occur. Sphingosine, which is too soluble to form a stable monolayer on water, is so attracted by cetyl alcohol as to form a stable mixed film.

Phenols and carboxylic acids penetrate and expand films of amines; but tannic and gallic acids, large molecules with many phenolic groups, solidify amine films, probably through cross-linking many amino molecules so that they cannot move independently in the surface. This must be a specific combination with the amino-groups, for gallic and tannic acids are very little adsorbed at an air-water surface. Soaps displace triglycerides, or proteins, from the surface.

The process of haemolysis is probably a penetration or displacement of the films normally surrounding the red blood corpuscles by the capillary active substances which constitute the haemolytic agents. Gorter and others[1] found that haemolysis was complete when just enough was present to cover an area equal in surface to the corpuscles. The correspondence between penetration in monomolecular films, and haemolysis, by various substances, has been discussed by Schulman and Rideal.[2]

32. Films between two immiscible liquids. Liquid-liquid interfaces are much commoner in biology than liquid-air, and in connexion with the emulsions (see Chap. III) they are of very great importance in non-biological systems. There is probably not a very large range of substances which are insoluble in either of two immiscible liquids, and also have an attraction for one solvent and a sufficiently small cohesion to spread at the interface. Askew and Danielli[3] have, however, recently succeeded in measuring directly the surface pressure of various films between bromobenzene and water. The apparatus was a modification of the trough and surface-pressure instrument of Adam and Jessop. The heavier bromobenzene was placed at the bottom of a brass trough, inside which, reaching about half-way up, was a trough made of glass; the bromobenzene-water interface was approximately level with the top of this inner trough. Glass barriers served to handle the film at this interface. The pressure-measuring instrument had a float of wood, and a thin strip of paper took the place of the platinum ribbons or vaselined silk threads. All barriers and the float were wet with water; the water takes the place of air, and the object is to produce a contact angle, of the liquid-liquid interface with the glass,

Proc. K. Akad. Wetensch. Amsterdam, **34,** 471 (1931). [2] *Proc. Roy. Soc.* B, **122,** 46 (1937). [3] *Proc. Roy. Soc.* A, **155,** 695 (1936); *Trans. Far. Soc.* (1940), 785.

of about 90°. If this is achieved the lower liquid fills the inner trough to the brim but does not run over the sides.

Egg albumin spread well at the interface; the speed of spreading was decidedly greater than at an air-water surface, the film settling down in a few seconds. The area of spreading appeared to be a minimum at the isoelectric point. The '*minimum*' was, however, in actual area, of the same order of magnitude as most of the *maxima* found by Gorter at the air-water surface; areas up to 60 per cent. larger being found on rather more acid solutions. Most long-chain compounds proved too soluble in one or the other phase, but α-aminopalmitic acid, and the amide of the straight chain acid with 20 carbon atoms, gave fairly stable gaseous films. This amide, at an air-water surface, is a condensed film expanding probably to a liquid-expanded (i.e. still coherent) film at about 67°. It is evident that the amount of lateral adhesion between the long chains when these chains are dipping into bromobenzene, is much less than when the chains are in air. This is to be expected, for the affinities of the long chains can be satisfied separately by proximity to molecules of bromobenzene, or indeed to any compounds containing much hydrocarbon, and these molecules are in constant motion in the liquid, and therefore tend to carry the chains along with them in their translatory motions parallel to the interface.

A methyl cellulose also spread in much the same manner as at a water-air surface.

33. The use of surface films as a micro-analytical method, and for elucidating constitution. The amount of material required to form a film of easily measurable area is a small fraction of a tenth of a milligramme, and the properties of many of the films are quite characteristic. Potentially, therefore, surface films offer a method of detecting and of estimating quantitatively small amounts of insoluble organic substances. It is necessary, however, as with other analytical methods, that some knowledge of the homogeneity or otherwise of the material should be available.

Gorter and Grendel[1] were the first to use surface films in this way; they estimated the amount of fatty material in red blood corpuscles from the area which was covered when this fat was spread on water surfaces, finding that it was sufficient to cover about twice the surface of the corpuscles; they also used spreading as a means of estimating protein.[2] More recently Wyatt and others[3] have used the extent to which the material will spread on water as a measure of the amount of water-attracting groups in the insulating sheaths of electric cables, and since the oxidation of the hydrocarbons in these sheaths is the principal cause of their deterioration, this is considered to be a measure of the extent to which the cable has deteriorated.

As a means of aiding in determining the constitution of unknown substances, the examination of surface films has also proved of considerable use. The first case was with batyl and chimyl alcohols, which are monoglyceryl ethers of long-chain alcohols. There was a question

[1] *J. exp. Med.*, **41**, 439 (1925); *Proc. K. Akad. Wetensch. Amsterdam*, **29**, 314 (1926); *Biochem. Z.*, **192**, 431 (1928). [2] *Biochem. Z.*, **201**, 391 (1928).
[3] *Trans. Amer. Inst. Elect. Eng.*, **52**, 1035 (1933), and March 1935.

whether the long-chain alcohol was attached to the end hydroxyl in the glycerine (α ether), or to the centre one (β ether). Knight[1] showed that the films formed were extremely similar to those of α-monopalmitin, in which the long-chain acid radical is attached to the end hydroxyl of the glycerine; measurements by Adam on octadecyl malonic acid, a molecule which would stand on the surface with two points of attachment, to support the single long chain, and therefore ought to resemble the octadecyl glyceryl ether in the film, gave quite different results. Knight correctly concluded that batyl alcohol is the α-octadecyl glyceryl ether. For some time this was not accepted, but Heilbron's synthesis of both the α- and the β-glyceryl ethers of octadecyl alcohol, with careful comparison with the natural products, both by the ordinary methods and by surface films, has placed the correctness of Knight's conclusion beyond doubt.[2]

Much light has been thrown also on the constitution of the sterols and the oestrin group by measurements on surface films, with comparison of the results with what would be expected from measurements on models of the molecules. Had the author, in 1929 or earlier, had the same confidence that he now has in the reliability of measurements on models of the molecules, the incorrectness of the older formulae for the sterols would have been apparent before it actually was; these formulae require about 50 per cent. more space on the surface than the newer formulae, and the measurements on surface films available as early as 1923 agree with the new formula, not with the old. The usefulness of the surface films for throwing light on constitutional problems may be expected to increase with additional landmarks for the investigator, through knowledge of the behaviour of more types of molecules in the films.

34. Films on mercury. The insolubility of organic substances in mercury, combined with its very high surface tension, renders this liquid, in theory at least, the ideal substratum on which to examine surface films. In practice, however, there are two grave difficulties, which have not yet been sufficiently overcome for much systematic work to have been done. The surface of mercury is exceedingly difficult to keep clean. Ordinary mercury, in ordinary air, very rapidly becomes covered with a film, which soon becomes visible and often solid. Tronstad and Feachem review the literature on this film.[3] It is still uncertain whether it is due to oxides (or other compounds) of mercury, or to oxides of metallic impurities in the mercury. Distillation alone does not clean the mercury, but it is well known that distillation fails to remove the more volatile of the oxidizable metallic impurities; oxidative treatments are more effective, e.g. distilling in a slow air current and treatment with sulphuric acid and dichromate.[4] Sheppard and Keenan[5] found that repeated covering of the mercury surface by collodion films, sweeping them off, removed impurities after a long time, so that the mercury is thereafter much less liable to spontaneous contamination; this points to the scum being due to base metals dissolved in the mercury. Burdon states that most kinds of glass contaminate mercury surfaces. Owing

[1] *Biochem. J.*, **24**, 257 (1930).

[2] Cf. *J.C.S.* (1930), 2542; (1934), 1232, and Adam, *ibid.* (1933), 164.

[3] *Proc. Roy. Soc.* A, **145**, 115 (1934).

[4] Cf. Burdon, *Proc. Physical Soc.*, **38**, 148 (1926). [5] Private communication.

to the great difficulty of removing the source of such scum, it is best to work in an oxygen-free atmosphere, and to keep moisture also out as far as possible. Apparatus for excluding oxygen has been described by Fahir.[1]

The second difficulty in working with mercury is that the contact angle with practically all solids (except metals which dissolve in mercury) is very large; if a trough of ordinary rectangular section is employed, the mercury is depressed at the edges, and a flat barrier travelling on the tops of the sides has a gap below at the sides of the trough, so that there is a curved channel along which the films pass any barriers. Devaux[2] made curved barriers of paraffin wax, which was solidified in place on the mercury surface, and consequently fitted the surface; another plan is to grind a sharp edge on the sides of the trough as indicated in Fig. 25. If the angle of this edge is less than the supplement of the contact angle the surface will be flat, and the barriers will work with the minimum chance of leakage. Devaux also used thin cellophane barriers, which adhere well to the mercury.

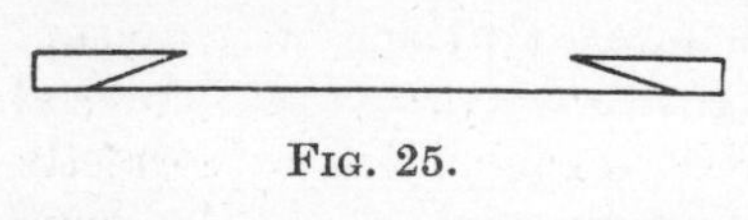

Fig. 25.

Fahir attempted to measure surface pressures of fatty acids on mercury, but obtained rather meagre results; a curve of oleic acid is given showing an area of 23 A. at 59·5 dynes, at which pressure the film collapsed; as the pressure was diminished to 15 dynes, the area increased to about 55 sq. A. per molecule, but no measurements were taken below this pressure. This film may be similar to the liquid-expanded films on water. The films of fatty acids required much higher pressures to bring about collapse on mercury than on water. Feachem and Tronstad[3] examined the effect of various fatty acids on the polarization of the light reflected from mercury surfaces, concluding that condensed and expanded phases probably exist. Devaux[4] found that the 'thickness' of films of cane sugar was 2 to 4 A., of glucose 1·4 to 2·1, of glycerine 0·6 to 0·8, and of sulphur 2 A. Sheppard, Nietz, and Keenan[5] have found that rubber gives a film of 'thickness' 1·5 A., cellulose 2·5 to 5 A., gelatine 7 A. The thickness of a single hydrocarbon chain lying flat is of the order 3 to 4 A., so that some of these figures must be taken with reserve. Keenan[6] suggests that the films are an open network, but this seems rather unlikely, as the lateral adhesion between film molecules of complex substances would probably close the gaps.

35. The formation of surface films by spontaneous spreading from solids. Pockels,[7] and more recent workers,[8] have noted that sometimes a substance placed in a liquid appears to dissolve much more readily at the level of the surface than elsewhere. This is due to spreading along the surface, which may be called a 'surface solution'. Cary and Rideal[9] have made very interesting studies of the spreading of long-chain, solid substances. There is a definite surface pressure of spreading, F_e, at each temperature for each substance. The substance spreads from the solid,

1 *J. Chim. Phys.* **27**, 587 (1930).
2 *Proc. Verb. Soc. Phys. Nat. Bordeaux* (1926–7), p. 152.
3 *Proc. Roy. Soc.* A, **145**, 129 (1934).
4 *J. Phys. Rad.*, **9**, 37 s. (1928).
5 *Ind. Eng. Chem.*, **21**, 126 (1929).
6 *J. Physical Chem.*, **33**, 371 (1929).
7 *Nature*, **43**, 437 (1891).
8 Cf. Volmer and Mahnert, *Z. physikal. Chem.*, **115**, 239 (1925).
9 *Proc. Roy. Soc.* A, **109**, 301–38 (1925).

to form a monomolecular film, until the pressure of this film reaches F_e, when spreading ceases. The rate of spreading is proportional to the perimeter of the solid, in contact with the liquid surface, and to the difference F_e-F, between the spreading pressure and the pressure of the film. The equation

$$\frac{dF}{dt} = k(F_e-F)$$

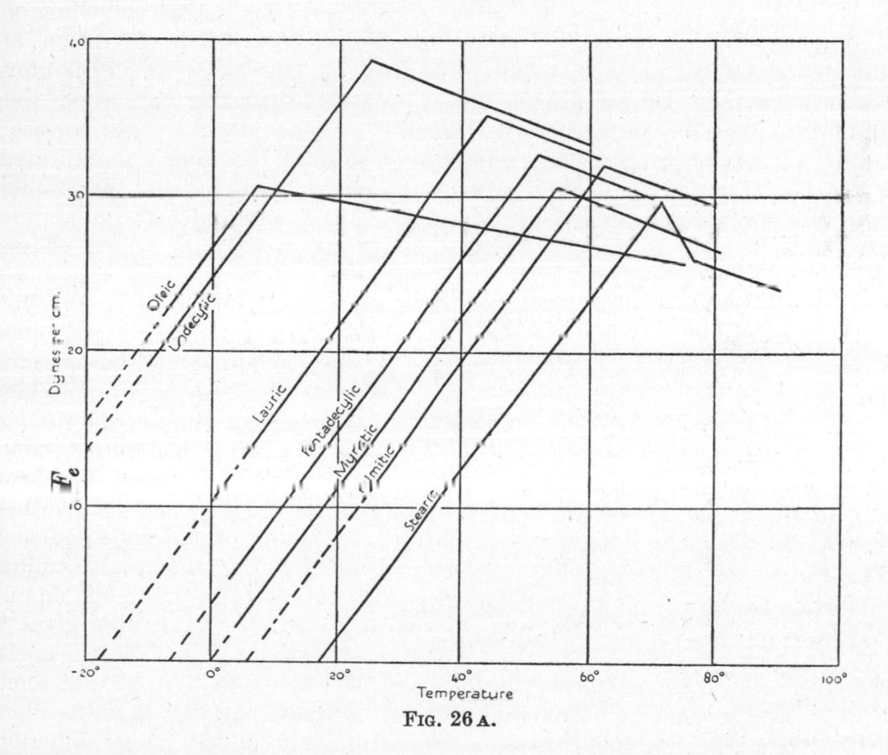

FIG. 26 A.

was accurately obeyed. Adam and Jessop[1] showed that the spreading of myristic acid in its initial stages covered the surface with a gaseous film, which subsequently condensed to an expanded film as the pressure of the film rose, the results conforming exactly to the above mechanism of spreading. The spreading is analogous to the evaporation, or solution, from the surface of a solid; in this case, however, the velocity of diffusion away from regions of the surface close to the solid is great compared with the actual rate at which the molecules leave the solid.

The spreading pressure F_e varies in an interesting way with temperature. Fig. 26 A (redrawn from the original to show surface pressures directly) shows the behaviour of several fatty acids.

Similar results were obtained on other long-chain compounds. Below a certain temperature there is no spreading. Above this temperature the pressure F_e increases linearly with the temperature until the solid melts.

[1] *Ibid.*, **110**, 441 (1926).

Then the pressure begins to fall. At still higher temperatures there are sometimes further discontinuities, which need further investigation; Cary and Rideal think they may be connected with an expansion of the film, but the connexion is not clear. In general, the shorter the chain the higher the spreading pressure; but there is an alternating effect between the odd and even acids, those with an odd total number of carbons in the molecule (n being even in the formula $C_nH_{2n+1}COOH$) having a higher spreading pressure than normal. Such alternations of physical properties are quite common in organic crystals, and must here be ascribed to the structure of the crystal, not to the film. No alternation between odd and even compounds has been found in the films.

The figure shows that many of the surface films, spread by the aid of solvents, are not thermodynamically stable, though they are often sufficiently stable in practice to be examined without serious collapse during some hours. The establishment of equilibrium between the film and the crystal is very slow from the film side; perhaps this is due to the absence of crystal nuclei of sufficiently large perimeter to allow collapse or condensation on the crystal to occur at an appreciable rate; or perhaps the aggregates formed when a film collapses have a considerably higher potential energy than properly formed crystals.

36. Evaporation through surface films. Rideal[1] has shown that surface films, both expanded and condensed, retard the rate of evaporation of water considerably. This retardation is not, however, at all easy to observe since the natural evaporation of water is already enormously retarded by the resistance caused by the slow diffusion of the evaporated molecules away from the surface. The real rate of evaporation can only be observed in a perfect vacuum; Rideal obtained, by evacuating to just above the pressure at which water boils, a rate from clean water surfaces about 0·4 per cent. of the theoretical rate into a vacuum. Under these conditions, both expanded and condensed films appreciably lowered the rate, the maximum diminution being about 50 per cent.

Langmuir[2] has used the reciprocal of the rate of evaporation as a measure of the resistance to evaporation, and considers the total resistance as the sum of the several partial resistances due to the water itself (a nearly negligible resistance), the film, and the vapour above. That of the water itself was taken as the reciprocal of the theoretical rate of evaporation, calculated from the vapour pressure as in Chap. I, § 6.

Using Rideal's measurements, he found the part of the resistance due to diffusion in the partially evacuated atmosphere to be about 770 units $\left(\frac{\text{cm.}^2 \times \text{sec.}}{\text{gm.}}\right)$. That due to the clean water surface was 3; to the films themselves, 300 for stearic acid, 570 for lauric acid, and 1,620 for oleic acid. These numbers may mean little except as regards their order of magnitude; the surprising result that the expanded film, oleic acid, offers five times as much resistance as the condensed film of stearic acid ought

[1] *J. Physical Chem.*, **29**, 1585 (1925). [2] *Ibid.*, **31**, 1719 (1927).

to be confirmed. Langmuir also found that cetyl alcohol films offer a very much greater resistance, of the order 60,000 units, which is enough to make a substantial reduction in the rate of evaporation into the open air; the work of Sebba and Briscoe (see Appendix) indicates that this exceptional obstructing power of cetyl alcohol is due to its possessing an unusually high spreading pressure, so that the film in equilibrium with the solid alcohol on the surface is under unusually high pressure, with fewer water molecules entangled in it than in the other films.

The effect of surface films on the evaporation of ether from its aqueous solutions was very marked, but was traced to the film stopping the convection currents, which usually stir up the layers near the surface and eliminate the slow process of diffusion of ether through the water to the surface. There was no evidence of any considerable resistance, offered by the film itself, to the passage of ether molecules.

37. The calming of waves by oil. Oil films do not diminish the height of large waves, but they damp out the small ripples which are constantly being formed by the action of wind, and lead to dangerous breaking of large waves, by their cumulative disturbance of the surface. Benjamin Franklin suggested that the oil lubricates the water surface, so that the wind cannot grip it as well as it does a clean surface; this is scarcely a probable explanation in view of the compact character of surface films. Moreover, Aitken[1] has shown that the oil films do not diminish the actual amount of motion imparted by the wind to the water, and possibly slightly increase it; he examined the motion both in the surface and in the layers slightly below the surface.

He showed that much of the action of the oil is due to its regularizing the motion imparted by the wind to the surface. A clean surface, having no surface skin, is blown in different directions, and with varying force, by a gusty wind; and this appears to be the main exciting cause of irregular, interfering ripples. An oil film, offering resistance to compression, distributes the motion uniformly over large areas, thus greatly diminishing the *excitation* of ripples.

Oil films also act to some extent by damping ripples already formed. Thus Pockels[2] showed that a coherent film, insufficient to cover more than a small fraction of the surface, damps ripples produced mechanically in a trough; the extent of damping increases with an increasing proportion of the surface covered, until the whole is covered. Further compression of the film, once the whole surface was covered, did not appear to produce a further damping effect. This shows that the diminution of surface tension alone, which does not commence till the film covers the whole surface, is not the cause of the damping. Probably the viscous resistance to motion of the separate islands of film through the water, as the surface expands and contracts, the jamming of these islands, and some dissipation of energy within the films, during the rapid alternate expansion and contraction which accompanies the ripples, all contribute to the damping.

It is scarcely necessary to say that good spreading power is essential for efficient damping of waves. Fish oils are supplied to ships, and to their lifeboats, for this purpose. Mineral oils are not good; but in emergency they might be very much improved by melting a few stearine candles, and mixing with the oil; the carboxyl groups in the stearine provide the necessary adhesion to water.

[1] *Proc. Roy. Soc. Edin.*, **12**, 56 (1883). [2] *loc. cit.*, § 2. See also Appendix.

CHAPTER III

SURFACE FILMS OF SOLUBLE OR VOLATILE SUBSTANCES: ADSORPTION ON LIQUID SURFACES

1. Changes of concentration at the surface of solutions. A pure liquid consisting of one species of molecule diminishes its surface free energy by diminishing its total surface to the minimum possible, molecules leaving the surface for the interior under the action of the inward attractive force exerted on the surface molecules. Its free energy per unit area cannot be altered, except by orienting the surface molecules so that the ends with the largest field of force point inwards. In the case of solutions of two or more substances, whose molecules differ in the intensity of the fields of attractive force round equal areas of the surfaces of their molecules, there is a second way in which the free surface energy may be diminished. The molecules which have the greater fields of force tend to pass into the interior; those with the smaller fields to remain at the surface. The surface layer of a solution will therefore be more concentrated in the constituents which have the smaller attractive fields of force, i.e. in those constituents whose intrinsic free surface energy is the smallest, than the interior. This concentration of one constituent of a solution, or of a gaseous mixture, at a surface, is called 'adsorption'. Positive adsorption of a constituent is an increase of concentration at a surface; negative adsorption a decrease.

The force which causes and maintains the change in concentration at the surface is the inward attractive force on the surface molecules. Suppose a new surface to be suddenly formed in a liquid; at the instant of formation its composition will be identical with that in the interior. The surface molecules are immediately attracted to the interior, but the inward pull acts more strongly on the molecules with the greatest attractive fields of force, and consequently these molecules move inwards more rapidly than the others, leaving the surface more concentrated in the other species of molecules. At the same time the surface will decrease in area to the minimum permitted by the external constraints on the system. The kinetic agitation of the molecules in the liquid (or gaseous mixture) is continually tending to restore equality of concentration throughout the system, but it cannot do so completely, because of the difference in rate at which the different species of molecules move inwards from the surface. The final equilibrium concentrations, which are usually established in a very small fraction of a second (except in the case of slowly diffusing substances), are determined by the balance between the osmotic forces or rates of diffusion tending to equalize the concentration and the surface forces tending to construct the surface wholly out of that constituent which has the least surface energy.

Qualitatively, the rule for adsorption is that, if the solution has a smaller surface tension than the solvent, the solute is concentrated at the surface; if it has a larger tension the solute is driven, as far as possible, into the interior. It is possible to obtain very considerable *decreases* in surface tension by adsorption of a substance which has, itself, a very low surface tension; in such cases the adsorption may proceed so far that the surface layer consists almost entirely of the molecules of the constituent with the smaller field of force. Large *increases* in surface tension cannot, however, be obtained in solutions by using solutes with fields of force much greater than the solvent. Such solutes are driven into the interior, and the surface layer tends to approximate to pure solvent containing few of the molecules with large fields of force. Consequently the surface tension is raised but little above that of the solvent, even though the solute may, intrinsically, have a very much higher surface tension than the solvent.

With water as solvent, organic substances containing more than two carbon atoms for each soluble group in the molecule usually show marked positive adsorption. In extreme cases the surface tension may be reduced, by adsorption of such substances, to about 28 dynes per cm., i.e. nearly the surface tension of paraffin hydrocarbons, the surface layer then consisting almost entirely of long, saturated, hydrocarbon chains. Inorganic salts are usually negatively adsorbed, and the tension may be raised, in strong solution, by a few dynes per cm.

The quantitative relation between the amount of adsorption and the change in surface tension was first deduced thermodynamically by Gibbs in 1878;[1] it was later calculated in a somewhat different form, by the methods of generalized dynamics, by J. J. Thomson.[2]

2. Gibbs's adsorption equation.* The precise meaning of the term 'concentration at a surface' must first be defined. We saw in Chapter I that a liquid surface is fairly sharply defined, but that the thermal agitation renders it indefinite to a thickness of one or two molecular diameters. The thickness of the transitional region between two phases is not great enough, nor can it be demarcated with sufficient accuracy from the bulk phases on either side of it, to use the term 'concentration in the surface layer' with the same precision as is associated with concentration in bulk. Gibbs's treatment compares the actual system with a physically impossible system in which two phases touch without any transitional layer; Guggenheim's new theory (see Appendix) discusses the composition of a region of definite thickness, including the surface transitional layer.

Gibbs defined the 'superficial density', now more commonly called the adsorption or 'surface excess', for a solution, as follows. In Fig. 26, I, let the horizontal dotted lines represent approximately the limits of the transitional region, between the upper phase α and the lower phase β; a normal to the surface is moved round so as to enclose a volume of cross-section A perpendicular to the surface. The volume is finally defined by drawing surfaces $P_\alpha Q_\alpha$ and $P_\beta Q_\beta$ parallel to the physical surface, in

* See also Appendix. [1] *Scientific Papers*, **1**, 219–37.

[2] *Application of Dynamics to Physics and Chemistry*, 190 (1888).

the bulk phases and at a sufficient distance from the actual surface for the composition of the matter in each phase to be exactly that of the interior. There is a definite amount of each component contained in this volume. Next, consider an idealized volume of the same length and cross-section, Fig. 26, II, in which the two phases are separated, not by an actual physical surface, but by a mathematical plane, *XY*, parallel to the physical surface of I, the composition of both phases remaining absolutely constant right up to the dividing surface. The amount of each component

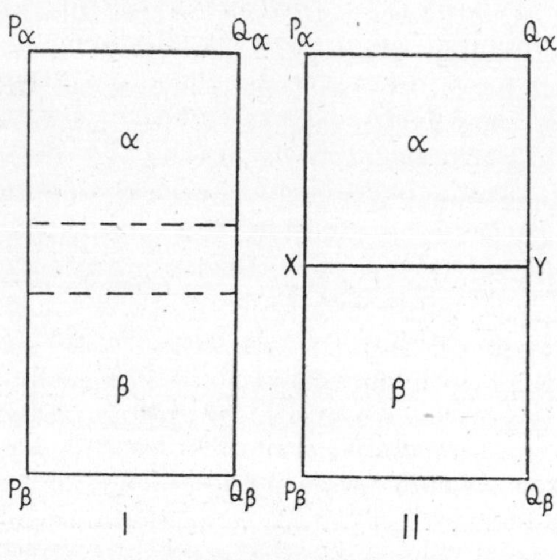

FIG. 26.

in this idealized system clearly depends on the precise position assigned to the surface *XY*, except in the special case where the concentration of that component is the same in each bulk phase.

The surface excess of any component is defined as the amount by which the total quantity of that component in the actual system I exceeds that in the idealized system II. The symbols used are Γ_1, Γ_2,..., Γ_i, for the surface excess of components 1, 2,..., *i*, per unit area; m_1^s, m_2^s,..., m_i^s, where $m_i^s = A\Gamma_i$, for the surface excess in the whole area *A* considered. Some of the quantities m_i^s, Γ_i, will usually be positive, others negative.

There is also, in general, a difference in the amount of energy and of entropy between the actual system I and the idealized system II; let the excess of energy in I over II be ϵ^s and of entropy η^s; per unit area ϵ_s and η_s, where $\epsilon^s = A\epsilon_s$. As the amount of any component, or of energy or of entropy, in the idealized system depends on the exact position assigned to the mathematical surface *XY*, the quantities Γ_1, Γ_2, Γ_i, are not precisely defined until the position of this surface is fixed. This must be done arbitrarily, and a number of different conventions have been considered. By far the most common convention is to fix *XY* in such a position that the surface excess of that component which is present in the bulk solution in amount much greater than any of the other components, i.e. the 'solvent', becomes zero. If this component is designated by 1, the values of the surface excess on this convention are written as $\Gamma_2^{(1)}$, $\Gamma_3^{(1)}$, $\Gamma_i^{(1)}$; $\Gamma_1^{(1)}$ is, by definition, zero. This convention is mathematically unsymmetrical, but it has very great convenience in the case of a binary solution which has one component in large excess, i.e. a dilute solution of a single substance. When dealing with concentrated solutions this choice of a position for the surface XY is less advantageous, especially if the range of solutions studied extends from nearly pure 1 to nearly pure 2 (see § 6).

Two proofs of Gibbs's adsorption theorem will now be given; they apply in general (from equations (1) to (7.1) below) to any of the possible positions of the dividing plane XY. The first is, essentially, Gibbs's original analytical proof; the second, a new proof involving an easily visualized process, due to Guggenheim. For further discussion of the analytical proof see Gibbs's *Collected Papers* and Rice's excellent commentary[1]; and Guggenheim's *Modern Thermodynamics*.[2]

The analytical proof assumes that the radius of curvature of the surface is small compared with the thickness of the transition layer between two phases, otherwise the position arbitrarily chosen for XY is of appreciable importance.[3] Gibbs proves that the temperature and chemical potentials of the components are uniform throughout the system when equilibrium exists; but we shall take this here as self-evident, as indeed it is from a physical standpoint, considering that temperature and potentials are measures of the escaping tendencies of heat and of each component from the different phases, and therefore equalize themselves automatically. The pressures in the different phases are not, however, equal unless the surfaces are strictly plane, as was pointed out in Chap. I, § 15.

The energy of the system, as always, may be expressed as a sum of terms, each of which is the product of a capacity factor and an intensity factor. Taking as capacity factors the entropy η, volume V, area A, and amounts of the components m_i, and indicating the phases referred to by suffixes α and β; also choosing the intensity factors temperature, pressure, surface tension, and chemical potentials μ_1, μ_2, μ_i, as the independent variables, the increase in energy of the actual system in any small reversible change when in equilibrium is

$$d\epsilon = T\,d\eta - P^\alpha dV^\alpha - P^\beta dV^\beta + \gamma dA + \mu_1 dm_1 + \mu_2 dm_2 + \ldots + \mu_i dm_i, \quad (1)$$

and the increase of energy of each phase of the idealized system separately is

$$d\epsilon^\alpha = T\,d\eta^\alpha - P^\alpha dV^\alpha + \mu_1 dm_1^\alpha + \mu_2 dm_2^\alpha + \ldots + \mu_i dm_i^\alpha, \quad (2)$$

$$d\epsilon^\beta = T\,d\eta^\beta - P^\beta dV^\beta + \mu_1 dm_1^\beta + \mu_2 dm_2^\beta + \ldots + \mu_i dm_i^\beta. \quad (2.1)$$

By the definition of surface excess,

$$\epsilon^s = \epsilon - \epsilon^\alpha - \epsilon^\beta,$$

$$\eta^s = \eta - \eta^\alpha - \eta^\beta,$$

$$m_i^s = m_i - m_i^\alpha - m_i^\beta,$$

[1] Gibbs, pp. 219 ff. Rice's commentary is Article L in the new commentary on Gibbs's works.

[2] Methuen (1933).

[3] Gibbs's work and Rice's commentary must be consulted for a discussion of this point.

and since there is no V_s, as the volume of the actual system is the same as that of the idealized system, subtracting (2) and (2.1) from (1), we have

$$d\epsilon^s = T\,d\eta^s + \gamma\,dA + \mu_1\,dm_1^s + \mu_2\,dm_2^s + ... + \mu_i\,dm_i^s. \tag{3}$$

Equation (3) has the same form as one of Gibbs's fundamental equations for a homogeneous phase, and owing to this formal similarity the term 'surface phase' is often used. It must be remembered, however, that the surface 'phase' is not physically of the same definiteness as an ordinary phase, with a precise location in space; neither do the quantities ϵ^s, η^s, m_i^s refer to the total amounts of energy, entropy, or material components present in the surface region as it exists physically; they are 'surface excesses', or the amounts by which the actual system exceeds the idealized system in these quantities. Care must be taken not to confuse the exact mathematical expression, 'surface phase', with the physical concept of the 'surface layer' or surface film.

Since (3) is a homogeneous function of the first degree it may be integrated to

$$\epsilon^s = T\eta^s + \gamma A + \mu_1 m_1^s + ... + \mu_i m_i^s, \tag{4}$$

an operation which corresponds physically to a finite increase of area without change of composition; differentiating (4)

$$d\epsilon^s = T\,d\eta^s + \eta^s\,dT + \gamma\,dA + A\,d\gamma + \mu_1\,dm_1^s + m_1^s\,d\mu_1 + ... + \mu_i\,dm_i^s + m_i^s\,d\mu_i, \tag{5}$$

and comparing with (3), we have

$$A\,d\gamma = -\eta^s\,dT - m_1^s\,d\mu_1 - ... - m_i^s\,d\mu_i, \tag{6}$$

or, for unit area of the surface,

$$d\gamma = -\eta_s\,dT - \Gamma_1\,d\mu_1 - ... - \Gamma_i\,d\mu_i. \tag{7}$$

Equation (7) is the general form of Gibbs's relation between surface tension, temperature, surface excesses, and chemical potentials for a system of any number of components, and if the surfaces are not very highly curved it holds good whatever convention is adopted for defining Γ_i, with any arbitrary position of the surface XY in the idealized system.

Guggenheim's beautiful new proof[1] brings out the close similarity between Gibbs's adsorption equation (7) and the well-known Gibbs-Duhem equation relating the amounts of each component in a homogeneous phase to the chemical potentials. In Fig. 27 let the small enclosure I be full to the level PQ with a solution of i components, of composition such that the fugacities, or vapour pressures if the vapour phase behaves as a perfect gas, are $p_1^*, p_2^*, ..., p_i^*$. The large enclosure II is full to the same level QS of a solution differing infinitesimally in composition, so that the fugacities here are $p_1^* + dp_1^*$, $p_2^* + dp_2^*, ...,$ $p_i^* + dp_i^*$. The volume of II is so large that it may be considered infinite in comparison with I, but the areas PQ and QS of the surfaces, which adjoin each other at the same level, are each equal to A. The wall QR which separates the solutions is hinged at Q so that it can be swung aside and the solutions mixed if desired.

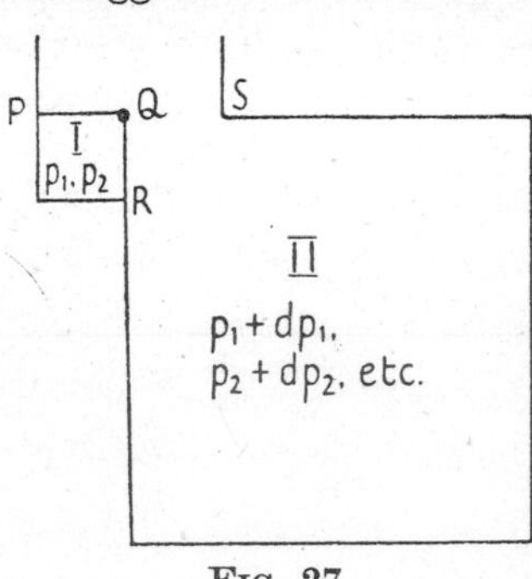

FIG. 27.

[1] *J. Chem. Physics*, **4**, 689 (1936).

There is a lid, of area A, which can be slid along the surface so as to cover the surface of either I or II completely, or both partially. This lid is made of material such that the interfacial tensions of the two solutions against it are equal, and the composition of each solution remains constant right up to contact with it; i.e. there is no adsorption of any of the components of the solutions, a condition which really follows from the first, by Gibbs's theorem.

Consider the free energy decrease, or reversible work gained, when the contents of I are mixed with II. This may be done in two ways. In the first, the partition QR is simply swung aside so that the solutions mix directly. The reversible work gained in transferring one mole of component 1 is

$$RT\log\frac{p_1^*}{p_1^*+dp_1^*} \quad \text{or} \quad -RT\,d\log p_1^*,$$

and so on for each component; the total work gained is therefore

$$-RT(m_1\,d\log p_1^*+m_2\,d\log p_2^*+...+m_i\,d\log p_i^*),$$

where m_1, m_2,..., m_i are the number of moles of each component present in I. But the Gibbs-Duhem relation states that the sum of the terms inside the bracket is zero;[1] it is strictly an infinitesimal of the second order compared with any one of the terms separately, i.e. zero in the case considered when the solutions differ infinitesimally in composition. Therefore the free energy change in mixing the small volume of solution in I with the large volume in II is zero.

In the second method of mixing, the partition QR remains closed at first, and the lid is gradually slid across from PQ to QS, thus uncovering the free surface of solution I, permitting adsorption to take place there, and covering the surface of II, terminating the adsorption at that surface. The quantities $A\Gamma_1$, $A\Gamma_2$, $A\Gamma_i$, adsorbed at first at QS, are transferred, reversibly, by isothermal distillation, or otherwise, to PQ, at such a rate that the compositions and the surface tensions in I and II are kept constant; the work gained in this transference is $A(\Gamma_1\,RT\,d\log p_1^*+\Gamma_2\,RT\,d\log p_2^*+...+\Gamma_i\,RT\,d\log p_i^*)$. In addition, the difference in surface tension $d\gamma$ between the two surfaces does work $A\,d\gamma$ in moving the lid. Next, the partition QR is swung open, and the solutions allowed to mix; for the reasons stated in considering the first method of mixing, no work is gained. Finally, the lid is slid back to its original position; as the solutions now have the same composition no work is done by the surface tension, nor by the transference of the amounts adsorbed back to the surface QS. The system is now in the same state as at the end of the first method of mixing, so that the total work done must be as in the first method, i.e. zero. Hence

$$d\gamma+\Gamma_1\,RT\,d\log p_1^*+\Gamma_2\,RT\,d\log p_2^*+...+\Gamma_i\,RT\,d\log p_i^* = 0,$$

which is identical with (7), since $d\mu_i = RT\,d\log p_i^*$ by (8) below, since $p_i^* = f_i\,N_i$.

The formal similarity between Gibbs's adsorption equation and the Gibbs-

[1] Cf. Guggenheim, *Modern Thermodynamics*, p. 15; Lewis and Randall, *Thermodynamics*, p. 209; Bjerrum, *Z. physikal. Chem.*, **104**, 410 (1923).

The physical meaning of the Gibbs-Duhem equation is that the free energy change, when a small volume of solution is mixed with a large volume of another solution, differing infinitesimally in composition, is zero (strictly an infinitesimal of second order). The equation holds for systems containing free surfaces, provided that (*a*) the surfaces are in equilibrium with the interior, (*b*) no free surfaces are created or destroyed during mixing.

Duhem relation is rather striking, and is not always recognized. The former may be written

$$d\gamma+\Gamma_1\,d\mu_1+\Gamma_2\,d\mu_2+...+\Gamma_i\,d\mu_i=0,$$

and the latter

$$m_1\,d\mu_1+m_2\,d\mu_2+...+m_i\,d\mu_i=0.$$

$\Gamma_1, \Gamma_2,..., \Gamma_i$ are the amounts of each component in the 'surface phase'; $m_1, m_2,..., m_i$ the amounts in a bulk phase.[1]

Gibbs's analytical proof of the adsorption formula is, *mutatis mutandis*, analogous to the analytical deduction of the Gibbs-Duhem relation; both depend on the integration of the formula for the increment in energy, followed by differentiation and comparison of the result with the original formula.

For systems of only two components, i.e. solvent and one solute, or a binary gaseous mixture, (7) becomes, at constant temperature

$$d\gamma=-\Gamma_1\,d\mu_1-\Gamma_2\,d\mu_2. \tag{7.1}$$

If the surface XY is fixed so that the surface excess of component 1 vanishes,

$$d\gamma=-\Gamma_2^{(1)}\,d\mu_2, \tag{7.2}$$

which may be written, for solutions where the activity coefficient of component (2) is f_2 and its mole fraction N_2,

$$d\gamma=-RT\Gamma_2^{(1)}\,d\log_e f_2 N_2, \tag{7.3}$$

since the activity coefficient is defined by the relation[2]

$$\mu_i=\mu_i^0+RT\log_e f_i N_i. \tag{8}$$

(7.3) is usually written

$$\Gamma_2^{(1)}=-\frac{f_2 N_2}{RT}\frac{\partial\gamma}{\partial(f_2 N_2)}. \tag{7.4}$$

If the component 2 is volatile and its vapour pressure obeys the perfect gas laws with sufficient exactness, the partial pressure in the vapour being p_2,

$$\Gamma_2^{(1)}=-\frac{p_2}{RT}\frac{\partial\gamma}{\partial p_2}. \tag{7.5}$$

(7.4) becomes, for ideal solutions with activity coefficient unity

$$\Gamma_2^{(1)}=-\frac{N_2}{RT}\frac{\partial\gamma}{\partial N_2}, \tag{7.6}$$

and for dilute and ideal solutions where the concentration c_2 is proportional to the mole fraction and $f_2=1$

$$\Gamma_2^{(1)}=-\frac{c_2}{RT}\frac{\partial\gamma}{\partial c_2}. \tag{7.7}$$

[1] The similarity is still more striking if the pressure is not taken as constant; then, for the bulk phase,

$$-dP+c_1\,d\mu_1+c_2\,d\mu_2+...+c_i\,d\mu_i=0,$$

where $c=m/V$ is the volume concentration of each component. (Cf. Gibbs, *Works*, **1**, equation (98).)

[2] Cf. Guggenheim, *Modern Thermodynamics*, p. 125.

If F is written for the difference between the surface tensions of the solvent and of the solution, i.e. for the surface pressure of the adsorbed film, dF can be written throughout for $-d\gamma$.

3. Experimental verification of Gibbs's equation. Two types of measurement have been employed in the attempt to obtain direct measurements of the amount of solute adsorbed at a surface, for comparison with the adsorption calculated from Gibbs's equation. The first, initiated by Donnan and his students, consists in passing a very large number of drops of a hydrocarbon liquid, or bubbles of a gas, up a column of the solution; the length and arrangement of the baffles in the column is such that the surface of the bubbles becomes fully saturated with the adsorbed substance. At the top the bubbles are made to pass through a narrow orifice into a chamber where they unite, their surface becoming negligibly small, so that the adsorbed material is discharged into the solution. The upper chamber thus becomes more concentrated than the lower column, owing to the material carried up on the surface of the bubbles or drops, and the amount adsorbed on unit area may be calculated from the increase in concentration and the estimated total area of the bubbles. Lewis[1] found that the adsorption of a bile salt, sodium glycocholate, at a hydrocarbon surface, was some eighty times that required by the approximate form of Gibbs's equation (7.7); congo red, methyl orange, and sodium oleate were also many times more adsorbed than required by theory; but caffeine and aniline, on a mercury-water surface, were adsorbed in roughly the calculated quantity. Donnan and Barker[2] found that the adsorption of nonylic acid at an air-water surface was of the same order of magnitude as that calculated; and Bancelin[3] found agreement as to order of magnitude, with dyestuffs adsorbed at water-air and water-mercury surfaces, the directly measured adsorptions being usually rather less than the calculated. Gibby and Addison,[4] however, obtained with five different dyestuffs very poor agreement between the adsorptions measured directly on benzene and chlorobenzene surfaces, and those calculated from the approximate form of Gibbs's equation (7.7). In some cases the observed adsorption was greater, in others less, than the calculated; and sometimes the observed adsorption rose to a maximum with increasing concentration, afterwards falling to a much lower value, zero in some cases, even though the surface tension of the solutions was considerably lowered. A possible explanation of these results would be the presence of some colourless, but surface-active substance, whose adsorption would be overlooked in the colorimetric determinations of the amounts adsorbed; yet from the care taken in purifying the dyes this would seem unlikely. Further experimental work, and a possible explanation, are given in the Appendix.

One difficulty, very hard to overcome in experiments of this nature, is that there is always risk of the more concentrated solution in the chamber where

[1] *Phil. Mag.*, **15**, 499 (1908); **17**, 466 (1909). *Z. physikal. Chem.*, **73**, 129 (1910).

[2] *Proc. Roy. Soc.* **A, 85**, 557 (1911).

[3] *J. Chim. Phys.*, **22**, 538 (1925).

[4] *J.C.S.* (1936), 119, 1306.

the bubbles break returning to the bulk of the solution in the column; this would render the measured adsorption less than the actual. McBain and others[1] have attempted to overcome this by causing the bubbles to pass finally into a tube bent downwards, so that they collect in a separate vessel. The results were invariably several times higher than the calculated, and it has recently been found that the results depend very much on the speed at which the bubbles move up the inclined tubes in which they become saturated with the solute. There are evidently considerable errors in this method of experiment, which have been variously ascribed to an electrical charge 'not in equilibrium', a rather indefinite and unsatisfactory explanation, and to oscillations in the bubbles causing the real surface to be much greater than it appears to be.

The 'microtome method' invented by McBain attacks the problem very directly.[2] By a very ingenious and accurately constructed apparatus they have succeeded in rapidly cutting off a thin layer, 0·05 to 0·1 mm. thick, from the surface of a solution contained in a long trough, with an accurately ground knife similar to that used in microtomes for cutting thin sections. This knife carried a small cylindrical vessel for the solution cut off the surface, and was catapulted along the surface at a speed of about 35 feet per second. The solution had been allowed to stand still in perfect equilibrium with the atmosphere, which was kept very carefully saturated to avoid errors due to evaporation. The maintenance of the saturated atmosphere required the provision of doors, opening and shutting automatically to permit the passage of the knife. The rails on which the knife was carried were most accurately levelled, and the whole apparatus constitutes a triumph of mechanical skill. The concentration of the solution cut off was compared with the original concentration by means of an interferometer.

If w is the weight of solution cut off from an area A, c' its concentration, and c the original concentration in the bulk of the solution, measured in grammes per gramme of solvent, then the weight of *solvent* cut off per unit area is

$$\frac{w_1}{A} = \frac{w}{(1+c')A}.$$

The amount of solute in this amount of solvent is, in the solution cut off, $w_1 c'/A$, and in the original bulk solution, $w_1 c/A$; the difference $(w_1/A)(c'-c)$ is, by the definition in §§ 2 and 6, $\Gamma_2^{(1)}$.

In every case so far examined, including four positively adsorbed organic substances and one negatively adsorbed salt, the adsorption measured by this method agreed with that required by Gibbs's equation (7) within experimental error. Fig. 28 shows the observed and calculated ('Gibbs') adsorption of phenol, together with the amounts found by McBain's moving-bubble method, which are very much higher.

A further, and rather striking, verification of Gibbs's equation will

[1] *J.A.C.S.* (1927) 2230; (1929) 3534. *6th Colloid Symposium Monograph*, 63 (1928). Cf. Harkins and Gans, *5th Colloid Symposium Monograph*, 40 (1927); *6th do.*, 36 (1928).

[2] McBain and Humphreys, *J. Physical Chem.*, **36**, 300 (1932); McBain and Swain, *Proc. Roy. Soc.* A, **154**, 608 (1936).

appear in the next paragraph. The areas per molecule of the adsorbed films of certain fatty acids, calculated by Gibbs's equation, are found to agree remarkably well with those directly observed for the same acids by the method of Chapter II.

The verification of Gibbs's equation may now be considered reasonably

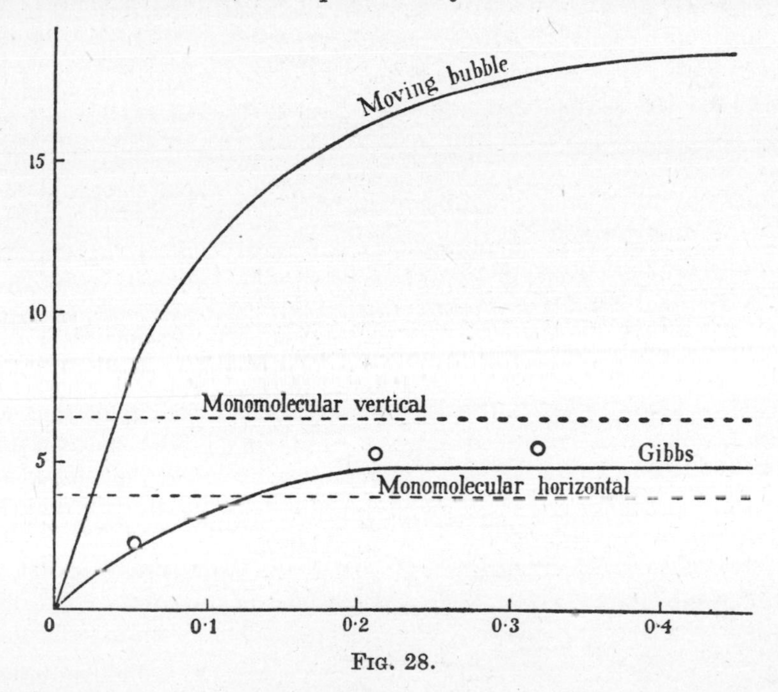

Fig. 28.

well established; a possible outstanding difficulty is that there appear to be cases in which the surface tension passes through a minimum as the concentration increases. This would involve a negative adsorption in the region where the surface tension rises with increase of concentration. Yet where there is any lowering of surface tension at all, the elementary considerations of § 1 require that the adsorption should be positive. It is possible that such cases will be explained by there being more than one capillary active component in the system, or by the presence of small amounts of an impurity which greatly increases the adsorption of the solute at certain concentrations.[1]

4. Structure of adsorbed films on dilute solutions. Gibbs's equations (7.1 to 7.7) permit the calculations of the area per molecule, if the surface tension is determined over a range of concentration of the solutions. The area per molecule is proportional to the slope of the curve relating the lowering of surface tension to the activity $f_2 c_2$ (the vapour pressure of component 2 if the vapour obeys the simple gas laws). This assumes

[1] C. Robinson, *Wetting and Detergency*, (1937), 141 150, traced a minimum in interfacial tension to very small amounts of polyvalent electrolytes present in ordinary distilled water.

that the total amount in the surface, per unit area, is equal to Γ_2; but the amount of 2 in dilute solution is so small that the difference is of little importance. The depression of surface tension is the 'surface pressure' of the adsorbed film, so that from a determination of surface tension and activity over a range of concentrations the relation between surface pressure F and area per molecule A, in the adsorbed films, may be mapped.

In every case yet worked out, the adsorbed films of soluble substances are of the gaseous type; there are always corrections, except in very dilute solutions, to the perfect gas equation due to the area actually occupied by the adsorbed molecules; and in many cases also there are corrections due to the lateral adhesion between them.

Traube,[1] in an extended investigation of the surface tension of aqueous solutions of many organic compounds, established several important points, of which the significance for the structure of the adsorbed films has been pointed out by Langmuir.[2]

For very dilute solutions of any one solute, the depression of surface tension F caused by the solute is proportional to the concentration, i.e.

$$F = Bc_2. \tag{9}$$

Differentiating,

$$\frac{dF}{dc_2} = B,$$

and combining with the approximate form of Gibbs's equation (7.7),

$$\Gamma_2 = \frac{Bc_2}{RT} = \frac{F}{RT},$$

or, since the area per molecule A is $1/\Gamma_2$,

$$FA = RT. \tag{10}$$

The proportionality of surface tension lowering to the concentration thus indicates that the adsorbed film is gaseous, with negligible corrections to the perfect gas equation.

As the concentration of the solution increases the lowering of tension F is no longer proportional to c_2, but increases more slowly than c_2. In the case of the fatty acids, Szyszkowski[3] found that the empirical equation

$$F = \gamma_0 - \gamma = C\gamma_0 \log_{10}\left(1+\frac{c_2}{a}\right) \tag{11}$$

expresses the relation between lowering of tension and concentration, with considerable accuracy, for the acids containing from 3 to 6 carbon atoms in the molecule. C has the constant value 0·411 for all the acids, while a is a constant for each acid, 0·165 for the three carbon, 0·051 for the four, 0·015 for the five, and 0·0043 for the six carbon acid, the ratio between the values of a for successive members of the series being about 3·1. γ_0 is the surface tension of water, 72·8 dynes at 20°.

[1] *Annalen*, **265**, 27 (1891). [2] *J.A.C.S.* (1917), 1883.
[3] *Z. physikal. Chem.*, **64**, 385 (1908).

Differentiating (11) and combining with Gibbs's approximate equation (7.7), we have

$$\Gamma_2 = \frac{13{\cdot}0}{RT}\frac{c_2}{a+c_2}, \tag{12}$$

an equation which is of the same form as Langmuir's adsorption equation (see Chap. VII, § 9)

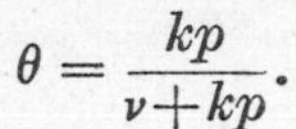

$$\theta = \frac{kp}{\nu+kp}.$$

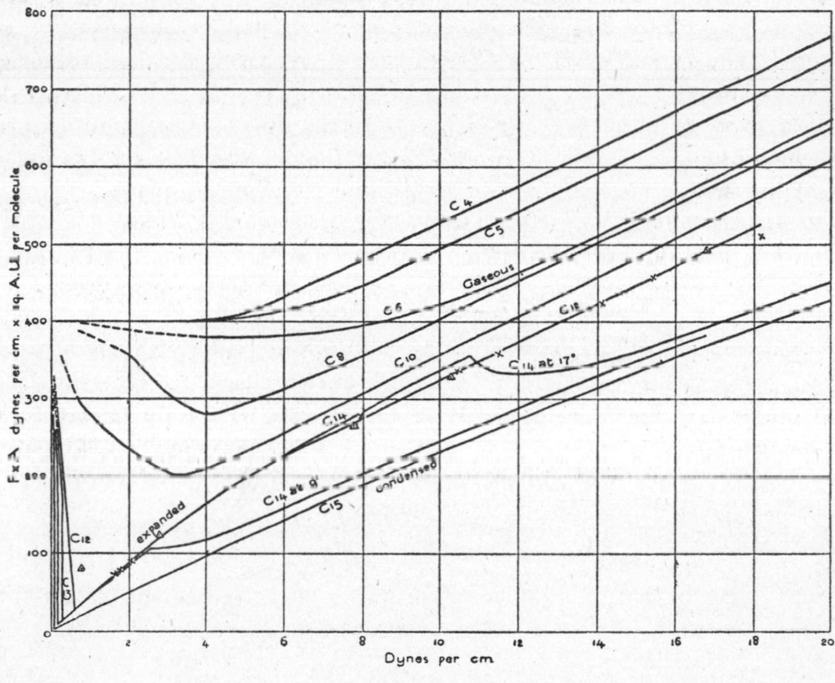

FIG. 29.

In this equation the pressure p of the gas corresponds to the concentration c_2 of the solute; the rate of evaporation from the adsorbed layer, ν, to a; and θ, the fraction of the surface covered, to the adsorption, Γ_2.

When the solutions are so dilute that c_2 is very small compared with a, expansion of (11) shows that the surface tension lowering is proportional to the concentration, as was found by Traube.

Schofield and Rideal[1] have mapped the relation between F and A for the longer chain, yet still appreciably soluble, fatty acids from 6 to 12 carbons long, using Frumkin's measurements of the surface tension of their solutions.[2] Their results are shown in the upper six curves of Fig. 29, the product FA being plotted as ordinates and the surface pressure F as abscissae. For comparison, the results for the acids from 12–15 carbon atoms, determined by spreading the acid and measuring the surface

[1] *Proc. Roy. Soc.* A, **109**, 57 (1925); **110**, 167 (1926).
[2] *Z. physikal. Chem.*, **116**, 480 (1925).

pressure directly as described in Chapter II, are added in the lowest curves. Two sets of points are given for the 12 carbon acid, one determined by the use of Gibbs's equation, the other by the technique appropriate for insoluble films. The agreement is very remarkable; quite unexpectedly so, since with the 12 carbon acid both methods are operating under disadvantageous conditions, the acid being slightly too soluble for the best results by the insoluble film method, but scarcely sufficiently soluble for really trustworthy measurements of the variation of surface tension with concentration. The agreement in the case of the twelve carbon acid, and still more the fact that the series of curves shows a continuous transition without a break, as the experimental technique is changed, indicates that the adsorbed, soluble films, and the insoluble films, have a similar structure, i.e. they are monomolecular. The agreement for the twelve carbon acid is a striking experimental verification of Gibbs's equation.

The curves of Fig. 29 show that, with all the acids, there is a steady rise of FA with increasing surface pressure above 4 dynes; this is due to the repulsions between the molecules, caused by their occupying a considerable fraction of the area of the surface. The dip of FA below 400, the value for a perfect gaseous film, is inappreciable with the 4 and 5 carbon acids (determinations were so few that a slight dip here may have been missed); it increases from 6 to 12 carbons. This dip is due to the lateral adhesions between the molecules in the films, which in the case of the thirteen carbon acid first become large enough to cause actual separation of a liquid-surface phase. The equation

$$FA = FB + RTx \tag{13}$$

fits the rising part of the curves reasonably well. B has the value about 25 sq. A. per molecule for all the curves, and x the following values:

C_4	0·73
C_5	0·63
C_6	0·43
C_8	0·4
C_{10}	0·3

The lateral adhesion is greater, the smaller x; B is the approximate limiting value to which the curves approach as F becomes very large. For the six carbon acid, B is 25, and the actual areas are: at 5 dynes pressure, 59 sq. A.; at 20 dynes, 33 sq. A.; at 40, 28·6 sq. A. It should be mentioned that the activity coefficients of the acids were not determined, though a correction to the approximate Gibbs's equation (7.7) was made for the ionization of the acids.

Goard and Rideal[1] made similar measurements on solutions of phenol, with determination of the activity coefficient. Fig. 30 shows the F–A and the FA–F curves calculated from their data; the adsorbed film is obviously gaseous, an equation of the form of (13) with $B = 18{\cdot}6$ sq. A. and $x = 0{\cdot}57$

[1] *J.C.S.* (1925), 780, 1668.

holding reasonably well. Other observations of the adsorption of phenol on salt solutions showed that the salt raised the tension of the phenol solutions almost as much as it ordinarily raises the tension of water, except at very high concentrations, when the rise of tension was rather less.

Rice[1] found that ammonia was slightly adsorbed at an air-water interface,

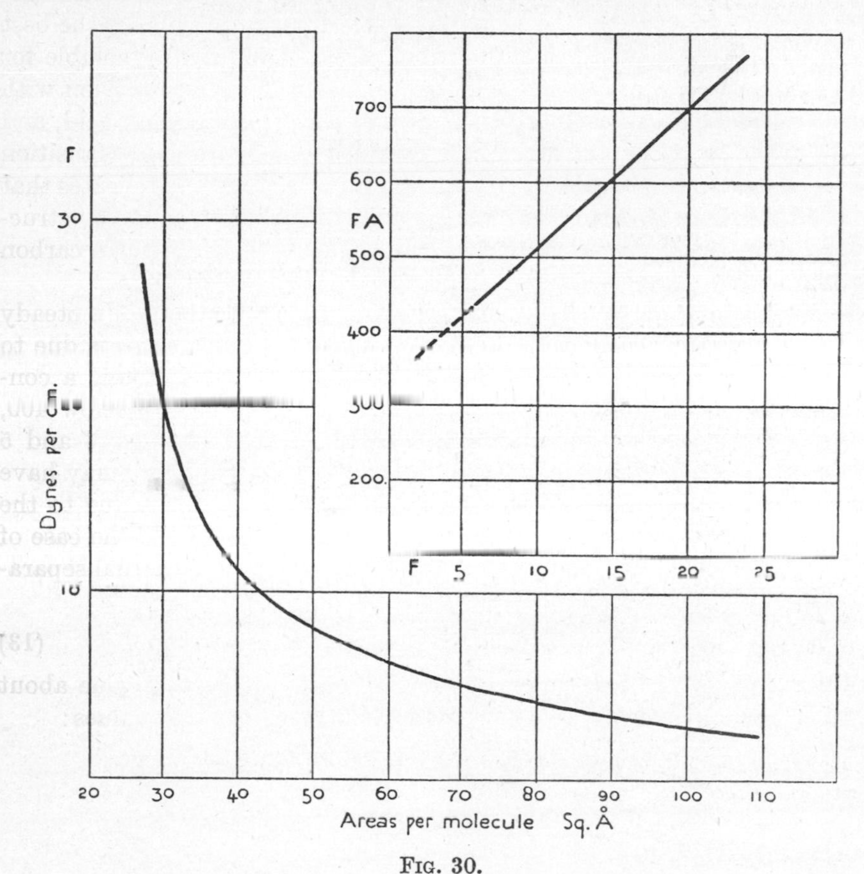

FIG. 30.

but never sufficiently to give a closely packed monomolecular layer. Harkins and Grafton[2] measured the surface tension of hydroquinone, resorcinol, and other polyphenols, calculating the adsorption by the approximate form of Gibbs's equation. The films appear to be gaseous below about 6 dynes pressure; above this pressure the area per molecule appears nearly constant, at 96 sq. A. for resorcinol, 55 for pyrocatechol, and 42·7 for pyrogallol. The *meta* derivative occupies much more space than the others, but all occupy more than would be required if the rings stood vertically on the surface. Frumkin's surface potential data (see § 10) indicate that the soluble polyphenols may lie with their benzene rings parallel to the surface.

In experiments with volatile solutes care must be taken to avoid errors due to evaporation. Bigelow and Washburn,[3] later Washburn and Shildneck,[4] have

[1] *J. Physical Chem.*, **32**, 583 (1928).
[2] *J.A.C.S.* (1925), 1329.
[3] *J. Physical Chem.*, **32**, 321 (1928).
[4] *J.A.C.S.* (1933), 2354.

shown that the surface tension of a solution of a moderately volatile surface active substance may be much greater if evaporation is permitted than if it is prevented. This is probably because evaporation of the molecules lowering the tension takes place more rapidly than the loss can be supplied by diffusion from the interior.

Two-dimensional equations of state for the adsorbed films, of the van der Waals type, have received some consideration, especially by Volmer and Mahnert,[1] and Cassel and Formstecher.[2] The former write, in formal analogy with the van der Waals equation for gases,

$$\left(F+\frac{a}{A^2}\right)(A-b) = RT, \tag{14}$$

and point out that b is, in two dimensions, twice[3] the actual area of the molecules, not four times, as in three dimensions. The usefulness of all such equations is limited to moderate pressures and, as in three dimensions, neither a nor b are really constant.

Cassel and Formstecher write

$$(F+aF^2)(A-b) = RT, \tag{15}$$

and deduce some interesting conclusions as to the effect of deviations from the perfect gaseous state on the relation between the partial vapour pressure of component 2 and the surface tension. If the adsorbed film is a perfect gas, obeying the equation

$$FA = RT, \quad \text{or} \quad F = RT\Gamma_2,$$

combining with (7.5)

$$F = kp_2, \tag{16}$$

i.e. a linear relationship between the lowering of tension and the activity of the solute denotes (as was also shown above) a perfect gaseous film.

Combining (15) with (7.5), putting $\Gamma_2 = 1/A$, and integrating, it is easy to show that

$$\log p_2 = \log F - \log(1+aF) + \frac{b}{RT}F + C. \tag{17}$$

Considering separately the effects of the correction b due to the area occupied by the molecules, and writing

$$F(A-b) = RT,$$

we find in the same way

$$\log p_2 = \log F + \frac{b}{RT}F + C', \tag{18}$$

and if we consider only the attractive term aF^2 so that

$$(F+aF^2)A = RT,$$

we have

$$\log p_2 = \log F - \log(1+aF) + C''. \tag{19}$$

(18) shows that the correction to the gaseous film, due to the space occupied by the molecules, causes F to increase with increasing partial pressure of the solute, less rapidly than a linear relation. (19) shows that if the attractive correction predominates, F increases with p_2 more rapidly than linearly. Hence a curve of F and p_2, concave to the axis of vapour pressure, indicates that the

[1] *Z. physikal. Chem.*, **115**, 239 (1925).

[2] *Kolloid-Z.*, **61**, 18 (1932).

[3] Cf. also Adam, *Proc. Roy. Soc.* **A, 101**, 526 (1922).

repulsive correction to the gaseous film predominates; a curve convex to the axis of p_2 indicates that the attractive forces predominate.

It is of interest to examine what equation of state of the adsorbed film would follow if the relation between the amount adsorbed and the vapour pressure or activity in solution obeyed Freundlich's 'adsorption isotherm' (Chap. VII, § 9)

$$\Gamma_2 = Kp_2^n.$$

Combining with (7.5) as before and integrating

$$F = \frac{RT}{n}\Gamma_2 = \frac{RTkp_2^n}{n}, \tag{20}$$

i.e. the adsorbed film is gaseous but the molecules are aggregated into groups averaging n molecules.

5. Traube's rule; calculation of work of adsorption. Orientation in the adsorbed films. Traube also showed that, in any one homologous series, the concentrations at which equal lowering of surface tension was obtained, in dilute solutions, diminished threefold for each additional CH_2 group in the hydrocarbon chain. Langmuir has shown that this indicates a constant *arithmetical* increase in the work done when a molecule passes from the interior to the surface layer, for each additional CH_2 in the chain. We may consider the surface layer as a region of thickness τ, so that the concentration in this surface region will be Γ_2/τ. The reversible work done in transferring a gramme-molecule of the solute from the interior to the surface will be

$$\lambda = RT\log\frac{\Gamma_2}{\tau c_2} \tag{21}$$

provided that both regions are dilute.

If λ_n and λ_{n-1} are the energies of adsorption for successive members of the series with n and $n-1$ carbon atoms, then

$$\lambda_n - \lambda_{n-1} = RT\log\frac{\left(\frac{\Gamma_2}{\tau c_2}\right)_n}{\left(\frac{\Gamma_2}{\tau c_2}\right)_{n-1}} = RT\log 3 = 640 \text{ cals. per gm.-molecule,}$$

assuming that the thickness τ of the surface layer is the same for n as for $n-1$ carbon atoms.[1]

Thus the work of adsorption increases by a constant amount for each CH_2 added to the hydrocarbon chain of the molecules. This must mean that each CH_2 group is situated in the same relation to the surface as every other such group in the chain, and this can only be the case if the chains lie parallel to the surface. Hence Langmuir concluded that Traube's rule—for this is the name given to the effect of increasing length of chain

[1] If this assumption is incorrect, the validity of the conclusion as to the orientation of the molecules will not be seriously impaired. Suppose that the layers are proportional in thickness to the number of carbons in the molecules, then $\lambda_n - \lambda_{n-1}$ will differ from that given by $RT\log_e\{n/(n-1)\}$, a quantity small compared with $RT\log_e 3$.

on the concentration required to reach a given degree of adsorption—implies that the molecules lie flat in the surface in the dilute gaseous films.

Considering other measurements by Traube, assuming the thickness of the surface layer to be 6 A., the work of adsorption of a large number of series was found to be approximately expressible by

$$\lambda = \lambda_0 + 625n,$$

λ_0 being a constant for each homologous series, characteristic of the end group, and n the number of carbon atoms in the molecule. The values of λ_0 were

TABLE V

Approximate work of adsorption at an air-water interface, for various organic groupings

Series	*End group*	λ_0
Monobasic acid	COOH	437
Primary alcohol	CH_2OH	575
Primary amine	CH_2NH_2	600
Ester	COOR	470
Amide	$CONH_2$	−510
Ketone	R CO R′	295
Dibasic acid	..	−700

A double linkage in the molecule decreases λ_0 by about 400 and every additional OH group in an acid decreases it by about 800.

Additional, and more accurate, data on these lines are likely to give information of some value to the theory of solution. λ_0 being the decrease in potential energy when a mole passes from the interior to the surface, a small value indicates a considerable tendency to dissolve, and vice versa. Langmuir pointed out that although hydroxyl and carboxyl groups increase the tendency to dissolve, this effect is not strictly additive, for two adjacent groups appear to enhance each other's tendency to make the molecule dissolve.

6. Films on concentrated solutions. On dilute solutions of strongly adsorbed substances $\Gamma_2^{(1)}$ increases with the bulk concentration, at first proportionally, then less rapidly as the concentration increases and the surface becomes filled with adsorbed molecules. On strong solutions of moderately capillary active substances $\Gamma_2^{(1)}$ rises to a maximum and then falls off fairly rapidly (see Fig. 31 below). It might be expected that when the solution reaches the stage of practically pure component 2 the 'surface excess' would fall to zero, since a layer of similar thickness in the interior would consist of almost pure 2, and the surface layer could not contain appreciably more of this component. This is not, as a matter of fact, the case with $\Gamma_2^{(1)}$, because this quantity is not at all as simple a concept, physically speaking, as the ordinary man's notion of what a surface excess should mean. The simplest *physical* concepts of the surface excess at a liquid-vapour surface would be the differences between the amount of solute contained in a given mass, or volume, containing unit area of free surface, and a similar mass, or volume, in the interior. These quantities do actually fall to zero with pure component 2. The $\Gamma_2^{(1)}$ of Gibbs's equation was chosen for mathematical convenience in *dilute* solutions, and is a much less easily visualized quantity.

Guggenheim and Adam[1] have discussed various alternative definitions of Γ, made by fixing the mathematical surface XY of the idealized system of Fig. 26 in different ways. For a two-component liquid solution whose volatility is small enough for the density of matter in the vapour phase to be neglected, it is possible to obtain a clear picture of the meaning of Γ defined by fixing the surface XY in different ways. Four different conventions were examined. Gibbs's choice, fixing XY so that Γ_1 vanishes, means that a portion of the liquid containing unit area of surface contains $\Gamma_i^{(1)}$ moles of component i more than a portion in the interior which contains *exactly the same number of molecules of component* 1. This may be called 'convention 1'.

A much simpler convention, physically, but much more complicated mathematically, is 'convention V'. The surface XY is so fixed that a portion of liquid containing unit area of surface contains $\Gamma_i^{(V)}$ moles more of i than *an equal volume* in the interior. On convention M, the portion of liquid containing unit area of surface is compared with *an equal mass* in the interior, and contains $\Gamma_i^{(M)}$ more moles of i. Finally, on convention N, the portion with unit surface contains $\Gamma_i^{(N)}$ more moles of i than a portion in the interior which contains an *equal total number of molecules of all species*. The $\Gamma^{(N)}$ are simple mathematically; the $\Gamma^{(M)}$ and $\Gamma^{(V)}$ rather more complicated.

The relations between the Γ_i were worked out for binary, slightly volatile solutions and numerical values calculated for water-alcohol mixtures. The general relations are

$$-\frac{N_1}{RT}\frac{\partial\gamma}{\partial\log N_2}=\frac{N_2}{RT}\frac{\partial\gamma}{\partial\log N_1}=\Gamma_2^{(N)}=-\Gamma_1^{(N)}=N_1\Gamma_2^{(1)}=-N_2\Gamma_1^{(2)}$$

$$=\frac{M_1N_1+M_2N_2}{M_1}\Gamma_2^{(M)}=-\frac{M_1N_1+M_2N_2}{M_2}\Gamma_1^{(M)}$$

$$=\frac{V_1N_1+V_2N_2}{V_1}\Gamma_2^{(V)}=-\frac{V_1N_1+V_2N_2}{V_2}\Gamma_1^{(V)},$$

M_1, M_2 being the molecular weights, and V_1, V_2 the partial molar volumes, of the components.

Fig. 31 shows the positive adsorption of alcohol and the negative adsorption of water, on the above conventions, from pure water to pure alcohol. In dilute solution it does not matter what convention is used for defining Γ, the Γ are all very nearly equal.

When the solution consists of nearly pure alcohol, the quantities $\Gamma_2^{(V)}$, $\Gamma_2^{(M)}$, and $\Gamma_2^{(N)}$ fall to zero, as would be expected on the 'ordinary man's' concept of what surface excess means, which is probably something close to $\Gamma^{(V)}$ or $\Gamma^{(M)}$. $\Gamma_2^{(1)}$ does not fall to zero.

Assuming that the non-homogeneous layer is one molecule thick, the proportions of water and alcohol in it were calculated, assuming probable values for the area occupied by each. At a mole fraction of 0·05, when only one in twenty of the molecules in bulk is alcohol, the surface consists of 50 or 60 molecular per cent. alcohol. This increases slowly up to slightly over 70

[1] *Proc. Roy. Soc.* A, **139**, 218 (1933).

per cent. for one molecule in five in bulk, increasing thereafter imperceptibly as the bulk concentration rises to 70 per cent. alcohol molecules. Thereafter the alcohol content of the surface rises almost linearly with increasing bulk concentration, reaching of course 100 per cent. on pure alcohol.

Butler and Wightman[1] conclude that the assumption that the transition layer is one molecule thick and no more leads to rather improbable values for the areas occupied in this layer by the water and alcohol, if, as seems likely *a priori*, the proportion of alcohol in the surface rises steadily with increasing

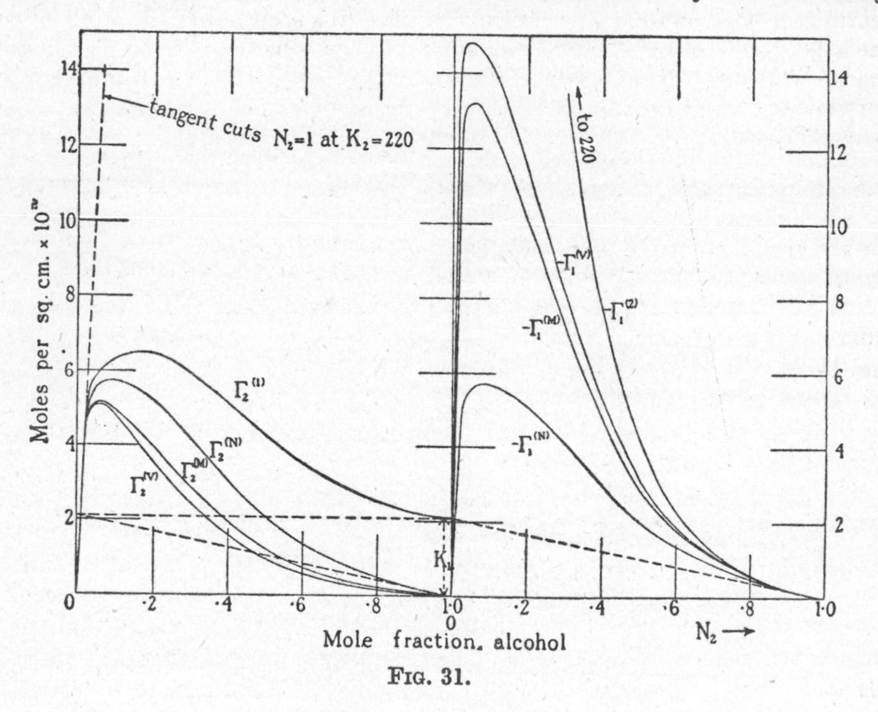

FIG. 31.

amounts of alcohol in the interior; and suggest that a little of the adsorbed alcohol is below the topmost layer of molecules in very strong solutions. The exact constitution of the surface is not yet fully understood.

7. Adsorption of solvent on salt solutions. If the surface tension increases with increasing concentration of the solute, by Gibbs's equation there is negative adsorption, i.e. less solute in the surface layers than in the interior. Most salts raise the surface tension of water, but very few organic substances do so, nor do salts which contain appreciable amounts of hydrocarbon in their composition. Sodium formate does, however, raise the tension of water;[2] the simple amino-acid, glycine, does so also,[3] the rise being somewhat greater at the isoelectric point than at other p_H, presumably because at this point the 'zwitterion' structure exists; i.e. both the amino and the carboxyl groups are ionized.

[1] *J.C.S.* (1932) 2095.

[2] Cf. Lottermoser and Baumgürtel, *Kolloid-Beih.*, **41**, 73 (1935).

[3] Jones and Lewis, *Biochem. J.*, **26**, 639 (1932).

In very dilute solution an expression for the rise of surface tension can be deduced for salts of known valency, on the assumption that the forces are purely electrostatic.[1] Agreement with experiment is, however, very indifferent at present. Some very remarkable observations are due to Grinnell Jones and Ray,[2] who found that in concentrations less than 0·002 normal several salts *decrease* the surface tension of water by a small but definite amount, the maximum lowering of tension being about one five-thousandth of the tension of water. At higher concentrations the salts raise the tension almost linearly with increasing concentration. The lowering is tentatively ascribed to a specific attraction between the ions of the salt and the oriented water molecules presumed to be present at the surface; but it is not clear why there should be positive adsorption in the very lowest concentrations and negative adsorption at all higher concentrations. Langmuir (see Appendix) ascribes the effect to an instrumental error.

Interesting results may be obtained, starting from the assumption that a single layer of water molecules, free from salt, covers the solution. Assuming that the salt solution remains constant in composition right up to the boundary of the surface layer of water, if $-\Gamma_2$ be the deficiency in solute of the surface layer per sq. cm., τ the thickness of this layer, m the molality of the solution, then $\tau = -1{,}000\Gamma_2/m$. Langmuir[3] first calculated the 'thickness' of the adsorbed layer of water in this way, finding τ from 3·3 to 4·2 A. The length of the side of a cube equal to the space occupied by a water molecule in the liquid form is 3·1 A., so that evidently the layer of pure water is of the order 1 molecule thick.

Goard,[4] Harkins and McLaughlin,[5] and Harkins and Gilbert,[6] have extended this work, using the accurate form of Gibbs's equation (7.4). They find values of τ which are not constant, but decrease in nearly all cases from 4 or 5 A. at low concentrations to about 2·5 A. at high concentrations. The most probable explanation of this variation in τ is that the surface layer does not, in the stronger solutions, consist of pure water, but some of the solute diffuses into it. It would be surprising if the diffusing tendency of the salt were unable to bring any of the solute molecules into the surface layer; but the greater inward pull on the salt ions keeps their concentration in the surface low.

The hydration of the ions has some influence on the extent of negative adsorption, the more strongly hydrated ions causing a slightly greater increase in tension; in order of decreasing effect, Cl $>$ Br $>$ I, and Li $>$ Na $>$ K.[7] Divalent cations are more powerful than monovalent for *equimolecular* (not equivalent) solutions; they have up to twice as great an effect on the tension. Salts also raise the interfacial tension between hexane and aqueous solutions, the effects of hydration and valency being similar to those at an air-water interface.[8]

In non-aqueous solvents, also, salts raise the surface tension, and the

[1] Cf. Wagner, *Physikal. Z.*, **25**, 474 (1924); Onsager and Samaras, *J. Chem. Physics*, **2**, 528 (1934).

[2] *J.A.C.S.* (1935), 957; (1937), 187.

[3] *Ibid.* (1917), 1897.

[4] *J.C.S.* (1925), 2451.

[5] *J.A.C.S.* (1925), 2083.

[6] *Ibid.* (1926), 604.

[7] Cf. *Int. Critical Tables*, **4**, 464–6.

[8] Kidokoro, *Bull. Chem. Soc. Japan*, **7**, 280 (1932).

extent of the rise depends on the nature of the solvent. Fig. 31A shows that the effect decreases very rapidly, in the series of alcohols, as the molecules of solvent increase in length.[1] In methyl alcohol the rise of tension is very large, reaching about 30 dynes at 12 normal sodium iodide; in ethyl alcohol it is about half this, and as each additional CH_2 group is added to the molecule of solvent the rise of tension produced by a given concentration of salt is approximately halved.

This is probably due to the outer layer of molecules being free from salt; the field of force of the salt below this layer making itself felt outside the

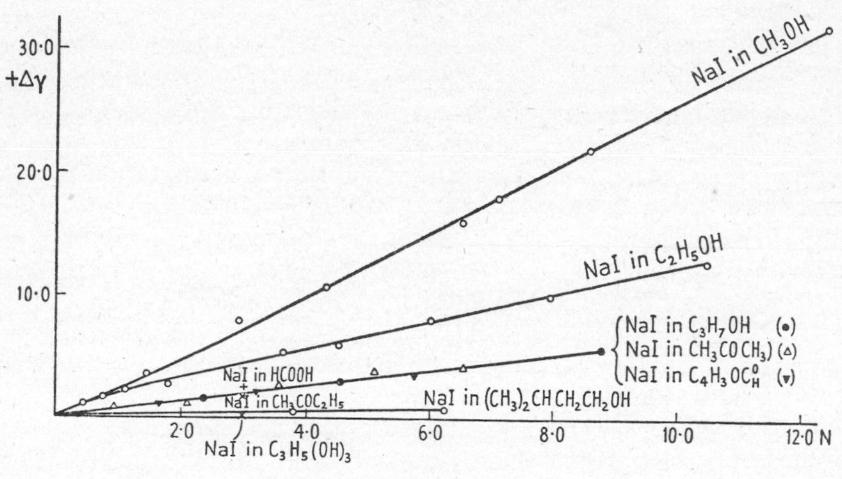

FIG. 31A.

liquid, in inverse proportion to the thickness of the hydrocarbon part of the outer layer. The screening effect of the monomolecular layer of methyl alcohol molecules is not great; but the five carbon atoms (with attached hydrogens) of iso-amyl alcohol form so effective a screen that the salts raise the external field of force, and the tension, but little.

8. Solutions of soaps and other long-chain colloidal electrolytes. The surface tension of soaps has been very extensively studied,[2] but for the most part the results in the literature are discordant far beyond the usual error of measurement of surface tension. In general the surface tension diminishes rapidly with increasing concentration, reaching a steady, or nearly steady, low value after a certain concentration is reached; this concentration is naturally lower the longer the hydrocarbon chain. The variation between the results obtained by different experimenters, and even by the same experimenter under different conditions, may

[1] Kosakewitsch, *Z. physikal. Chem.*, **133**, 1; **136**, 195 (1928).

[2] Some of the more important papers are: Donnan and Potts, *Kolloid-Z.*, **7**, 208 (1910); Walker, *J.C.S.* (1921), 1521; Lascaray, *Kolloid-Z.*, **34**, 73 (1924); Lottermoser and others, *Kolloid-Z.*, **63**, 295 (1933) (extensive bibliography); **66**, 276 (1934); **73**, 155, 276 (1935); *Trans. Faraday Soc.*, **31**, 200 (1935); *Kolloid-Beih.*, **41**, 73 (1935)

perhaps be explained by hydrolysis of the soaps, the extent to which neutral and acid soaps are adsorbed being very different. Lottermoser has found that solutions of neutral soap decrease slowly in surface tension on exposure to air containing carbon dioxide, and that the nature and treatment of the glass with which the solutions are in contact affects the

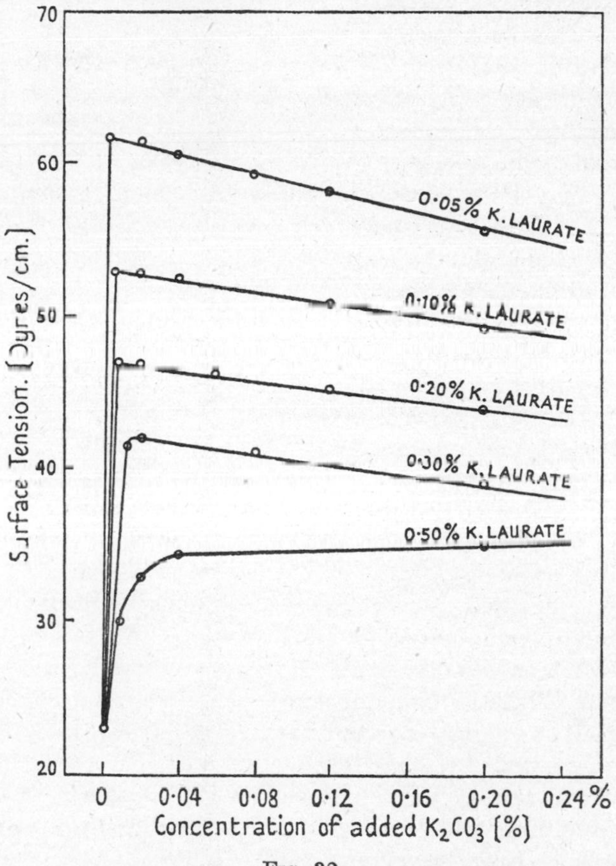

FIG. 32.

results obtained. An observation by Harkins and Clark,[1] followed up by Ekwall[2] and recently by Powney,[3] gives a clue to the effect of hydrolysis. Powney's results on potassium laurate are shown in Fig. 32; similar results were obtained with all the fatty acids tried from 9 to 18 carbons. The neutral soap, at all concentrations above the most dilute tried (roughly N/500), has a tension about 22 dynes per cm. Minute traces of alkali raise the tension to a maximum, which is greater the more dilute the solution, and the amounts of alkali required to reach this maximum of surface tension are smaller the more dilute the solution. As further, much larger,

[1] Harkins and Clark, *J.A.C.S.* (1925), 1854.
[2] Ekwall, *Acta Akad. Åboensis* (*Math. Phys.*), **4**, 6 (1927).
[3] Powney, *Trans. Faraday Soc.*, **31**, 1510 (1935).

quantities of alkali are added, the tension decreases slowly, almost linearly, with increasing quantities of alkali.

The changes can probably be explained as follows.[1] When the p_H is more acid than about 8, some acid soap is present, and this is far more strongly adsorbed than neutral soap. The fact that the surface tension in the supposedly neutral solutions is independent of concentration is due to the surface tension-concentration curve of the acid soap having reached its minimum at the lowest concentration here studied, the surface being saturated with adsorbed molecules. It would be expected, *a priori*, that an acid soap would be more strongly adsorbed than a neutral soap, on account of the much greater attraction of COONa for water than COOH; also Miss Laing and McBain[2] have shown that the soap in the froth obtained from neutral sodium oleate solutions contains about 0·7 molecules of oleic acid for each molecule of neutral soap, but on slightly alkaline solutions the surface layer is not acid.

Addition of alkali suppresses the hydrolysis, and when sufficient alkali has been added for complete suppression of hydrolysis, the adsorbed layer consists of neutral soap. This is probably the state of affairs at the maxima of surface tension in Fig. 32. More alkali is required to reach the maximum with the stronger solutions, because more alkali is needed to suppress hydrolysis completely. The maximum surface tensions in Fig. 32 are probably very near to the surface tension of solutions of neutral soap only of the concentration indicated on each curve. The subsequent slow fall of tension, as more alkali is added, is probably due to a salting out of the soap by the alkali, an increase in escaping tendency caused by the presence of comparatively large amounts of another solute. It would be interesting to find whether addition of neutral salt, in addition to the small amount of alkali needed to reach the maximum, produces a fall in tension similar in amount to that given by additional alkali.

So-called 'neutral' soap solutions are more complex systems than at first appears, and the fairly small amounts of hydrolysis in the interior of the solution are very much magnified by the great difference in adsorbability between a neutral soap and an acid soap, or free fatty acid. A close approximation to the true surface tension-concentration curve of neutral soap can probably be obtained by plotting the maxima of tension shown in Fig. 32 against the concentration on each curve. It does not seem possible as yet to plot the true surface tension-concentration curve for acid soap, as the concentration of acid soap, and even the ratio of acid to soap molecules in any compound which may be formed in the interior, is unknown.

According to Lottermoser and Baumgürtel,[3] the final surface tension of soap solutions is reached in a few minutes; Ekwall, however, records a fall lasting at least two hours in solutions more dilute than N/20,000.

[1] Adam, *Trans. Faraday Soc.*, **32**, 653 (1936).

[2] *Proc. Roy. Soc.* A, **109**, 28 (1925); *6th Colloid Symposium Monograph*, 63 (1928).

[3] *Kolloid-Beih.*, **41**, 89 (1935); but contact with glass or metal may produce slow changes.

Paraffin-chain salts, similar in general constitution to the soaps but containing a strongly dissociated end group such as a sulphonic acid or a quaternary ammonium atom, are not subject to hydrolysis, and might be expected to behave in a simpler manner. The surface-tension measurements of Adam and Shute,[1] R. C. Brown,[2] and Lottermoser and others[3] indicate, however, a curious, very slow attainment of the final surface tension in solutions so dilute that there are few, if any, ionic micelles present in the interior. The tension may take several days to reach the final value; and when the final tension is reached it appears to be independent of the concentration, at least for solutions over 0·003 per cent., i.e. of the order N/10,000. The amount of this final tension depends somewhat on the nature of the end group; it is usually about 30 dynes per cm.

For solutions sufficiently concentrated for ionic micelles to be present in considerable quantity (this occurs with the twelve-carbon compounds at about N/100 and with the sixteen-carbon at about N/1,000)[4] the surface tension reaches the final value in a few seconds and this value is usually the same as that attained slowly in the very dilute solutions. Additions of salt to the very dilute solutions accelerate the attainment of the final tension. Doss (see Appendix) ascribes the slow adsorption to an electrical effect.

It is evident from the low values of the surface tension of all these solutions of paraffin-chain salts that the surface is fairly completely covered with the adsorbed molecules. The surface films are probably all 'gaseous' however. Adam[5] found that even with the 20- or 22-carbon homologues of the pyridinium bromides or the trimethylammonium iodides, which are insoluble enough to be examined by the methods of Chapter II, the films are gaseous; and Adam and Miller[6] found the same with fatty acids on alkaline solutions for chain lengths up to at least 18 carbons at room temperature: and naturally the much shorter chain potassium laurate (12 carbons) gives a gaseous adsorbed film.[7]

Traube's rule holds, at least qualitatively, for the surface tension, i.e. the concentration at which a definite degree of lowering of surface tension occurs is lower the longer the hydrocarbon chains. Many of the published observations on the change of surface tension with concentration show a minimum at a certain concentration followed by a rise of a few dynes per cm. as the solution becomes stronger. The existence of this minimum can perhaps not be considered fully established as yet, owing to the fact that the measurements were usually made very rapidly, and the surface tension changes slowly with time; R. C. Murray[8] has pointed out that if, as is probable, the surface-active constituent of the solution is the unaggregated single ions, not the ionic micelle, a minimum is not unlikely, as the equilibrium between ionic micelle and single ions changes

[1] *Trans. Faraday Soc.* (1938), 758.
[2] *Ibid.*, **31**, 205.
[3] *Kolloid-Z.*, **73**, 155 (1935).
[4] Cf. G. S. Hartley, *Aqueous Solutions of Paraffin Chain Salts* (Paris, 1936).
[5] Unpublished.
[6] *Proc. Roy. Soc.* A, **142**, 401 (1933).
[7] Cf. Powney, *loc. cit.*, and Adam, *Trans. Faraday Soc.*, **32**, 653 (1936).
[8] *Trans. Faraday Soc.*, **31**, 206 (1935).

in such a way as the solution increases in strength that at one point the concentration of single ions goes through a minimum.

The effect of the formation of the ionic micelle in the interior of the solutions of these long-chain salts, on their surface tension, is interesting. Although the ionic micelle is, itself, much more soluble and probably much less capillary active than the single ions, its presence in the interior causes the surface tension to be diminished to the minimum very much more rapidly than if no ionic micelles are present. The reason for this is not clear, but it is possible that electrostatic forces between the heavily charged micelles and the single ions tend to concentrate the latter at the surface.

9. Adsorption from vapours on liquid surfaces. From measurements of the change of surface tension of water caused by contact with various pressures of hydrocarbon vapours Micheli[1] and Cassel and Formstecher[2] have found the adsorption of these substances. They produce a surface-tension lowering of a few dynes per cm., and there is no doubt that the films are gaseous. Micheli found that the lowering of tension is nearly proportional to the partial pressure of the hydrocarbon vapour, indicating a dilute gaseous film with but small corrections to the perfect gaseous state; but according to Cassel and Formstecher the surface pressure increases more rapidly than linearly with increasing vapour pressure, indicating considerable adhesion between the hydrocarbon molecules in the films, a result which, if correct, is somewhat surprising.[3] A rule analogous to Traube's holds, the longer chain paraffins being more adsorbed than the shorter, and the heat of adsorption of each additional CH_2 group in the molecule is of the order 500 calories per mole. Benzene is more strongly adsorbed than heptane, no doubt owing to its partially unsaturated character.

Many workers have studied adsorption from vapour on mercury surfaces, the substances used ranging from the rare gases to organic compounds of fairly high boiling-point. There is great confusion in the published results, arising probably from variations in the purity of the mercury used, with consequent variations in the amount of contamination present on the supposedly clean mercury surfaces.[4] A *slow* fall in surface tension in a gas is often found, and may

[1] *Phil. Mag.*, **3**, 895 (1927).

[2] *Kolloid-Z.*, **61**, 18 (1932).

[3] D. C. Jones and Cutting (unpublished 1937) have very recently confirmed the predominance of the lateral adhesion in these adsorbed films, and also the validity of Traube's rule. When the vapour phase is nearly saturated with the hydrocarbon they find films more than one molecule thick. Adsorption on heavy water is rather less than on ordinary water.

[4] Although it has been known for over half a century that distillation carries over appreciable amounts of less volatile, but much more easily oxidizable, metals with the mercury, papers still appear describing measurements purporting to be of great accuracy, in which the purification of the mercury is not described further than by saying that it has been 'distilled'. Prolonged treatment with wet oxidizing agents, followed by a lengthy treatment with air, and subsequent distillation, is probably the indispensable minimum of care if the mercury is to be freed from oxidizable impurities; and also the apparatus which comes into contact with the mercury requires most scrupulous cleaning. A really clean surface of mercury is very difficult

be due, not to a film of oxide or other compound slowly forming on the surface of the mercury, but to a more readily oxidizable metal, present in traces in the interior, diffusing slowly to the surface and combining with the gas there.

Values up to 480 or 490 dynes per cm. have been obtained by the most careful workers for the surface tension of mercury in some permanent gases at about 20°; the temperature coefficient of the tension is about 0·23 dyne decrease per degree rise. Many workers record no increase in a vacuum, but it is also recorded that, once a mercury surface is covered by a layer of adsorbed gas, it is exceedingly difficult to remove this layer merely by pumping. The highest, apparently reliable, result recorded for mercury in a vacuum is that of Cook,[1] 515 dynes at 31°; this could only be reached by using extreme care in outgassing the whole apparatus and renewing the mercury surfaces by overflowing. Bradley,[2] in very careful work, found 503 dynes at 16·5°, this being reduced a few dynes by hydrogen, the rate of lowering of tension being very slow. Burdon[3] found that adsorbed hydrogen, carbon dioxide, or air, which could not be removed by evacuation, were displaced from the surface as gas, simply by contracting the surface. The amount thus displaced was approximately equal to a layer one molecule thick on the mercury surface. Kazda,[4] and Dunn,[5] found it necessary to renew the surface by overflowing before the correct photoelectric threshold could be obtained; and even with mechanical renewal of the surface it is evidently essential to eliminate all greased taps, and all moisture, from the apparatus or clean surfaces cannot be obtained. Burdon[6] gives 488 dynes per cm. as the tension of mercury, at 25°, in a vacuum and in dry air. When, as frequently happens, results much lower than this are recorded, there is a strong presumption that the surfaces were contaminated with some compound of a more readily oxidizable metal, present as impurity in the mercury; or, that there was a layer of moisture, of or greasy matter, present on the surface. Water vapour is very hard to pump off.

In view of the difficulty in deciding whether or not the initial tension is that of pure mercury, attempts to deduce the equation of state from measurements of the lowering of surface tension at various vapour pressures are open to doubt. Most workers have abandoned the attempt to do this with ordinary gases.[7] Oliphant[8] and Bosworth[9] have, however, measured directly the amounts of carbon dioxide, sulphur dioxide, water vapour, and hydrogen adsorbed on a stream of freshly formed mercury drops. These were found to adsorb the maximum, final amount of gas in a fraction of a second; and this was liberated,

to obtain for more than a very short time; and it is probable that much of the work recorded describes the change in tension by adsorption of vapours, not on a clean mercury surface, but on one already considerably contaminated. In the present state of the subject it is to be hoped that authors will record in full detail, not only the methods used for cleaning the mercury, but also its surface tension and how this tension alters with time.

[1] *Physical Rev.*, **34**, 513 (1934). [2] *J. Physical Chem.*, **38**, 231 (1934).
[3] *Proc. Physical Soc.*, **47**, 460 (1935). [4] *Physical Rev.*, **26**, 643 (1925).
[5] *Ibid.*, **29**, 693 (1927). [6] *Trans. Faraday Soc.*, **28**, 866 (1932).

[7] Binné's measurements of the decrease in surface tension, caused by xenon and krypton on mercury, made by Cassel's technique, are puzzling (*Diss.*, Berlin (1932); R. Noske, Leipzig). Although his initial surface tension was a good deal lower than that of most careful workers, he records smooth curves of the lowering of tension by different pressures of these chemically inert gases.

[8] *Phil. Mag.*, **6**, 422 (1928). [9] *Trans. Faraday Soc.*, **28**, 896 (1932).

and swept away, at the bottom of the column down which the drops fell, as the drops coalesced. The amount released from the coalescing drops was found to be approximately a closely packed monomolecular layer. If two gases were present, the total amount adsorbed was practically constant at a monomolecular layer. Carbon dioxide rapidly displaced hydrogen from adsorption on the surface.

Vapours lower the surface tension of mercury. Gibbs[1] suggested the measurement of the surface tension of mercury in water vapour as a suitable case for calculating the amount of a vapour adsorbed, but did not actually carry out the calculation owing to paucity of data. Iredale,[2] Micheli,[3] Cassel,[4] Bosworth,[5] and Bartell[6] and others have in recent years made systematic measurements of the lowering of the tension of mercury by various vapours. Bartell worked only with saturated vapours, finding that water causes a small depression of tension; organic vapours reduced the tension to within a few dynes of 395 at 25°. Iredale and Micheli worked with various pressures of vapour, all, however, sufficiently high for a good deal of adsorption to take place; the surface pressures were high, the area per molecule in the adsorbed films changing but slowly with increasing pressure; the films, nevertheless, were almost certainly gaseous. Water gave a linear F–p_2 curve, but at the greatest dilution measured, the surface pressure was already 9 dynes and the area per molecule about 19 sq. A. With methyl acetate, benzene, various lower paraffins, and some aliphatic halides, Iredale and Micheli found the F–p_2 curves concave to the axis of pressure, indicating (as would be expected from the small areas per molecule) that the corrections to the gaseous state of the films, due to the space occupied by the molecules, preponderate over those due to lateral adhesion; this concavity was less with the lower alcohols than with the hydrocarbon vapours, indicating more lateral adhesion. Bosworth worked with the lower fatty acids, down to concentrations which gave quite small depressions of tension, finding the F–p_2 curves also concave to the pressure axis, at low and at high concentrations.

Cassel's results indicate gaseous films, the hydrocarbons giving the same direction of curvature as above, i.e. a preponderance of the 'b' correction in the van der Waals type of equation; but the lower alcohols and nitromethane showed opposite curvature in the F–p_2 curves, except at very high pressures; this indicates strong lateral adhesion; the F–A relations for the adsorbed films, deducible from his results, indicate association into double molecules even at great dilutions. Butyl and iso-amyl alcohols formed adsorbed films intermediate in properties between the lower alcohols and the hydrocarbons. No lowering of tension at all was observed with water. Cassel's results differ considerably from those of other workers; since the surface tension of his supposedly clean mercury was some 25 dynes lower than the best values of several other workers, and since no adsorption of water was found, there may have been a considerable amount of contamination initially on the mercury.

Iredale found the tension to become very indefinite when the vapours were saturated; results anywhere between those lying on the F–p_2 curves found

[1] *Works*, **1**, 235.
[2] *Phil. Mag.*, **45**, 1088 (1923); **48**, 177 (1924); **49**, 603 (1925).
[3] *Ibid.*, **3**, 895 (1927).
[4] *Z. physikal. Chem.* A, **155**, 321 (1931); *Z. Elektrochem.*, **37**, 642 (1931).
[5] *Trans. Faraday Soc.*, **28**, 903 (1932).
[6] *J.A.C.S.* (1933), 2769.

for lower pressures, and much lower figures, appearing more or less capriciously. This is probably due to condensation of drops on the mercury surface, or possibly to the surface-tension measurements having been spoiled by condensation on the tips used for forming the drops, whose volume was taken as a measure of the surface tension.

Cassel's further results[1] on carbon tetrachloride are interesting; very sharp breaks in the Γ–p_2 and F–A curves were obtained at an area per molecule of 32 sq. A. This is believed to be a saturated monomolecular layer; it is reached at a fraction of 1 millimetre pressure, and as the pressure increases further, the adsorption increases very much more slowly, until the adsorption reaches approximately three molecular layers.

From the fact that all workers have found considerable lowering of tension by organic vapours, it seems likely that these displace the layers of oxide or other contamination that may be present initially. Owing to the discordant results, it is difficult to say more, with certainty, than that the adsorbed films of organic vapours on mercury are usually gaseous, and that there may be more lateral adhesion in the films of short-chain, polar substances than of hydrocarbons.

10. Surface potentials of solutions. If a dissolved substance is adsorbed at the surface of a solution it alters the contact potential between the solution and air, or between the solution and any other phase with which it may be in contact. The change in potential due to the solute, called as usual the 'surface potential' of the solute, may be due to electrical double layers set up by the orientation of the molecules adsorbed, re-orientation of the solvent molecules, redistribution of ions, or to all these causes.

The method first used for measuring surface potentials of solutions is often known as the method of 'flowing junctions'. It was used by Bichat and Blondlot,[2] Kenrick,[3] and more recently by Frumkin.[4]

The solvent, and the solution, are made to flow, one in a column down the centre of a vertical tube, the other down the walls, so that there are constantly renewed surfaces of solvent and solution, of large area, in fairly close proximity. The difference in the air-liquid potential between the two liquids (which is the 'surface potential' of the solute) causes a difference in potential between the liquids, and since the liquids are constantly renewed, current must be supplied to one liquid, and taken from the other, in order to maintain this difference. This current is large enough to be measurable by an electrometer. A circuit is therefore constructed with reversible electrodes in contact with the insulated reservoirs containing a supply of each of the liquids, an electrometer to detect the flow of current, and a potentiometer to impose any desired potentials on the liquids. The potentiometer is adjusted until the electrometer shows no flow of current; then the applied potential is equal to the difference in

[1] *Trans. Faraday Soc.*, **28**, 177 (1932).
[2] *J. Physique*, **2**, 533 (1883).
[3] *Z. physikal. Chem.*, **19**, 625 (1896).
[4] *Ibid.*, **109**, 34; **111**, 190 (1924); **123**, 321 (1926); a modified form in *Acta Physicochim. U.R.S.S.*, **2**, 1 (1935).

air-liquid potential between the liquids, provided that the solute does not affect the junction potentials between the liquids and the reversible electrodes through which the connexion to the potentiometer is made. There is no transfer of electricity across the air gap in this method, as there is when an air electrode covered with some radioactive material is used.

The method would probably give erroneous results for solutions of substances adsorbed too slowly for the surface to reach equilibrium very quickly with the interior, but for solutions of salts and organic substances of moderate molecular weight it is probably trustworthy. Frumkin and Donde[1] have used a thin stream of falling mercury instead of the inner column of aqueous solution.

Sawai[2] applied the technique of the air electrode covered with a radioactive substance, described for insoluble films in Chapter II, to stationary solutions contained in a funnel filled to the brim; the funnel was first filled with the solvent, which was quickly replaced with solution. The difference between the potentials when solvent and solution are in the funnel is the surface potential. The method works quite well and is to be preferred to a flowing junction for solutes which diffuse slowly to the surface.

Kenrick found that many organic substances cause a considerable positive surface potential—the outer layer being more positive than the inner half of the double layer, just as most insoluble organic substances have a positive surface potential; most of the following results are due to Frumkin.

Most salts produce a rather small potential at a water-air surface, the double layer having the outer side negative. This indicates that, on the average, the anions are nearer the surface than the cations. The amount of the negative charge increases with decreasing hydration of the ions, the charges being in the order F < Cl < Br < I < CNS, no doubt because the least hydrated ions penetrate to the surface most easily. The fluorides produced a small positive charge. The nature of the cation makes little difference, but complex anions containing metals are usually more inclined to come to the surface than simple anions, so that the negative charge is larger.

The surface potentials of solutions of surface active organic substances run generally parallel with those on insoluble monomolecular films; the surface potential naturally increases with increasing number of adsorbed molecules per unit area of surface. It is found that, for any one substance, as the concentration increases, the surface potential increases with the adsorption, though not always in direct proportion. For different members of a homologous series containing the same polar group, Traube's rule holds; the concentration required to give a certain potential decreases about three times with each additional CH_2 in the chain.

As with the insoluble films, the amount of the surface potential depends on the vertical component of the dipole of the molecules, and therefore on the orientation of this dipole and of the molecules to the surface. All

[1] *Z. physikal. Chem.*, **123**, 339 (1926). [2] *Trans. Faraday Soc.*, **31**, 765 (1935).

the adsorbed films appear to be gaseous, and with the aliphatic compounds there is sometimes an upward trend in the contribution of each molecule to the potential, measured by

$$\mu = \Delta V / 4\pi n,$$

discussed in Chap. II, § 10, as the area is decreased to those at which the molecules must be standing up to some extent. Frumkin made a very large number of measurements on solutions of substances of various constitutions, some in a good deal of detail, but others at a few concentrations only. Table VI shows his principal results: the approximate values for μ and A are given when the data permit. The expressions for the potential, 'small', 'large', etc., are purposely left vague, as without knowledge of the amount of adsorption the figures for potential at any single concentration mean little.

With the aliphatic compounds the contribution (as measured by μ) of each molecule to the surface potential is similar to that of insoluble molecules with the same end groups in spread films. In some cases there may be some change in μ as the film becomes more crowded, indicating a change in tilt of the dipoles to the surface; in others, μ apparently remains constant; the data are scarcely full enough, however, to afford much information on this point.

With the aromatic compounds, however, fairly certain deductions as to orientation can be made. The polyphenols, with two or three hydroxyl groups in the ring, all gave negative potentials of rather small amount at all areas. This is probably due to the rings lying flat in the surface; the $\overset{+}{C}—\overset{-}{O}$ bonds being parallel to the surface and the $\overset{-}{O}—\overset{+}{H}$ bonds tilted somewhat with the positive H below. Phenol itself gives small positive values, increasing as the molecules are crowded in the film; probably a few of the molecules are slightly tilted at great dilutions, and the number tilted, and the angle of tilt to the horizontal, increase as the area decreases so that there is no longer ample room for all the molecules to lie flat. *p*-cresol gives larger positive values, which also increase on crowding; probably the effect of the CH_3 group at the opposite corner to the hydroxyl is to make the molecules tend to aggregate with the rings more or less perpendicular to the surface, thus bringing the $\overset{+}{C}—\overset{-}{O}$ bond at a sufficiently steep angle to the surface to make a considerable positive contribution to the potential. With *o*-cresol the molecule evidently prefers to remain flat, and *m*-cresol is intermediate. The unusual change of sign of the potential with benzoic acid is probably due to a change in orientation, but as usual with the salts of the carboxylic acids, the resultant moment is quite small.

The halogenated derivatives show a strong negative effect of the halogen atoms, covalently linked; the positive μ of acetic acid is turned into a negative, through superposition of the

```
      CHCl⁻
       |
       C⁺
     ╱   ╲
   HO     O
```

dipole above the carboxyl; and the effect is very much increased on introducing two, or three, halogens. The increased dissociation of the acid also increases the negative dipole of the hydroxyl group.

TABLE VI

Surface Potentials of Solutions of Organic Substances (Frumkin)

Substance	Surface potential		Approximate contribution by each adsorbed molecule	
	Sign	Order of magnitude	μ e.s.u. $\times 10^{-19}$	Area sq. A.
Butyric acid . . .	+	Moderate	1·7 2·14 to 3·0	280 130 40 and below
Other fatty acids, also phenyl acetic and β-phenyl propionic acid . . .	+	Moderate	Same order as above	
Na and K salts of above .	—	Very small		
Benzoic acid . . .	+	Large	c. 4·3*	
Sodium benzoate:				
dilute solutions . .	—	Very small		
strong solutions . .	+	Small†		
Esters	+	Large	c. 6	Constant below 240
Aliphatic alcohols, also benzyl alcohol and cyclohexanol .	+	Moderate	c. 2·2	
Glycol and glycerol . .	+	Moderate		
Aliphatic amines and benzylamine	+	Large	c. 5	
Ethylene chlorhydrin . .	—	Very small		
Mono-halogenated acetic acid	—	Small		
Di- ,, ,, ,,	—	Moderate		
Tri- ,, ,, ,,	—	Large		
Chloral hydrate . . .	—	Large		
α-Chloropropionic acid . .	Practically none			
β- ,, ,, . .	+	Very small		
Phenol	+	Small	< 0·1 to 0·44	80 37
o-Cresol	+ ?	Very small	Variable, maximum 0·2	
p-Cresol	+	Moderate	1·0 1·5 to 2·0	700 110 30
m-Cresol	Intermediate between ortho- and para-			
Polyphenols . . .	—	Small		
Aniline	+	Moderate	c. 1·7	
Toluidine, methylaniline, dimethylaniline . . .	+	Moderate		

* Frumkin ascribes the high value for benzoic acid to association in solution having rendered the calculation of Γ incorrect. It is possible, however, that μ is really much larger than for the saturated fatty acids; large values of μ occur in aliphatic acids having double bonds close to the carboxyl group (cf. Chap. II, § 22).

† The change in sign of the potential, as the surface layer becomes more crowded with adsorbed molecules, is very unusual.

11. Adsorption from organic solvents. No large amount of work appears to have been done on the surface tension of solutions in organic solvents, and hence on the adsorption at an air-solvent interface. Gilbert[1] found a very slight diminution of the surface tension of a heavy hydrocarbon oil by long-chain fatty acids, indicating slight adsorption. No great amount of positive adsorption would be expected, as the field of force round hydrocarbon parts of molecules is less than that round most other groups; hence no diminution of surface tension would be expected. On the contrary, a negative adsorption at an air-liquid surface is perhaps more likely.

At the interface between solids and organic solvents, however, specific attractions between the solid and the adsorbed substances may come into play and produce considerable adsorption. Some such cases are of importance in lubrication; long-chain fatty acids, and some of their salts, are adsorbed from solution in hydrocarbon oils at the surface of many metals, and the result is a 'boundary' lubricating layer (see Chap. VI).

Traube's rule does not hold for adsorption from organic solvents. While, on charcoal, from aqueous solution, the adsorption of organic compounds increases as the hydrocarbon chains are lengthened,[2] this rule is reversed in the case of fatty acids on silica. Holmes and McKelvey[3] found much greater adsorption of the shortest chain acids, from toluene on silica, than of longer chain acids; and Bartell and Fu[4] obtained similar results with solutions in carbon tetrachloride.

There is no reason to expect Traube's rule to hold good except for aqueous solutions; it is only an expression of the tendency of long hydrocarbon chains to escape from solution in water.

12. Adsorbed films between two immiscible liquids.* Schofield and Rideal,[5] calculating from the data of Harkins and King,[6] find no perceptible lateral adhesion between the molecules of butyric acid adsorbed at the interface between water and benzene, the only perceptible corrections to the perfect gaseous state of these films being those due to the space occupied by the molecules; the same acid at an air-water surface shows a small amount of lateral adhesion. Harkins and McLaughlin,[7] on the other hand, consider that acetic acid is more closely packed between water and benzene than between water and air; but the lateral adhesion is not necessarily greater, as the effect may be due to attraction of the benzene for the methyl groups in the acetic acid bringing more molecules to the surface for a given surface pressure. The data are as yet rather meagre; the same considerations as those given in § 32 of Chapter II would indicate that the lateral adhesion should be smaller than at the water-air surface, but the difference ought to be less with the short-chain acids than with the long, since these lie flat in a water-air interface and so are more likely to move with the water molecules than longer chain molecules which stand upright closely packed.

[1] *J. Physical Chem.*, **31**, 543 (1927).
[2] Cf. Freundlich, *Kapillarchemie*, **1**, 257 ff. (1930).
[3] *J. Physical Chem.*, **32**, 1522 (1928).
[4] *Ibid.*, **33**, 680 (1929).
[5] *Proc. Roy. Soc.* A, **109**, 67 (1925).
[6] *J.A.C.S.* (1919), 985.
[7] *Ibid.* (1925), 1610.

* See also Appendix.

Hartridge and Peters,[1] and Peters,[2] find that the interfacial tension between various liquids and aqueous solutions varies with the p_H, if there are fatty acids or long-chain amines dissolved in the hydrocarbon phase. With dilute benzene solutions of fatty acids the tension was high, over 30 dynes per cm., if the p_H was less than about 5·5; with increasing alkalinity it fell, reaching practically zero at about 9. Benzene solutions of the amines had the high tension on the alkaline side of p_H 9, the tension falling with increasing acidity to very low values at p_H 5. The natural explanation is that the ionization of the carboxyl or amine groups begins at the point where the tension begins to fall, and is due to repulsion between the similar electrical charges developed on the end groups of the molecules in the interfacial films (cf. Chap. II, § 21). The range of p_H over which the tension changes is close to the range in which ionization occurs, but Danielli shows[3] that it probably differs by one or two units, owing to the p_H in the surface layer being slightly different from that in the interior of the solution.

An α-hydroxyacid showed similar changes in interfacial tension, commencing at a lower p_H; an ester showed a fall beginning at a much higher p_H, perhaps owing to some hydrolysis occurring at the interface.[4]

13. Displacement of equilibria in adsorbed layers.* If an equilibrium exists in solution between two or more constituent substances, and one of these is adsorbed more strongly than another, that one will be more concentrated in the surface and the equilibrium in the surface layer will be shifted in the direction of that constituent. It often happens, owing to electrolytic dissociation or to hydrolysis, that a single pure substance when dissolved in water consists of such an equilibrium mixture, and if the bulk solution alone were under consideration, an aqueous solution of such a substance would naturally be treated, according to the phase rule, as a two-component system. But when surfaces enter into consideration, unless the ease of adsorption of both the constituents of the equilibrium mixture in solution is identical, the adsorption of each has to be considered separately and consequently the system must be regarded as consisting of three components at least, not two.[5]

One such case has already been met with, in §8; undissociated fatty acids are concentrated at the air-liquid surface of soap solutions made by

* See also Appendix. [1] *Proc. Roy. Soc.* A, **101**, 351 (1922). [2] *Ibid.*, **133**, 140 (1931). [3] *Ibid.*, B, **122**, 155 (1937). [4] Peters (private communication, 1936).

[5] Although most of the references given in this section are comparatively recent, it must not be forgotten that the influence of surfaces on chemical equilibria, and on reactions, was clearly seen by J. J. Thomson. In the *Application of Dynamics to Physics and Chemistry* (1888, p. 236) he wrote: 'Thus in very thin films the influence of capillarity might be sufficient to modify completely the nature of chemical equilibrium, though we should not expect it to do much in the body of a fluid. If the surface tension increases as the chemical action goes on the capillarity will tend to stop the action, while if the surface tension diminishes as the action goes on, the capillarity will tend to increase the action.' Cf. also Liveing, *Proc. Camb. Phil. Soc.*, **6**, 66 (1887); Liebreich, *Naturwiss. Rundschau*, **1**, 405 (1886).

dissolving carefully neutralized soap in water. A similar phenomenon occurring on charcoal and silica has been termed by Bartell and Miller 'hydrolytic adsorption'. That charcoal (and textile fibres, when dyestuffs are adsorbed) may change the p_H of a solution of an electrolyte from which it adsorbs the solute has long been known.[1] This would mean a preferential adsorption of either anions or cations. A good deal probably depends on the nature and preliminary treatment of the charcoal, but with activated, pure sugar charcoal two rules appear reasonably well established; organic ions or molecules of large size are usually much more strongly adsorbed than inorganic ions, and, for molecules or ions of similar size and constitution, organic acids and anions are usually more easily adsorbed than bases or cations.

Particularly clear results have been obtained by Bartell and E. J. Miller,[2] and Kolthoff.[3] There is some effect on solutions of inorganic salts, but the most striking instances of hydrolytic adsorption were found with salts of organic acids, and in a few cases of organic bases also. The salts of basic dyes became acid in solution owing to adsorption of the large organic base; those of acid dyes became alkaline. Miller[4] showed that the solutions of salts of several simple organic acids become alkaline in the presence of charcoal, and that if the charcoal is then removed and extracted with a neutral, organic solvent, the adsorbed acid is dissolved off in amount quantitatively equivalent to the alkali set free during adsorption in the aqueous solution. The charcoal adsorbs the organic acid, probably in the undissociated form, though it is just possible that some adsorption of the anion also takes place, with the hydrogen ion attracted near the surface as the aqueous half of the double layer. Phelps and Peters[5] find a correlation between the amount of undissociated acid present and the amounts adsorbed, with simple fatty acids, which indicates that the undissociated form is generally adsorbed. They also found that most amino-acids are not adsorbed on charcoal; this may perhaps be due to these acids existing in the 'zwitterionic' form, with both amino and carboxyl groups dissociated. Phelps[6] finds evidence that the unionized form of dibasic acids is the most strongly adsorbed, the singly ionized less so, and the doubly ionized acid is probably not adsorbed at all, on pure charcoal; and further that there are differences between the adsorption of fumaric and maleic acids probably due to stereochemical differences in structure. Propylamine and butylamine are adsorbed only as unionized molecules.[7] These findings are all in accord with the well-established rule that an ion is a very hydrophilic, or water-attracting, group.

[1] Cf. Freundlich and Losev, *Z. physikal. Chem.*, **59**, 284 (1907); Michaelis and Rona, *Biochem. Z.*, **94**, 240; **97**, 57, 85; **103**, 19 (1919–20); Odén and others, *J. Physical Chem.*, **25**, 311, 384 (1921).

[2] *J.A.C.S.* (1922), 1866; (1923), 1106; Miller (1925), 1270.

[3] *Rec. Trav. Chim. Pays-Bas*, **46**, 549 (1927) (further references here).

[4] *J.A.C.S.* (1924), 1150.

[5] *Proc. Roy. Soc.* A, **124**, 554 (1929).

[6] *J.C.S.* (1929), 1724.

[7] *Proc. Roy. Soc.* A, **133**, 155 (1931).

Bartell and Fu[1] find a similar hydrolytic adsorption of organic acids, from their salts, on silica.

The undissociated form of almost any organic electrolyte is more strongly adsorbed at the interface between an aqueous solution and air, or an immiscible organic liquid, than its (organic) ion, which usually differs in constitution only slightly from the undissociated molecule. The cause is again that the ionized group has a much stronger attraction for water than the ionized. In cases such as coloured indicators the shift of equilibrium in the surface caused by the preferential adsorption of the unionized form of the indicator is very beautifully shown by a change in colour. Deutsch[2] has studied this in detail, and showed that if an aqueous solution of a coloured indicator which is an acid, such as thymol sulphone phthalein, adjusted to a p_H slightly on the alkaline side of its usual colour change, is shaken with any immiscible hydrocarbon liquid so as to produce a large interface, the interface becomes strongly coloured with the colour appropriate to the *acid* form of the indicator. Conversely, a basic indicator, such as malachite green, when the p_H is adjusted slightly on the acid side of the range of change of colour in bulk, shows the colour of the *alkaline* form of the indicator when a large amount of interface is produced in the solution. The colour change in the interface may be equivalent to that produced in bulk by a shift of 1 to 1·5 units of p_H. The explanation is quite simple: with the acid indicators the colour shown on the acid side is that due to the unionized form of the indicator, and therefore it is this colour which tends to appear in the interface; with basic indicators the unionized form, that predominant in the interface, is the 'alkaline' colour.

Deutsch also showed that an ionizable dye whose undissociated form is soluble in benzene, such as Rhodamine O, assumes the colour of the ionized form at the interface with water, when a benzene solution of the undissociated dye is shaken with water. Similar changes of colour may occur on glass or silica, cellulose, or on any solid surface; Fajans[3] has suggested that deformation of the adsorbed molecules may sometimes be responsible for the colour change.

The preferential adsorption of one or other constituent of an equilibrium mixture, at an interface, requires that the equilibrium constant in the surface should be different from that in the interior. This may be of great importance in biology. For instance, the p_H of an interface may be as much as two or three units different from that of a bulk phase in equilibrium with it.

The influence of the *charge* of a surface on its adsorption may be very important. In general, a positively charged surface adsorbs negatively charged ions preferentially, and vice versa.[4] Hartley[5] has recently shown

[1] *J. Physical Chem.*, **33**, 682 (1929). [2] *Z. physikal. Chem.*, **136**, 353 (1928).
[3] *Z. Elektrochem.*, **29**, 495 (1923); *Z. anorg. Chem.*, **137**, 221 (1924).
[4] Cf. Freundlich, *Kapillarchemie*, **1**, 304 (1930).
[5] *Trans. Faraday Soc.*, **30**, 444 (1934).

how such effects may seriously affect the use of indicators in solutions of colloidal electrolytes, where the ionic micelles, or aggregated ions of long-chain salts, behave as if they had a very highly charged surface. If the micelles are composed of aggregated anions, carrying therefore a negative charge, the equilibrium of the indicator in the solution is shifted so that more of the positively charged form of the indicator, or less of the negatively, is present; ionic micelles composed of cations have the opposite effect.

The specific constitution of the surface may also be important. B. A. Adams and E. L. Holmes[1] have shown that synthetic resins formed from phenols, while they have a general tendency to adsorb cations on account of their acidic properties, show considerable specific differences according to the nature of the phenols used; resins made from aromatic bases adsorb anions preferentially. These adsorptive properties probably have important technical applications, e.g. to water purification. The varying adsorptive powers of all sorts of solids furnish a valuable means of separating mixtures of complex organic compounds as well as inorganic ions. These have been of the greatest use in separating biochemically important substances, especially enzymes and pigments. The use of adsorbents for such separations is quite old. Danilewski[2] in 1862 separated amylase from trypsin, in pancreatic juice, by adsorption on freshly precipitated collodion; in more recent times the voluminous hydroxides of iron and aluminium, also kaolin and charcoal, have proved of very great service in fractionating enzymes.[3] For dealing with plant or animal colouring materials the method known as 'chromatographic analysis' is now standard technique; the mixed colours are passed in solution through a porous column of the adsorbent, which acquires a scale of colours as the different pigments are adsorbed at different rates; the column is subsequently cut up according to colour and the colours washed off by appropriate reagents. The method has been extended to colourless substances by Karrer and Schöpp,[4] by using ultra-violet light; they have employed solid carbon dioxide as the adsorbent, which disposes of the problem of liberation of the adsorbed substances later in a remarkably simple manner, for the adsorbent evaporates completely when allowed to warm up! Tswett[5] was one of the first to use selective adsorption, for separating chlorophylls; its use is described by Zechmeister, Winterstein, and others.[6]

This subject really belongs to Chapter VII; there is not yet much systematic information as to the relation between the constitution of the

[1] *J.S.C.I.*, **54**, 1T (1935).

[2] *Arch. Path. Anat. Physiol.* (Virchow's), **25**, 285.

[3] Cf. Haldane, *Enzymes*, 170 ff. (1930).

[4] *Helv. Chim. Acta*, **17**, 693 (1934).

[5] *Ber. deut. bot. Ges.*, **24**, 316, 384 (1906).

[6] Cf. Palmer, *Carotenoids and Related Pigments* (Chem. Catalog Co.); Zechmeister, *Carotenoide* (Springer), 1934; Winterstein, Klein's *Handb. d. Pflanzenanalyse*, **4** 1403 (1933); Winterstein and Stein, *Z. physiol. Chem.*, **220**, 247 (1933); cf. Ruggli and others, *Helv. Chim. Acta*, **18**, 624 (1935); *Chim. et Ind.*, **33**, 1072 (1935).

adsorbing surfaces and the substances adsorbed, but it will be seen there that different faces of a crystal may have quite different, and specific, adsorbing capacities.

The specific differences in ease of adsorption between oppositely charged ions has already been seen to be an important factor in the potential difference across the boundary between two phases; we have seen that chemical equilibria of many kinds may be drastically changed at surfaces, and it may be no exaggeration to say that selective adsorption of the various constituents of a solution may be a controlling factor in a great variety of natural processes, for the power of regulating concentrations confers also the power of influencing the rate of chemical reactions. At liquid surfaces this power is not fully developed; but in Chapter VII we shall see instances of the enormous power of surfaces in modifying, and even initiating, chemical reactions.

14. Stability of isolated liquid films; soap films; foams. Pure liquids rarely, if ever, foam, but most solutions of capillary active substances do so to a greater or less extent, and long-chain colloidal electrolytes, particularly the soaps, have an almost miraculous power of rendering liquid films stable. Dewar[1] has maintained soap films unbroken for over a year (one for three years!), with due precautions against evaporation, mechanical and thermal shocks, and absorption of carbon dioxide.

A foam, or an isolated film or lamina[2] of liquid, naturally tends to contract by virtue of its surface tension, and a low surface tension might be expected to be a necessary accompaniment of good foam-forming qualities. Low surface tension is not, however, the main requisite; a much more important factor in the stability of a film of liquid is that the solution of which it is composed should have a surface tension easily, and quickly, variable. Gibbs[3] described this quality as an 'elasticity' of the film. To meet mechanical shocks, which will generally (owing to the flexibility of the film) be in effect extensions or contractions, more or less localized, the film must be able to respond to a local extension by a rise, and to local contraction by a fall of surface tension, the change in tension being of sufficient duration to outlast small sudden disturbances. To meet permanent differences of stress in different parts of the film, the film must be able to maintain slight differences of tension in its different parts. Clearly a pure liquid, whose tension is constant, cannot do this; but many solutions of capillary active substances can. The most stable bubbles or foams are usually (not always) obtained where the surface tension is varying rapidly with concentration, not where the tension has reached the minimum.

Methods for the study of the stability of liquid films are semi-quantitative at present; the two commonest are (*a*) Hardy's method of timing single bubbles

[1] *Proc. Roy. Inst.*, **22**, 179, 359; **24**, 197 (1917–23).

[2] The term 'lamina' will sometimes be used in order to avoid confusion with the monomolecular surface films which are so important for the stability of isolated liquid films.

[3] *Works*, **1**, 300 ff.

which rise to a free surface of the liquid; the bubbles form a thin lamina of the liquid over their surface at the top of the liquid, and the time which elapses between the arrival of the bubble at the surface and its bursting is taken as a measure of the stability of the film; (b) forming a foam by a standard process of shaking, usually in a closed vessel, and observing the time taken for this foam to disappear after the shaking ceases. Hardy's experiments[1] were mostly on the duration of bubbles at surfaces of water covered by insoluble monomolecular films; working with coherent films, generally of the liquid-expanded type, he found that the bubbles burst instantly at areas per molecule greater than the limiting area of the film, i.e. if the surface was not completely covered, so that there was an appreciable surface pressure, the film had no effect in increasing the stability. As soon as the area was diminished sufficiently for the surface pressure to reach a very few dynes per cm., the stability had increased to a maximum; further compression of the film resulted in a steady decrease in the stability of bubbles, until when the film was so much compressed that the molecules must have been standing nearly upright, the stability of the bubbles had returned to a small value, only slightly above that on the pure water surface.[2]

Those who have studied the stability of masses of foam on solutions of surface-active substances find rather different results according to whether evaporation can, or cannot, take place. Bartsch[3] examined the durability of foams on an extensive range of solutions, in closed cylinders, where the air space was saturated with water vapour; the maximum of stability occurred at concentrations where there was some depression of surface tension, but far below those at which the maximum depression of tension was obtained. With moderately surface-active substances such as amyl alcohol, the maximum stability of the foams occurred at a reduction of tension roughly 12 dynes per cm.; naturally the bulk concentration required to reach this varied with the length of hydrocarbon chain in the compound, but it was always only a small fraction of saturation. The stability of the foams rose very rapidly, as the bulk concentration increased from zero up to that at which the maximum fall of tension was obtained;

[1] *Proc. Roy. Soc.* A, **86**, 627 (1912).

[2] Talmud and Suchowolskaja (*Z. physikal. Chem.*, **154**, 277 (1931)) record numerous, but rather puzzling, observations on the effect of the closeness of packing in an insoluble monomolecular film on water on the stability of bubbles. They found a maximum similar to Hardy's, but if the areas per molecule in the surface films are calculated from their results, it appears in nearly every case that the maximum of stability was obtained at an area greater than the maximum which the coherent films can occupy; these areas were, for palmitic acid, 54 sq. A.; for stearic acid, 32·5; oleic acid, 61; cetyl alcohol, 26; ethyl oleate, 185 sq. A. per molecule. The surface pressure, and the variation of surface tension with area per molecule in the film, ought to have been practically nothing at these areas, the films being two-phase systems of islands of coherent film in equilibrium with very dilute vapour films, except possibly in the case of ethyl oleate, which is probably a vapour-expanded film. It seems so unlikely that the maximum of stability would be obtained without any lowering of tension at all or complete covering of the surface with a film, that confirmation of these areas seems desirable.

[3] *Kolloid-Beih.*, **20**, 1 (1924).

it fell off rather less rapidly with further increase of concentration. The relation between surface pressure and stability was much the same as in Hardy's work on insoluble monomolecular films on water. Talmud and Suchowolskaja found that the maximum stability of bubbles and foams, formed on solutions from which evaporation could take place freely, occurred at much greater concentrations, sometimes no sharp maximum being obtained. These results have not been fully explained.[1] It is probable that, with solutions of organic substances of moderate molecular weight whose foam-forming properties are fairly good, the maximum stability of the foams occurs at concentrations where the surface layer is not over half to two-thirds saturated, and there is a rapid variation of surface tension with changes of concentration.

With soap solutions, however, exceedingly stable foams and isolated films are obtained at concentrations high enough for the surface tension to have fallen practically to the minimum obtainable. Nevertheless, owing to the slow diffusion of soaps, there is probably a considerable temporary increase in surface tension if the surface is locally stretched; the molecules in the surface move apart somewhat, and the gaps in the surface layer are filled first by water molecules, which come to the surface much more rapidly than more soap, from the interior, and these of course increase the free energy of the surface. Similarly, a local contraction crowds the soap molecules in the surface layer together, so that there is a strong resistance to the mechanical disturbance, as the soap molecules can escape but slowly into the interior of the film. Probably the speed with which the adsorbed molecules can diffuse from interior to surface, or vice versa, is of considerable importance for the stability of a liquid film.

Soap films, when first formed, are usually too thick to show interference colours. They rapidly thin through some of the liquid draining away, either to form drops adhering to the lower edge, or to accumulate in a thick ridge at the junction of the film with its supports. The progress of thinning is shown by the development of interference colours; and the final stages are the well-known 'black' films. The thinning of soap films has been very extensively studied by Plateau,[2] Boys,[3] Reinold and Rucker,[4] Johonnot,[5] Perrin,[6] Wells,[7] Dewar,[8] Lawrence,[9] and others. There are five stages of black films, the thickness being from one to five multiples of the unit, finally formed black film. The thickness of this unit

[1] Theories purporting to explain the results as due to more or less 'hydration' of certain parts of the molecules do not seem to clarify the situation much; the word 'hydration' is all too frequently employed so vaguely by writers on colloids that its use increases, rather than relieves, the mystery!

[2] *Statique Experimentale, &c., des Liquides* (1873), vol. 2.

[3] *Soap Bubbles, and the forces which mould them* (S.P.C.K., 1890).

[4] *Phil. Trans.*, **172**, 447 (1881); **174**, 645 (1883); **177**, 627 (1886); **184**, 505 (1893).

[5] *Phil. Mag.*, **47**, 501 (1899); **11**, 746 (1906).

[6] *Ann. de Physique*, **10**, **160** (1918).

[7] *Ibid.*, **16**, 69 (1921).

[8] *Loc. cit.*

[9] *Soap Films* (Bell, 1929).

film is about 50 A.; Perrin gave it as 54, Wells as 42, and previous workers' measurements average about 50 A. In all probability it consists of two monomolecular layers of soap molecules, one on each face of the film, with the water-attracting groups in the centre, these groups approaching so close that there is a fairly strong adhesion between the molecules forming the monomolecular layers on the two faces of the film. The amount of water in the unit film is unknown, but there must be a fair amount present, and its amount must be of importance, since evaporation must be prevented if films are to be kept a long time. The most stable soap films contain a high proportion of glycerine, whose function may be to retard draining by increasing the viscosity, or to increase the resistance to shocks. Perrin showed that if a small amount of a fluorescent dye is added to the solution, thinning takes place discontinuously in a series of steps, right up to thicknesses many times the unit black film, comprising several orders of colour. He says that the general appearance is like what would be obtained 'by superposition of extremely thin, transparent leaflets, with rigorously parallel faces, cut out with a punch'. And the thickness of each of the superposed leaflets appears to be exactly the same. This stratification is stimulated, in some unknown way, by absorption of light by the fluorescent dye; it does not occur so easily in the dark, nor if the light which falls on the film has previously passed through a layer of the same dye sufficiently thick for much absorption of the rays which excite the dye to have taken place. It seems possible that the reason for the extraordinary stability of these bimolecular leaflets of soap solution is the attraction between the water-soluble groups on the monomolecular layers belonging to opposite faces of the film; and presumably the fluorescent dye acts by activating the combination between adjacent groups; but the mechanism is not understood.

When stratification occurs, liquid is squeezed out; this is probably water, or a very much more dilute solution than that remaining in the film. Droplets lying on the films, even on the thinnest black film, are generally in Brownian motion if small enough, showing that the monomolecular layers at the surface are liquid in character. The surface of a soap film may become solid, if instead of oleates, which are generally used for the most permanent soap films, stearates or soaps from other saturated acids are employed: and in this case draining is retarded. Woog[1] found that, under rather rough conditions, foams made from stearates last longer than those from oleates; but Dewar's soap films, which lasted phenomenally long, were made of oleate and glycerine solution.

The exact state of the monomolecular layers on the two faces of soap films is unknown, but would almost certainly be, on bulk solutions of the same concentration, a very highly compressed gaseous film. Possibly the attraction between the molecules on opposite faces of the films exercises some restraint on the motions in the surface layers; but it is usually insufficient to solidify the films.

[1] *Graissage, Onctuosité, Influences Moléculaires* (1926), 103 ff.

Naturally, other paraffin-chain salts with one water-soluble end group also form fairly stable films and foams. Proteins, saponins, gamboge, resinates are also capable of forming stable foams; the two last named were found by Perrin to form stratified films, just like the stratified soap films.

The composition of the soap solution used has a great influence on the stability and properties of the films. For good results very highly purified oleic acid must be used; and the best results cannot apparently be obtained without the use of a trace of ammonia or an amine. Excess of alkali is said to be fatal; this points to the hydrolytic equilibrium between acid and neutral soap being of great importance. A 5 per cent. solution of ammonium oleate in 50 per cent. glycerine makes a good solution for ordinary work; details of this may be found in Lawrence's *Soap Films*. Perrin, however, used a $2\frac{1}{2}$ per cent. solution of 'ordinary soap'.

A most ingenious use for soap films has been discovered by Griffith and Taylor.[1] The equations representing the deformation under torsion of an elastic, solid bar of any cross-section are of the same form as those for the displacement of a soap film stretched over a hole in a flat plate, the hole being of the same shape as the section of the bar. The mathematical solution of these equations may be difficult, but it is easy to measure the displacement of the soap film; hence by forming a soap film on a box, in the lid of which is a hole of the same shape as the bar, and measuring the contour lines of the film when pressure is applied inside the box, by means of a spherometer, the effect of torsional stress on bars of the most complicated section may be ascertained.

In technical practice foams are often a nuisance, particularly in the evaporation of liquids in boilers. When, however (as in fire-fighting), it may be desired to cover a large area semi-permanently with liquid, foams are used. The 'froth flotation' process for the separation of minerals requires a great volume of foam (see Chap. V); here the powdered mineral itself greatly aids the stability of the foam. As soap solutions possess such an exceptional foaming power, it is often thought that foaming power is an essential for good detergent action; this is certainly not the case, however; the detergent action and the foaming power both arise from the surface activity of the substances used, but do not appear to be quantitatively correlated. Some paraffin-chain salts show better detergent action than soaps, but do not froth nearly as much.

Boilers usually 'prime', i.e. carry water over in large amounts with the steam, when the amount of salt in the water exceeds a definite quantity. This is probably associated with foaming inside the boiler. The cause may be that the films of liquid over the bursting bubbles of steam, which are evaporating rapidly, begin to crystallize out, and the particles of solid in the film naturally tend to hinder its collapse and so to prolong the life of the bursting bubbles and promote foaming.

15. The role of surface films in emulsification.* Emulsions, or dispersions of one liquid in another, are of two types. One consists of a very dilute dispersion of small droplets of oil in water, in the stabilization

* See also Appendix.

[1] *Proc. Inst. Mech. Eng.*, Dec. 1917.

of which the electric charges at the surface appear of primary importance, and surface films of less importance; these are well described in Clayton's *Emulsions and their Technical Treatment*, chap. i (3rd ed., 1935). These approach more nearly to the lyophobic than to the lyophilic type of colloid; they are of technical importance in connexion with oil in condensed water, which may subsequently give trouble if used in the boilers.

The more common type of emulsion depends largely for its stability on the nature of the interfacial film, generally of a third substance different from either phase, but slightly soluble in one of them, present between the two liquids when one is dispersed in the other. One of the principal functions of the interfacial film is to decrease the interfacial tension, by increasing the adhesion between the two phases, and thus lowering the amount of work that must be done in creating the (often very large) area of interface between the liquids, as one is dispersed in the other.

Donnan[1] showed that the interfacial tension against water, of hydrocarbon liquids and glycerides, is very much diminished if there is acid in the oil and alkali in the water. Hartridge and Peters (see § 12) found that this fall in interfacial tension is a function of the hydrogen-ion concentration of the water, commencing at a p_H of about 4·5 and continuing up to about 10. Danielli[2] concluded that there is a slightly different p_H in the surface film from that in the bulk of the aqueous solution, and Harkins and Zollmann[3] found that the interfacial tension (like the air-water tension of these solutions, § 8) takes time to reach its final value, especially in dilute solutions. Even quite small concentrations of suitable paraffin-chain salts will lower the interfacial tension to a fraction of 1 dyne per cm., and at this point a very small amount of stirring causes emulsification; indeed emulsification may even take place spontaneously without any deliberate agitation.[4] When the interfacial tension falls below 5 or 10 dynes per cm. emulsions can be formed by shaking.

Polyvalent ions have very large and striking effects on the interfacial tension between dilute solutions of paraffin-chain salts and oils.[5] With a pure mineral oil and a 0·005 per cent. paraffin-chain salt solution ('Igepon T'), whose end group consists of a sulphonated and substituted amide group, and forms paraffin-chain anions, in the absence of salt the tension was 11 dynes per cm. Sodium chloride lowered the tension rather gradually; calcium chloride rapidly, down to 0·8 dynes at N/400; while the trivalent lanthanum chloride reduced the interfacial tension to only 0·25 dynes at N/10,000, the concentration of the paraffin-chain salt remaining constant throughout. The valency of the ion of opposite charge to the long-chain ions of the paraffin-chain salt is thus of very great importance, in increasing the effectiveness of the long paraffin-chain ion in lowering the interfacial tension.

[1] *Z. physikal. Chem.*, **31**, 43 (1899).
[2] *Proc. Roy. Soc.* B, **122**, 155 (1937).
[3] *J.A.C.S.* (1926), 69.
[4] Cf. McBain and Ts-Ming Woo, *Proc. Roy. Soc.*, A, **163**, 182 (1937), and references therein.
[5] C. Robinson, *Symposium on Wetting and Detergency*, p. 144 (London, 1937).

While a low interfacial tension is one of the most important factors promoting easy emulsification and stability of the emulsion, it is probably by no means the only factor. A good deal probably depends on the mechanical qualities of the interfacial film, whether it is mobile or rigid. Among the best emulsifiers are the natural, complex, colloidal compounds, particularly proteins such as gelatine, which have a strong tendency to form semi-solid structures in liquids, causing 'structural viscosity' (a variation of the observed viscosity with the rate of shear applied to the liquid), or even gelation. These substances are generally strongly adsorbed at surfaces;[1] they diffuse slowly and therefore tend to remain at the surface during sudden changes of form, and to set up changes of tension similar to those caused by soap in stabilizing isolated films of liquid. They also show viscous, almost elastic properties at surfaces (cf. Chap. II, § 28). Hence they tend to remain in any interface and to resist changes in its form, and thus stabilize the emulsions by resisting any diminution in, or even any deformation of, the interface between the two liquids. Their impartation of some degree of structure to the aqueous phase may also help to stabilize the cushion of water between two oil drops in contact, and thus delay, or prevent, their coalescence.

Harkins and others[2] have measured, simultaneously, the number of drops of different sizes, and the amount of soap adsorbed at the interface, in emulsions stabilized by soaps, thus finding the area per molecule in the interfacial film. The most interesting fact was that, if the soap solutions are dilute, the emulsions can be stabilized for some time by interfacial films with only one soap molecule in an area of the order 50 sq. A., and sometimes the films are even more sparsely occupied by molecules. These emulsions, however, gradually change until, after some ten days' standing, the area of the interface between the liquids has diminished so that the soap molecules are closely packed, with an area of the order 20 sq. A. per molecule. When this stage is reached the emulsions remain stable with very little further change for many months. Whether or not these interfacial films are strictly similar to the condensed films at an air-liquid surface seems doubtful, since the lateral adhesion between the long chains of oleate ions, particularly when these are immersed in an oil, will probably be insufficient to keep the films coherent; but it does seem that the area of interface can diminish until the soap molecules are so closely packed that there is a considerable lateral compression in the interfacial films, and then further breaking of the emulsion is almost prevented.

The reason why a closely packed film of stabilizer, such as soap, is more effective than a loosely packed one, is probably simply that when the packing is loose, the molecules may be pushed out of the way, away from the parts of the surfaces of two droplets which approach nearest when two molecules are about to collide. Assuming, as is probably the case, at

[1] Cf. du Nouy, *Surface Equilibria of Colloids* (Chem. Catalog Co., 1926).
[2] *J.A.C.S.* (1929), 1674; *J. Physical Chem.*, **36**, 98 (1932).

any rate with the paraffin-chain salts (including soaps), that the electric charges in the interface due to the paraffin-chain ions aid stability by electrostatic repulsion between approaching droplets, Rideal[1] and Conmar Robinson[2] have shown that a tightly packed film should be better than a dilute film. The argument need not, however, be confined to the stability arising from electrical charging at the interface.

Harkins's results appear to show that the stabilizing film of soap is never thicker than monomolecular.

The size distribution curve of the droplets in the emulsions varied little if soaps of sodium, potassium, or caesium were used. As a rule the curves had a marked peak, at a diameter of about 2μ, which apparently depended little on the manner of preparation of the emulsion, and slightly on the nature of the oil. Emulsions of water in oil, stabilized by magnesium or aluminium soaps, had a similar distribution of sizes among the droplets.

The scientific study of emulsions would seem to involve, of necessity, a thorough study of the size distribution among the droplets and its dependence on other factors, and it is to be hoped that more workers will follow Harkins's example in carrying out these essential measurements. One difficulty in the study of emulsions is that it does not even yet appear certain how far they are in a state of true, or apparent, equilibrium. Hardy, however, records[3] a very interesting case of an emulsion of oil, in which the droplets, if left to themselves, always settled down to a diameter of 3 mm.; violent shaking would break them up, but on standing they always reverted to this large size. As a rule, however, stable emulsions have very much smaller droplets, of the order a few μ across.

A more mysterious phenomenon, probably due to the interfacial film, is the 'inversion' of emulsions. Sometimes one liquid, sometimes the other, is the 'internal' phase, i.e. is dispersed as separate droplets in a continuous, 'external' phase of the other. The reasons for this are as yet imperfectly understood. It was suggested at one time that the relative volume of the two liquids might be the deciding factor; it is possible to pack rigid spheres, as Wa. Ostwald pointed out,[4] to fill 74 per cent. of the available space, and it might be expected that if the volume of one liquid exceeded 74 per cent. of the whole volume, this liquid must become the external, continuous phase. That this is not so is probable from Pickering's preparation of emulsions of paraffin oil,[5] containing about 99 per cent. of oil in separate droplets, with 1 per cent. of water as a continuous phase enclosing them. Such emulsions, stabilized with soap, are quite stable; they are fairly rigid. The reason why this 'phase-volume' theory as to which liquid forms the internal phase is not wholly true is partly that the drops

[1] *Surface Chemistry* (1930), p. 384. [2] *Trans. Faraday Soc.*, **32**, 1426 (1936).

[3] *6th Colloid Symposium Monograph*, 8 (1928).

[4] *Kolloid-Z.*, **6**, 103; **7**, 64 (1910).

[5] *J.C.S.* (1907), 2001; A. S. C. Lawrence points out, however, that some of the oil may have been actually dissolved in the interior of the soap micelles (*Trans. Faraday Soc.*, **33**, 815 (1937)).

of liquid are deformable; but the conditions at the interface are probably the determining conditions.

Nevertheless there is some tendency for either breaking of an emulsion or inversion to occur if the amount of liquid originally present as separate globules is much increased.[1]

There is no difficulty in testing whether a given emulsion is of the oil-in-water or water-in-oil type. Three methods are available: the oil-in-water type has a much higher electrical conductivity than the inverted type, because the conducting phase is the continuous one; the oil-in-water type mixes easily with a drop of water, but not with oil, while the water-in-oil type mixes with oil, not water; and the oil-in-water type is easily stained with water-soluble dyes, the other type being stained by oil-soluble dyes such as Scharlach R or Sudan III.

If soaps are used as emulsifiers, the nature of the cations present at the interface is most important. Newman[2] showed that while sodium oleate as emulsifier always forms an emulsion of oil dispersed in water, magnesium oleate disperses water in oil, and other divalent soaps have the same effect. Briggs and Schmidt[3] confirmed this, and Clowes[4] showed that as the proportion of divalent to monovalent ions is increased, there comes a critical ratio at which neither the oil-in-water nor the water-in-oil emulsion is stable; as this critical point is passed, inversion of the type of the emulsion takes place. Bhatnagar[5] and Parsons and Wilson[6] have studied this inversion by the antagonistic action of ions (which is very much like the antagonistic action of ions on living tissues) more closely. The ratio, not the absolute quantities, of the mono- and divalent ions is the more important matter, although there seems to be some variation with the dilution of the solutions of the soap or ions.

The inversion of emulsions is probably of great importance in biology; and it may be that the well-known need for the correct balance of mono- and divalent cations, in preserving a suitable environment for many biological activities, is connected with similar phenomena within the cells.

At one time a very attractive theory of the inversion of emulsions, called the 'oriented-wedge' theory, was rather generally accepted. Starting from the fact that the soaps of divalent metals usually form water-in-oil emulsions, while those of monovalent metals form oil-in-water emulsions, it was suggested[7] that, since in the divalent soaps there are two hydrocarbon chains attached to one metal atom, while in the monovalent there is only one chain, the molecules of these soaps are wedge-shaped, being wider at the water-soluble end in the case of the monovalent soaps, and at the oil-soluble end with the di- and trivalent soaps. A closely packed layer of these molecules would therefore naturally curve with the concave side towards the oil in the case of the monovalent soaps, with the convex side towards the oil in the case of the divalent soaps; thus the

[1] Cf. Parke, *J.C.S.* (1933), 1458; (1934), 1112.

[2] *J. Physical Chem.*, **18**, 34 (1914). [3] *Ibid.*, **19**, 478 (1915).

[4] *Ibid.*, **20**, 407 (1916). [5] *J.C.S.* (1920), 542; (1921), 61, 1760.

[6] *Ind. Eng. Chem.*, **13**, 1116 (1921).

[7] Harkins, Davies, and Clark, *J.A.C.S.* (1917), 595; cf. Finkle, Draper, and Hildebrand, *ibid.* (1923), 2780.

water phase would be the internal phase, as this has the curvature convex outwards, if divalent soaps are used as stabilizers.

Unfortunately this theory, in its original simple form at any rate, does not seem tenable, for several reasons. First, it requires the soap molecules to be closely packed in the interface; this does not appear always to be the case; second, it requires that the metallic ions should be rigidly attached to the hydrocarbon chains, which is not possible as they are, at any rate in the case of the soaps of the alkali metals, dissociated. Finally, unless the taper of the molecules, from one end to the other, were excessively small, the radius of curvature imposed by the interfacial film on the droplets should be comparable with the length of the soap molecules, and the only really stable sizes of droplets in emulsions should be of the order perhaps 100 A. in diameter. Actually, the droplets are generally about a hundred times larger than this.

Powdered solids are very useful emulsifiers, and are frequently used, and it is found that emulsions of either the oil-in-water or the water-in-oil type can be stabilized by them. Here it has been shown (Chap. V, § 21) that the liquid which forms the internal phase in the emulsion is the one which wets the solid least; this is very easily understood in terms of the contact angle formed by the liquid interface with the solid surface, and the theory is easy.

It appears probable that much the same holds also with the soluble emulsifiers; e.g. gelatine, a water-soluble substance, tends to form oil-in-water emulsions, while rosin soaps (soluble in oil) form emulsions of the opposite type.[1] Though the actual mechanism in terms of molecules is rather difficult to understand, the rule is correct for the soaps, for the soaps of polyvalent metals are soluble in oil, those of monovalent metals are soluble in water. Tartar and others,[2] in studies which have brought to light some rather complicated cases of the inversion of emulsions, show that emulsions stabilized by monovalent soaps may be inverted to the water-in-oil type by adding sufficient sodium chloride, especially if the soaps used were originally rather difficult to dissolve in water; here the agency which lowers the solubility of the soap in the water tends to produce the water-in-oil type. Conversely, raising the temperature promotes the oil-in-water type, the solubility of the soaps in the water being increased. Finally, adding oleic acid to the hydrocarbon promoted the water-in-oil type.

One might perhaps retain a part of the oriented-wedge theory to explain the different solubility of the monovalent and the polyvalent soaps. If the molecules are wedge-shaped, with the hydrocarbon ends the thicker, then they will naturally pack into a micelle, or aggregate, with the hydrocarbon ends outwards and the water-soluble groups in the centre. Then the soap should be soluble in oils, not in water, as is actually the case with the polyvalent soaps. But if the water-soluble end is the wider, the micelle should have the water-soluble ends of the molecules outwards, and be itself soluble in water, as is the case with the monovalent soaps.

[1] Cf. Freundlich, *Kapillarchemie*, **2**, 500 (1932).

[2] *J. Physical Chem.* **(1929)**, **435**; (1930), 373.

Seifriz[1] has produced some very interesting multiple emulsions, in which the drops of the dispersed liquid are themselves an emulsion, containing the other phase as smaller droplets inside them. In one case this multiplying process had proceeded so far that there were five kinds of drops each inside the other, three of oil and two of water! Such complex phenomena may require the presence of two different emulsifying agents.

It will be seen that the scientific understanding of the mechanism of emulsification has not yet proceeded very far. The reader can gain from Clayton's *Emulsions* some idea of the great complexity of the phenomena.

Schulman and Cockbain (see Appendix) have recently put forward a new theory of emulsion stability and inversion.

[1] *Amer. J. Physiol.*, **66**, 124 (1923); *J. Physical Chem.*, **29**, 738 (1925).

Page 153, *note* 1. *Int. Critical Tables*, **4**, 434 (1928). The surface tension of 'heavy' water, according to most observers, differs very little from that of ordinary water (see *Ann. Rep. Chem. Soc.* (1937), 36); but Cockett and Ferguson (*Phil. Mag.*, **28**, 685 (1939)) report that over a long range of temperature it is roughly one dyne per centimetre lower.

Liquid helium suffers no obvious change in surface tension at the transition (λ) point (J. F. Allen and A. D. Misener, *Proc. Camb. Phil. Soc.*, **34**, 299 (1938)).

CHAPTER IV

RESULTS OF THE MEASUREMENT OF SURFACE TENSION

IN this chapter attention will be directed to the conclusions which can be drawn as to the molecular structure of liquids, from the measurement of surface tension. No attempt will be made to tabulate the great amount of accurate data now available on surface tension; this task has already been performed by Harkins and Young,[1] by Bakker,[2] and by many others.

1. Disorienting effect of the molecular motions. The molecules in liquids are in constant violent translatory and rotatory motion. It is true that there are nearly always forces at the surface, tending to orient molecules whose chemical constitution renders their fields of force unsymmetrical, in some definite position on the surface; but in liquids this orientation is rarely perfect, as the molecular motions mix up the molecules at a rate comparable with their rate of orientation. In discussions of the orientation of molecules at the surfaces of liquids misunderstandings have sometimes arisen, because the problem was treated as if the molecules were stationary and the orientation fixed and definite.[3]

2. The work of adhesion between two liquids; orientation at liquid-liquid interfaces. Much the clearest conclusions at present available as to the structure of the surfaces of liquids (except those covered by films of another substance) concern the interface between two liquids. They have been obtained by considering the work of adhesion between the liquids, or the perpendicular attraction across the interface. This work of adhesion can be ascertained by measurement of the surface tensions of the two liquids separately, and of the interfacial tension between them, and applying Dupré's equation (Chap. I, § 8):

$$W_{AB} = \gamma_A + \gamma_B - \gamma_{AB}.$$

Hardy[4] found that the value of the adhesion of a number of organic liquids to water was almost entirely determined by the active, water-attracting groups in the molecule. For the aliphatic hydrocarbons it was small, about 45 ergs per sq. cm.; for the cyclic hydrocarbons it was slightly larger; but for the fatty acids and alcohols containing a COOH or OH group at the end of the molecule, it was much larger, about 95. The molecular weight had practically no influence on the value of W_{AB}. From this

[1] See note at foot of page opposite (p. 152).
[2] *Kapillarität u. Oberflächenspannung*, chap. vii (1928).
[3] Cf. Sugden, *Trans. Faraday Soc.*, **22**, 488 (1926).
[4] *Proc. Roy. Soc.* A, **88**, 311 (1913).

he concluded that the active, water-attracting group of the alcohols and acids was oriented towards the water, so that the interface consisted largely, or entirely, of these active groups on one side and of water on the other.

Harkins and his colleagues[1] have extended these measurements of the work of adhesion to water, and also to mercury.[2] The measurements of surface tension were made by the drop-weight method, using the corrections necessary for accurate results; as three separate measurements of surface tension are required, considerable accuracy is desirable for trustworthy results in the work of adhesion.

The results confirm Hardy's general conclusions, although there are minor variations within each class of compound; there is sometimes a fall of 10 or 20 per cent. in the case of compounds with a specific water-attracting group, as the molecular weight increases from the shortest chain compounds up to long-chain compounds. The work of adhesion increases, however, with the paraffins, as the molecular weight increases.

TABLE VII

Work of Adhesion to Water

	Ergs per sq. cm.
Paraffins	36 to 48
Aromatic hydrocarbons . . .	63 to 67
Halogen derivatives	66 to 84
Nitriles	*c.* 90
Esters	*c.* 75
Primary alcohols	92 to 97
Acids	90 to 100

Clearly the oxygen-containing groups, and the CN group in the nitriles, provide the main part of the adhesion between the organic liquids and water; this must mean a specific attraction between these groups and the water, and the fact that the influence of the constitution of the rest of the molecule is so small indicates a tendency of these water-attracting groups to fill the layer next to the water—that is, to be orientated to the water. But it cannot be concluded that the orientation is complete and the molecules are stationary in this position; the experimental results would be equally well accounted for if the molecules near the interface were in motion but under the influence of forces which cause the water-attracting groups to be directed towards the water for a decidedly larger fraction of the time, than in the case of molecules in the interior of the liquids. The results also indicate that the partially unsaturated aromatic nucleus attracts water more than paraffin chains.

[1] *J.A.C.S.* (1917), 356; (1920), 702.

[2] *Ibid.* (1920), 2543; the electrical potential difference between the mercury and the other liquid was not controlled, which may render the results somewhat uncertain (see Chap. VIII, § 7).

A similar set of measurements, though less complete, have been made on mercury, and it is clear that a different set of groups tend to be oriented to mercury.

TABLE VIII

Work of Adhesion to Mercury

	Ergs per sq. cm.
Paraffins	c. 120
Aromatic hydrocarbons	c. 150
Alcohols	c. 150
Acids	c. 160
Halogen derivatives	c. 200

Here the oxygen-containing groups do not produce a very marked increase in the adhesion, but the halogens obviously attract the mercury strongly.

A further hint that the orientation in these liquid liquid interfaces is incomplete may be obtained by comparing the values of the adhesion between the liquid acids and alcohols in Table VII with those for the solid members of the same series (Chap. V, § 6). When the solid surface is formed by cutting across the sheets of molecules, the adhesion is about 120 ergs per sq. cm.; yet it is nearly certain that the molecules are so oriented that only a small proportion of the surface consists of water attracting OH or COOH groups; there are probably at least a dozen CH_2 groups for each OH or COOH. The adhesion between the liquid acids or alcohols and water is roughly 25 per cent. smaller than this, so that it is unlikely that the interface consists solely of molecules with their OH or COOH groups directed to the water.

There must, however, be some tendency to orientation, for the approximate constancy of the adhesion within each group points to the water-soluble group spending nearly the same fraction of the time in contact with the water in the long- as in the short-chain members of each series.

3. The free surface of pure liquids. There is some evidence in favour of a tendency for the hydrocarbon ends of molecules to be oriented outwards when one end of the molecule is hydrocarbon in character and the other has a greater residual affinity.[1] The most direct evidence is gained by comparing the work of cohesion, or twice the surface tension (Chap. I, § 8), of compounds of related constitution with their work of adhesion to water. The surface tension is half the work that must be done in order to pull apart a bar of the liquid of 1 sq. cm. cross-section, for 2 sq. cm. of fresh surface are formed in this operation. The work of cohesion therefore measures the intensity of the attraction between two free surfaces of the same liquid about to come into contact.

[1] These ideas were put forward first by Langmuir (*Met. Chem. Eng.*, **15**, 468 (1916), and *J.A.C.S.* (1917), 1848) and Harkins (*J.A.C.S.* (1917), 354, 541).

The following data, from Harkins, Clark and Roberts,[1] are significant.

TABLE IX

Comparison of Work of Cohesion with Work of Adhesion to Water, at 20°

	Work of cohesion	*Work of adhesion*
	(Ergs per sq. cm.)	
Paraffins	37–45	36–48
Alcohols	45–50	92–97
Ethyl mercaptan . .	43·6	68·5
Methyl ketones . . .	*c.* 50	85–90
Acids	51–57	90–100
Nitriles	*c.* 55	*c.* 90

The cohesional work varies much less than the adhesional work to water—that is, the attraction of the free surface of a liquid such as an alcohol or acid of medium length of chain for a similar surface is but little greater than the attraction of one purely paraffin surface for another. There can be little doubt that two OH or COOH groups in contact would attract each other strongly; therefore the data indicate that these groups are, partly at any rate, buried beneath the hydrocarbon groups at the surface. The table indicates that the SH, $COCH_3$, and CN groups also have some tendency to be covered up by hydrocarbon chains at the surface. It seems unlikely, however, that the orientation is complete or fixed in the surfaces of liquids: probably the molecules turn with their active ends upwards occasionally in the surface, but much less frequently than in the interior.

Harkins and Langmuir at one time considered that the total surface energy (Chap. I, § 13)

$$\epsilon_s = \gamma - T\frac{d\gamma}{dT},$$

which usually varies very little with temperature, gave an indication of the degree of exposure of groups with a high residual affinity. A high total surface energy indicated that an active group was uncovered. An attempt was made to discover the orientation of various benzene derivatives in the surface, assuming that only the outermost groups could affect the total surface energy, and that different groups could be brought to the exterior by suitable tilting of the benzene rings. This leads, however, to inconsistent results, and Sugden[2] has shown definitely that all the substituents in a benzene ring make their contribution to the total surface energy, although these contributions do not combine to make up the total energy in any very simple manner. It seems doubtful if the values of the total surface energy can be made to furnish information as to the orientation in the surface of benzene derivatives; the kinetic agitation is quite large enough to bring all parts of the molecules to the exterior for some part of the time, since the total surface energy contains a potential energy term, γ, and a kinetic energy term, $-T\,d\gamma/dT$; it is difficult to visualize the physical meaning of total surface energy in terms of molecules.

[1] *J.A.C.S.* (1920), 702.

[2] *J.C.S.* (1924), 1167; *Trans. Faraday Soc.*, **22**, 486 (1926).

4. Definiteness of the surface tension of a pure liquid. The surface tension of an aggregate of precisely similar molecules, differing only in their different energies of motion according to the ordinary law of distribution of velocities, should be constant, as it is the average work required to drag the molecules in 1 sq. cm. of free surface, from the interior, against the inward attractive force which is exerted on the surface molecules. It is frequently true, however, that an ordinary 'pure' liquid is really an aggregate of different molecular species, the molecules differing either in degree of polymerization, or degree of excitation or chemical activity, and attempts have been made to show that freshly formed surfaces of pure liquids have a different surface tension from that existing after a time. If this were the case, it would show that the liquid was formed of at least two molecular species, one of which had a higher surface tension than the other; the freshly formed surface would have the two species in the same proportion as in the interior, but in time that with the higher surface tension would tend to go into the interior.

In the case of ordinary liquids, the author knows of no clear evidence of a change in surface tension with time (except of course when the time is sufficiently long for contamination from outside to occur). Schmidt and Steyer,[1] following up an earlier suggestion of Lenard and work by Hiss,[2] caused rapid evaporation to take place at the surface of water in a capillary tube by blowing a jet of air over it. This air jet was suddenly cut off, the column of water falling rapidly to the height corresponding to the normal surface tension of water in about $\frac{1}{200}$ second. The surface tension was apparently some 10 per cent. above the normal at the beginning of this period; but the hydrodynamic suction of the air jet may reduce the air pressure above the column, thus raising it above the normal height, and it is practically impossible to disentangle the purely mechanical effect due to this cause from any elevation above the normal height which may occur through the surface tension being abnormally great. It can only be concluded that water has its normal surface tension after its surface is 0·005 second old, and that satisfactory methods have yet to be devised for investigating surfaces of less age than this.

Baker's experiments[3] indicate that the surface tension of benzene and bromine is considerably raised by prolonged drying, and that the molecular weight of many liquids is also increased by drying; apparently also some effect on the surface tension is produced by prolonged contact with charcoal and other solid catalysts.[4] The meaning of these changes is obscure at present.

5. The influence of temperature on surface tension. An immense number of investigations have been carried out on this subject, but clear conclusions as to the meaning of the results in terms of molecules are as yet difficult to reach. Surface tension, or the free energy per unit area

[1] *Ann. Physik*, **79**, 442 (1926).

[2] Cf. Freundlich, *Colloid and Capillary Chemistry*, p. 51.

[3] *J.C.S.* (1922), 573.

[4] *Ibid.* (1927), 956.

of the surface, is the work done in dragging the molecules required to form the fresh surface from the interior to the surface against the inward pull of the molecules underlying the surface, which is exerted on the surface molecules. It is therefore a measure of the intensity of this inward pull.

The kinetic agitation of the molecules and the tendency of the molecules to fly outwards increases as the temperature rises; consequently the net inward pull may be expected to become less, even if the real cohesion remains unchanged by the temperature. In fact, the surface tension almost invariably decreases with rising temperature, the only exceptions known being with a few substances over a restricted range of temperature. As the temperature rises towards the critical, the restraining force on the surface molecules diminishes and the vapour pressure increases; when the critical temperature is reached, of course, the surface tension vanishes altogether. 'Negative surface tension' is impossible for a liquid; it could only occur above the critical temperature, where the liquid cannot exist.

6. Eötvös's 'law'. In many cases the diminution of surface tension as the temperature rises is approximately linear, over long ranges. Eötvös[1] and Ramsay and Shields[2] drew attention to a certain resemblance between the alteration of surface tension with temperature in these cases and the alteration of gaseous pressure with temperature. The surface tension increases linearly as the temperature *falls* below a certain temperature (which is about 6 degrees below the critical), while the gaseous pressure increases linearly as the temperature *rises* from absolute zero. Ramsay and Shields's equation for the variation of surface tension with temperature was

$$\gamma(Mv)^{\frac{2}{3}} = k(T_c - T - 6), \tag{1}$$

Eötvös having previously given a rather less accurate equation in which the constant 6° was not subtracted from the critical temperature. Mv is the molecular volume and T_c the critical temperature.

Eötvös deduced his equation theoretically from considerations of 'corresponding states' of liquids of similar molecular constitution, which are rather difficult to follow. The central point of the theory is, however, that surfaces should be compared on the basis of the number of molecules per unit area, which is, if the molecules are similar in shape and symmetrically packed, proportional to $(Mv)^{\frac{2}{3}}$.

Differentiating (1),

$$-\frac{d}{dT}\{\gamma(Mv)^{\frac{2}{3}}\} = k. \tag{2}$$

The constant k was found, for a great number of 'normal' liquids, to have a value close to the mean value, 2·12. Some liquids, notably water and others containing hydroxyl groups, gave a decidedly lower value for k, the temperature coefficient of $\gamma(Mv)^{\frac{2}{3}}$, a quantity called the 'molecular

[1] *Ann. Physik*, **27**, 448 (1886).
[2] *Phil. Trans.* A, **184**, 647 (1893); *J.C.S.* (1893), 1089.

free surface energy'; for the alcohols k varied from about 0·95 to 1·5 and for the acids from 0·90 to 1·7, decreasing as the hydrocarbon chains were lengthened up to five carbons. For water, k was not constant, but increased from 0·87 at 0° to 1·21 at 140°.

These abnormally low values were supposed to be due to association of the molecules of the liquid, M being higher than calculated from the formula. Assuming that the whole change in the number of molecules in the surface is due to simple association of molecules of molecular weight M to molecules of weight M_1, Ramsay and Shields calculated the degree of association thus

$$\frac{M_1}{M} = \left(\frac{2\cdot 12}{k}\right)^{\frac{3}{2}}.$$

Later research has shown that the earlier workers were much too optimistic in thinking that a method had been discovered of revealing the molecular complexity of liquids. It is now abundantly clear that there is no '*constant* of Eötvös'. Walden and Swinne[1] gave values ranging from 0·56 for ethylene cyanide up to 5·7 for tristearin; and Jaeger,[2] who re-measured the surface tension and density of some 200 organic and 50 inorganic compounds over long ranges of temperature, gives even more remarkable variations in k. Methyl alcohol was 0·67, tristearin 6·75; fused salts varied from 0·3 up to about 1·9; but the most remarkable results were obtained with some substances which form liquid crystals. Anisaldazine, for instance (*loc. cit.*, p. 153), gave a positive value for k of 19·3 over a short region of temperature in the anisotropic liquid, and nearly all this class of substances gave very high *negative* values of k in the very short range in which the anisotropic liquid becomes isotropic.

According to the original theory, low values of k indicate association of the molecules, and, conversely, high values a dissociation. But the fused salts, which are certainly dissociated electrolytically, generally show very small values; and high values, which are in fact very common, ought to be impossible with organic compounds which do not decompose. Also many substances show variations of 100 per cent. or even more in k. It can only be said that experiment has proved Eötvös's 'law' absolutely unreliable; yet so great is the need for a method for determining the molecular complexity of liquids that it was widely accepted for a long time, and it is apparently still sometimes considered to be a fairly reliable method of detecting, or measuring, association in liquids.

Bennett and Mitchell[3] showed that practically all the liquids usually recognized as unassociated have a constant value of the *total* molecular surface energy

$$\left(\gamma - T\frac{d\gamma}{dT}\right)(Mv)^{\frac{2}{3}}$$

and suggest that the behaviour of this quantity over a considerable range of temperature is a guide as to whether or no the degree of association

[1] *Z. physikal. Chem.*, **82**, 271 (1913) [2] *Z. anorg. Chem.*, **101**, 1 (1917).
[3] *Z. physikal. Chem.*, **84**, 475 (1913).

remains constant; constancy of the quantity indicates no change in the degree of association. Bennett[1] has used this test to show that acetic acid does not change its association between 15° and 150°, and that certain long-chain compounds which gave very high values for the Eötvös constant k are also normal. The total molecular surface energy appears to be an approximately additive function of contributions due to the individual atoms in the compound.

In terms of molecular theory the meaning of this test for molecular association is rather obscure, and it does not appear to be an independent method of determining molecular association, as it has been discovered as an empirical rule obtaining among compounds known from other evidence to behave normally. Until the kinetic theory of liquids is better understood it seems useless to look to the data of surface tension for information as to molecular complexity.

7. Kinetic considerations. Ramsay and Shields stressed the analogy between the rise in surface tension as the temperature *falls* from the critical, and the rise in gaseous pressure as the temperature *rises* from absolute zero. For a proper comparison in terms of molecules it is little use comparing a rather intangible quantity like surface tension, which alters in one direction with temperature, to another property like pressure, which alters in the opposite direction; there is an error of sign in one of the quantities. And, as has so often appeared already in this book, the error in sign has arisen through the unfortunate practice of regarding surface tension as a physical pull parallel to the surface instead of as the mathematical fiction for free surface energy.

By considering the effect of the bombardment or thermal pressure of the molecules of the liquid against a barrier in the surface it is possible to gain some insight into the meaning of Ramsay and Shields's comparison. The following discussion is perhaps open to criticism, on the ground that the 'surface' is not properly defined, and that the simplifications are far too sweeping; yet although it cannot give trustworthy quantitative results, it illustrates the effect of temperature, in terms of molecules.[2]

Consider a barrier in the surface, separating two parts of the surface at temperatures T and $T+dT$. This barrier is analogous to the float of Chapter II, which divides a clean surface from one covered by a film; but it is purely ideal, as no barrier can be constructed which distinguishes between the 'surface' molecules and those in the interior. Let the pressure due to the horizontal bombardment of the surface molecules on either side of this barrier be F and $F+dF$ per cm. length. Then the difference, or the net force on the barrier dF, is clearly equal to the difference in surface tension between the two surfaces, with the sign changed, $-d\gamma$, for the work done in moving the barrier through dx, towards the warmer side, may be expressed either as $dF \,.\, dx$ or as $-d\gamma \,.\, dx$.

The decrease of surface tension with rise of temperature simply means that the horizontal component of the bombardment pressure on the float increases with the temperature; and the approximately linear rate of decrease of surface tension with temperature means that the lateral bombardment pressure of the surface molecules on this ideal float, which is affected only by the surface molecules, increases proportionally to the temperature. Thus if we focus attention

[1] *J.C.S.* (1913), 351; (1924), 958.

[2] Cf. Adam, *Phil. Mag.*, **8**, 539 (1929).

on the thermal pressure in the liquid surface instead of on the surface tension, the comparison between the liquid and the gas is seen to be very close.

Using this surface pressure F, (2) becomes

$$\frac{d}{dT}\{F(Mv)^{\frac{2}{3}}\} = k,$$

and if the molecules are symmetrical and may be taken as occupying cubical space, N_0, the number per square centimetre in the surface is

$$n\left(\frac{N}{Mv}\right)^{\frac{2}{3}},$$

N being the Avogadro number and n the number of molecules in the thickness of the surface. Then

$$\frac{d}{dT}\left(\frac{F}{N_0}\right) = \frac{k}{n(N)^{\frac{2}{3}}} = 1{\cdot}395\times10^{-16}\frac{k}{n}. \tag{3}$$

But if A is the area per molecule, $F/N_0 = FA$, and (3) is of the same form as the equation

$$\frac{d}{dT}(FA) = R = 1{\cdot}372\times10^{-16}, \tag{4}$$

obtained if we differentiate the equation of state of a perfect two-dimensional gas, $FA = RT$.

Now suppose that the rate of increase of the thermal bombardment pressure F is identical with the rate of increase of the surface pressure of the ideal two-dimensional gas; comparing (3) and (4) shows that $k = 0{\cdot}985n$.

It is probably more than a coincidence that this value for k is of the same order of magnitude as the observed values of the Eötvös constant; n, the number of molecules in the thickness of the surface, being unknown, though certainly small, a closer comparison is not possible.

The effect of association of the molecules will be the same as in Eötvös's theory, the number N_0 of molecules in the surface layer being diminished. Elongation of the molecules, and orientation perpendicular to the surface, will also increase the number in the surface and increase k. If the molecules are x times as long as thick, then the number in the surface is $nx^{\frac{1}{3}}(N/Mv)^{\frac{2}{3}}$ and the constant is increased in the ratio $x^{\frac{2}{3}}$. Thus molecules eight times as long as thick, if orientated perpendicular to the surface, will increase k four times.

The most important causes of deviation of k from the normal value will, however, be those properties of the molecules which cause the rate of increase of F with temperature to differ from the rate of increase of gaseous pressure. These may be very large, as the molecules are closely packed in the surface, and will no doubt be determined by details of the shape and size of the molecules, as well as by the lateral attractions between them. Unfortunately, evaluation of these factors is quite impossible at present.

Yet another cause for deviation from Eötvös's law may be found in Born and Courant's theory[1] of the motions of the molecules of liquids, which follows the lines of Debye's theory of the specific heat of solids. Assuming three degrees of freedom for the motions of the molecules, they obtained good agreement with experiment for several liquids for which the constant is about 2·1. If the number of degrees of freedom is n, the constant is altered on their theory in the ratio $(n/3)^{\frac{1}{3}}$.

[1] *Physikal. Z.*, **14**, 731 (1913).

Thus additional possibilities of motion in the surface molecules, capable of affecting F, may increase the Eötvös constant. In the next section we shall see evidence that such additional degrees of freedom probably come into play in the case of the triglycerides.

Thus, besides association, the orientation and shape of the surface molecules, their number of degrees of freedom for thermal motion, and their mutual attractions and details of their shape, size, and packing, and also the number of molecules in the thickness of the surface layer, may all affect the value of the Eötvös 'constant'. It is not surprising that experience has already shown that this 'constant' varies enormously, and that it cannot be used for drawing trustworthy conclusions as to the degree of molecular association.

8. The temperature coefficient of surface tension in homologous series. Some insight into the behaviour of molecules at surfaces may be

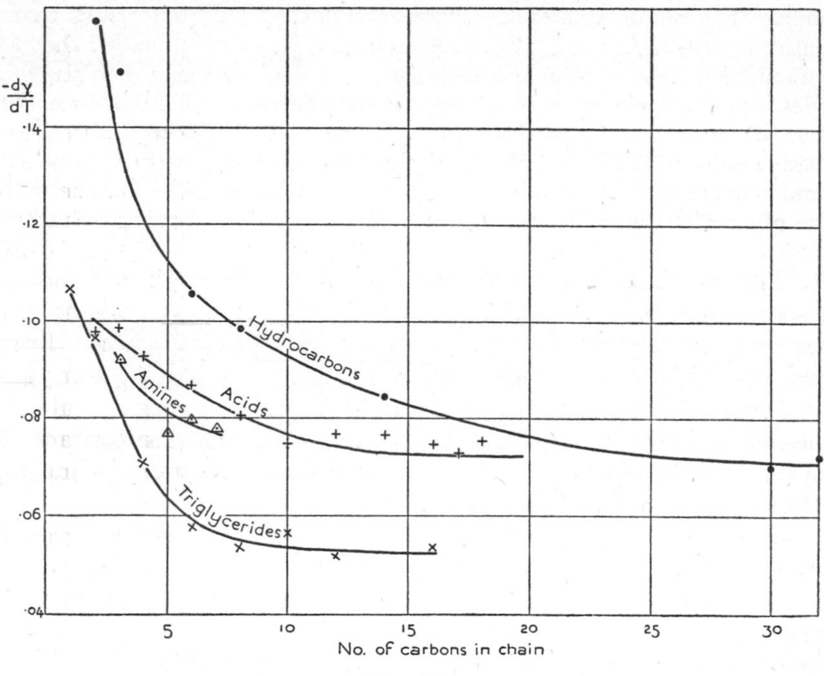

Fig. 33.

obtained by considering the values of the temperature coefficient of surface tension over a long range of compounds in a homologous series. Fig. 33 shows how $-d\gamma/dT$ varies with the number of carbon atoms in the chain, in the case of four series, the hydrocarbons, acids, amines, and triglycerides. In nearly all cases the value of $-d\gamma/dT$ was constant over the whole range of temperature investigated for each compound; in all cases it was constant over a considerable range of temperature, within the experimental error.

All the four series have high values of $-d\gamma/dT$ or dF/dT for the shorter chain compounds, which fall gradually to a nearly constant value as the chains are lengthened. The limiting value for the hydrocarbons, acids, and probably the amines also, is about 0·07; the triglycerides approach a decidedly lower value, about 0·053. The limiting value is practically reached with the three series of compounds with polar, water-attracting groups at the end, when the chains are about ten carbons long; but with the hydrocarbons, whose molecules are not loaded at one end, the limiting value is not reached till at least double this length of chain.

Probably the occurrence of this limiting value means that the long chains are orientated in the surface, so that the structure of the surfaces of the hydrocarbons, acids, and amines is practically the same, both in the arrangement of molecules and in the motions of the molecules. The orientation may be approximately perpendicular to the surface, but all that can be definitely stated is that it is probably the same for all the compounds.

The triglycerides have a lower limiting value of dF/dT, that is, the rate of increase of the thermal bombardment pressure of the surface molecules, laterally on a barrier, is less than that of the compounds with single chains. It seems probable that the attainment of a constant value for dF/dT means that the orientation of the surface molecules becomes nearly complete when the chains are about ten carbons long, and that the lower limiting value with the triglycerides is due to some restriction on the motions of the chains. This is no doubt due to the chains being bound together at their bases, in groups of three, by the glycerine ends of the molecules. There seems certainly, however, to be a considerable amount of independent movement of the long chains, for the limiting value of dF/dT is much more than one-third of that for the single chain compounds.

9. The surface tension of metals. The accurate determination of the surface tension of metals presents great difficulties, which arise largely from two causes: first, metals very easily combine with gases, forming layers of compounds on their surface which have a much lower tension than the metal; second, the cohesion of metals is so high, while their adhesion for other solids is not comparably high, that the contact angle between metals and other solids is often large, thus invalidating many of the usual methods of measurement.

Hogness,[1] Burdon,[2] Bircumshaw, and Sauerwald have done a great deal to render accurate measurements possible; the best method is probably the maximum bubble pressure method, but the measurement of sessile drops (see Chap. IX), and of drop volumes, are also useful. Metals always have a very high surface tension. Table X gives typical results.

The most remarkable features are the high surface tensions, greater, often many times greater, than those of any other substances; and the occasional *positive* temperature coefficients of tension. There is no obvious correlation between the tension and other physical properties; though (except for the last four metals in the table) the surface tension is higher for the metals with the higher melting-points, a fact which indicates that the cohesional forces in the liquid and in the solid state are similar in kind.

For the remarkable rise in tension sometimes found with increasing temperature there is no satisfactory explanation as yet; there is no reasonable doubt of the fact, although quantitatively the measurement of temperature coefficients is so difficult that there is often considerable

[1] *J.A.C.S.* (1921), 1621. [2] See Chap. III, §9.

TABLE X

Surface Tension of Metals

Metal	*γ dynes per cm.*	*Temperature*	*dγ/dT*	*Temperature range for dγ/dT*	*Reference*
Iron (various alloys with up to 10 per cent. other elements)	1,220 to 950	*c.* 1,300°	+1·0 to +0·3	*c.* 1,150–1,500°	9
Iron (grey cast)	880	1,300°	+0·8	1,225–1,350°	9
Copper	1,160	1,200°	+0·7	1,130–1,250°	8, 9
Gold	1,120	1,200°	−0·1	1,130–1,210°	9
Silver	923	1,000°	−0·13	990–1,160°	9
Zinc	770	600°	−0·2	510–700°	3, 9
Cadmium	600 (max.)	430°	Variable: positive below 430°, negative above 430°	..	3
Tin	510	900°	−(0·09)	880–1,050°	3, 8, 10
Mercury*	485±5	20°	−0·22	−25 to 60°	1, 2, 4, 5
"	..	..	Slight positive ?	Near f.p.	5
Thallium	460±20	320°	..	..	11
Lead	438	400°	−0·07	350–800°	6, 8
Antimony	350	900°	−(0·06)	700–1,100°	3, 8
Bismuth	340	960°	−0·07	300–960°	3, 7

1. See references in Chap. III, § 9.
2. Bircumshaw, *Phil. Mag.*, **2**, 341 (1926).
3. *Ibid.*, **3**, 1286 (1927).
4. *Ibid.*, **6**, 510 (1928).
5. *Ibid.*, **12**, 596 (1931).
6. *Ibid.*, **17**, 181 (1934).
7. Sauerwald and others, *Z. anorg. Chem.*, **154**, 79 (1926).
8. *Ibid.*, **162**, 301 (1927).
9. *Ibid.*, **181**, 353 (1929).
10. *Ibid.*, **213**, 310 (1933).
11. *Ibid.*, **223**, 84 (1935).

* Cook (*Physical Rev.*, **34**, 513 (1934)) found 515 at 31° in the highest vacuum.

discrepancy between different observers (the figures in brackets are cases in which there are discrepancies of over 100 per cent.). It is just possible that the positive coefficients are characteristic of impure metals, there being a large reduction in the adsorption of the substance with the smaller residual affinity on raising the temperature, or there may even be volatilization of an adsorbed impurity, but there is no evidence for these suggestions at present. There may possibly be films of adsorbed gases tenaciously held; possibly it is these that are removed from the surface as the temperature is raised.

The author knows of no other cases of a positive temperature coefficient of tension, except some rather discordant results of Zickendraht,[1] with sulphur, and the observations of Jaeger[2] on liquid crystals. In every one of five cases the tension increases abruptly by a small amount, up to

[1] *Ann. Physik*, **21**, 141 (1906).

[2] *Z. anorg. Chem.*, **101**, 152 (1917).

1·5 dynes, at the transition point where the anisotropic liquid becomes isotropic. In the case of the liquid crystals the sudden loss of anisotropy at this point indicates a sudden loss of orientation of the molecules, and the increase in tension probably arises through the molecular motions, suddenly freed, bringing parts of the molecules with greater residual affinities to the surface. In the case of the metals such marked orientation in the liquid state seems improbable.

If the positive temperature coefficient of surface tension is a genuine property of the pure metals, it may mean that there is a decrease in the components of kinetic energy, parallel to the surface, as the temperature rises. The matter appears worthy of further investigation.

The surface tension of various alloys has been recorded in several of the above papers (6, 8, 10, 11). Qualitatively, at least, there is a similarity between the tension of these alloys and that of mixtures of any other two substances differing in surface tension; small amounts of the metal of lower surface tension lowering the tension of the mixture much more than comparatively large amounts of the metal of higher tension raise it (6).

Lorenz and Adler[1] record measurements of the tension of metals against fused salts.

10. Empirical relations between surface tension and temperature. Although no simple equation can be constructed which will accurately express the variation of the surface tension of all liquids with temperature, yet in many cases formulae can be found which are sufficiently accurate to be used for interpolation purposes.

The simplest of these is the expression of the nearly linear variation of surface tension with temperature

$$\gamma = \gamma_0(1-bT). \tag{5}$$

Since the surface tension vanishes at the critical temperature, this may be approximately written

$$\gamma = \gamma_0\left(1-\frac{T}{T_c}\right). \tag{6}$$

The accuracy of (5) is within the limits of experimental error for many liquids. As the linear relation does not usually hold near the critical temperature, (6) is less accurate, though it is preferable theoretically as containing one less arbitrary constant. Refinements of the linear equation have usually been made along one of two lines: the first is to follow Eötvös's plan of introducing the two-thirds power of the molecular volume, as in equation (1) of Ramsay and Shields, or Katayama's modification[2]

$$\gamma\left(\frac{M}{D-d}\right)^{\frac{2}{3}} = kT_c\left(1-\frac{T}{T_c}\right), \tag{7}$$

in which D is the density of the liquid and d that of the vapour; the second

[1] *Z. anorg. Chem.*, **173**, 324 (1928).
[2] *Sci. Rep. Tôhoku Imp. Univ.*, ser. 1, **4**, 373 (1916).

is to raise the second factor $1-(T/T_c)$ to a power slightly greater than unity:

$$\gamma = \gamma_0\left(1-\frac{T}{T_c}\right)^n. \tag{8}$$

Equation (8) was first proposed by van der Waals[1] as a result of thermodynamical theory, the constant γ_0 having the value $K_2 T_c^{\frac{1}{3}} p_c^{\frac{2}{3}}$, where K_2 is a universal constant for all liquids, p_c is the critical pressure, and n also should have the same value for all liquids. In practice, van der Waals' universal constants are not accurately the same for all liquids. Ferguson[2] has tested the power equation (8) with experimental data, finding a mean value for 14 common organic liquids, for n, of 1·21, with variations of a few per cent. only.

Finally, McLeod's empirical equation,[3] which connects density and surface tension, must be mentioned:

$$\frac{\gamma}{(D-d)^4} = C, \tag{9}$$

where C is a constant, different for each liquid. It holds accurately for the majority of organic liquids over a long range of temperature; it may be obtained by eliminating $1-(T/T_c)$ from (7) and (8), if n has the value 1·2. The chief value of McLeod's equation lies in its use as a rational means of comparing densities, or molecular volumes.

In the case of liquid metals McLeod's equation does not appear to hold well; Bircumshaw[4] finds that C varies with temperature.

Fowler[5] has shown that McLeod's relation can be deduced from general statistical considerations.

11. Sugden's 'parachor'. It has long been recognized that the molecular volume of organic compounds depends on chemical constitution, and may be used in the case of liquids of uncertain constitution as a guide to their constitution. The principle underlying this view is that different atomic groupings have characteristic shapes and sizes and will therefore probably occupy characteristic volumes in liquids, the total volume of the liquid being the sum of the characteristic volumes of the separate parts of the molecules. The difficulty in the practical application of this principle has always been that the volumes of liquids change with temperature, as the thermal motions of the molecules gradually overcome the cohesional forces between them, and no really satisfactory basis for choosing the correct temperature at which to compare the molecular volumes was found for a long time. Sugden,[6] however, pointed out that McLeod's relation affords a basis for the comparison of molecular volumes under conditions where the effect of temperature is neutralized by taking account of the surface tension.

1 *Z. physikal. Chem.*, **13**, 716 (1894).

2 *Phil. Mag.*, **31**, 37 (1916); *Trans. Faraday Soc.*, **19**, 408 (1923).

3 *Trans. Faraday Soc.*, **19**, 38 (1923).

4 *Phil. Mag.*, **2**, 350 (1926).

5 *Proc. Roy. Soc.* A, **159**, 229 (1937).

6 *J.C.S.* (1924), 1177; (1925), 1525, 1868, 2517; (1927), 139, 1173, 2877; (1928), 263, 410, 989; (1929), 1058, 1291, 1298; *The Parachor and Valency* (Routledge, 1930); 'A List of Parachors', *Brit. Assoc. Report*, 1932.

The fourth root of the constant of McLeod's equation (9), multiplied by the molecular weight,

$$\frac{M}{D-d}\cdot\gamma^{\frac{1}{4}},$$

is a molecular volume multiplied by the fourth root of the surface tension, and does not vary with temperature. Sugden has termed this the 'parachor'. It can be dissected into parachors for different atoms, and special atomic arrangements such as double bonds (the ordinary non-polar double linkage of four shared electrons and the 'coordinate' or 'semi-polar' linkage having quite different values), closed rings, etc.; and these 'atomic parachors', when added up, reproduce the observed parachor in the case of substances of known constitution with exceptional accuracy. The parachor is much the most satisfactory convention as to molecular volumes, truly comparable for different substances, which has yet been found; and its rational basis is that the compounds are compared under similar conditions of surface tension, which is nearly the same as comparing them under equal degrees of self-compression by the intermolecular cohesional forces.

The values of several atomic and constitutive parachors are as follows:

TABLE XI

Parachors

	H 17·1						
He 20·5	Li (50)	Be 37·8	B 16·4	C 4·8	N 12·5	O 20·0	F 25·7
Ne 25·0	Na (80)	Mg —	Al 38·6	Si 25·0	P 37·7	S 48·2	Cl 54·3
A 54·0	K (110)	Ca (68) Zn 50·7	Sc — Ga 50	Ti 45·3 Ge [36]	As 62·5	Cr 54 Se 62·5	Br 68·0
Kr [68]	Rb (130)	Sr — Cd (70)	..	Sn 57·9	Sb 66·0	Mo (80) Te [81]	I 91·0
Xe [91]	..	Ba (106) Hg 69	..	Pb 76·2	Bi 80	..	..

Non-polar double bond .	23·2	3-membered ring . .	16·7
Semi-polar bond	−1·6	4-membered ring . .	11·6
Triple bond	46·6	6-membered ring . .	6·1

Numbers in round brackets are only approximate, those in square brackets are estimated by interpolation.

The atomic parachors are an approximation to the volumes of the atoms in coordinate or covalent combination; it will be seen that there is a rough correspondence between the atomic parachors and the atomic volumes in Lothar Meyer's curve.

Some quite small deviations between the observed parachors of compounds and those calculated from the sum of the atomic and constitutive parachors have been pointed out by Hunten and Maass,[1] and by Mumford

[1] *J.A.C.S.* (1929), 153.

and Phillips.[1] Recently, however, Mann and Purdie[2] have shown that, in several series of coordinated compounds of metals and organic radicals, there is a large deviation from the additive property of atomic parachors, progressively varying with the size of the hydrocarbon chains in the radicals. The parachor of palladium, for instance, appears to decrease from a moderate positive value to a negative value, as the hydrocarbon chains on the organic radicals in the compounds are increased.

It must be remembered, however, that in these compounds, when the hydrocarbon chains are short, a great part of the cohesion of the liquid will be provided by the comparatively unsaturated metal, and the phosphorus, arsenic, or sulphur atoms which are also present. When these are more completely covered by the hydrocarbon groups the cohesion, and consequently the self-compression of the molecules in the liquid state, will be less, and their volume less. It may be that this is insufficiently compensated by multiplying the molecular volume by the fourth root of the surface tension.

12. The influence of pressure on surface tension. It might be expected that a high pressure of vapour over the surface of a liquid would diminish surface tension by bringing a fairly large number of gaseous molecules within reach of the surface. The attractions of these molecules on the surface molecules of the liquid would neutralize, to some extent, the inward attraction on the surface molecules, and so diminish surface tension. High compression of the gas above the liquid is equivalent to putting a second liquid, of rather small attraction for the first, in place of air.

Kundt's measurements[3] confirm this expectation and show decreases in the surface tension of several common liquids, increasing regularly with increase of pressure of the gas above them; the decrease amounted to some 50 per cent. in some cases at about 150 atmospheres. The amount of decrease caused by the same pressure of gas increased in the order hydrogen–air–carbon dioxide, as would be expected from the fact that the residual affinities and tendency to condense of these gases increases in the same order.

If the air in the tube is evacuated, leaving only the vapour of the liquid, there is usually a slight, barely measurable, increase in the surface tension.[4]

[1] *J.C.S.* (1929), 2112. [2] *Ibid.* (1935), 1549.
[3] *Ann. Physik*, **12**, 538 (1881); *Int. Critical Tables*, **4**, 475.
[4] Richards and Carver, *J.A.C.S.* (1921), 847.

CHAPTER V

SOLID SURFACES, GENERAL PROPERTIES

1. Limited mobility of the molecules of solids. The essential difference between liquids and solids is that the particles of liquids can move, easily, long distances, while those of solids are practically fixed in position. The effects of this limited mobility, on their surface properties, are of two principal kinds. In the first place, those properties of liquid surfaces which are due to the free motion of the particles are absent, or very much less conspicuous, in solids. Thus solid surfaces do not contract spontaneously as a general rule, and it will be seen in Chapter VI that liquids do not spread over the surface of solids to form surface films, nearly as easily as they do on liquids, even when the attraction of the liquid for the solid is great enough for such a film, once spread, to be very stable.

In the second place, the non-mobility of the surface particles of a solid results in the surface being often extremely uneven, unless special means such as polishing have been employed to smooth out the irregularities. The atoms in a solid surface stay where they are placed when the surface is formed, and this may result in no two adjacent atoms or molecules having the same properties.

We saw in Chapter I that the surface of a liquid is definite within one or two molecules' thickness, and that the molecules in it are in constant agitation. An instantaneous photograph, taken with a camera capable of detecting individual molecules, would reveal the surface of a liquid as an irregular collection of small elevations and pits, none of them, however, more than a molecule or two in height or depth. A time exposure would show a continuous smooth blur. A solid surface would usually show, both in an instantaneous and a time photograph, pits and elevations of much greater size and more irregular shape. Liquid surfaces are equipotential, solid surfaces are not.

The heterogeneous character of solid surfaces is a matter of the greatest importance to Chemistry, as it is on the exceptional state of strain in certain atoms in the surface that the catalytic properties of surfaces usually depend. This subject will be dealt with in Chapter VII; in this chapter, those properties which can be averaged over considerable areas of the solid surface, such as their power of being wetted by liquids, will be considered. The average properties of solids are often of very great industrial importance.

2. Effects due to partial mobility. The immobility of the particles of many solids is not absolute. Apart from the power of slowly flowing possessed by such solids as pitch, a large number of crystalline substances show a certain small degree of flow. Spring's experiments[1] showed

[1] *Bull. Acad. Roy. Belg.*, **28**, 23 (1894); cf. also *ibid.*, **37**, 790 (1899).

that most metals flow under pressures of thousands of atmospheres sufficiently to unite into coherent masses. Diffusion of metals into metals is a well-known phenomenon;[1] it may occur along the crystal boundaries in a solid mass of metal, or (if the two metals are capable of forming solid solutions with each other) even through the space lattice of single crystals. Metals frequently exhibit mobility, below their melting-points,[2] the corners and edges of the crystals becoming rounded. In the next chapter frequent reference will be made to the 'sintering', or alteration of nature, and probably of the form, of the irregularities in the surface of solids which are of such importance for catalytic action. These effects are evidence of the existence of surface tension in solids; the inward pull on the surface atoms must always be present, owing to the cohesion, exactly as in liquids; the effects of this surface free energy or surface tension are not manifested in changes of form, in solids, except in those cases where the mobility is sufficient for the atoms to move under fairly small forces. Changes of form, due to surface tension in solids, are always very much slower in solids than in liquids; this is due not to the forces being less, but to the mobility being very much less.

3. Polishing and surface working of solids. That repeated rubbing of a solid surface may result in a rapid smoothing out of minute irregularities and a great increase in lustre and reflecting power has been known to polishers for an indefinite time. Rayleigh[3] showed microscopically that it is probably a different process from even the finest grinding; in polishing, it is usual to have a yielding substance such as pitch, leather, or some textile material moving over the solid; the abrasive need not be different from that used in the finest grinding; it is, however, supported on a yielding backing, and does not cut and splinter the surface being worked, but drags the surface about by adhesion. Rayleigh considered polishing to be a molecular process. Beilby[4] showed that the polished layer appears amorphous to the highest powers of the microscope, resembling a film of viscous liquid, painted over the irregularities of the ground surface, and then suddenly congealed into a glass-like film. Usually the film had completely filled the visible cracks and pits left by the previous grinding, but occasionally small pits, up to 0·01 mm. across, were flowed over with a translucent film. The depth to which the polishing altered the structure of the surface of calcite was investigated by dissolving away the surface with acid; the completely amorphous layer was roughly 50 A. thick, i.e. a layer of a good many molecules deep had been rendered amorphous to microscopic examination. Flow lines, produced by the fibres of the moving wash-leather, were found at depths of 250–500 A., and some traces of the original ground surface down to 5,000–10,000 A.

The introduction of electron diffraction, a most powerful new tool[5] for

[1] Cf. Desch, *Chemistry of Solids* (1934), chap. ix.

[2] Desch, *J. Inst. Metals*, **11**, 57 (1914); **22**, 241 (1919); Thompson, *J. Iron Steel Inst.*, **93**, 155 (1916).

[3] *Nature*, **64**, 385 (1901).

[4] *Aggregation and Flow in Solids* (1921), sect. 5.

[5] Cf. Finch, *J.C.S.* (1938), 1137.

the investigation of the structure of surfaces, has yielded detailed information about the effects of polishing.[1] In the case of metallic surfaces, fully polished, the surface layers are amorphous to the limit of the powers of the electron-diffraction method; there is a strong probability that the first few layers of atoms are arranged in as random a manner as in a monatomic liquid. An unpolished metal shows diffraction patterns indicative of the normal crystalline structure of the metal. As polishing proceeds, the pattern becomes gradually more diffuse, indicating a reduction in crystal size; finally, the rings or spots of the crystalline metallic structure disappear, giving place to two very diffuse rings.[2] For over a dozen elements of metallic or metalloidal nature the ratio of the diameters of these rings is within 2 per cent. of 1·85, which is that to be expected for a random arrangement of spherical atoms, and has been found for liquid mercury by X-ray methods. It is therefore practically certain that the polishing of metals changes the surface into a completely amorphous assemblage of atoms, packed as in liquids. There appears to be only one difference, which occurs occasionally: in a few cases the atoms appear, from the size of the diffuse rings, to occupy less than their normal volume, as if the process of polishing brought about a certain rearrangement of the outer electrons. This apparent decrease in atomic volume at present appears mysterious; it looks as if the simple mechanical operation of polishing tended to diminish the differences in atomic volume between the members of different groups in the periodic table.

The depth of the amorphous layer is of the order 30 A., according to the findings of electron-diffraction photographs. Hopkins[3] determined it by removing successive layers by sputtering *in vacuo*, and Lees[4] by electrolytic solution. To optical standards, the polished surfaces appear flat, but Thomson[5] considers that they are probably wavy, the angle of different submicroscopic areas of the surface varying by several degrees. The length of these wavelets in the surface must be considerably less than the wave-length of light.

Crystalline solids other than metals examined, by electron diffraction, show some disturbance of the normal structure on polishing, but do not usually form a completely amorphous layer.[6] Polishing tends to disintegrate the crystals at the surface, but not to the same extent as in metals; and it often happens that continued polishing removes the

[1] French, *Nature*, **129**, 169 (1932); *Proc. Roy. Soc.* A, **140**, 637 (1933); Raether, *Z. Physik*, **86**, 82 (1933); Darbyshire and Dixit, *Phil. Mag.*, **16**, 961 (1933); cf. also Finch and Quarrell, *Nature*, **137**, 516 (1936); Dobinski, *Phil. Mag.*, **23**, 397 (1937).

[2] Examination by means of X-rays does show lines corresponding to a finely divided crystalline structure on a polished metal (Boas and Schmid, *Naturwiss.*, **20**, 416 (1932); but this is almost certainly because the X-rays penetrate below the amorphous layer and reveal the microcrystalline structure below. Electrons do not penetrate to more than a few atoms depth.

[3] *Trans. Faraday Soc.*, **31**, 1095 (1935).

[4] *Ibid.*, p. 1102.

[5] *Phil. Mag.*, **18**, 640 (1934).

[6] Cf. Hopkins, *Phil. Mag.*, **21**, 820 (1936).

disintegrated crystalline particles, restoring the original surface structure more or less completely. It would appear that the cohesion of the finer crystalline fragments was to some extent overcome by the dragging action of the polisher, but the temperature did not rise sufficiently to liquefy the surface, so that a coherent amorphous surface layer cannot be produced. Raether records that, by careful surface treatment, he could obtain patterns from sodium chloride and some other non-metallic solids indicative of a fibrous structure produced at the surface. These differences from the effects found with metals may, however, depend on the nature of the polishing material, particularly its melting-point.

The amorphous Beilby layer (as it is often called) has properties markedly different from the rest of the solid. It is much harder, and is usually more soluble and electrolytically more anodic, a fact of considerable importance in the corrosion of metals, as it is often found that corrosion starts at those points (such as the neighbourhood of a punched hole) where some degree of surface flow, or damage to the crystalline structure, has taken place in the metal. It has, apparently, powers of dissolving other metals, not possessed by a crystalline surface. Thus Finch, Quarrell, and Roebuck[1] found that if small amounts of metals were deposited by condensation from vapour on to a *polished* surface of another metal, patterns indicative of the crystalline structure of the deposited metal were obtained temporarily, but disappeared after a few minutes or even seconds. Permanent patterns of zinc on copper could only be obtained by very many successive depositions. If, however, metals were similarly deposited on *crystalline* surfaces of other metals, one deposition was always sufficient to give the pattern of the deposited metal.

The heat of solution of the surface layers of polished, drawn, or cold-worked metals is greater than that of the metal in its usual state,[2] indicating the storage of energy in the surface layers of energy in potential form. The surface layers of glass (to a depth of about 3,000 A.) are rendered doubly refracting[3] by polishing and mechanical working, and many other substances show a similar change at the surface. There is no doubt that a part of the energy of motion of a body rubbing on a solid surface is transferred to this surface, by the local adhesion of the surfaces in contact, and that the stresses so imposed on the surface layers are sufficient to produce profound disintegration of its structure, and rearrangement to less orderly structures, which have a higher potential energy than the orderly crystalline arrangement; in this way some small part of the kinetic energy of the moving polisher is not dissipated as heat but is stored as potential energy in the surface layers of the solid.

The actual mechanism by which the amorphous surface layer is produced is probably a combination of many processes; very large shearing

[1] *Proc. Roy. Soc.* A, **145**, 676 (1934).

[2] Cf. Desch, *Chemistry of Solids* (1934), p. 165.

[3] Zocher and Coper, *Z. physikal. Chem.*, **132**, 295 (1928).

stresses are set up in the surface crystallites, causing slip along various planes in their structure and disintegration; in the case of the sharper projections some disintegration may be caused by mere compression; pieces of the surface, varying in size from single atoms upwards, may be pushed or pulled about in the surface. But there is now little doubt that, when a fully amorphous, highly polished, surface layer is produced, the surface layers are actually liquefied by heat momentarily, through the friction produced by the moving polisher. This view has been held for some time by many workers;[1] it was not accepted in the first edition of this book, owing to the apparent difficulty of maintaining a sufficiently high temperature in the surface layers when considerable opportunities are present for conducting away the heat liberated by friction. But the recent work of Bowden and others[2] has shown, both theoretically and experimentally, that the *surface* temperature can, and does, rise quickly to the melting-point of the solid during sliding friction, and never rises higher than this; the surface temperatures were measured by using different metals sliding on each other as a thermocouple. Polishing only occurs if the melting-point of the polisher is higher than that of the substance being polished; thus camphor (m.p. 178°) polishes Wood's metal, but not tin or lead; oxamide (m.p. 417°) polishes tin, lead, bismuth, but not speculum metal (m.p. 745°); speculum metal can, however, be polished by lead oxide (m.p. 888°); calcite (m.p. 1,339°) is polished by stannous oxide (1,625°) or by zinc oxide (1,800°), but not by cuprous oxide (1,235°). Hardness alone is of little importance; but a few cases have been found with very ductile metals, such as gold or platinum, where the metal can be polished with a material of melting-point far below that of the metal.

The disturbance of the normal structure of the solid gradually decreases, from the completely amorphous surface layer, down through layers of varying degrees of crystal size and distortion, to the undistorted structure several thousand A. below the surface.

The various forms of cold-working of metals all seem to produce a more or less perfect Beilby layer on the surface, with consequent increase in hardness and resistance to mechanical wear. Some of Finch, Quarrell, and Wilman's[3] recent observations on materials employed for the cylinders of internal-combustion engines appear very significant. The sleeves of aeroplane-engine cylinders, honed ready for use, but not actually used, showed electron-diffraction patterns indicating a microcrystalline structure with α-iron rings prominent. Other sleeves which had been 'run in' showed only the diffuse rings of a polished surface layer, which were found even after a fair thickness of the surface had been rubbed away. It would seem that the running in of cylinders consists in the production of Beilby layers to an appreciable depth on the internal surface. It was also noticed

[1] Cf. discussion with Macaulay, *Nature*, **118**, 339 (1926); **119**, 13, 162, 279 (1927).
[2] *Proc. Roy. Soc.* A, **154**, 640 (1936); **160**, 575 (1937).
[3] *Trans. Faraday Soc.*, **31**, 1078 (1935).

that rubbing cast iron, of the quality generally used for cylinders, brings graphite to the surface, and it seems possible that the reason why cast iron is suitable for cylinder walls is that surface friction tends to bring graphite to the surface, and so, to some small extent, to cause the walls to become self-lubricating.

Polishing and cold-working are the nearest phenomena found in solids to the normal changes in surfaces which take place in liquids. In the formation of smooth, polished layers we have the phenomenon corresponding to the natural smoothing out of the irregularities of liquid surfaces under surface tension; in the bringing of graphite to the surface of cast iron by rubbing, something resembling adsorption of a substance with a smaller residual field of force, from the interior of a liquid, is taking place. In the liquid the molecular motions produce the phenomena quickly and unaided; in the solid they require assistance by mechanical means.

4. The cleanliness and condition of solid surfaces. Unless very special precautions are taken a solid surface is nearly always contaminated with foreign matter in a thin layer. The cleanest and most perfect solid surfaces are probably those obtained by cleaving a single crystal. G. P. Thomson[1] brings evidence from electron-diffraction observations indicating that the greater part of many freshly cleaved surfaces is exactly parallel to a given direction, to an accuracy of 10 minutes or less; there may, however, be shallow steps or ridges bounded by cleavage planes. Surfaces produced by etching in a polycrystalline material, or by sandpapering or machining, usually have crystalline projections of the order of thickness 100 A., or rather more. If the surface is prepared by etching, chemical changes may be produced on the surface, oxide or other films being present.

If a solid surface is left unprotected in ordinary air for a short time, its surface usually becomes coated with a film of greasy material. Even if these films are only one molecule thick, they may profoundly alter the properties of the surface. An hour, or less, according to the cleanliness of the air and other conditions, may suffice for very considerable alteration in the properties of the surface. The presence of these films of grease is shown in many different ways. Quincke[2] found that *freshly split* mica surfaces will seize to each other if brought into close contact, sliding being impossible unless great force is applied, when the surfaces are much torn and scratched. After a short exposure to air the surfaces no longer seized, and were obviously lubricated to some extent. Hardy's classical work on boundary lubrication[3] required careful purification of the air from traces of greasy matter, moisture, etc., before consistent results could be obtained. Macaulay[4] has recently shown that this greasy layer is probably deposited mainly by simple settling from the air, since (in the middle of the city of Glasgow) the power of seizing was lost much more rapidly if the freshly cleaved surfaces were placed uppermost, than if they were placed vertically with some protection against air currents which might bring

[1] *Phil. Mag.*, **18**, 640 (1934).

[2] *Ann. Physik*, **108**, 326 (1859).

[3] Cf. Chapter VI.

[4] *J. Roy. Tech. Coll.* (Glasgow), **3**, 357 (1935).

suspended grease on to them; if placed with the clean faces downwards, the flakes retained their power of seizure for two days or longer. The accidental traces of grease also greatly decrease the ease of wetting and increase the contact angle against water; this is easily shown by the 'breath figures'.[1] If one breathes suddenly on a cool surface of glass or mica, the moisture condenses in minute droplets on any slightly greasy regions, and is easily visible as a temporary mist; on perfectly clean regions the condensation occurs as a continuous film which may be invisible, or may show interference colours momentarily. These breath figures are an exceedingly sensitive method of showing traces of grease on those surfaces which, if perfectly clean, would be wetted; it should not be forgotten, however, that some surfaces would naturally show a misty appearance, however clean, on condensation of moisture. The insulating property of various materials depends on their surface condition. Reiss[2] noted that mica gains in insulating qualities after exposure to the air; Rayleigh[3] attributed this to partial replacement of the condensed layer of water present on clean mica by grease, which prevents the formation of a continuous conducting film of moisture.

Another consequence of these films of grease is the prevention of 'oriented overgrowths'.[4] It is often found that if a crystal with a clean, freshly cleaved surface, is moistened with a solution of an isomorphous, soluble salt, which is then allowed to evaporate, the crystals deposited from the soluble salt are oriented with their edges parallel to those of the original crystal. Such overgrowths are well shown by sodium nitrate deposited on calcite. They are only obtained in perfection, however, if the surface of the first crystal is free from contamination; the power of orienting deposited isomorphous crystals is much diminished if the freshly cleaved surface is left in the air.

The presence of such films of grease often complicates the electron-diffraction patterns, and sometimes, in extreme cases, only the patterns due to the grease itself are obtained.[5] Usually, however, the grease can be removed sufficiently to give the proper electron-diffraction pattern for the clean surface, by washing with carefully purified benzene or other solvents: with careful work the grease patterns need not appear. A glass surface can be more effectively cleaned by holding in a flame for a short time than in any other way, provided it is not too dirty at first.[6] Most surfaces would have their structure much altered by heating, however,

[1] Moser, *Ann. Physik*, **56**, 177; **57**, 1 (1842); Waidele, *ibid.*, **59**, 255 (1843); Rayleigh, *Nature*, **86**, 416 (1911).

[2] *Die Lehre v. der Reibungs-elektrizität*, **2**, 220 (1853).

[3] *Phil. Mag.*, **33**, 220 (1892).

[4] For literature, see Barker, *J.C.S.* (1906), 1120; *Z. Krist.*, **45**, 1 (1908); Bunn, *Proc. Roy. Soc.* A, **141**, 567 (1933).

[5] Cf. Trillat, *Trans. Faraday Soc.*, **31**, 1127 (1935).

[6] Glass surfaces seem to become dirty more quickly than most others; this is very likely due to the contamination having penetrated below the surface into cracks, and coming out gradually after cleaning the actual surface.

the small ridges and projections becoming sintered and rounded off. In a few cases, e.g. bismuth,[1] it is recorded that polishing with a clean wash-leather will remove a lubricating layer of grease; but more often a polishing cloth will deposit more grease than it removes. Polishing will also alter the structure of the surface by forming a Beilby layer.

The best chance of obtaining a perfect solid surface appears to be by cleaving a single crystal; and in cleaving, pre-existing cracks should be avoided if possible, as they may have accumulated contamination. A very simple test for some kinds of detachable contamination on a solid surface was used by Fräulein Pockels;[2] the solid was dipped into a clean water surface covered by a clean powder such as ignited talc; the contamination usually spreads out along the water, clearing the powder away. Pockels called this spreading of the grease on to the water 'solution currents'; if these occur, contamination is present. Their absence does not necessarily indicate a clean solid surface, however; the contamination may either be of a non-spreading character, or adhere too strongly to the solid surface.

Adsorbed films of gas are probably present on most solid surfaces. On metals the adsorbed films are held with great tenacity, the first layer of atoms of oxygen being combined by covalent forces with the underlying metal. Some account of the properties of these adsorbed films will be given in Chapter VII. Most metals will form, with continuous exposure to air, especially at high temperatures, thick films of oxide; these may, in extreme cases such as aluminium, form so rapidly that it becomes very difficult to wet the surface of the metal with another molten metal, and to solder or weld the metal. These films vary considerably in tenacity and in their adhesion to the underlying metal, and exert a greater or smaller degree of protection to corrosion of the metal, according to their tenacity and power of preventing the access of ions in solution to the metal.

On most non-metallic surfaces little systematic information exists as to the nature or effect of any adsorbed films of gas. There have been attempts, from time to time, to ascribe slow changes in the properties of surfaces to the adsorption of air;[3] Ehrenberg[4] considers that the difficulty of wetting soils which have been dry for some time is due to the accumulation of adsorbed air on the particles; Spring[5] found that sand settles to a different volume in the absence of air from that to which settling occurs in air, and that heating of the sand to redness affects the volume of settling. The settling of powders is such a complex matter, however, depending on the shape of the particles, on the friction between them, and on the amount of mechanical agitation, that it appears very doubtful if the changes observed can be taken as conclusive evidence of thick layers of air held firmly on the surface of the sand; and it seems much more likely that the difficult wetting of soil particles after a drought is due to accumu-

[1] Hardy, *Phil. Mag.*, **40**, 201 (1920).
[2] *Ann. Physik*, **8**, 854 (1902).
[3] Cf. Quincke, *Ann. Physik*, **108**, 326 (1859).
[4] *Die Boden Kolloide* (1915), p. 223.
[5] *Bull. Soc. Belg. Geol.*, **17** (mém.), 13 (1903).

lated greasy contamination, than that it is the result of adsorption of air. There is every reason to expect that adsorbed films of air will be formed practically instantaneously on exposure to the atmosphere.

The conductivity of surface films of adsorbed moisture may be a serious trouble in high voltage engineering practice.

5. The surface tension, and total surface energy, of solids. Strictly speaking, the work required to produce a fresh surface of a solid varies from atom to atom, and the surface tension is therefore not uniform. It is, however, possible to speak of the surface tension of a solid as the average work necessary to produce one square centimetre of fresh surface; if a sufficiently large area of surface is taken, the irregularities will be averaged out.

At present there is no trustworthy method for measuring the surface tension of most solids. An estimate for mica[1] depends on the work required to cleave the crystal. Ostwald's older solubility method involves large and incalculable errors in practice. The usual methods for liquids fail, because of the non-mobility of the surface.

Ostwald[2] pointed out that, just as the vapour pressure of small drops of liquid is greater than that of large drops, so the vapour pressure and solubility of small solid particles is greater than that of large. The relation between the radius, surface tension, and vapour pressure or solubility of spherical particles is the same as that deduced in Chap. I, § 15, for small drops.

Unfortunately, the methods necessary for reducing a solid to the state of fineness necessary to produce a measurable alteration in solubility or vapour pressure are certain to alter their surface properties profoundly, generally in the direction of increasing their intrinsic solubility by disturbing the space lattice of the crystalline solid. The small particles, whether prepared by rapid condensation from vapour or solution, or by mechanical subdivision of large particles, will have the surface atoms in much less regular arrangement than in the large particles, unless these are already wholly amorphous. The mechanical processes of grinding always result in the formation of a certain amount of the amorphous 'Beilby' layer which is obtained by polishing. This enhanced intrinsic solubility will be added to that due to the greater curvature of the small particles, so that the 'surface tensions' calculated from the formula will be too high, perhaps much too high.

Hulett,[3] Dundon and Mack,[4] and others have worked with salts, finding values ranging from 130 to 3,000 dynes per cm. for the surface tension of the solid-liquid interface. F. C. Thompson[5] has estimated the surface tension of solid iron carbide against iron as 1,350, by this method. The

[1] Obreimoff, *Proc. Roy. Soc.* A, **127**, 290 (1930).

[2] *Z. physikal. Chem.*, **34**, 503 (1900). Through a mistake, Ostwald gave the factor 3 instead of 2 in the original formula, and this was followed by some of the earlier experimenters.

[3] *Ibid.*, **37**, 385 (1901); **47**, 357 (1904).

[4] *J.A.C.S.* (1923), 2479, 2658.

[5] *Trans. Faraday Soc.*, **17**, 391 (1922).

numerical results are of little value for the reasons stated. Proof must be given that the surfaces of the small particles are in the same condition as those of the large, before the results can be trusted.

Lipsett, Johnson, and Maass[1] have measured the heat of solution of small and large particles of sodium chloride, in order to determine the total surface energy of this salt, this quantity being the same as the total surface energy ϵ_s of Chap. I, § 14. This total energy will appear entirely as heat when the particles are dissolved, so that more heat will be evolved on solution of the small than of the large particles. Sodium chloride dissolves with absorption of heat, so that the heat of solution is negative, and is less with the small than with the large particles. The difference amounted to about 14 calories per mole for small particles prepared by subliming the salt, and to 30 calories per mole for ground particles, each of about $1 \cdot 3\ \mu$ diameter. The total surface energy for the interface salt-liquid was about 380 ergs per sq. cm. for the sublimed particles; that of the ground particles was probably larger, but the difficulty of estimating the surface of the ground particles was so great that this is not certain. The objections described above to the comparison of small and large particles, because their surfaces may be intrinsically different, apply to these determinations also, so that the figure obtained must be taken as a maximum value only.

6. The work of adhesion between solids and liquids: contact angles. Although no method has yet been found of determining the surface tension of solids against air or other liquids, yet the work of adhesion W_{SL}, of a solid to a liquid, analogous to the work of adhesion W_{AB} between two liquids, can be measured easily. This work of adhesion, like that between two liquids described in Chap. I, § 8, is the work necessary to separate the liquid from the solid by separating them perpendicularly from each other, against the adhesive forces between them.

Dupré's equation (2) of Chapter I holds good for the case of a solid and a liquid:

$$W_{SL} = \gamma_{SA} + \gamma_{LA} - \gamma_{SL}; \quad (1)$$

γ_{SA} and γ_{SL} being the surface tensions of the solid against air and liquid, and γ_{LA} the surface tension of the liquid. This involves the difference between the two unknown solid surface tensions; but this difference may be found as follows.

Liquids frequently rest on solids at a definite angle θ (measured in the liquid). The relation between the surface tensions and the contact angle θ may be deduced from Fig. 34, by treating the surface tensions as mathematical tensions pulling parallel to the surfaces, and resolving parallel to the solid surface. This is legitimate, as the mathematical surface tension can always be substituted for the physical free surface energy, to obtain the conditions of equilibrium

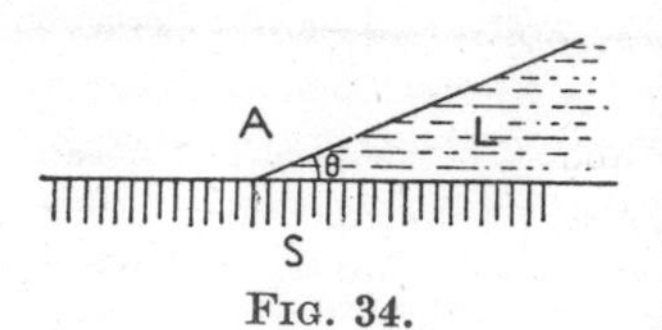

FIG. 34.

[1] *J.A.C.S.* (1927), 925, 1940; (1928), 2701.

when only the consequences of this free energy are concerned. We have

$$\gamma_{SA} = \gamma_{SL} + \gamma_{LA} \cos\theta. \tag{2}$$

Combining (1) and (2), the unknown solid surface tensions are eliminated,

$$W_{SL} = \gamma_{LA}(1+\cos\theta). \tag{3}$$[1]

Equation (3) shows that the contact angle is determined by the relative strengths of the adhesion of the liquid to the solid, and to itself, for the latter is $2\gamma_{LA}$. If the contact angle is zero, $W = 2\gamma_{LA}$, so that the liquid attracts the solid as much as it attracts itself; and the angle will also be zero if the liquid attracts the solid more than it attracts itself. A contact angle of 90° indicates that the attraction of the liquid for the solid is half that for itself, and 180° would indicate no adhesion between the liquid and the solid. As there is always some adhesion, angles of 180° are unrealizable.

This equation has been known for over a century; it was given by Young[2] (without proof!) and by Dupré;[3] it can be deduced also from Laplace's theory of Capillarity, or indeed from any theory of the cohesive forces, since it can be obtained from consideration of energies only. Until recent years it has been little noticed, which is unfortunate, as the meaning of the contact angles is much clarified when the work of adhesion is introduced, and the surface tensions of the solid surfaces, which are not measurable, are eliminated. Most authors are now, however, expressing their results in terms of the work of adhesion or of closely related expressions.

The quantity $\gamma_{LA}\cos\theta$ was termed by Freundlich the 'adhesion tension', and is frequently used; it is equal to the difference between the solid-air and solid-liquid surface tensions, that is, to $W_{SL}-\gamma_{LA}$.

The meaning of the term 'wetting' of a solid by a liquid has been much discussed; it is really only a matter of definition. The simplest plan seems to be to define wetting in terms of the contact angle and therefore of the relative adhesions between the liquid for the solid and of the liquid for itself. In this book a solid will be said to be completely wet if the contact angle is zero; incompletely wet if there is a finite contact angle. As there is always some adhesion between solids and liquids in contact, on this definition there is no such thing as complete non-wettability (an angle of 180°). Many writers, however, refer to such solids as paraffin wax, which have a contact angle greater than 90°, as being unwettable by water. This is possibly convenient in describing the macroscopic appearance of the surface with water standing on it, or in discussing whether the liquid will, or will not, penetrate at all into capillaries in the solid; as, however, there

[1] Bangham and Razouk (*Trans. Faraday Soc.* (1937), 1459) correctly pointed out that the work of adhesion W_{SL} is not fully defined above, since it is not stated whether the work of detachment of liquid from solid is that required to leave a *clean* solid surface, or one covered with an adsorbed film. The former work is definite, but difficult to measure; the latter depends on the partial pressure of the vapour of the liquid in the gaseous phase, which may be anything from zero up to the vapour pressure.

[2] *Phil. Trans.* (1805), 84; *Works* (ed. Peacock), **1**, 432.

[3] *Théorie Mécanique de la Chaleur*, p. 393 (1869).

is no qualitative distinction between the adhesions when the angle is greater or less than 90°, this definition will not be used here.

7. Measurement of contact angles: hysteresis. The experimental determination of contact angles is complicated by two factors: first, that the angle depends on the surface tension of the liquid surface; second, that the angle is rarely definite, but may have any value between two extremes, according as the liquid is tending to advance over a dry surface, or to recede from a previously wetted one.

The effect of contamination of the liquid surface is to diminish the contact angle. This is clear from equation (3); the value of W_{SL} will not be affected by contamination on the liquid-air surface such as insoluble grease on water, but γ_{LA} will be diminished. Hence the value of $\cos\theta$ must be greater if the liquid surface tension is diminished by contamination, and θ must be less. The importance of a clean liquid surface for determining contact angles has not always been recognized; some of the results in the literature are probably considerably too low owing to no provision having been made for cleaning the surface.

The second complication, that the angle depends on whether the liquid is advancing over or receding from a solid surface, has also been too often overlooked; mathematical works on Capillarity rarely mention it at all. It may, however, be observed without any apparatus with almost any rain drop travelling down an ordinarily dirty window pane;[1] these appear to stick somewhat in their downward path and the lower edge has a much larger angle than the upper. The angle is much larger, usually, if the liquid is advancing than if it is receding; forces insufficient to move the line of contact of liquid and solid raise or lower the angle anywhere within the limits of the 'advancing' and 'receding' angles, beyond which the line of contact moves along the surface. This difference between advancing and receding angles is often called the 'hysteresis' of the contact angle. Early references to it in the literature are scarce; Rayleigh[2] referred to it in 1890; Pockels[3] measured it for several liquids; Sulman[4] studied it in connexion with the flotation of minerals. It is well known to those who have measured surface tension by the rise in a capillary tube, for the rise is often less if the liquid is pushing its way up from below than if it is falling from a point above its final equilibrium height.

The cause of the 'hysteresis' of contact angles is still obscure. It looks superficially as if there was a frictional resistance to motion of the liquid edge over the solid. Sometimes, if sufficient time is allowed, the liquid settles down to an equilibrium, stationary angle, the same after either advancing or receding motion; Ablett[5] thought that this was the arithmetic mean of the 'advancing' and 'receding' angles obtained with advancing or receding motions of equal speeds. More commonly, however, the edge of the liquid sticks permanently, with a difference between

[1] Cf. A. A. Milne, *Now We Are Six*, p. 89 (1927).
[2] *Phil. Mag.*, **30**, 397 (1890).
[3] *Physikal. Z.*, **15**, 39 (1914).
[4] *Trans. Inst. Min. and Met.*, **29**, 88 (1919).
[5] *Phil. Mag.*, **46**, 244 (1923).

the angles left after advancing or receding motion sometimes as much as 40°, or more.

Adam and Jessop[1] attempted to formulate the hysteresis as an effect of a frictional force F, operating along the surface with equal intensity, when advancing and receding motions were just prevented. Equation (2) would be modified, for advancing motion, to

$$\gamma_{SA}-\gamma_{SL} = \gamma_{LA}\cos\theta_A+F, \tag{4}$$

and for receding motion to

$$\gamma_{SA}-\gamma_{SL} = \gamma_{LA}\cos\theta_R-F, \tag{5}$$

θ_A and θ_R being the advancing and receding angles. Combining (3), (4), and (5), the equilibrium angle θ, which would be obtained in the absence of friction, and the magnitude of the friction F, are given by

$$2\cos\theta = \cos\theta_R+\cos\theta_A, \tag{6}$$

$$2F = \gamma_{LA}(\cos\theta_R-\cos\theta_A). \tag{7}$$

This treatment is probably nothing but a formal description, however. It is very difficult to see how there can be a permanent frictional resistance to the motion of a liquid over a solid. No doubt the layer of molecules next the surface can move with great difficulty, if at all, but the molecules above this could easily roll over the edge of the stationary layer next the solid.

An alternative explanation of the hysteresis is that the work of adhesion between the liquid and the solid surface is actually different for a dry surface and for one that has previously been wetted, even for a very short time. Most writers have taken this view in some form; Edser[2] says 'it is probable that the liquid is absorbed in the solid surface, which it penetrates to a finite distance', and points out that this absorption increases instead of decreasing the surface tension of the solid-air surface. The previous treatment of the solid surface often has a marked influence on the 'hysteresis' of the contact angle. Pockels[3] found that the difference between the advancing and receding angles with various liquids and platinum or glass was always diminished, and sometimes abolished entirely, after heating the solid surface to redness. Bartell and Wooley[4] found, with glass and silica surfaces and various organic liquids, that the receding angle depends very little on the previous treatment of the surface, but the advancing angle may be diminished until in some cases it becomes equal to the receding angle, by heating first in the vapour of water or benzene, finishing by heating to a maximum temperature of 625° C. in dry clean air. It is probable that the structure and the composition of the surface undergo considerable changes in this treatment.

As far as the available evidence goes, it appears that the cleaner the surface, the smaller is the hysteresis of the contact angle. It seems possible that the large advancing contact angle (small adhesion between liquid and solid) is due to the presence of some film which prevents the liquid adhering closely to the solid; after contact with the liquid, this film is wholly or

[1] *J.C.S.* (1925), 1865.
[2] *4th Colloid Report*, p. 292 (1922).
[3] *Physikal. Z.*, **15**, 39 (1914).
[4] *J.A.C.S.* (1933), 3518.

partially removed, so that the contact between the liquid and the solid becomes more complete, and the work of adhesion rises, giving the smaller receding angle. This film may be merely air, in which case its removal may be termed soaking of the liquid into the surface of the solid, or 'sorption'; it may possibly be a film of some greasy material, which is very easily deposited on solid surfaces from ordinary air; a short period of contact with the liquid may remove it either by solution or by replacement at the

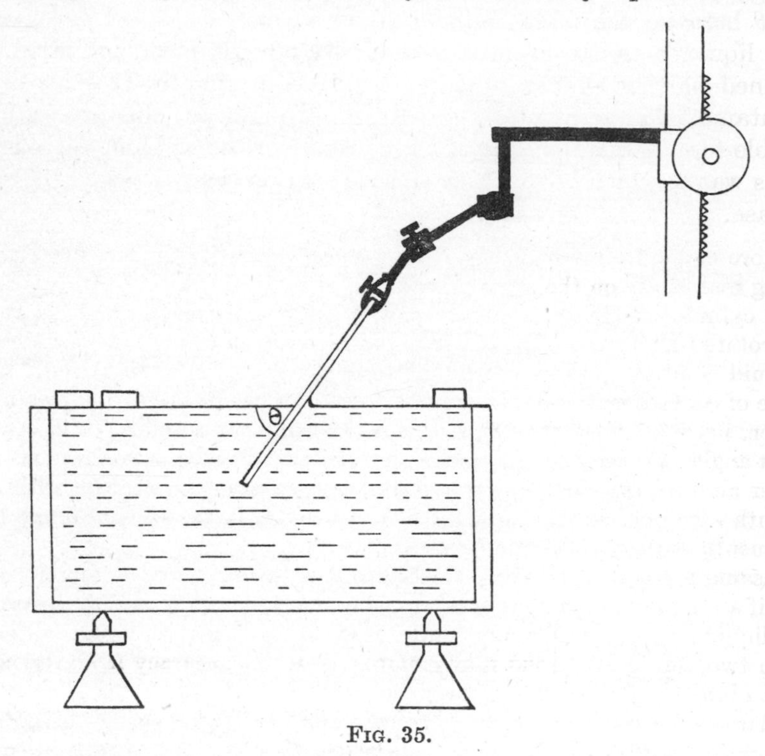

FIG. 35.

surface by the molecules of a liquid such as water, which has usually a stronger attraction for solid surfaces than has greasy matter. Such a film need not be over one molecule thick, perhaps not even a complete monomolecular film (see § 9; and Appendix).

When the solid surface can be obtained in the form of a reasonably flat plate a few centimetres across, the easiest method of measuring the contact angles is that commonly known as the 'plate' method. The solid is held in an adjustable holder capable of being tilted to any angle; provision should also be made for raising and lowering it slowly with respect to the water surface, so as to measure the angle under advancing and receding conditions. The plate is set at various angles until a position is found at which the water surface remains undistorted right up to the line of contact with the solid. Fig. 35 shows the form of apparatus used by Adam and Jessop.[1] For the advancing angle the plate is lowered slightly and the

[1] *J.C.S.* (1925), 1865; cf. Adam and Morrell, *J.S.C.I.*, **53**, 255T (1934).

angle is taken after about a minute; for receding motion it is raised and the angle taken at a similar time. Care must be taken to avoid waves on the water; and the setting of the plate to the required angle should be done before, not after, the raising or lowering. This will require usually two or three trials. For a great many purposes, since the angle of contact is not constant within two or three degrees over the whole surface, simply dipping a protractor into the liquid is sufficient for the measurement of the angle θ between the plate and the liquid surface.

The liquid is contained in a trough filled to the brim, provided with paraffined barriers similar to those described in Chapter II for sweeping up contamination accidentally present on the surface; this precaution is desirable for the maintenance of the normal surface tension, with liquids such as water, which have a high surface tension easily lowered by traces of grease.

A more elaborate method, which may be called the 'cylinder' method, depending essentially on the same principle, was used by Ablett.[1] An accurately turned cylinder of the solid, mounted with its axis horizontal and capable of being rotated about this axis, is partially immersed in the liquid. The level of the liquid is adjusted until the liquid surface remains horizontal right up to the line of contact with the solid, under prescribed conditions of rotation of the cylinder, i.e. with prescribed speeds of advancing and receding motion. The contact angle can easily be calculated from the relative heights of the axis of the cylinder and the level of the water. This method is more accurate with large than with very small angles; it should be combined with some device for cleaning or frequently renewing the liquid surface.

The same method in principle can be used with thin wires, or single textile fibres, if a microscope (preferably a travelling microscope) is used for inspection of the liquid surface. Adam and Shute[2] have studied contact angles with one, or with two, liquids and solid fibres, finding that the accuracy is almost equal to that obtainable by the plate method.

For large angles of contact simple inspection of the liquid surface is sufficient to determine, within two or three degrees, whether the adjustment is correct so as to give a water surface flat right up to the line of contact with the solid. For smaller angles the reflection of an illuminated slit, held at an oblique angle to the line of contact of the solid and liquid, gives a sensitive test; if the liquid surface is not flat up to the line of contact, the reflection is curved near to the solid. Alternatively, ruled lines held underneath the surface, obliquely to the line of contact, may be viewed through the liquid surface; if the liquid surface is not plane, these appear curved near the solid surface.

Two very sensitive methods for detecting the presence of any contact angle, in cases where it is nearly zero, are described by Richards and Carver,[3] and by Bosanquet and Hartley.[4] The former photographed the reflection of an illuminated slit from the liquid surface and also from the solid surface; if the reflections from the solid and the liquid are continuous, the contact angle is zero; a finite angle causes a break in the reflected line of light. The latter workers poured the liquid

[1] *Phil. Mag.*, **46**, 244 (1923).

[2] *J. Soc. Dyers and Col.* (1937), p. 125; *Symposium on Wetting and Detergency*, p. 53 (1937).

[3] *J.A.C.S.* (1921), 827.

[4] *Phil. Mag.*, **42**, 456 (1921).

into a shallow glass trough, tilted so that the liquid formed a prism with a small angle. A line ruled on paper, held parallel to the edge of this prism below the trough, was observed through the liquid and the glass. If there is a finite contact angle, there is an area above the liquid in which this line is invisible.

Various optical means for observing the direction of reflection of light from the solid surface and from the liquid surface, very close to the edge, and so deducing the contact angle. have been given by Pockels,[1] Herstad,[2] and Langmuir.[2a]

In tubes of glass, silica, or other transparent material the contact angle may be found by microscopic observation.[3] The optical distortion due to the curvature of the walls of the tube should be eliminated by immersing in a flat-sided bath of a liquid of the same refractive index as the tube.

With surfaces of rather small extent, but still sufficiently large to be approximately plane under a low power of the microscope, Taggart's bubble method[4] gives fairly accurate results. A bubble of air on the end of a vertical tube is brought into contact with the solid and the tube is slowly moved upwards. If the contact angle is not too small, the bubble sticks to the solid for some time, and the angle between the edge of the bubble and the solid may be observed and measured by means of a microscope fixed horizontally at the level of the solid surface. This method has been much used with mineral surfaces. Wark has also used a relation between the volume of a bubble, area of contact with the solid, and contact angle, to determine the angle.[5]

The contact angle can also be determined by measuring the height of rise of the liquid, whose surface tension must be known, in a capillary tube. For small tubes the rise is

$$\frac{2\gamma \cos \theta}{gDr},$$

where r is the radius of the tube and D the density of the liquid. The hysteresis can be investigated by using both rising and falling columns of liquid. This method has been used by many workers, including Bosanquet and Hartley, and Owen and Dufton,[6] who determined the contact angle of mercury against steel as 154°, using X-rays to measure the depth to which the mercury was depressed ($\cos \theta$ being negative, there was a depression, not an elevation). Haller[7] has used a modification of this method, measuring not the rise of the liquid in a vertical tube but the pressure required to move the liquid forward or backward along a horizontal capillary tube.

Another method is to measure the thickness of a drop of liquid resting on a horizontal plate, or of a bubble underneath a plate. If the bubble or drop is large, so that the curvature at the apex can be neglected and this part of the surface treated as flat, the contact angle is given by the equation[8]

$$1 \pm \cos \theta = \frac{gDh^2}{2\gamma}, \tag{8}$$

[1] *Physikal. Z.*, **15**, 39 (1914). [2] *Kolloid-Z.*, **55**, 169 (1931). [2a] See Appendix.

[3] Bartell and Merrill, *J. Physical Chem.*, **36**, 1178 (1932); Carter and Jones, *Trans. Faraday Soc.*, **30**, 1028 (1934).

[4] Taggart, Taylor, and Ince, *Am. Inst. Min. Met. Eng.* (Milling Methods), Tech. Pub. 204 (1929); Wark and Cox, *ibid.*, 461 (1932); Siedler, *Kolloid-Z.*, **68**, 89 (1934).

[5] *J. Physical Chem.* (1933), 623.

[6] *Proc. Physical Soc.*, **38**, 204 (1925).

[7] *Kolloid-Z.*, **54**, 7 (1931).

[8] Cf. Poynting and Thomson, *Properties of Matter* (1909), p. 156.

D is the density, h the total thickness of the bubble, or drop. In this method it is difficult to ensure the angle being either the advancing or the receding; it is likely to be intermediate between the two extremes: probably near the advancing angle for the drop and near the receding angle for the bubble. The positive sign in (8) is applicable to the bubble, the negative to the drop.

8. Factors modifying contact angles: greasy layers; moisture on or just below the surface; roughness of surfaces. Layers of grease not more than one molecule thick can increase the contact angle very considerably; it may not even be necessary for the layers to have their molecules closely packed on the surface. Langmuir[1] showed that a glass plate brought up through a water surface covered by a monomolecular film of some fatty substance had its contact angle very much increased. Blodgett[2] finds that the wetting of glass covered by a layer of stearic acid three molecules thick is no better than that of paraffin wax. Devaux[3] also found a considerable diminution of wetting by layers one molecule thick. Some of the adsorbed layers on minerals, which increase the contact angle sufficiently to ensure flotation, are probably only one molecule thick (§ 17).

Prolonged soaking of organic materials in water, including varnished or painted surfaces, and even paraffin wax, produces a greater or smaller decrease in the contact angle,[4] without, however, abolishing the hysteresis, as far as the author's experience goes. If many substances are allowed to crystallize in contact with water the angles against water are often lower than when they crystallize in air; this was attributed by Devaux[5] to an orientation of the water-attracting groups outwards, but is more probably due to water-molecules becoming entrapped in the surface layers, and increasing the adhesion of the surfaces for water. Such penetration into the surface layers, with consequent change in the contact angles, is a very frequent phenomenon; its amount depends on the surface porosity of the solid, and also on the nature of the liquid.

With mercury and glass or silica the presence of moisture on or near the surface increases the contact angle. This angle is usually in the neighbourhood of 140°, but this high value is probably due to the moisture which is so firmly held by these solids near their surfaces. Young[6] quotes Casbois, of Metz, as having shown that prolonged boiling of mercury in a barometer tube may change the meniscus from convex to concave upwards; Schumacher[7] produced a capillary rise of mercury in glass and silica by baking out, instead of the usual fall; and Manley[8] has achieved the same result both by boiling the mercury in the tube and by prolonged electrical discharge.

The films of oxide so tenaciously held by aluminium are well known to

[1] *Trans. Faraday Soc.*, **15**, 69 (1920).
[2] *J.A.C.S.* (1934), 495; (1935), 1007.
[3] *J. Phys. Radium*, **4**, 293 (1923).
[4] Adam and Jessop, *J.C.S.* (1925), 1863; Pockels, *Kolloid-Z.*, **62**, 1 (1933).
[5] *J. Phys. Radium*, **4**, 184s (1923); **6**, 90s (1925); *Kolloid-Z.*, **58**, 266 (1932).
[6] *Phil. Trans.* (1805), 73. [7] *J.A.C.S.* (1923), 2255. [8] *Phil. Mag.*, **5**, 958 (1928).

be the cause of the difficulty in wetting this metal with liquid metals, and consequently of obtaining a satisfactory solder.

If the surfaces are markedly rough, the contact angle observed will not be the true angle representing the work of adhesion of the liquid to the solid. The effect of roughness is to increase the apparent angle if the true (advancing) angle is greater than 90°, but to decrease it if the true angle is less than 90°. This is because the liquid penetrates into the hollows if the true angle is less than 90°; part of the supposedly plane surface consists not of the solid but of the liquid, which has a zero contact angle against itself. If the true angle exceeds 90°, no liquid penetrates into the hollows, the apparently plane surface of solid consists therefore partly of solid and partly of air, for which the liquid has practically no adhesion. Coghill and Anderson[1] noted an equilibrium angle of about 145° and an advancing angle of 160° for powdered galena thickly sprinkled on a plate; a plane surface of galena has a much smaller angle. A similar phenomenon has been noticed by the author, with plates covered with fine mineral powders on which a layer of stearic acid had been deposited. The true contact angle of the solid was probably about 100°; the observed angle on the rough granular surface was about 160°.

9. Approximate values of some contact angles. Most organic liquids and water form zero angles with *clean* glass and silica, also with clean metallic surfaces. A few dilute solutions of organic bases, containing quaternary nitrogen groups at the end of a long fatty chain, form quite considerable angles with glass, because the solutes are adsorbed on to the glass with the long chains outwards. The largest contact angle found with solids and water appears to be that of paraffin wax, 105°. Equation (3) shows that this value corresponds with a work of adhesion between the water and the wax, of 54 ergs per sq. cm., a value in fair agreement with the adhesional work of a long chain liquid paraffin for water, 48 ergs per sq. cm. (Chap. IV, § 2). The value of 105° against a clean water surface indicates that the solid surface consists of CH_3 and CH_2 groups, or of other groups having no greater adhesion for water than these, if there are any such groups.

The contact angle of water against mineral surfaces varies with the state of the mineral surfaces. Edser[2] gives values from 13° to 58° receding, 62° to 91° advancing. Wark,[3] however, reviewing more recent work, considers that really clean surfaces of most minerals, including sulphides, have quite small angles.

Molten metals on glass and silica have high contact angles, usually greater than 90°; this is because the cohesion 2γ of the liquid is much greater than W_{SL}. Young's value of 140° for mercury on glass seems as trustworthy as any later values. Mercury on steel gives 154°,[4] but on amalgamated copper, zero angle.

[1] *U.S. Bureau of Mines*, Tech. Paper 262, 47 (1923).
[2] *4th Colloid Report*, p. 290 (1922).
[3] *Am. Inst. Min. Met. Eng.*, Tech. Pub. 461, 12 (1932).
[4] Owen and Dufton, *Proc. Physical Soc.*, **38**, 204 (1925).

10. Contact angles and molecular orientation at solid surfaces. Just as the work of adhesion between two liquids (Chap. IV, § 2) gives information as to the orientation of molecules of an organic liquid in contact with water, so W_{SL}, deduced by (3) from the contact angle, may indicate the orientation of the surface molecules in a solid. The problem is easier in one respect, for the surface molecules of a solid are not in constant motion with changes of orientation, as are those of a liquid. On the other hand, the soaking of the liquid into the surface layers of the solid may confuse the results in a way not likely to occur with the liquid surface; also the surface of the solid may be difficult to clean. This last difficulty has, in the author's experience, proved surprisingly small.

Adam and Jessop[1] found that pure long chain acids and alcohols, solidified in contact with air, showed contact angles against clean water of about 100°, nearly as large as the value (105°) obtained for paraffin wax. If a cut was taken through the solid mass, the contact angles of the surfaces so exposed proved to be very variable. In some cases they were high, about 100°, in others about 50°, which corresponds to an adhesion to water of about 120 ergs per sq. cm., more than double that of the purely hydrocarbon surface. It is evident that cutting through the interior sometimes exposes a number of water-attracting groups, but sometimes does not.

This variation, while at first sight surprising, is in perfect accord with the known arrangement of the molecules in the crystals of these compounds. These crystals consist of double sheets of molecules, bimolecular leaflets of indefinite extension in two dimensions, the molecules in each half having their polar groups in the middle of the leaflet and the hydrocarbon ends outwards. The character of the cut surface depends on the direction which the knife takes, relative to these sheets of molecules. If it travels parallel to the sheets, only hydrocarbon groups are exposed, so that the angle will be about 105°; if perpendicular to the sheets, one water-attracting group will be exposed for each molecule, or every 15 CH_2 or CH_3 groups. This is the maximum number of groups which can be exposed without destroying the orientation of molecules in the crystals; it is probably this surface which shows the attraction for water of 120 ergs. Clearly only a small proportion of COOH or CH_2OH groups in the surface is sufficient to produce a great increase in the attractive power for water.

A long chain iodide gave the same high angle when cut as on the naturally solidified surfaces; this is in accord with the known low adhesion of organic halides for water. Cut surfaces of paraffin wax showed the same angle as the natural surfaces.

An attempt was made to obtain a surface with all the water-attracting groups oriented outwards, by crystallizing the acids on a water surface. This failed, probably because the lowest layer of molecules next the water, although it probably was oriented with the hydrophilic groups to the water, stuck to the water instead of to the solid cake when this was removed. The adhesion between the carboxyl ends of the molecules of this

[1] *J.C.S.* (1925), 1863.

layer and the water would naturally be much greater than that between the hydrocarbon ends of the molecules and the next layer in the crystal. Had it been possible to leave an outer layer of molecules with the carboxyl groups all pointing outwards, so that the surface consisted entirely of carboxyl groups, a zero contact angle would have been expected.

Some rather similar measurements were made by Nietz,[1] using a much greater variety of organic substances, but they are not strictly comparable with the preceding, as he did not clean his water surfaces. There was an interesting alternating effect between the odd and even fatty acids, which was probably due to differences in the spreading pressure (Chap. II, § 35) of the acids causing different degrees of lowering of the surface tension of the water. The odd acids have a higher spreading pressure than the even.

The fact that the angle is practically the same as that obtained with paraffin wax, when the fatty acids and alcohols are oriented with their long chains outwards, shows that the attraction of the water for the hydrophilic groups buried some 20 A. below the surface is inappreciable. Crystal flakes of the long chain amine hydrochlorides, which presumably also have their hydrocarbon chains oriented outwards, gave smaller angles (45°); these are electrolytically dissociated and it is possible that the range of attraction is greater than with the undissociated carboxyl or alcohol groups.

Whether or not the influence of polar groups buried below the surface, at the end of long hydrocarbon chains, extends to the surface depends on the test used for them. Adam, Morrell, and Norrish[2] found that the COOH or CH_2OH groups in long chain acids or alcohols, buried so that they scarcely attract water at all as judged by the contact angle, nevertheless exert a very considerable catalytic effect on the combination between ethylene and halogens. Paraffin wax does not catalyse this combination. The depth of the 'surface' is therefore much greater, when judged by the penetration of gaseous ethylene and halogens, than when estimated by contact with liquid water.

11. Contact angles with two liquids and a solid. The mathematical treatment of the case of two liquids A and B, and a solid S, is similar to that of a single liquid and a solid. In Fig. 36 the angle θ_{AB} will denote that in the liquid A, its supplement, the angle in B, will be written θ_{BA}. Resolving the surface tensions, as before, parallel to the solid surface, the condition of equilibrium, in the absence of hysteresis, is

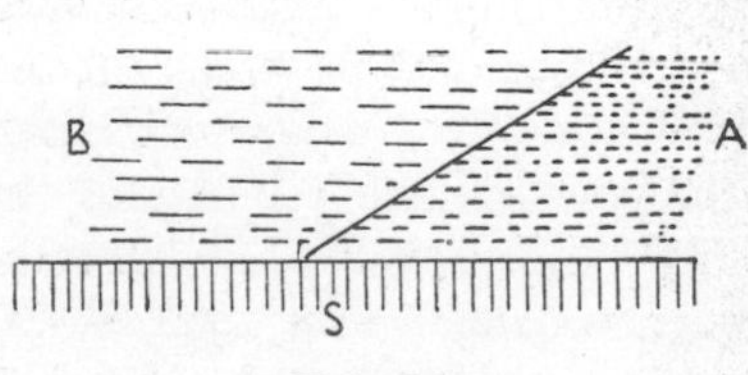

FIG. 36.

$$\gamma_{BS}-\gamma_{AS}=\gamma_{AB}\cos\theta_{AB}.$$

The values of the adhesional work between the two liquids and the solid, W_{AS} and W_{BS}, are given by Dupré's equation

$$W_{AS}=\gamma_{A}+\gamma_{S}-\gamma_{AS}$$
$$W_{BS}=\gamma_{B}+\gamma_{S}-\gamma_{BS}.$$

[1] *J. Physical Chem.*, **32**, 255, 620 (1928).

[2] *J.C.S.* (1925) 2793.

Combining, $$W_{AS}-W_{BS} = \gamma_A-\gamma_B+\gamma_{AB}\cos\theta_{AB}, \quad (9)$$
which reduces, as it should, to (3) if the fluid B is air, so that γ_B and W_{BS} are zero, and $\gamma_{AB} = \gamma_A$.

12. Determination of the work of adhesion when the contact angle is zero. Bartell and Osterhof[1] pointed out that the work of adhesion of a single liquid to a solid can be determined, even though the contact angle is zero and equation (3) is not directly applicable, if a second liquid can be found which gives a finite angle with the same solid, both against air and against the first liquid. If the second liquid is B, then W_{BS} can be found from (3), and W_{AS} from (9). The precaution ought to be taken of showing that the two liquids do not affect each other's surface tensions, or of mutually saturating each liquid with the other, before determining the angles and surface tensions. If this is not done, the values of γ_A and γ_B may be different in the various equations, and the final result will be erroneous.

13. Measurement of contact angles with two liquids. Little work has yet been done on this problem, important though it is. Scarlett, Morgan, and Hildebrand[2] attempted to use a plate method like that of § 6; their results indicate the existence of a large difference between advancing and receding angles, the displacement of a film of one liquid already formed on the surface, by the other liquid, being very slow. Their results are in general agreement with those of Hofmann,[3] for glass surfaces; when the liquids are water and a hydrocarbon liquid, the angle in the water is acute; the 'receding' angle seems to be very small, and the 'advancing' angle fairly large, possibly nearly 90°.

14. Displacement of one liquid from a solid by another. One liquid will displace another from a solid powder if the contact angle in that liquid, made by the liquid-liquid interface with the solid, is acute. This is because the powder may be taken as an aggregate of capillary tubes; if the angle in A, θ_{AB}, is acute, the meniscus between the liquids is concave towards B, and the boundary between the liquids is driven towards B by the hydrostatic pressure difference set up by the curved surface. Equation (9) gives the conditions for the angle θ_{AB} to be acute; it is necessary, not that the work of adhesion W_{AS} should exceed W_{BS}, but that the quantity $W_{AS}-\gamma_A$ should exceed $W_{BS}-\gamma_B$. These quantities, the difference of the work of adhesion and the surface tension of the liquid, have been termed by Freundlich the 'adhesion tensions' of the liquid against the solid. By equation (3), the adhesion tension is also equal to $\gamma_A\cos\theta_A$, where θ_A is the contact angle of A against S. For A to displace B, the adhesion tension of A must exceed that of B. Bartell and Osterhof have made use of these adhesion tensions graphically, to exhibit the energy levels of different combinations of solids and liquids, and to determine when displacement will occur.

[1] *5th Colloid Symposium Monograph*, p. 113 (1927).
[2] *J. Physical Chem.*, **31**, 1566 (1927).
[3] *Z. physikal. Chem.*, **83**, 393–403 (1913).

This displacement of one liquid by another is sometimes important in oil mining, when water may displace oil by capillary forces from porous strata.[1]

It should be noticed that the theory indicates that equilibrium is possible between two liquids, on *a single surface* of a solid, if the contact angle is finite. But in a granular mass, or a porous system equivalent to fine capillaries, displacement of one liquid by another will occur through the curvature of the meniscus, provided that the 'advancing' angle of contact is less than 90° in one liquid. It is possible for the advancing contact angle to exceed 90° in both liquids, for although the equilibrium contact angle cannot be obtuse in both liquids, the advancing angle is always greater than the equilibrium angle.

15. Contact angles of powders. The contact angle of a powder is often of great technical importance, but its measurement is difficult. Some information may be obtained, with moderately large particles, by direct examination under the microscope; also the ease of flotation of the powder on a liquid-air surface gives qualitative information. A powder which is easily blown about on water is probably floating far out, and has an angle probably near 90°; one which floats but looks fairly low in the water and is not easily blown about has a smaller angle, and one which cannot be floated at all has a very small angle. For angles when two liquids are present, shaking the powder with the liquids, and observing the type of emulsion formed, is some guide (see § 21).

Freundlich, Enslin, and Lindau[2] obtained a semi-quantitative estimate of the contact angle by placing a standard quantity of the powder, ground and elutriated to standard size, on a porous sintered glass disk. The liquid was brought into good contact with the under side of this disk, and the rate at which the liquid entered the powder observed. Quartz powder was quickly wetted, but if certain basic dyestuffs were adsorbed on it, the rate of wetting diminished very greatly.

The work of Bartell and his collaborators[3] gives a quantitative measure of the contact angle and adhesion tension of a powder, either against one liquid, or at the interface between two liquids. The pressure exerted by the liquid entering a highly compressed plug of the powder is measured; reproducible results are obtained if the pressure on the compressed powder exceeds 2,500 lb. per sq. in. The angle so measured is probably the advancing angle. The powder is compressed in a brass cell, connected with a manometer, and liquid is admitted at one end. If the contact angle is less than 90°, the liquid enters, and the pressure P required to prevent the liquid moving forwards in the plug is proportional to the surface tension of the liquid and the cosine of the contact angle. The apparatus has been recently modified so that the pressure required to displace the liquid from

[1] Cf. Bartell and Miller, *Ind. Eng. Chem.*, **24**, 335 (1932).

[2] *Kolloid-Beih.*, **37**, 242 (1933).

[3] *4th Colloid Symposium Monograph*, p. 240 (1926); *5th do.*, p. 113 (1927); *Z. physikal. Chem.*, **130**, 715 (1927); *Ind. Eng. Chem.*, **19**, 1277 (1927); **21**, 1102 (1929); *J. Physical Chem.*, **34**, 1399 (1930); **36**, 1178 (1932).

the powder can be measured,[1] this gives the receding angle. With silica powder the adhesion tension for receding liquids was found to be about 6 ergs per sq. cm. lower than for advancing liquids—a strange result, for the receding angle is smaller than the advancing, which requires a larger adhesion tension. It is thought that the newer apparatus gives more reliable results than the older; the results agree well with those obtained by the microscopic inspection method.[2] Bell, Cutter, and Price have recently studied the method.[3]

If the plug were a system of uniform, cylindrical, straight capillary tubes of radius r, the pressure would be

$$P = \frac{2\gamma}{r}\cos\theta.$$

The difficulty lies in the fact that the pores between the particles are neither straight, nor of uniform bore, nor even of known cross-section. Bartell and Osterhof[4] circumvent these difficulties fairly satisfactorily, obtaining a value for r, the radius of the equivalent cylindrical capillary tube, by measuring the pressure set up by a liquid known to wet the powder completely, so that θ is zero, and also by measuring the rate of flow of liquids, under pressure, through the plugs, and applying Poiseuille's law for the flow through capillary tubes. The formula for the flow through the plug becomes, when the unknown number of tubes is eliminated from the ordinary formula and the volume V of the liquid in the powder is introduced,

$$Q = \frac{R^2PVt}{8\eta l_0^2}.$$

Q is the volume of liquid passing in time t under pressure P, l_0 is the length of the tubes, and η the viscosity of the liquid. The length of the tubes, l_0, is taken as $\frac{1}{2}\pi l$, l being the length of the plug, this factor being introduced to account for the bending of the tubes round each particle of the powder, and some other complications. The errors due to departure of the tube from circular cross-section would be quite small, if they were elliptical and of moderate eccentricity; and are neglected, although it seems too much to hope that an elliptical cross-section would be found in the channels between grains of a powder. The simplifications appear somewhat sweeping, but in the cases where the radius of the equivalent capillary tube has been calculated both by this method and by the use of a liquid giving a known zero angle, there has been very fair agreement. There is a slow decrease in the measured 'radius' of the tubes, determined by the second method, as the experiment proceeds, which is probably due to very fine particles being washed into, and obstructing, the passages.

The method has been applied to the determination of the contact angle of a powder with single liquids, and also with the interfaces between two

[1] *J. Physical Chem.*, **36**, 3115 (1932); **38**, 495 (1934).
[2] Bartell and Merrill, *J. Physical Chem.*, **36**, 1178 (1932).
[3] *Symposium on Wetting and Detergency*, p. 19 (London, 1937).
[4] *J. Physical Chem.*, **32**, 1553 (1928).

liquids. In the case of the technical problem, of the displacement of one liquid from a powder by another, the uncertainties in the theoretical deduction of the contact angle do not matter much, as it is generally the measured pressure of displacement which is the important quantity.

16. Conditions for the stability of solid particles at a liquid interface. Flotation. It is well known that a waxed needle will float on the surface of water, although it is of much higher density. Small particles of many solids, particularly if coated with a substance which gives them an exterior surface of a hydrocarbon nature, also float, sometimes most obstinately. They attach themselves to air-bubbles and sometimes, if sunk by violent agitation, drag down air-bubbles with them, or if the bubbles are large, are refloated by reason of the bubbles attached to them. This flotation is wholly due to surface forces; gravity tends to sink the particles, but the surface forces resist the complete wetting of the surface. If the solid is once wholly submerged, it does not spontaneously rise again to the surface; but if taken to the surface, it floats afresh, unless it has become so much soaked in the liquid as to have its surface properties changed.

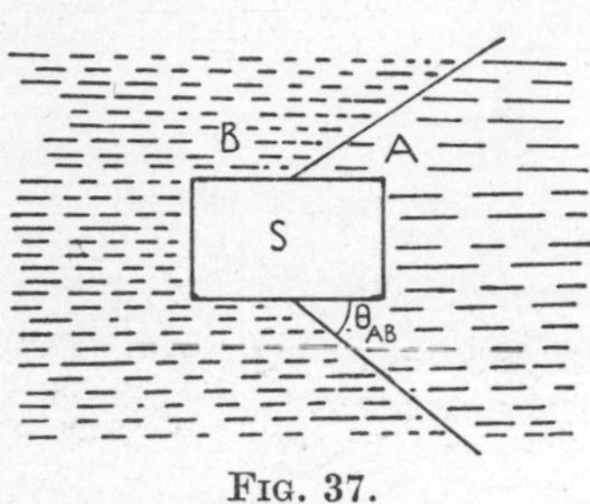

Fig. 37.

A very similar phenomenon is the attachment of solid particles to the interface between two liquids. Solid particles which go to the interface will stabilize emulsions of one liquid in the other.

The theory of the two phenomena is mathematically the same; the condition for adherence of the solid to the interface is simply that the contact angle must be finite. In practice, for stability in flotation, it is desirable that the angle should not be too near zero. The theory is due to des Coudres[1] and Hofmann.[2]

Neglecting first the weight of the particles, consider first the case of a particle S with straight sides, in two liquids A and B, the contact angle in A being θ_{AB} (Fig. 37). The equilibrium of the line of contact depends only on the free surface energies, or surface tensions, so that we can use the mathematical fiction of surface tensions pulling parallel to the surfaces. With a finite angle, equilibrium is obtained; none of the tensions is greater than the sum of the other two. If γ_{BS} becomes stronger, the contact angle θ_{AB} must become smaller, until, when it becomes zero, the line of contact is pulled right off the solid, which goes wholly into A. Thus if $\gamma_{BS} > \gamma_{AS}+\gamma_{AB}$, the solid goes into A; if $\gamma_{AS} > \gamma_{BS}+\gamma_{AB}$, it goes into B, and if neither of the solid tensions exceeds the sum of the other and the liquid tension, the solid is stable at the interface with a contact angle.

The theory applies of course to air-liquid systems as well as to systems

[1] Quoted by Rhumbler, *Arch. Entwickelungsmechanik*, **7**, 325 (1898).

[2] *Z. physikal. Chem.*, **83**, 388 (1913). See also Freundlich, *Kapillarchemie*, **1**, **222** ff. (1930).

of two liquids; if B be air, θ_{AB} becomes the ordinary contact angle. One possibility of the two-liquid systems is absent from the single liquid system; since θ cannot become 180° the solid cannot be drawn up wholly into the air.

Nevertheless, a solid of suitable shape can float with more than half its bulk out of water,[1] as is shown for circular cross-sections in Fig. 38. If the contact angle is greater than 90°, the spherical particle floats with its middle line out of the water.

The weight of solid substances causes them to float in a slight depression in the liquid, whose dimensions vary with the size and weight of the

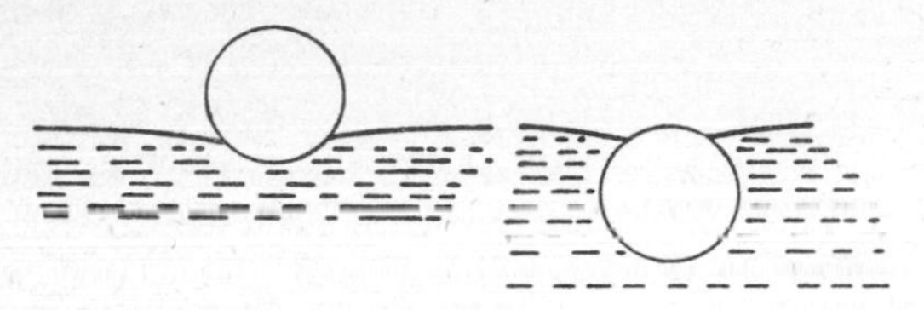

FIG. 38.

particles; let l be the perimeter of the particle following the line of contact, α the angle which the water makes with the horizontal at the line of contact, and $W-w$ the difference between the weight of the particle and of the liquid which it displaces, then $W-w = \gamma l \sin\alpha$, γ being the surface tension.

All particles of sufficiently small size and convex cross-section can float in the manner indicated in Fig. 38, provided the contact angle is finite. It remains to consider whether the angle in question is the receding or the advancing angle. Since the weight of the particle tends to immerse the particle, it would at first sight appear that it is the advancing angle which is concerned. But the receding angle also must be finite if the flotation is to be stable; for stable flotation involves that, if the line of contact is moved accidentally up the particle, it will tend to return down the particle before complete immersion takes place. A displacement of the line of contact upwards diminishes the angle, by Fig. 38, but the line of contact will not move downwards spontaneously, until the diminution brings the contact angle below the receding angle, at which the surface forces can move it back again against the friction. If the particle is immersed before this occurs, flotation will not be stable; hence it is the receding contact angle that must be finite for stable flotation. With care, however, temporary flotation should be possible, with a fairly small advancing angle. For flotation of long duration, there should be a margin of safety, for the contact angle may be diminished by soaking of the liquid into the solid.

Coghill and Anderson[2] have shown that sharp edges on solid substances increase the stability of flotation. In Fig. 39 suppose the liquid forms a

[1] Cf. Coghill and Anderson, *J. Physical Chem.*, **22**, 245 (1918).
[2] *U.S. Bureau of Mines*, Tech. Paper **262** (1923).

moderate advancing angle θ_A with the solid. Then the liquid edge can easily travel up the steep face PQ, but in order to start travelling along the horizontal face QR, it must be swung through an angle $180°-\phi$, where ϕ is the angle of the solid edge, into the position shown dotted. Experimentally, they found that it is necessary, in order to make a liquid pass a sharp edge at the top of a stationary solid object (such as the edge of a tumbler), to raise the level of the liquid sufficiently to produce nearly this change in the direction of the liquid surface. This edge effect is the reason why a tumbler of water can be overfilled, and why flaky minerals have an unusual tendency to float on water.

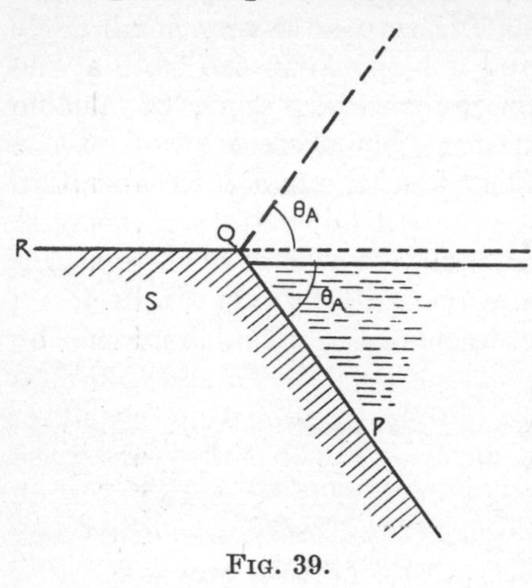

Fig. 39.

By taking advantage of this edge effect, solids with quite small contact angles, such as glass plates and prisms, can be floated; and the effect can be enhanced by cutting grooves on the solid surfaces.

17. Technical processes for separating minerals by flotation. Since the beginning of this century advantage has been taken, on an enormous scale, of the differences in ease of wetting of the various minerals and their different powers of adsorbing small traces of oils and other reagents, in separating the valuable from the valueless constituents of ores. It was more or less accidentally found that the different constituents of many ores often have a very different tendency to float on the surface of water, and that these differences can be greatly increased by addition of small quantities of various oils. The natural surface of a pool of water has not, however, nearly sufficient area, nor is it sufficiently easy to bring large amounts of ground ore gently on to the surface of water, to enable separation on a large scale to be achieved simply by sprinkling on to the surface of water. In practice, the 'froth-flotation' process is practically always employed; the ore is ground with water to a fairly fine powder, and a very large air-liquid surface is then produced in the suspension of ore and water, by forming a voluminous froth of fine bubbles. These bubbles, as they rise through the suspension, collect on their surface those particles which have a large angle of contact, carrying them up to the surface of the liquid, where the froth, highly charged with the valuable minerals, is swept off.[1]

[1] Until about 1919 the practice of flotation was conducted with much secrecy, and was on a semi-empirical basis. Since then the literature has become voluminous and in recent years the scientific principles underlying it have been fairly well elucidated. A long paper by Sulman (*Trans. Inst. Min. and Met.*, **29**, 44–204 (1919)) gave the first comprehensive description of the froth-flotation process and showed the fundamental importance of the contact angle. The reader will find excellent text-books in Gaudin's *Flotation* (1932), Luyken and Bierbrauer's *Flotation* (1931),

It is clear from § 16 that solid particles which have a large contact angle will adhere to the surface of the rising air bubbles, once they are brought into contact with them, while those having zero or a very small angle will remain in the bulk of the liquid and not appear in the froth at the surface. There are often differences between the contact angles of valuable and unwanted minerals in the natural state, but these are not, except in a few unusually favourable cases, sufficient to achieve a good separation by flotation. Advantage is taken of the property of various reagents to be selectively adsorbed at, or to combine with, the surface of the minerals which it is desired to float. Such reagents are usually termed 'collectors'; their function is to increase the contact angle of the valuable mineral by forming a film on its surface which is difficult to wet. In addition, it is usually necessary to add a small amount of some reagent which stabilizes the froth of small bubbles (the 'frothing agent'). In the early years of the process, complex mixtures of various oils such as pine oil, eucalyptus oil, etc., easily available at the mine, were generally used; these often contained sufficient amounts of both frothing and collecting agents to cause efficient flotation alone. The modification of the surface of the mineral was then usually termed 'oiling'. Perkins,[1] in a series of important patents in 1921, showed that a great many slightly soluble organic compounds acted as collectors for sulphide minerals; most of these contained, in addition to a reasonable proportion of non-polar hydrocarbon groups in the molecule, nitrogen or sulphur-containing groups. Two of the most important modern types of collectors for sulphides are the xanthates[2] (I) and 'aerofloats'[3] (II),

$$\underset{\text{I}}{\mathrm{RO{-}C({=}S){-}SM}} \qquad\qquad \underset{\text{II}}{\mathrm{(RO)(S{=})P(OR)(SM)}}$$

R being a hydrocarbon group and M a metal or other base, usually an alkali metal. They are used in exceedingly small amounts; under the best conditions it may be unnecessary to use more than the amount needed

and Petersen's *Schwimmaufbereitung* (1936). Taggart's *Handbook of Ore Dressing* (1927), pp. 779–904, gives a full account of patent literature and practice; Gaudin, Taggart, and their respective collaborators have published many illuminating papers in *Trans. Am. Inst. Min. Met. Eng.* and elsewhere; Bartsch (*Kolloid-Beih.*, **20**, 50 (1924)), Petersen (*Kolloid-Z.*, **58**, 121 (1932)), Siedler and others (*ibid.*, **60**, 318 (1932); **68**, 89 (1934)), Wark and others (*J. Physical Chem.* (1933), 797, 805, 815), and del Giudice (*Eng. and Min. Journ.*, May 1934), have written admirable accounts of the theory; other references will be found in the following pages. The importance of the process may be judged from the fact that, in 1931, it was said that about one hundred million tons of ore were being treated by flotation annually, and that this included nearly all the copper and lead-zinc ores mined throughout the world, together with an increasing proportion of numerous other ores. Much of the ore treated is of such low grade that its recovery by other means would not be commercially practicable.

[1] U.S.P. 1,364,304–8.

[2] Keller, U.S.P. 1,554,216; Lewis, U.S.P. 1,554,220; 1,560,170 (1925).

[3] Cf. Petersen, *Kolloid-Z.*, **58**, 121 (1932).

for a layer one molecule thick on the surface of the valuable mineral. There is little doubt that they form surface films with the alkyl group oriented outwards. Wark and Cox[1] have measured the contact angles of several minerals treated with a series of xanthates differing only in the length of the hydrocarbon chains, finding that the angle was practically independent of the nature of the underlying mineral, provided that this surface was of such a nature that the xanthates became attached at all, but increased steadily from 50° with methyl xanthate, to 74° with *n*-butyl and 96° with cetyl xanthate. In actual practice the xanthates such as cetyl, with very long chains, are too insoluble in water to be brought quickly enough on to the surface of the mineral; the best results are said to be obtained with a chain length of four or five carbon atoms, but considerations of cost may indicate the use of ethyl xanthate.

The precise method by which the sulphur-containing collectors, such as xanthates, attach themselves to the surface of the sulphide minerals, has been much discussed. There is a good deal of evidence that it is not usually simple adsorption, but an actual combination of the xanthate ion with the surface layer, forming an oriented film firmly attached to the heavy metal atoms of the mineral surface, with the hydrocarbon groups outwards; in other words, an oriented thin film of lead xanthate, in the case of galena, is formed as the outer layer of the space lattice of the mineral, by double decomposition with the soluble xanthate in the liquor. Taggart, Taylor, and Knoll's observations[2] on the interaction between powdered galena having a slightly oxidized surface and solutions of xanthates, showed that the xanthate was abstracted from solution; lead was not increased in the solution, but there was a decided increase in the concentration of sulphate and hydroxide in the solution; the oxidized layer appears to have contained both oxide and sulphate, the reactions at the surface being as below:

$$Pb(OH)_2+2KS\cdot CS\cdot OC_2H_5 = Pb(S\cdot CS\cdot OC_2H_5)_2+2KOH,$$
$$PbSO_4+2KS\cdot CS\cdot OC_2H_5 = Pb(S\cdot CS\cdot OC_2H_5)_2+K_2SO_4,$$

the lead atoms being firmly fixed to the underlying body of the mineral. It seems likely that a slight degree of oxidation of a sulphide surface is necessary for the formation of the surface film with xanthate and similar collectors; there is, however, practically certain to be sufficient oxidation unless very special precautions are taken to avoid access of air. Lintern and Adam[3] found that if a freshly cleaved surface of galena is kept in an atmosphere of hydrogen and continuously reduced electrolytically, its potential when used as an electrode does not change appreciably when xanthate is added; whereas if oxygen is allowed access to the surface, xanthate forms a surface film which lowers the electrode potential very considerably. In practice, too much oxidation, which might occur through

[1] *Am. Inst. Min. Met. Eng.*, Tech. Paper **461** (1932).
[2] *Ibid.* (Milling Methods), Tech. Paper **204** (1929).
[3] *Trans. Faraday Soc.*, **31**, 564 (1935).

the ore being exposed to moist air for long periods, is unfavourable for the flotation of sulphide ores.

Quite frequently the natural surface of a mineral requires preliminary chemical treatment before it will form the surface film required for collection. One of the commonest instances of this is with sphalerite (zinc sulphide), which does not float properly when treated with xanthates. If, however, it is given a preliminary treatment with dilute copper sulphate solution, a very small amount of copper sulphide is deposited on the surface and the ore becomes floatable, the surface being now capable of reaction with xanthates. Such treatment is usually termed 'activation'; in general, an activating solution for a sulphide mineral should contain a metallic ion whose sulphide is less soluble than that contained in the mineral; for zinc sulphides, silver, copper, mercury, cadmium, and lead salts are all effective activators.

Further, by suitable treatment of surfaces, the attachment of the collector and flotation may be prevented in special cases. This is often called 'depression'; it is particularly useful with complex sulphide ores for differentiating between the sulphides of different metals, several of which may be valuable if separated before smelting. Thus iron and zinc sulphides are frequently separated from lead sulphide[1] by the addition of cyanide to the liquor before the xanthate is added; this does not affect the flotation of the lead sulphide but prevents the iron and zinc floating. After the lead has been removed, the addition of copper salts permits the attachment of xanthate to the other sulphide minerals and they are floated off. Wark and Cox[2] have published a valuable study of the influence of cyanide concentration and alkalinity on the flotation of mixtures of iron, lead, and zinc sulphide ores. Lipetz and Rimskaja[3] give many valuable data on the influence of collectors and various activating and depressing reagents on the contact angle at various mineral surfaces.

By the use of other reagents certain oxidized ores may be floated. For the oxides and carbonates of basic metals, fatty acids such as oleic, and soaps, are frequently useful. These no doubt form an oriented thin film of the soap of the heavy metal present in the mineral, by double decomposition with the surface layer; the long hydrocarbon chain is probably oriented outwards. By special activation it is said that even quartz may be floated by the judicious use of soaps, if its surface is contaminated naturally or artificially with small amounts of heavy metals. There would appear to be a vast range of possibilities in the separation of complex minerals, by proper selection of reagents capable of modifying their surfaces. A detailed study of the flotation of various silicate minerals, with oleic acid, has been given by Patek.[4]

In addition to collectors, frothers usually have to be added. The best

[1] Sheridan and Grisewold, U.S.P. 1,421,585; 1,427,235 (1922).
[2] *Am. Inst. Min. Met. Eng.*, Tech. Paper **495** (1933).
[3] *Kolloid-Z.*, **68**, 82 (1934).
[4] *Am. Inst. Min. Met. Eng.*, Tech. Paper **564** (1934).

of all frothing agents, soaps, saponins, etc., are generally unsuitable, for they lower the surface tension of the air-liquid interface so much that the contact angle also becomes low (see § 7). It can easily be shown that the work required to detach, reversibly, 1 sq. cm. of solid surface from a bubble is $\gamma_{LA}(1-\cos\theta)$; the most stable flotation will therefore be obtained with the largest values of this expression. Hence in seeking a frothing agent great lowering of surface tension should be avoided, or the froth becomes 'barren', containing little or no mineral. Some degree of lowering of surface tension is, however, probably a necessary accompaniment of frothing power. One of the commonest frothers is crude cresol ('cresylic acid'); many others may be found in the literature cited above.

The question has been frequently raised, whether the electrostatic potential differences at the air-liquid and solid-liquid surface play any part in the flotation process. There would appear no doubt that the adhesional surface forces which determine the angle of contact are all that is necessary to maintain the mineral particles adhering to the surface of the bubbles once they are brought into contact therewith. It appears possible,[1] however, that if the surfaces of the bubble and of the mineral are oppositely charged, electrostatic forces will bring the mineral particles into contact with the bubbles more rapidly than would occur in the absence of such aid, or if the charges were of the same sign. Conclusive evidence on tl is point is lacking; Ridsdale Ellis's[2] and Bull's[3] papers may be consulted. It is clear, however, that the principal quality of the solid surface required for flotation is that it should be sufficiently 'hydrophobic' to have a large contact angle; this property does not appear to be connected with the potential differences in the liquid near the solid surface. Tables of electrokinetic potential[4] show no correlation of this quantity with the adhesion to water.

18. Other practical applications of the contact angle, or wetting power. The water-proofing of textile fabrics is achieved by coating the threads with a composition having a high contact angle. The mode of action of the waxed surface in preventing the passage of rain through the fabric is as follows. Fig. 40 shows the cross-section of a set of parallel threads as circles. If the contact angle is larger than 90°, then the equilibrium position of the water level is *BB*, well on the outside of the cloth. It will require considerable pressure to force the water through to the middle, *AA*, for here the curvature of the surface is considerable if the contact angle (advancing) exceeds 90°. The pressure required to force the water through varies directly as the surface tension, and inversely as the width of the channel, so that it is important that the

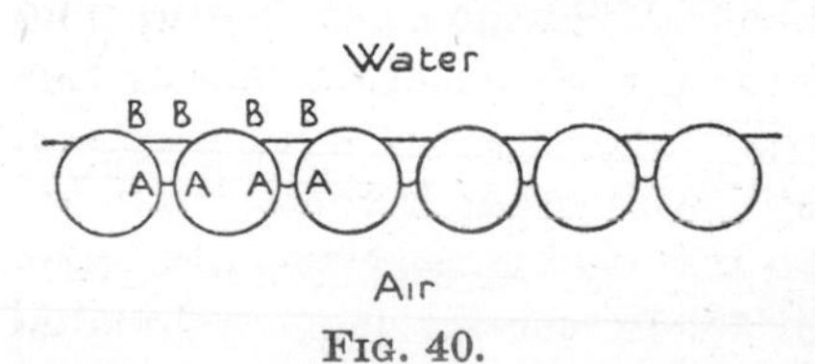

FIG. 40.

[1] Ridsdale Ellis, private communication.
[2] U.S.P. 1,425,185; 1,425,187; 1,555,915 (1922–5).
[3] *7th Colloid Symposium Monograph*, p. 115 (1930).
[4] Cf. Freundlich, *Kapillarchemie*, **1**, 363 (1930).

weave should be close, and that the waxy material chosen should be free from a tendency to contaminate the water surface (its spreading pressure, Chap. II, § 35, should be zero).

The materials used in practice include various compositions of waxes, petroleum residues, asphalt, or soaps of polyvalent metals which leave a surface consisting probably entirely of hydrocarbon groups outside, and have an equilibrium contact angle of 105° and an advancing angle greater than this. An essential qualification for a good proofing substance is that it shall not easily soak up water, and thereby suffer a lowering of the contact angle.

In many operations good wetting power is essential. 'Dips' for cattle, sheep, and other animals, 'sprays' for killing insect pests on plants, and in general any disinfectant or parasite-destroying liquid needs to be spread evenly over the surface of the leaf or animal, or other surface.[1] As many of these surfaces are greasy or wax-like, with a high angle of contact against water, their wetting can only be achieved by adding to the 'dip', or 'spray', some wetting agent which decreases the angle of contact of the liquid against the solid. In most cases the wetting agents are soluble substances which both increase the adhesion W_{SL} to the solid and decrease the surface tension of the liquid, thus operating in both ways to diminish the angle of contact according to (3).

Whether it is the 'advancing' or the 'receding' contact angle which is of importance depends on the conditions of the problem. For 'dips' where the animal is wholly immersed in the bath and subsequently drains, it is probably the amount of liquid retained on the surface, or rather the time for which it is retained as a complete film, which is of importance; and therefore a low 'receding' angle is necessary. Evans and Martin,[2] in a very careful study of many factors involved, find that the amount of liquid retained on the surface, when excess is drained away, is for a large number of solutions in close correlation with the 'receding' angle; the area of spread, however, determined by measuring the area covered by a drop of standard size delivered from a capillary tube on to the surface, depends on the 'advancing' angle. The difference between advancing and receding contact angles depends on the constitution both of the solutions and of the solid surface; Evans and Martin find the difference $\cos\theta_R - \cos\theta_A$ approximately constant, however, for the long chain type of wetting agent and wax surfaces, although the time taken to reach the final angles varies a good deal with the different solutions. Saponin solutions showed unusually low receding contact angles, accompanying moderately high advancing angles.

The rate of penetration of liquids into solid powders, or capillary tubes, may also be of great importance; e.g. in the laying of dust in mines.[3] Here the penetrating pressure or the difference in pressure across the meniscus into a tube of radius r and advancing contact angle θ_A is $2\gamma\cos\theta_A/r$; if

[1] Cf. Woodman, *J.S.C.I.*, **49**, 93 T (1930). [2] *J. Pomology*, **13**, 261 (1935).
[3] Cf. Tideswell and Wheeler, *Trans. Inst. Min. Eng.*, **87**, 1 (1934).

we can take it that W'_{SL} is the work of adhesion of the liquid to the solid before wetting, then, combining with (3), the penetrating pressure is

$$\frac{2}{r}(W'_{SL}-\gamma), \quad \text{or} \quad \frac{2A'_{SL}}{r},$$

where A'_{SL} is the adhesion tension of the liquid against the dry solid. Thus a low surface tension and a high adhesion for the walls of the capillary, or for the solid powder, will be required for good penetration. No simple theory of the penetration into powders is possible, as the particles are of irregular shape, but it will probably be found that these factors are the important ones. Washburn[1] has discussed the theory of the penetration of liquids into capillary tubes, the pressure set up by the curved meniscus being the driving force, and viscosity the resistance to motion.

It must be remembered that *in cases when a liquid penetrates into spaces of small cross-section, the important quantity is the 'adhesion tension', $\gamma \cos \theta$ or $W_{SL}-\gamma$. For the distribution of a loose solid powder between two fluid phases, the contact angle is the important quantity, and this must be between* 0 *and* 180° *for the powder to be stable at the interface.*

The efficiency of condensers in steam engines may be very much enhanced if the steam can be induced to condense in separate drops instead of as a continuous film on the condensing surfaces.[2] The parts of the metal condensing surfaces that are covered by liquid do not conduct heat nearly as rapidly as those which are dry, or nearly dry; and if the water condensing runs into drops locally as soon as it is condensed, the power of the condenser to transfer heat across the surfaces is much increased. For condensation as drops, the contact angle between the condensed water and the metal must be as high as possible; and this can, as a rule, only be ensured by the addition of small amounts of contaminating organic materials to the steam. These may, on occasion and temporarily, be supplied by such details of the steam-pipe system as a newly fitted washer containing linseed oil, or some rubber compounds. Nagle, Drew, and others[3] have studied the conditions for dropwise condensation in detail. The smoother the surfaces the greater the chance that the steam will condense in drops; rough surfaces usually condense as a film. Oil promotes dropwise condensation, but the oils must have a good adhesion to the metal; fatty acids especially, and to a lesser extent all fatty substances, assist the maintenance of a sufficiently greasy surface to condense steam as drops. Some sulphur-containing substances, notably mercaptans, xanthates, and dithiophosphates, also promote condensation as drops. The nature of the metal is also important; it was much more difficult to treat mild steel and aluminium so as to produce dropwise condensation, than copper and its alloys, or chromium plate.

[1] *Physical Rev.*, **17**, 273 (1921).

[2] Cf. Schmidt, Schurig, and Sellschopp, *Tech. Mech. Thermodynamik*, **1**, 53 (1930); Spoelstra, *Arch. Suikerind. Neder.-Indie*, III, 905 (1931).

[3] *Trans. Am. Inst. Chem. Eng.*, **30**, 217 (1933); **31**, 593 (1935).

The successful use of solders depends mainly on obtaining a zero contact angle between the liquid solder and the surfaces to be soldered.[1] The importance of removing adhering films of grease, oxide, etc., from the surfaces is due to the fact that the liquid metal solder has a much higher cohesion for itself than adhesion for grease or oxide; its adhesion to clean metals is, however, high.

To a large extent detergent action also seems to depend on wetting,[2] but here it is a question whether the grease or the detergent solution (generally an aqueous solution of soap, or other paraffin chain salt) wets the cloth, or other solid being cleaned, most easily. A dirty cloth is one in which the fibres are generally wet with grease, and the problem of cleaning is to displace the grease by water. Water alone does not displace the grease, but a good detergent solution will do so, by changing the contact angle formed by the water-grease surface, from zero in the grease and 180° in the water, to 180° in the grease and zero in the water. By (9)

$$\cos\theta_{AB} = \frac{W_{AS}-\gamma_A-(W_{BS}-\gamma_B)}{\gamma_{AB}} = \frac{A_{AS}-A_{BS}}{\gamma_{AB}}, \tag{10}$$

where A_{AS}, A_{BS} are the adhesion tensions of the water and the grease for the solid.

For complete displacement of the grease by the aqueous solution θ_{AB} must be zero when the water is advancing over a greasy surface. Hence the right-hand side of (10) must be equal to or greater than unity. This equation shows the relative importance of the different adhesions and surface tensions in detergent action. Low surface tension of the aqueous solution and low interfacial tension are both desirable, but neither *alone* is a sufficient condition for good detergent power.

19. Adhesion between solids immersed in a liquid; sedimentation volume, flocculation, 'adhesion number'. The completeness of dispersion, or separation of the particles, of a powder immersed in a liquid depends on the balance between the adhesion of the solid particles to each other and their adhesion to the liquid. If the mutual adhesion between solid particles is high, and the adhesion to the liquid not so high, they will tend to stick together instead of being dispersed as single particles in the liquid. Conversely, a low mutual adhesion accompanied by a high adhesion to the water is likely to produce good dispersion. The adhesion to the liquid can be measured by the surface tension and contact angle; at present no quantitative method exists for measuring the adhesion between solid particles in units comparable with those used for the liquid-solid adhesion, and indeed there may be great difficulty in devising such a method of measurement, since the actual area of contact between two solid particles is very uncertain. There are, however, several ways in which the adhesion between particles suspended in a liquid can be

[1] Cf. Daniels and Macnaughtan, *Symposium on Wetting and Detergency*, p. 77 (1937).

[2] Adam, *J. Soc. Dyers and Col.* (1937), p. 121; cf. also C. Robinson, *Symposium on Wetting and Detergency*, p. 137 (1937).

estimated semi-quantitatively. One of these is the tendency to flocculate; another, more easy to express quantitatively, is the 'sedimentation volume', or the volume occupied by a given weight of a powder allowed to settle under standard conditions; a third is the velocity of filtration; a fourth is the rate of flow of pastes under pressure; and a fifth is afforded by v. Buźagh's recent measurements of the tendency of the particles of solid powders to stick to solid surfaces.

The sedimentation volume naturally depends on the density, size, and shape of the solid particles, but it is found also to depend very markedly on the adhesion between them. If this is high, so that the particles do not easily slide over one another, they pack into a volume very much greater than that occupied if there is less adhesion, i.e. better 'lubrication', between the particles. Quite small changes in the surface of the powders may affect the ease of sliding of the particles over one another. One such case is the lubrication of an insoluble powder by adsorbing a monomolecular layer of some long chain substance on its surface. Harkins and Gans[1] found that adsorption of a monomolecular layer of oleic acid on *dry* titanium dioxide in *dry* benzene causes the sedimentation volume to decrease to one-third of that for the same powder with a clean surface. The particles become lubricated so that they slide over each other and pack more closely. But if a little water is present on the surface of the powder, the adhesion between the particles is not destroyed to nearly the same extent, and the sedimentation volume remains large. This is, in part, at any rate, due to the oleic acid being less easily adsorbed on moist than on dry titania. Thus it is clear that two solid surfaces of dry, or of moist, titanium dioxide adhere much more strongly than surfaces lubricated with an adherent monomolecular film of oleic acid; this is in accord with the well-known fact that the residual affinity of polar groups is greater than that of non-polar groups. A practical application of this lubricating effect of long chain substances adsorbed on the surface of pigments has been made by Gardner;[2] many pigments treated with aluminium stearate have a lower 'oil absorption' per gramme of powder, i.e. they require less oil to fill the interstices between the particles, and therefore less oil is required to make a paint than with ordinary clean mineral pigments. The importance of the surface of pigments for the properties of paints is very great; and Gardner[3] has also claimed that treatment of zinc oxide with soap, sodium resinate, gave paints with better initial properties and more stability than those made from untreated zinc oxide, the wetting of the oxide by the oil medium being much improved.

The sedimentation volume of mineral powders is also affected by the electric charge on the surface of the particles,[4] just as the state of dispersion of suspensions and suspensoid colloids depends on the amount of this

[1] *J. Physical Chem.*, **36**, 86 (1932).
[2] *Am. Paint and Varnish Manufacturers Assoc.*, Circular **321**, p. 100 (1923).
[3] U.S.P. 1,979,379 (1934). [4] Cf. Freundlich, *Kapillarchemie*, **2**, 166 ff. (1932).

charge. Thus silica powder, negatively charged in water, occupies the smallest sedimentation volume when few cations are present and the charge is high; the sedimentation volume increases with increasing concentration of cations, the usual valency rule holding good, that monovalent ions are less effective than divalent, and divalent less than trivalent.

The velocity of filtration of a liquid through a powder appears to be greater the greater the adhesion between the particles, and consequently the greater the free space in the powder.

Bartell and Hershberger[1] studied the flow of pastes of zinc oxide, zinc sulphide, and carbon, made up with various organic liquids whose adhesion tensions against the solids were approximately known. In general, there was a remarkably close correlation between the adhesion between the liquid and the solid, and the constants characterizing the flow. The 'yield value' was high, and the 'mobility' low,[2] for a given powder, with liquids which wetted it poorly; conversely, the yield value was low, and the mobility high, for liquids wetting the powder well. This is presumably because the high adhesion between liquid and solid tends to separate the particles, so that the paste offers less resistance to flow than if there is a tendency to stick together. Comparing two different powders, naturally properties of the powders are important, in addition to the adhesion between the liquid and solid.

The adhesion of particles of powders to solid walls runs closely parallel with the adhesion of solid particles to each other. It has been tested in two ways: in the first, a powder containing particles of various sizes is allowed to settle, inside a closed tube, on a quartz plate;[3] the tube is turned upside-down, so that the particles tend to fall from the plate, and observed with a microscope. The number remaining attached is a measure of the adhesion (the 'adhesion number'). The size of the particles is important in two opposite directions: if they are very small, the Brownian motion tends to dislodge them; if large, they are more prone to fall off than those of moderate size. Particles of about 2–3 μ diameter stick best. In another method the particles are allowed to settle on a horizontal plate, at the lower end of a vertical tube; the tube and plate are then tilted gradually and the angle at which the particles begin to slide downhill is observed.[4] This is, in effect, an observation of the angle of friction of the powder.

As a rule the adhesion increased with increasing amounts of salts, cations being the important ions with the negatively charged silica; the

[1] *J. Rheology*, **2**, 177 (1931).

[2] For the definition of the terms 'yield value' and 'flow' see also Bingham, *Fluidity and Plasticity*. This abstract of Bartell and Hershberger's paper differs from that given by the authors, but it seems to be justified on a careful analysis of the data recorded.

[3] v. Buźagh, *Kolloid-Z.*, **47**, 370 (1929); **51**, 105, 230; **52**, 46; **53**, 294 (1930); *Kolloid Beih.*, **32**, 114 (1930). Cf. Freundlich, *Kapillarchemie*, **2**, 106 ff. (1932).

[4] Krauss and Rüger, *Kolloid-Beih.*, **25**, 314 (1927); v. Buźagh, and Freundlich, *loc. cit.*

effect increases with the valency of the cation. Thorium has a curious effect, however; the adhesion increases very rapidly to a sharp maximum, but then decreases again with further increase in concentration to a value much the same as in water. It then increases again gradually, and remains high. Here there is a correlation with the electrokinetic ζ potential (Chap. VIII, § 8).

These experiments are an attempt to imitate, on a scale large enough to be visible, the adhesional forces which control the stability of suspensoid colloids, and are of very great interest. Protective action has been investigated to some extent also, but the results published so far are rather meagre.

20. Heat of wetting. When a liquid is brought into contact with a solid, the affinity of the liquid for the solid usually results in the evolution of heat. The heat of wetting has been measured very often. It is often called 'Pouillet's effect',[1] but Leslie[2] observed it twenty years earlier. The earlier experimental results are not of any great scientific interest, for experimenters generally adopted the easy course of measuring the heat per gramme of powder, without attempting the difficult task of determining the extent of the surface. Parks,[3] however, measured the heat of wetting of different silica powders by water, finding that the heat is proportional to the surface of the powder, the heat per square centimetre being 0·00105 calories, or about 44,000 ergs, at about 7° C.

Junck[4] and Schwalbe[5] found that silica and water evolve heat above 4°, but absorb heat below this temperature. This indicates that the second term of (11) becomes negative below 4°, so that there must be a maximum in the work of adhesion between water and silica at 4°. Direct test of this may be possible by contact angle measurements, and would be very interesting.

Patrick,[6] however, has found that the heat of adsorption of water on silica *gel* is positive below 4°. This is ascribed to the surface of the gel consisting largely of water, not dry silica.

Schwalbe and Parks give bibliographies of the earlier literature; Gaudechon[7] gives values for numerous liquids and solids; Gurwitsch[8] gives another table of results, which are widely divergent from those of Gaudechon, agreeing only in that both find, in a very general way, that water and some alcohols generally have a considerably higher heat of wetting on various solids than saturated hydrocarbons and carbon tetrachloride and disulphide. Andress and Berl[9] give other results on *activated* charcoal, which are, however, higher for organic liquids than for water. The discordance between various workers' results is marked. Freundlich's section should be consulted for further information and references.[10]

[1] *Ann. Chim. Phys.*, **20**, 141 (1822).
[2] *Tilloch's Phil. Mag.*, **14**, 201 (1802).
[3] *Phil. Mag.*, **4**, 240 (1902).
[4] *Ann. Physik*, **125**, 292 (1865).
[5] *Ibid.*, **16**, 32 (1905).
[6] *J.A.C.S.* (1921), 2144.
[7] *Compt. rend.*, **157**, 209 (1913).
[8] Cf. Langmuir, *J.A.C.S.* (1917), 1898.
[9] *Z. physikal. Chem.*, **122**, 81 (1926).
[10] *Kapillarchemie*, **1**, 235 ff. (1930).

Harkins and Dahlstrom[1] have carried out a very interesting analysis of the heat of wetting of titanium dioxide by various pure and mixed liquids. The heat evolved on immersion of the dry powder in dry benzene or other hydrocarbon is small; if butyric acid, or alcohols, or water are present, in very small amounts, the heat evolved is about doubled; esters produce an increase in the heat of wetting, but less than compounds with OH or COOH groups. The maximum heat appears to be evolved as soon as enough of these polar substances are present to form a layer one molecule thick on the surface of the powder. This seems to indicate that the affinity of the solid surface is practically completely satisfied when a layer one molecule thick of butyric acid is adsorbed, so that nearly all the heat of adsorption arises from the adhesion of this layer.

These experiments are significant, for they indicate a possible reason for the very divergent values recorded in the literature; the observed heats of wetting may not really be those of the pure liquids, but of the impurities, or moisture, present therein, in amount not necessarily more than is required to give a monomolecular film over the surface of the solid.

The heat of wetting is related to the free energy change on wetting by the Gibbs-Helmholtz equation. When one gramme, a solid, with an area of *clean* surface S sq. cm. effective for adsorption, is immersed in a liquid, then the free energy decrease is $S(\gamma_{SO}-\gamma_{SL})$, where γ_{SO} is the surface tension of the clean solid surface against a vacuum. This will in general be greater than the surface tension γ_{SV} of the solid surface against the vapour of the liquid, perhaps much greater. Bangham and Razouk[2] call the quantity $\gamma_{SO}-\gamma_{SL}$, F_L, showing its analogy with the surface pressure of Chapter II.

Then the heat evolved on immersing one gramme of the clean solid in the liquid is

$$-(\Delta H_{SL}) = S\left(F_L - T\frac{dF_L}{dT}\right). \qquad (11)^3$$

F_L would be the adhesion tension of the *clean* solid against the liquid; but $\gamma_{SV}-\gamma_{SL}$ is what is generally measured as adhesion tension. Bangham terms F_S, equal to $\gamma_{SO}-\gamma_{SV}$, the surface free energy decrement on saturation (with vapour).

[1] *Ind. Eng. Chem.*, **22**, 897 (1930).

[2] *Trans. Faraday Soc.* (1937), 1459, 1463; *Proc. Roy. Soc.* A, **166**, 572 (1938); cf. also Razouk, *Ph.D. Thesis*, Cairo (1939), pp. 44 ff., for details of the measurement of the heat of wetting.

[3] There has been some confusion as to the correct quantity to take for the free energy of wetting. The quantity F_S was used by A. M. Williams in 1918, and in earlier editions of this book the work of adhesion, W_{SL}, was used instead of F_L. Harkins and Ewing (*J.A.C.S.* (1921), 1797) and Bartell and others (*7th Colloid Symposium Annual* (1930), 138 ff.; *J. Physical Chem.* (1932), 985) gave the theory, though Bartell makes the further statement, probably not true in general, that F_L is proportional to the surface tension γ_{LV} of the liquid. The importance of the difference between γ_{SO} and γ_{SV}, i.e. of the adsorbed film of vapour of the liquid on the solid, has been rather overlooked except by Bangham and his colleagues.

For one specimen of charcoal, Bangham and Razouk measured the heat of wetting directly as 16·0 calories per gramme. The validity of equation (11) was tested in the following ingenious manner: as described in Chapter VII, p. 254, charcoal expands on adsorbing vapour, and somewhat further when immersed in the liquid. F is assumed to be proportional to the expansion, X, thus:

$$X_L = kF_L, \tag{12}$$

where the subscript L indicates the expansion or free surface energy decrease on immersion of the clean solid in the liquid. Gibbs's adsorption equation (III, 7.5) gives, if the amount in moles adsorbed per gramme is s/M, $\Gamma = s/MS$, so that

$$\frac{s}{MS} = \frac{dF}{RT\,d\log p}, \tag{13}$$

p being the vapour pressure of the liquid. Then

$$\frac{k}{S} = \frac{M\,dX}{sRT\,d\log p}, \tag{14}$$

so that although the specific surface S of the solid cannot be easily measured, nor the ratio k of the expansion to the free energy decrease F_L, their ratio k/S can be found by (14) from measurements of the variation in the amount adsorbed and the expansion, with the pressure.

Combining (11) and (12),

$$-(\Delta H_{SL}) = \frac{S}{k}\left(X_L - T\frac{dX_L}{dT}\right). \tag{15}$$

The heat of wetting calculated from (15) was 15·8 calories per gramme, in excellent agreement with the measured value.

If the expansion X_S found when the charcoal is placed not in the liquid but in the saturated vapour is substituted for X_L in (14), the heat (strictly of saturation of the charcoal with the vapour) is found to be about 3 calories less. Charcoal saturated with vapour both expands further, and evolves heat, when immersed in liquid at the same temperature.

The heat of wetting has been taken by Gurvich[1] as a measure of the affinity of the solid and the liquid. This may be a reasonable approximation to the truth, just as the heat of a reaction is generally some approximation, if a rough one, to the free energy. It will not be accurately true, except near absolute zero, or if dF_L/dT is zero. Bartell and others attempted to use equation (11), substituting the measured adhesion tension (here $\gamma_{SV}-\gamma_S$) for F_L, to calculate the specific area S of a powder, by comparison with the measured heat of wetting. The results may be of the right order, if the heat of wetting is measured on the solid already saturated to the same extent with the vapour as when the adhesion tension is measured; but they cannot be trustworthy, if the heat of wetting is measured on the *clean* solid surface, since F_L of equation (11) is usually much greater than $\gamma_{SV}-\gamma_{SL}$.

21. Emulsification by solid powders. It has long been known that solid powders can sometimes emulsify one liquid in another; that is, can stabilize one liquid in the form of small drops in the other. This can occur in all cases where the surface relationships between the solid and the two

[1] *Kolloid-Z.*, **32**, 80 (1923).

liquids are those required by § 16 for stability of the solid at the interface between the liquids. Just as the mineral particles were seen, in § 17, to act as stabilizers of a froth, so powders may act as stabilizers of liquid-liquid emulsions. The mode of action in both cases is that the liquid interface cannot contract without crowding the foreign particles together, and eventually driving them into one liquid or the other; and this expulsion of the powder from the interface involves an increase in the free energy of the system.

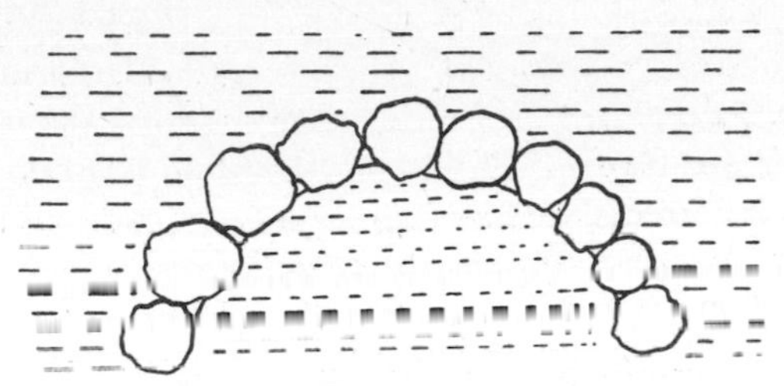

FIG. 41.

Pickering[1] appears to have been the first to make a scientific study of the behaviour of solid emulsifiers. He found that basic sulphates of iron or copper are excellent emulsifiers for paraffin oil in water, and by microscopic observations he showed that the particles do actually form an envelope round the liquid globules at the interface. Bancroft[2] suggested that particles more easily wetted by oil than by water ought to form emulsions of the water in oil type, and Schlaepfer,[3] using carbon black, obtained such emulsions. Briggs[4] found that an antagonistic action was possible between different emulsifiers resembling that found for the two types of soluble emulsifiers (Chap. IV, § 12). Silica emulsifies kerosene in water, and carbon black emulsifies water in kerosene, but a suitable mixture of silica and carbon prevents the formation of any emulsion at all.

The mechanism of this emulsification has been explained in detail by Finkle, Draper, and Hildebrand,[5] and by Ramsden.[6] It was seen in § 17 that if the contact angle is acute in liquid A, the greater part of the bulk of the particles, including the widest cross-section, is in that fluid. Fig. 41 shows a number of particles in contact in an interface, their greatest cross-section being in A. Any contraction of the interface must bend the surface with its load of solid particles so as to become concave to fluid B. Thus the contraction of the interface, after bringing the particles into contact, curves the interface towards that fluid which wets the powder least, in which the contact angle is obtuse.

This simple and attractive theory is certainly, however, insufficient to cover the whole of the facts, just as the 'oriented wedge' theory of soluble

[1] *J.C.S.* (1907), 2001.
[2] *J. Phys. Chem.*, **16**, 475 (1912).
[3] *J.C.S.* (1918), 522.
[4] *Ind. Eng. Chem.*, **13**, 1008 (1921).
[5] *J.A.C.S.* (1923), 2786.
[6] Clayton's *Emulsions and their Technical Treatment*, 2nd ed., Appendix I (1928).

emulsifiers is inadequate. Other factors have a great influence on the stability; lateral adhesion between the particles seems very important. Thus Moore[1] found that highly calcined carbon blacks would not emulsify kerosene in water, possibly because of the lack of adhesion between neighbouring solid particles in the surface. Briggs also found that adhesion between the solid particles, amounting to flocculation, can be carried too far; while the addition of 'mild' flocculating agents (salts) to the aqueous phase increases the stability of the emulsions, the addition of more drastic agents tends to make the solid clump together and spoils the emulsion, although the solid is driven into the interface.

Bhatnagar,[2] following Donnan,[3] thinks that electrical effects at the interfaces also are important, and finds that the formation of a water-in-oil or an oil-in-water emulsion depends on the ions present in the solution, which are no doubt adsorbed on the surface of the solid. The rule that monovalent ions promote oil-in-water emulsions, which are reversed by polyvalent ions, appears to hold good with solid emulsifiers as well as with soluble soaps. Developments of the theory in this direction will be of great interest.

One final complication in emulsions must be mentioned. It seems unlikely that true equilibrium is ever reached in forming an emulsion with a solid emulsifier. Shaking or other forms of mechanical agitation are necessary to bring the solid to the interface, but they are much too coarse physical operations to produce equilibrium. The globules are divided up and also reunited by the shocks, and the solid particles are violently driven in and out of the interface, so that the distribution of solid in the interface is partly an accidental effect of the means used to agitate the mixture.

22. Multilayers. Langmuir and Miss Blodgett's new 'multilayers', formed on solids by successive deposition of monolayers from a water surface, are discussed in the Appendix.

[1] *J.A.C.S.* (1919), 940.
[2] *J.C.S.* (1921), 1760.
[3] *Kolloid-Z.*, **7**, 214 (1910).

CHAPTER VI

SPREADING AND LUBRICATION

1. Energy requirements for stable spreading. When a drop of a liquid is placed on the surface either of another immiscible liquid, or of a solid, it may spread to a film, or may remain as a drop without spreading. The surface tensions of the two liquids, and the interfacial tension between them, determine whether or no the liquid spreads; and the same holds if the lower phase is a solid.

Fig. 42 shows a drop of high boiling paraffin, which does not spread[1] even on clean water. At the edge of the drop, three fluid surfaces meet;

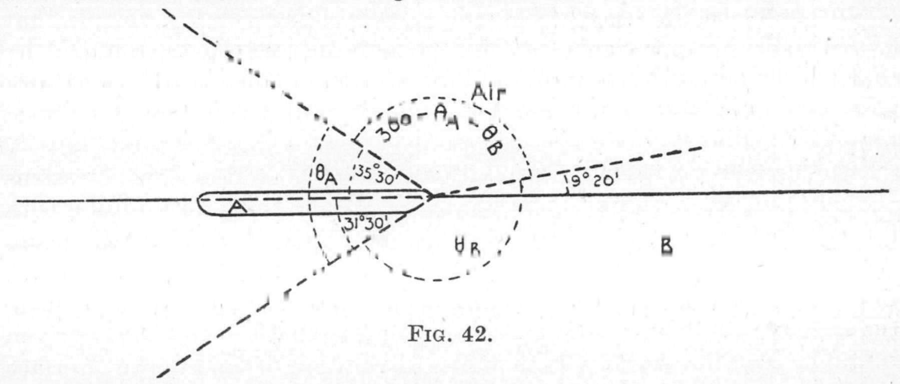

FIG. 42.

the condition of equilibrium is that the three surface tensions should be in equilibrium; therefore, by the well-known statical theorem that the magnitude of each of three tensions meeting at a point is proportional to the sine of the angle between the other two,

$$\frac{\gamma_B}{\sin\theta_A} = \frac{\gamma_A}{\sin\theta_B} = \frac{\gamma_{AB}}{\sin(360^\circ - \theta_A - \theta_B)}, \quad (1)$$

γ_A, γ_B being the surface tensions of the upper and lower liquids, and θ_A, θ_B the angles in the liquids A and B. This condition of equilibrium is often called Neumann's triangle. If one liquid rests as a drop on another, without spreading, then none of the three surface tensions is greater than the sum of the other two.

Coghill and Anderson found that the angles, and probably the surface tensions, of various liquids resting on water changed with time, so that the experimental verification of Neumann's triangle was not very accurate.

If now the surface tension of the lower liquid B increases, the angle θ_A will gradually diminish until it becomes zero. At this point

$$\gamma_B \geqq \gamma_A + \gamma_{AB}$$

and equilibrium becomes impossible. The energy will be diminished by a spreading of A on B, and the liquid A will spread on B, therefore, if

[1] Coghill and Anderson, *U.S. Bureau of Mines*, Tech. Paper **262** (1923).

the surface tension of B exceeds the sum of γ_A and γ_{AB}. Using Dupré's equation (Chap. I (2)), this condition of spreading can be transformed into

$$W_{AB} \geqq 2\gamma_A. \tag{2}$$

These conditions of spreading were formulated by Dupré[1] and Hardy;[2] Harkins has called the difference $\gamma_B-\gamma_A-\gamma_{AB}$, or $W_{AB}-2\gamma_A$, the 'spreading coefficient' of A on B. Since W_{AB} is the work of adhesion of A to B, and $2\gamma_A$ the cohesion of A, the condition of spreading is simply that the upper liquid must adhere to the lower more strongly than it adheres to itself. For solids, by (3) of Chapter V the spreading coefficient becomes $\gamma_A(\cos\theta_A-1)$, the angle of contact being usually the advancing angle θ_A.

The actual form of lenses of non-spreading liquids on the surface of another immiscible liquid has been recently studied by Lyons[3] and Langmuir.[4] Langmuir shows that, in addition to the surface tension, if the lens is not of very large size, the 'linear tension' f at the curved line of contact between the two liquids makes an appreciable difference to the thickness of the lens. The actual shape of the lenses is dependent on a rather complicated balance between the spreading coefficient F_S, the densities of the liquids, and the linear tension f round the perimeter of the lens, whose radius is R. If D_1, D_2 are the densities of the lower and the upper liquids, respectively, the thickness t of a lens so large that its upper surface may be taken as flat, in the centre, is

$$t = t_\infty \sqrt{\left(1-\frac{f}{F_S R}\right)}, \tag{3}$$

where t_∞, the thickness which the lens would have if there were no linear tension at the boundary, is given by

$$t_\infty^2 = -\frac{2F_S D_1}{gD_2(D_1-D_2)}. \tag{4}$$

As F_S is a negative quantity for a non-spreading liquid which forms lenses, this expression is positive. The linear tension f can be calculated from measurements of stationary lenses; Bradley[5] has deduced its amount from measurements on oscillating lenses. It may amount to several dynes.

Water has a high cohesion, and therefore does not spread on organic liquids. Organic liquids have usually a moderate cohesion, and spread on water unless the adhesion to water is unusually low. Practically all liquids will spread on clean mercury, but the surface of mercury is so difficult to obtain clean, that it is not at all common for water to be found spreading on mercury. If water will spread, the mercury has an exceptionally clean surface.

Any diminution of the surface tension of the lower liquid, by a film, diminishes the tendency of the upper liquid to spread. This may be regarded as due to the surface pressure of the film opposing the outward spreading pressure of the liquid A.

The condition of spreading is clearly the same as that for zero contact angle in the liquid A, and is therefore the same as that for complete

[1] *Théorie Mécanique de la Chaleur*, p. 368.
[2] *Proc. Roy. Soc.* A, **88**, 313 (1913).
[3] *J.C.S.* (1930), 623.
[4] *J. Chemical Physics*, **1**, 756 (1933).
[5] *Trans. Faraday Soc.* (1940), 999.

wetting of a solid surface by a liquid. If A spreads on B, then it is clearly impossible, by Fig. 42, for B to spread on A; it is, however, possible for neither liquid to spread on the other.

A non-spreading liquid such as a heavy paraffin may be caused to spread on water by dissolving in it a fatty acid or some substance which increases W_{AB}, the adhesion between the oil and the water.

Harkins gives the following typical values of spreading coefficients; any positive value causes spreading to occur on a clean surface, while a high positive value permits spreading against the surface pressure of a considerable amount of contamination.

TABLE XII

Spreading Coefficients on Water (20°)[1]

(a) Spreading Liquids	*Coefficient, ergs per sq. cm.*
n-propyl alcohol	10·0
n-butyl alcohol	48·3
n-octyl alcohol	36·7
n-butyric acid	45·7
Heptylic acid	37·8
Undecylenic acid (25°)	32·0
Oleic acid	24·6
Ethyl capronate	25·0
Butyronitrile	34·8
Aniline	24·4
Anisole	11·0
Benzene	8·9
Toluene	6·8
p-xylene	6·7
Chlorobenzene	2·3
Hexane	3·1
Octane	0·2
(b) Non-spreading Liquids	
Monobrombenzene	−3·3
Carbon disulphide	−6·9
Phenyl mustard oil	−7·7
Monoiodobenzene	−8·8
Medicinal paraffin (average)	−13·5
Methylene iodide	−26·5

Spreading Coefficients on Mercury (20°)[2]

Ethyl iodide	135
Oleic acid	122
Carbon disulphide	108
n-octyl alcohol	102
p-xylene	97
Benzene	90
Hexane	79
Acetone	60
Water	32

[1] *J.A.C.S.* (1922), 2665; *6th Colloid Symposium Monograph*, p. 31 (1928).
[2] *J.A.C.S.* (1920), 2543.

A rise of temperature generally reduces the spreading coefficient slightly, in the case of long chain spreading compounds. With non-spreading liquids the spreading coefficient increases as the temperature rises, eventually becoming positive.

The figures in Table XII show some of the effects of chemical constitution in the upper liquid. Groups which dissolve in water and promote stability of a surface film give high spreading coefficients. Halogens give low coefficients, in accordance with their low adhesion for water, already known from the behaviour of surface films. Halogen groups have, however, a high attraction for mercury. In homologous series the spreading coefficient for a given end group diminishes as the chains are lengthened.

If neither liquid will spread on the other, a denser liquid can be made to float on a lighter, in just the same way as solid substances which have a finite angle of contact can float on water. The author has floated mercury on water, by a preliminary shaking with sulphuric and chromic acids, which contaminates the surface of the droplets of mercury.[1] Kremnev[2] describes the flotation of carbon tetrachloride, and also quotes Rehbinder and Serb-Serbina[3] as having floated mercury with alizarin red.

2. The mechanism of spreading on liquids. The *energy requirements* for spreading are the same on solids as on liquids, but the *mechanism* of spreading is quite different on solid and on liquid surfaces. On liquids the mechanism is revealed by an experiment first described closely by Osborne Reynolds.[4] He showed that when oil spreads on a dust-covered surface of water, the dust does not move until the advancing edge of the oil reaches it, and then the dust is heaped up as a rib, being swept up by the advancing oil. He wrote: 'The result is to give the impression that the dust is being driven back by the oil, as if the oil were spreading by some inherent force,' continuing, 'but, as a matter of fact, the oil is being drawn forward by the contraction of the dust-covered surface of the pure water.' He later called the phenomenon 'very remarkable, for it would be inferred from other hydrodynamical phenomena that viscosity would tend to distribute the action over a considerable area'.

It is interesting to see how Reynolds's first impression, based on his own observation, of the mechanism of spreading was that it was due to an expansive force. At that time, however, the predominance of the theory that liquids have skins in tension was so complete, that he felt obliged to abandon his own, correct, impression, and to wonder why the pulling power of this supposed skin was not apparent as a contraction some distance in advance of the spreading oil. Many reasons have been given already, in Chapters I and II particularly, for the view that there is no such skin on the surface of liquids; and the absence of motion of the water surface in front of the spreading oil is a further, and rather striking, demonstration that this surface contractile skin is a myth.

[1] *Nature*, **123**, 413 (1929).
[2] *Kolloid-Z.*, **68**, 21 (1934).
[3] *J. Phys. Chem. Russ.*, **2**, 768 (1931).
[4] *Works*, **1**, 410; *Brit. Assoc. Report* (1881).

The motions of the molecules of the water cause the expanding movement of the oil drop.[1] The molecules of water are in constant motion parallel to the surface, diffusing long distances. The oil molecules adhere to them, and are carried outwards along the surface by reason of these surface diffusing motions. If the liquid is one which spreads stably, then the spread film has a lower potential energy than the drop, so that the molecules which have left the drop to form a film stick to the surface; the surface diffusing motions go on continually underneath the drop, and the oil molecules which spread first are continually being pushed out farther by the surface pressure of those just leaving the drop. If the liquid is a non-spreading one, a few molecules may diffuse out along the surface a little way, but being less stable on the surface than in the drop, they will soon return to the drop, and will not stick to the surface.

Spreading liquids spread first as a film of visible thickness, sometimes showing interference colours, but often too thick for this. As soon as the whole surface is covered, however, this thick film breaks up, and after passing through a variety of stages settles down as a monomolecular film in equilibrium with visible drops of liquid; the final stage is a film in equilibrium with one drop,[2] if sufficient time is allowed. These changes have been described by Devaux,[3] Hardy,[4] Beilby,[5] Taylor,[6] and Feachem and Rideal.[7] Volatile substances spread in a similar manner, but equilibrium is never reached, since the drops and particularly the film are evaporating rapidly, and there is constant motion from any unspread liquid to make up losses from the film. Hardy found that some substances of quite high boiling-point (e.g. ethyl hydrocinnamate) evaporate with extraordinary rapidity from the sheets.

This spreading as a thick, unstable sheet, is probably due to the motions of the molecules of the oil, diffusing in contact with the water, transmitting the outward motion to the upper layers of the oil by viscosity.

Leslie's explanation,[8] that the spreading is due to an attraction exerted by the lower liquid on molecules of the upper liquid beyond the first layer, squeezing out those in the first layer, cannot be correct, or the final state could not be a monomolecular film in equilibrium with excess liquid in drops—the drops would be squeezed out along the surface.

The velocity of spreading on water has been observed by Brinkman,[9] Cary and Rideal,[10] Ramdas,[11] Woog,[12] and others. It is often of the order 20 cm. per

[1] Cf. Langmuir, *Trans. Faraday Soc.*, **17**, 673 (1922).

[2] With *mixtures* of substances, thick spread sheets may persist for a very long time (Hardy, *Proc. Roy. Soc.* A, **88**, 316 (1913)). This is familiar when paraffin oil is spilt on puddles, and is of vital importance in killing mosquito larvae on water.

[3] *J. Phys. Radium*, **2**, 891 (1912).

[4] *Proc. Roy. Soc.* A, **88**, 315 (1913).

[5] *Aggregation and Flow in Solids*, sect. 2 (1921).

[6] *Ann. Physique*, **1**, 134 (1924).

[7] *Trans. Faraday Soc.*, **29**, 409 (1933).

[8] *Tilloch's Phil. Mag.*, **14**, 193 (1802).

[9] *Biochem. Z.*, **139**, 274 (1923).

[10] *Proc. Roy. Soc.* A, **109**, 312 (1925).

[11] *Proc. Indian Assoc. Cult. Science*, **10**, 1 (1926).

[12] *Graissage, Onctuosité, Influences Moléculaires*, p. 88 (1926).

second, but the speeds found by Woog were a good deal lower than this. It is probable that the form of the boundary of the water surface, over which spreading occurs, affects the rate of spreading.

Camphor, and some other substances which spread rapidly on a water surface, execute rapid irregular movements during this spreading. Ramdas[1] has studied the camphor movements, and finds that the form of the perimeter of the camphor is important for the motion, as it determines the stream-lines along which the spreading proceeds; and consequently the temporary crowding of the molecules in different parts of the spread film varies according to the shape of the camphor.

Spreading on mercury is sometimes similar to that on water, but complicated phenomena which deserve further investigation are reported by Burdon;[2] Harkins[3] has also noticed points which seem difficult to explain on existing theories. Water, for instance, spreads very slowly, and it is doubtful whether a monomolecular film is ever formed. There appears to be a definite limit to the area of a spread film, while it is still quite thick, and it has not yet been definitely ascertained whether or no an invisible film extends beyond this. This limiting area of a visible film varies in a very remarkable way; minute traces of substances in solution affect it greatly, and passing electric currents through the upper liquid, from a platinum electrode dipping into it, the mercury serving as the other electrode, affected the spreading strongly, possibly because electrolysis altered the concentration of ions at the interface between the water and the mercury. Sharply curved surfaces seem to impede spreading, an effect which may be similar to the 'edge' effect on solids. The reader is referred to Burdon's papers for further details of these largely unexplained phenomena.

Solids spread on liquids to a monomolecular film, as has been described in Chapter II.[4] Owing to the non-mobility of the particles of a solid, the molecules which are driven out next the water cannot drag a thick layer of the solid along with them, as happens when liquids spread.

3. Equilibrium between two liquids saturated with each other: Antonow's rule. A liquid which spreads on another usually does so with considerable violence at first, overshooting the final equilibrium by dragging out a sheet much thicker than the final equilibrium layer, this sheet breaking up into droplets or lenses of small diameter and considerable thickness. It is not at once obvious what would be the final angle of contact θ_A (see Fig. 42) in the lenses. If, however, the spreading is imagined to take place very slowly, with time allowed for the complete mutual saturation of the upper and lower liquids, the spreading coefficient will gradually diminish, as the surface of the lower liquid B becomes covered by a surface film of liquid A, and its surface tension diminishes. The contact angle remains zero so long as the spreading coefficient is positive, the sum of the two tensions $\gamma_A+\gamma_{AB}$ being less than γ_B. The spreading ceases when γ_B is equal to $\gamma_A+\gamma_{AB}$; at this point the contact angle is still zero, but any further diminution in the surface tension of the lower liquid, γ_B, would result in the angle becoming finite.

Hence, in the case of two liquids whose surface and interfacial tensions are such that one will spread on the other, *before they are mutually saturated*, it is to

[1] *Proc. Indian Assoc. Cult. Science*, **10**, 1 (1926).

[2] *Proc. Physical Soc.*, **38**, 148 (1926); *Trans. Faraday Soc.*, **23**, 205 (1927).

[3] *J.A.C.S.*, **44**, 2680 (1922).

[4] Cf. also Volmer and Mahnert, *Z. physikal. Chem.*, **115**, 239 (1925).

be expected that, *when they are mutually saturated,* one will rest on the other with zero contact angle, and

$$\gamma_A+\gamma_{AB} = \gamma_B. \tag{5}$$

If the liquids do not spread on each other when not mutually saturated, the contact angle will be finite and the slight diminution in the spreading coefficient which takes place when the liquids are saturated with each other will result in the angle becoming larger; in this case we may expect

$$\gamma_A+\gamma_{AB} > \gamma_B. \tag{6}$$

Antonow[1] claimed that it is a general rule that, for two liquids mutually saturated with each other, the interfacial tension is equal to the difference between the surface tensions of the two liquids separately, i.e. that all liquids, when mutually saturated, obey (5). This rule has attracted a great deal of attention, and many attempts have been made to verify it, or otherwise. Antonow's[1] own measurements, and Reynolds[2] confirmed it; Bartell, Case, and Brown[3] find that it holds for mercury and water, also for mercury and several organic liquids. Harkins and Ginsberg,[4] also Carter and Jones,[5] find that liquids with negative 'initial' spreading coefficients, i.e. before they are mutually saturated, do not obey the rule, but the inequality (6) holds. Rather surprisingly the sum of the tensions $\gamma_A+\gamma_{AB}$, with several alcohols, phenols, or acids, was found to be from 1 to 5·6 dynes per cm. higher than γ_B, after saturation; i.e. the 'final' spreading coefficients were negative, instead of zero, as they should be if Antonow's rule held. Carter and Jones ascribe this to the orientation of molecules in the surface, but the explanation is not clear.

If (5) is combined with Dupré's equation (Chap. I (2)), we see that $W_{AB} = 2\gamma_A$; i.e. the work of adhesion for two liquids mutually saturated with each other is equal to the work of cohesion of the liquid of lower surface tension, after saturation with that of higher tension. This must mean that the surface of B, after saturation, becomes very similar to that of A as regards external field of force—not necessarily identical as regards molecular composition.

4. Spreading on solids. The principal mechanism of spreading on liquids, namely the dragging out of the upper liquid by the translational motion along the surface of the molecules of the lower liquid, being absent in solids, naturally such spreading as does occur is a much slower phenomenon. There is no doubt, however, that *some* lateral motion of the molecules in films adsorbed with greater or less intensity on the surface of solids can, and frequently does, occur.

If the liquid resting on a solid is volatile, it can distribute itself along the surface of the solid through the vapour; thus Hardy[6] found that only those acids and alcohols which have a sensible vapour pressure distribute themselves along the surface, from a drop in one spot, so as to lubricate it in any reasonable time. It does not appear to be necessary, for this kind of spreading to occur to some extent, that the contact angle should be zero; it was found that the coefficient of friction of paraffin wax was

[1] *J. Chim. Phys.*, **5**, 372 (1907); *Kolloid-Z.*, **59**, 7 (1932); **64**, 336 (1933).
[2] *J.C.S.* (1921), 466. [3] *J.A.C.S.* (1933), 2769.
[4] *6th Colloid Symposium Monograph*, p. 23 (1928).
[5] *Trans. Faraday Soc.*, **30**, 1027 (1934). [6] *Proc. Roy. Soc.* A, **100**, 573 (1922).

lowered by a slight condensation of water vapour. Woog,[1] on the other hand, finds that some spreading of the practically non-volatile medicinal paraffin, and some other oils, occurs on steel and other metal surfaces. Beilby[2] describes the slow creep of mercury along a compact gold leaf.

Alty and Clark[3] studied the creep of mercury up cylinders of tin, a process easily visible on account of the amalgamating action of the mercury. There was certainly a surface diffusion, much more rapid than any volume diffusion; for polished surfaces the rate of travel of the mercury was of the order a few millimetres a minute, and was not much less if the exposed surface of the tin was in a bath of mineral oil, instead of in air, so that no distribution of the mercury by evaporation and condensation on other parts of the surface was possible.

The rate of travel up the surface of the cylinder depended on the state of the surface, being much slower up a cylinder with the surface as left by turning, than on a ground or polished surface. The authors ascribe the difference to roughness actually lengthening the path; but it would appear possible that the rate of diffusion is intrinsically more rapid on a surface which has been worked or polished, and therefore has a Beilby layer. The course of the worked portion of the surface, up the turned cylinder, would be a helix with a very slow rate of ascent, i.e. a very long path.

These experiments are sufficient to prove that lateral motion of molecules along the surface of a solid can, and often does, occur. But there is much further evidence, pointing particularly to a rather high degree of mobility along the surface, of atoms or molecules which have just hit the solid from the vapour phase. The first such observations appear to be those of Volmer and Estermann[4] on the growth of crystals of mercury from vapour, at about $-50°$ C. The mercury condenses as very thin hexagonal leaflets, which are found to grow at their thin ends very much faster than the rate at which mercury atoms can possibly strike these ends directly, but along their flat sides much more slowly. The rate of growth at the ends was actually 1,000 times as great as the rate at which, from kinetic theory, the mercury atoms could hit a target of the size of these ends. The rate of growth of the crystal perpendicular to the large flat sides was less than the rate at which molecules could hit these sides. Volmer[5] considers that when the molecules first hit the sides of the crystals they give up only a part of the final heat of condensation, and are not incorporated into the crystal lattice but are free to rush along the surface until they reach the ends, where they become bound with the full heat of condensation, and their mobility is very much diminished. Further evidence comes from observations on the condensation of metallic atoms on glass or similar surfaces. Cockcroft[6] placed a metallic wire in the path of a stream of atoms moving in a vacuum so high that the atoms moved in parallel streams (molecular rays) without being deflected by collisions.

[1] *Graissage, Onctuosité*, etc., p. 92.
[2] *Aggregation and Flow in Solids*, p. 27.
[3] *Trans. Faraday Soc.*, **31**, 648 (1935).
[4] *Z. Physik*, **7**, 13 (1921).
[5] Cf. *Trans. Faraday Soc.*, **28**, 359 (1932).
[6] *Proc. Roy. Soc.* A, **119**, 93 (1928).

The shadow thrown by the wire on the walls, though not so dark as the surrounding parts, still contained a good deal of deposited metal, which could only have come by travelling along the surface from regions outside the shadow. Estermann[1] also brings evidence that surface migration plays an important part in building up the requisite density of atoms on a surface for visible and permanent condensation to take place. Other evidence, along the same general lines, comes from Chariton, Semenoff, and Schalnikoff,[2] Ditchburn,[3] and the work cited by Volmer.[4]

Volmer and Adhikari[5] found that needle-shaped crystals deposited from liquid or from solutions are apt to grow beyond the boundary of the liquid, without any film of liquid being perceptible on the surface; it was concluded that the molecules moved along the surface of the solid crystal immediately after deposition. The proof of the absence of a liquid film on the surface does not, however, appear quite complete.

It is thus evident that atoms or molecules in process of being deposited on a crystal are mobile. There is some reason to suppose that the surface molecules even of crystals, or adsorbed layers, which have been formed for some time and may be considered stable, can also move along the surface. Volmer and Adhikari washed the surface of crystals of benzophenone by a stream of drops of mercury, finding that material was removed from points some little distance from where the mercury touched the crystal; also[6] if a glass plate on which a crystal of benzophenone was placed was similarly washed a short distance away from the edge of the crystal, the crystal disappeared, indicating diffusion across the empty space on the glass. This diffusion was, however, exceedingly small, roughly 3×10^{-5} gm. per hour only across a gap only 0·01 mm. wide.

The mobility of surface atoms increases with temperature. Becker[7] has shown this particularly clearly by measuring the change in thermionic emission on tungsten caused by an adsorbed layer of barium. The barium was deposited on one side of a flat tungsten ribbon, which was periodically heated to about 1,000° K. for short periods, during which the thermionic current was measured. At first practically all the emission was from that side on which the barium had been deposited; later, as the barium migrated round, the emission began, and increased, from the back of the ribbon, until it was finally equal to that from the front. The rate of migration of the source of the emission (i.e. the barium atoms) from the front to the back increased with increasing temperature. Potassium migrates similarly on tungsten.[8]

[1] *Z. Physik*, **33**, 320 (1925); cf. Fraser, *Molecular Rays*, pp. 91 ff. (Cambridge, 1931).

[2] *Trans. Faraday Soc.*, **28**, 169 (1932).

[3] *Proc. Camb. Phil. Soc.*, **29**, 131 (1933).

[4] *Trans. Faraday Soc.*, **28**, 359 (1932).

[5] *Z. Physik*, **35**, 170, 722 (1925).

[6] *Z. physikal. Chem.*, **119**, 46 (1926).

[7] *Trans. Am. Electrochem. Soc.*, **55**, 153 (1929); *Trans. Faraday Soc.*, **28**, 148 (1932); *Phil. Mag.*, **29**, 129 (1940). Benjamin and Jenkins, however, contradict this, though they find a migration of thorium over tungsten (*Phil. Mag.*, **26**, 1049 (1938)).

[8] Bosworth, *Proc. Roy. Soc.* A, **154**, 112 (1936).

Lennard-Jones's consideration[1] of the potential energy of the adsorbed atoms has thrown a great deal of light on the probable mechanism of migration along the surface. On the scale of atoms the field of force of the surface will vary not only perpendicular, but also parallel to the surface. An atom near enough to the surface to be well within the range of the attractive forces, i.e. within the 'adsorbed layer', will have a potential energy which depends on whether it is directly over an atom of the underlying solid, or intermediate between them. Suppose an atom approaches the solid perpendicularly until it reaches the minimum of potential energy along its line of approach; the actual value of this minimum will depend on whether the atom is directly above an atom of the underlying solid, or intermediate between them. Lennard-Jones has shown that the potential energy of an atom adsorbed over a lattice point, i.e the centre of a surface atom of a crystal such as potassium chloride, is higher than the potential energy over the centre of the unit cell of this crystal. In general, the potential energy of an atom adsorbed on the surface, so closely that its potential energy is the minimum possible along a given line of approach, can be represented by a surface with peaks and hollows, which are repeated at regular intervals, if the underlying crystalline surface is regular. The peaks of energy are over the atoms and the hollows over the mid-points of the lattice cells. Normally, an adsorbed atom or molecule will move to the absolute minimum of potential energy, i.e. the hollows, and stay there. To pass along the surface it would have to climb out of the hollow. But thermal agitation may cause it to reach the level of one of the equipotential contours which, like height contours on the map of a mountainous region, run continuously along the surface for long distances, from the slopes of one peak to another. Then it can diffuse easily along the surface, until it loses energy either by collison with other moving atoms, or by interaction with the field of force of the solid at some irregularity, and falls into a different hollow.

Fig. 43 is a sketch[2] of the potential field parallel, and normal, to a surface; the dots are the maxima of energy and the crosses the minima. Thus a rise of temperature may make it possible for the adsorbed atoms to migrate from one hollow in the potential energy surface to another, perhaps far distant. And the amount of kinetic energy required to bring an adsorbed atom to this level of energy will be definite, so that there will be a definite 'energy of activation' for the migration along a solid surface.

The very striking phenomenon of surface migration during condensation is presumably due to the molecules striking the surface with considerable kinetic energy, so that they take some time to settle down into thermal equilibrium with the underlying solid, the oscillations of the atoms when

[1] *Trans. Faraday Soc.*, **28**, 333 (1932); *Proc. Roy. Soc.* A, **158**, 242 (1937).

[2] From *Trans. Faraday Soc.*, **28**, 347 (1932); better worked out though more complicated diagrams may be found later in the same paper and in *Proc. Roy. Soc.* A, **158**, 244 (1937).

first hitting the solid bringing them once, or more often, above the level of energy where migration can occur; also in some cases perhaps the surface migration is due to the atoms hitting a crystalline face where the binding force is not so strong, and the energy hollows not so deep, as on other faces, so that migration may occur on one face of a crystal at a temperature when it does not occur on another.

Lennard-Jones suggested that the migration of surface atoms may be the first stage of melting of a solid; this may be one of the preliminaries of large scale melting. It is very probable that migration of adsorbed

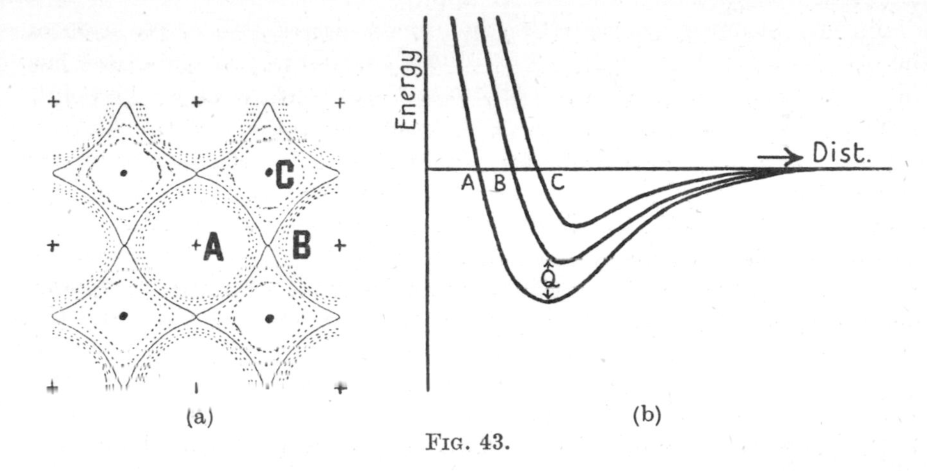

FIG. 43.

atoms helps to bring them into positions where they react with each other, on the surface, or to regions where they acquire exceptional reactivity, so that the surface migration may be an important factor in controlling the rate of heterogeneous catalysis.

5. Friction: seizure of clean solid faces. Sliding friction is almost certainly due to the exceedingly strong adhesion between those parts of the surfaces which come into real contact with each other, when two solid bodies touch. The unsatisfied molecular attractions at the surface of solids extend outwards a very short distance, not more than a few A. Two solid bodies in apparent contact will probably approach each other within the range of these attractive forces, only at a very few points of small area, as it is impossible as a rule to prepare solid surfaces true to an accuracy of closer than a few hundred A. There is reason to believe that two *clean* surfaces of most solids adhere to each other with a strength equal to that of the solids in bulk, at those points where they really touch, and that this highly localized welding of the surfaces occurs at ordinary temperatures, almost instantaneously.

It is usually found that *clean* surfaces cannot be made to slide on each other without considerable damage. Hardy[1] found that a curved slider of clean glass, moving on a flat glass plate, tears a track which begins

[1] *Phil. Mag.*, **38**, 32 (1919); cf. Macaulay, *J. Roy. Tech. Coll.*, **3**, 353 (1935).

about 1 μ wide, but widens to about 50 μ in a short distance. The track consists of small pits, and is littered with loose thin plates torn off the surface; it apparently consists at first of a single track not more than 1 μ wide, which later gives place to several parallel tracks which spread and unite into an apparently broader track. This widening appears to be caused by oscillations of the slider from side to side as it travels forwards. Even the first movement of a clean solid body, resting on another clean surface, seems usually to tear away some of at least one of the surfaces; it makes very little difference whether the surfaces are highly polished or moderately rough.

There seems little doubt that much of the destruction of the surfaces is due to very strong adhesions, amounting to welding of the projections on the surfaces on to the opposite faces, taking place when these projections come within the range of molecular attraction of the opposite surface. Bridges appear to be formed between the surfaces, which have to be broken before sliding can occur; and the force of friction is (at any rate with unlubricated surfaces) the force required to shear these bridges across. The detailed analysis of sliding friction, described below, indicates, however, that some of the destruction may be due to a kind of 'ploughing' action by the projections on the metal of higher melting-point, through the metal of lower melting-point.

Until recently the real area of contact between two surfaces was a matter of speculation only. Bowden and Tabor,[1] however, have by an ingenious electrical method made approximate estimates of the area of real contact, and of the way in which this changes as the load pressing two pieces of metal together is varied. Most of the electrical resistance between two pieces of metal, joined only by narrow bridges, is located in the bridges, and by measuring the resistance the extent of real contact can be fairly closely ascertained. In this way the *real* area of contact was found to depend very greatly on the load, but for a given load, to vary but little with the shape and apparent extent of the surfaces. Thus two practically flat pieces of steel, 0·8 sq. cm. in area, had almost exactly the same area of real contact, for a given load, as two similar pieces of area 21 sq. cm.; and there was little difference in the extent of real contact between these flat plates, and two cylinders with axes at right angles, or a 3-mm. sphere resting on a flat plate, with which the apparent area of contact was very small. With the curved surfaces, at high loads, independent estimates of the area of contact could be obtained by observing the extent of the impressions left on the surfaces microscopically, and these agreed well with the estimates by the electrical method, in cases where a well-defined track was left after sliding.

The area of real contact was, with a curved slider, moving on a flat plate, approximately proportional to the load pressing the two surfaces together. It was also nearly equal to the area which would be theoretically required to support the metals under the applied load, calculating from

[1] *Proc. Roy. Soc.* A, **169,** 391 (1939).

the approximately known pressures at which the metals commence to undergo plastic flow. This indicates that the regions of real contact are produced by plastic deformation of the small projections to be found on every surface.

The proportionality between the area of real contact and the applied load supplies at last a rational explanation of the well-known Amontons'[1] or Coulomb's[2] law of friction, that the frictional force F is directly proportional to the total load P pressing the surfaces together. The meaning of this law has long been mysterious. Under ordinary circumstances the law holds fairly accurately, i.e. there exists a nearly constant coefficient of friction, $\mu = F/P$. The frictional force is naturally proportional to the total area of these bridges; consequently the frictional force should be proportional to the load.

With both surfaces flat, the area of real contact was more difficult to estimate absolutely and appeared to increase more rapidly than in direct proportion to the load; but there is some uncertainty here as to the actual number of regions of real contact.[3]

It should be noted that the area of real contact is, as a rule, the minimum area required to reduce the pressure produced by a given normal load to that at which the metal no longer flows plastically. It is therefore necessarily proportional to the applied load. If the deformation were elastic, not plastic, the area of contact would be proportional to the two-thirds power of the load, assuming that the projections at which real contact commenced were segments of spheres.

It is very difficult to detect the existence of these welded bridges by means of a direct pull apart, perpendicular to the surfaces. *Dry* solid surfaces, even if very accurately trued, do not usually stick together. If a little moisture is present, they may adhere with considerable force: thus Budgett[4] found that very accurately plane gauges would fall apart by their own weight if dry, but if moist, a pull up to 90 lb. per sq. in. might be required to separate them. The reason why extremely little force is required to break the adhesions between two solid surfaces is that these are of very small area, and further, it is almost impossible to apply a perfectly perpendicular pull apart, so that the bridges will tend to be broken one by one, and also sheared as well as broken in pure tension. If there is moisture present, between accurately plane surfaces, this may form a continuous film of liquid, so that the considerable pull required to separate Budgett's gauges when moist was probably a measure of the tensile strength of water.

It is not quite obvious why, if the friction is the force required to break the welded bridges formed by plastic deformation of projections, under load, the friction should decrease when the load is diminished. Yet, under most ordinary circumstances, the friction is well known to be determined by the load present at a given moment,[5] alone, and to be independent of whether or not a higher

[1] Amontons, *Mém. Acad. Roy. Sci.* (1699), 206; (1704), 96.

[2] Coulomb, *ibid.* (1785), 161.

[3] Bowden and Tabor, *Proc. Roy. Soc.* A, **169**, 403 (1939).

[4] *Proc. Roy. Soc.* A, **86**, 25 (1911).

[5] This has been verified for some metal surfaces, not specially cleaned, by Bikerman and Rideal (*Phil. Mag.* **27**, 687 (1939)). Paraffin wax, however, showed a higher

load has previously been applied. If the friction is determined by the cross-section of the bridges formed between the surfaces, at the regions of real contact, why do not the area of these bridges, and the friction, remain at the value characteristic of the maximum load applied during the time when the two metals have remained stationary in contact? There are probably two reasons for this: in most ordinary experiments the technique is so imperfect that the act of decreasing the load probably causes sufficient motion to break previously formed welded bridges; and also it must be remembered that, above those extreme projections which are plastically and presumably permanently deformed, the metal undergoes elastic and temporary deformation, and so will spring back to its original shape when the load is removed. This is likely to break the junctions formed under the heavier load, so that new junctions have to be formed each time the load is changed.

Bowden and Tabor[1] describe some 'hysteresis' in the adjustment of the area of real contact to the load, when this was altered without vibration; successive increases and decreases in the load may not alter the electrical resistance across the surfaces much. A source of complication in such measurements is the formation of oxide films at the surfaces where the welded bridges are broken.

The friction between metals, as ordinarily observed, is the friction between metals covered with adsorbed gases, usually oxygen, or even thin oxide films. The coefficient of friction is usually less than unity for such surfaces. If the metals are *thoroughly* de-gassed, by heating in a vacuum, the coefficient of friction rises[2] to very high values, often to 5 or 6, and in the case of gold to nearly 30. On readmission of oxygen the coefficient of friction fell, but usually not below unity; the results varied very much with different metals; and pure nitrogen and hydrogen did not decrease the friction below that of the de-gassed metal. The effect of the films of adsorbed gas, or of oxide, must be to reduce the attractive force at the surface, thus rendering the cohesion between the surfaces less strong and weakening the welded bridges. These results show that practically all the observations on friction of metals are really on metals whose surfaces are far from clean chemically; in view of the extremely high friction found with really clean metals it is fortunate, for engineering, that metals are not found with perfectly clean surfaces in practice.

Kinetic friction, that is, the force required to maintain sliding at an appreciable speed, is not usually very different from static friction, the

friction after a moderately large load had been applied and then decreased than when the smaller load was applied in the first instance. It is difficult, however, to be convinced by their conclusion that, in the case of metal surfaces in their ordinary condition, molecular cohesion is not the cause of friction, and that the old theory of Coulomb, that the friction is the force required to drag the projections on one surface out of the hollows in the other, both being in reality perfectly smooth, is adequate to explain friction. This would deny the existence of friction for mathematically smooth surfaces; but other experiments show that friction is certainly no less with the most carefully trued and polished surfaces obtainable than with slightly rougher surfaces; indeed, it may be rather greater with the polished surfaces.

[1] *Proc. Roy. Soc.* A, **169**, 396.

[2] Bowden and T. P. Hughes, *Proc. Roy. Soc.*, **172**, 263 (1939).

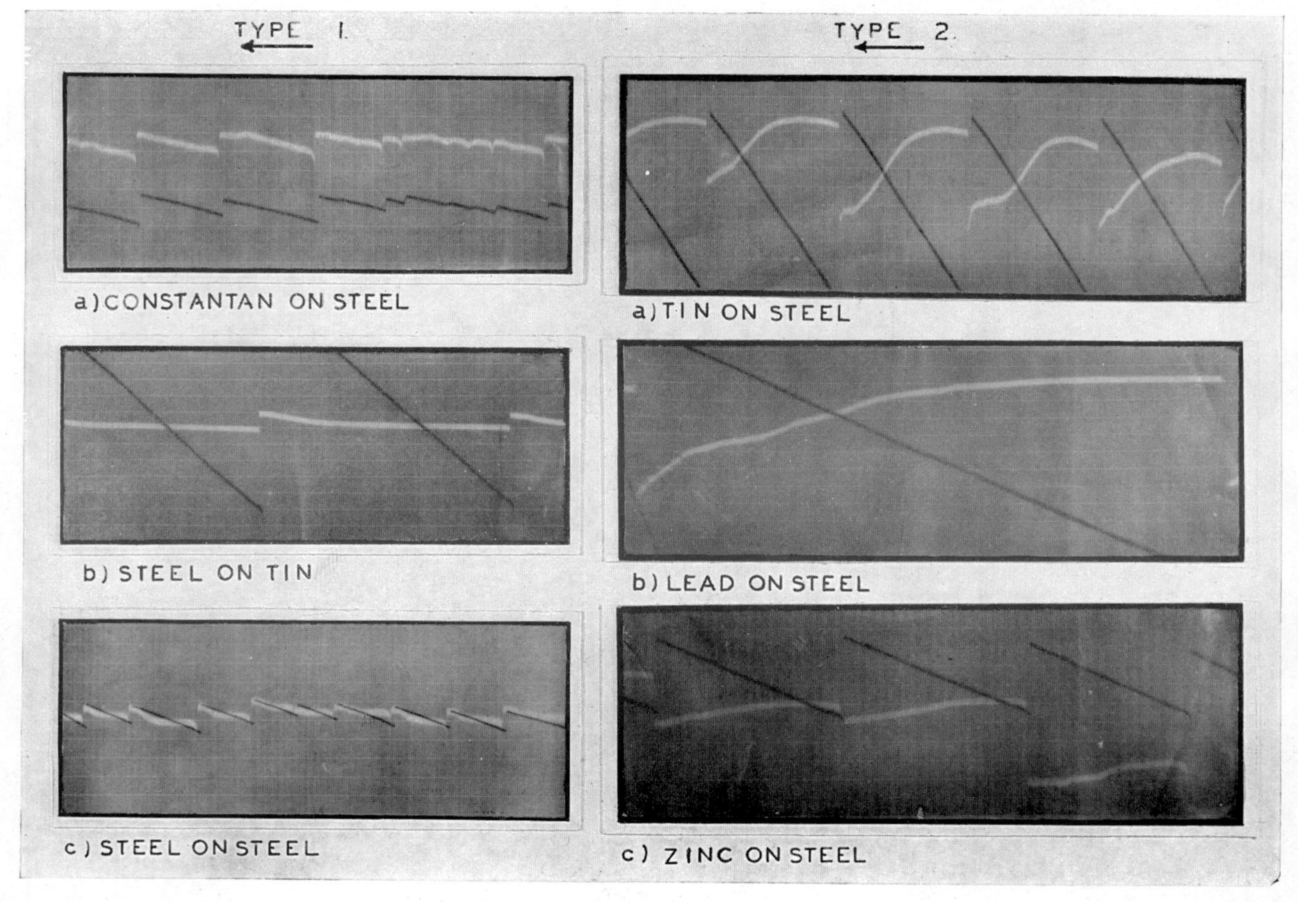

Fig. 44. 'STICK-SLIP' SLIDING

force required to start sliding, according to most observers. Coulomb considered them to be identical; it is often stated that kinetic friction is a little lower than static, but Deeley[1] found that at low speeds kinetic friction is almost the same as static; Beare and Bowden,[2] with unlubricated surfaces, found the same coefficient of friction at 600 as at 60 cm. per second, while later work indicates little, if any, change down to much lower speeds. It is scarcely possible, however, to make a very exact comparison between static and kinetic friction, since if the surfaces are moving the heat evolved by friction must alter the conditions of the surface somewhat.

It has now been shown beyond doubt[3] that, with unlubricated metals, and also with slightly lubricated metals, sliding takes place in a series of discontinuous jerks, the surfaces alternately sticking, without any motion at all, then slipping suddenly to a new position. This 'stick-slip' motion is shown in Fig. 44; in the photographs the friction appears as a dark trace and the conductance (a measure of the real area of contact) across the junction between the metals as a light trace. Motion is from right to left. The upper metal (named first in the descriptions) was a small sphere, pressed by a spring on a moving flat plate of the metal named second; the upper metal was fixed to a stiff vertical torsion device, capable of slight movement which was recorded on the moving photographic film. In these records the lower flat plate was moved slowly, so that the speeds of sliding were slow; during the 'stick', which was complete and without any relative motion, the friction always rose and fell very suddenly, in less than a thousandth of a second, when slip occurred. The area of real contact behaved in a different manner during the 'stick', according as the upper (curved) metal had a higher or a lower melting-point than the lower. If the curved upper metal had a higher melting-point the area of real contact, indicated by the conductance, increased slightly until slip took place, as if the curved metal projection ploughed through the more fusible lower metal; if the curved piece of metal had a lower melting-point the area of contact decreased during the slip, to be re-established by the next 'stick' at a higher level. This looks as if the two metals form welded bridges, which are pulled out during the increasing stress as the 'stick' nears its end, with a consequent diminution of cross-section.

Using the two metals as one junction of a thermo-electric element it was found that, at the 'slip', the temperature rose and fell with extreme suddenness, the whole surge of temperature being over in a thousandth of a second or less. When the two sliding pieces were of the same metal the 'stick-slips' were much less regular.

The photographs of Fig. 44 were obtained with a string galvanometer, whose natural period did not permit of the detection of changes taking

[1] *Proc. Physical Soc.*, **32**, 8 s (1919).

[2] *Phil. Trans.* A, **224**, 329 (1935).

[3] Bowden and Leben, *Proc. Roy. Soc.* A, **169**, **371** (1939); *Phil. Trans.* A, **239**, 1 (1940); Bowden and Tabor, *Proc. Roy. Soc.* A, **169**, 401 (1939).

place in less than 0·001 second. With a cathode-ray oscillograph, however, the 'slip' was found to be quite complex; there was extremely rapid clutching and breaking away of the surfaces all occurring within about 0·001 second; and the conductance across the junction fell for an extremely brief instant to a lower figure than that shown in Fig. 44. This is evidence that the area of contact falls suddenly as the welded bridges are broken, then rises as new bridges are formed as soon as the sliding ceases after each 'slip'.

Naturally the possible duration of the 'stick' depends on the freedom of independent motion of at least one of the two surfaces. In an engine usually one surface is held very rigidly, while the other is driven steadily on; some observations on the conductance across the junction between rigidly held surfaces indicated, however, that even here the motion was not quite continuous, though the restraint on motion of the surfaces restricted the 'sticks' to very short distances.

If the curved slider was of a higher melting-point than the lower plane surface a groove was ploughed out in the lower metal. If the upper curved surface had the lower melting-point the lower surface was not grooved, but was smeared with some of the upper metal. With both metals the same a different type of groove was formed, as if the metal had flowed and then solidified.

There was evidently some tendency to fusion of the lower melting metal during the sliding. Bowden and Ridler,[1] using the two dissimilar sliding metals to record their own surface temperature thermoelectrically, found that the surface temperature was proportional to the speed of sliding, and to the normal force between the surfaces, up to a few degrees below the melting-point. When the surface temperature had reached the melting-point of the lower melting metal, there was no further rise of temperature. With the low melting gallium the highest temperature reached was only 30° C., the melting-point; with constantan on steel the temperature rose to over 1,000° C., but did not reach the melting-point of either metal. Even with lubricated metals the temperature may rise some 500° C. locally.

6. Lubrication. Lubricants separate the solid surfaces, either so completely that the projections on the two surfaces cannot touch, or they provide sufficient covering on the surfaces, so that if any projections do really touch the other surface the intensity of seizure is much less than if the metals were clean. We have already seen that adsorbed films of oxygen, or oxide films, reduce the friction far below that of chemically clean metal surfaces; in a sense, therefore, such films might be considered lubricants. But the practical problem of lubrication consists in reducing the friction between ordinary metal surfaces, with their surface films, to the lowest practicable value.

While a considerable degree of lubrication can be achieved even by a monomolecular layer of many organic substances, particularly those

[1] *Proc. Roy. Soc.* A, **154**, 640 (1936); cf. Herbert's analogous measurements of the temperature attained by cutting tools (*Proc. Inst. Mech. Eng.*, **1**, 289 (1926)).

with long hydrocarbon chains, the engineer aims, wherever possible, at separating the moving surfaces by a layer of lubricant thick enough to have the properties of liquid in bulk. This is 'complete', or 'film', lubrication, and is mainly a problem in hydrodynamics. The theory was first given by Osborne Reynolds;[1] Boswall[2] gives a good account of it. In practice the bearings are designed as far as possible to drag the oil in automatically; this is often possible without external aid, if the relative speed of the moving surfaces is high enough and the pressure between the bearing surfaces not too high; often, also, the oil is forced into the bearing under pressure from a pump. But if the pressure between the faces is high, and the speed low, as may be the case with the teeth of gear wheels, or still more in the cold pressing of metals by forcing them through dies, or, temporarily, when machinery is started up after the oil has drained from the bearings, it may be impossible to have the complete thick layer of oil present. In such cases the surfaces touch, except for a 'boundary' film of lubricant, and the properties of this boundary film are very important, in order that it should provide a safeguard against wear. Osborne Reynolds, and practically all later writers, have distinguished sharply between 'complete' and 'boundary' lubrication.

For complete lubrication a high viscosity aids the dragging in of the oil into the bearings, and hinders its being squeezed out under pressure. Therefore, as a rule, a high viscosity, up to the highest temperatures to which the oil may be raised under severe conditions of loading and a somewhat overheated engine, is usually desirable; since in complete lubrication the only friction is fluid friction, the viscosity should not be very much higher than that necessary to maintain the film complete, with a reasonable margin for any likely lowering of viscosity, through dilution with fuel, or decomposition. Since the engine may have to run over a range of temperatures the temperature coefficient of the viscosity should not be larger than necessary, though all liquids do decrease rapidly in viscosity with increasing temperature. A most important consideration is the chemical stability of the oil, under conditions of high temperature, and some oxygen present, with metals such as copper which may catalyse the oxidation of organic substances. 'Anti-oxidants', such as tin soaps, may be added to inhibit the oxidation, which in its later stages may give rise to tarry or asphaltic sludges and so block the oil channels or filters and stop the supply of oil to the bearings. The very general use of mineral oils as lubricants in internal combustion engines is largely due to their stability.

In practice, besides a good 'body' or high viscosity, it has long been recognized that another property, usually termed 'oiliness', is desirable. 'Oiliness' was long a mystery, but is now generally recognized to be the power of forming a satisfactory 'boundary' lubricating film. Deeley[3] and

[1] *Phil. Trans.*, **177**, 157 (1886).

[2] *The Theory of Film Lubrication* (Longmans, 1928).

[3] *Proc. Physical Soc.*, **32**, 10 s (1919).

Allen[1] suggested that oiliness is largely due to the power of forming a strongly adherent film at the surface of the metal. There is a general consensus of opinion that good lubricants adhere more strongly to metals than inferior lubricants. Von Dallwitz-Wegener[2] found a lower contact angle, against metals, with the better lubricants; his angles were rather higher than those found, in a few cases, by the author. It is probable that angles quite near to zero can fairly easily be obtained with most metals and oils. A low contact angle will aid complete lubrication by facilitating the penetration of oil into narrow channels.

It seems probable, however, that the efficiency of an oil can be improved by increasing its adhesion to the metal above that required to give zero contact angle. This would not affect complete lubrication, unless cavitation of the liquid tended to make holes in the film and detach it from the bearing; but the higher the adhesion the less likely is a boundary film of the lubricant to be rubbed or volatilized away under severe conditions. The earliest lubricants employed were vegetable and animal oils and greases, consisting mainly of glycerides with small amounts of free fatty acids. Mineral oils were introduced later; they have the necessary viscosity and better chemical stability, but are somewhat deficient in 'oiliness'. Mineral oils may often be very much improved as boundary lubricants by adding quite small amounts of free fatty acids with long hydrocarbon chains, or rather larger amounts of glycerides. Hyde[3] and Wells and Southcombe[4] found that a quite small proportion (1–2 per cent.) of fatty acid added to a mineral oil gives results as good as the best mixtures with much more glyceride. Soaps of heavy metals have also been employed to improve lubricating power. For lubricants required to work under extremely high pressures small additions of sulphur-containing compounds, or chlorinated wax, or lead soaps, have been found very useful;[5] and since the fragments worn away from the metal contain sulphur or chlorine, when these are present, it appears that there is actual surface combination between these atomic grouping in the molecules and the metals.

Bachmann and Brieger[6] have found a correlation between the heat of wetting of metals by oils and lubricating efficiency. The heat of wetting is a rough guide to the affinity or adhesion of the metal for the oil. Parish and Cammen[7] have described a centrifugal machine, capable of rotating up to 18,000 revolutions per minute, for indicating the adhesion of oils to metals. The oils which adhere best require higher speeds to throw them off. There is some evidence, however, that a strong adhesion is not alone

[1] *Proc. Physical Soc.*, **32**, 165.

[2] *Petroleum*, **16**, 245, 285 (1920); Lunge-Berl, *Chem. Tech. Untersuchungsmethode*, **3**, 471 (1923).

[3] *Engineering*, **111**, 708 (1921).

[4] *J. Soc. Chem. Ind.*, **39**, 51 T (1920).

[5] F. L. Miller, *General Discussion on Lubrication and Lubricants, Inst. Mech. Eng.*, **3**, 102; J. E. Southcombe, J. H. Wells, and J. H. Waters, *ibid.*, **4**, 172 (1937).

[6] *Kolloid-Z.*, **36**, 142 (1925); **39**, 334 (1926).

[7] Cf. *Petroleum Times*, 12 Nov. 1932.

sufficient to ensure good boundary lubricating qualities. Wilson and Barnard[1] found that *p*-cresol impairs the lubricating efficiency of mineral oil, yet it is probably strongly adsorbed at metal faces, since it lowers the interfacial tension between water and mercury. Something besides strong adhesion appears to be required in order to produce good boundary lubrication; it is possible that this may be flexibility in the molecules.

7. Boundary lubricating films. Even a monolayer of a long chain substance on a solid surface diminishes the friction very greatly. Rayleigh[2] and Hardy found that invisible films of greasy matter lubricate; Devaux[3] showed, by measurement of the amount put on directly, that these need not be more than one molecule thick, and Langmuir[4] in 1920 transferred a monolayer of oleic acid from the surface of water to a glass plate, by dipping the plate into water covered by the monolayer, in the manner which has since been developed so extensively for the preparation of multilayers (Chap. V, § 22).

Hardy and his colleagues,[5] between 1919 and 1932, made very extensive studies of boundary lubrication and static friction. Great care was taken to exclude accidental traces of lubricating substances, including moisture, other than the lubricant studied, and the experiments were conducted in a stream of air purified from dust, grease, and water vapour. Usually the tangential force required to start motion of a spherical slider on a horizontal plate was measured. Films were deposited from vapour, or by oiling the surface slightly and polishing off with a clean cloth; most frequently, however, the measurements were made with a spherical slider in a pool of the liquid lubricant; in a very short time the slider falls through the lubricant until only a boundary layer remains.

Whether this boundary layer was one molecule thick (on each surface) or thicker is not certainly known. Trillat's work[6] indicates that orientation, in the case of long chain acids and similar compounds, may extend some distance from a surface into the interior of a liquid, and Andrews's electron diffraction studies[7] also indicate orientation extending beyond the first layer. The heavy slider may, or may not, penetrate through to the layer of molecules next to the solid.

According to Hardy, in general, ring compounds reduced the friction less than aliphatic compounds. In aliphatic homologous series a steady diminution in the static friction was observed with increasing length of

[1] *J. Soc. Automotive Eng.*, **11**, 149 (1922).
[2] *Phil. Mag.*, **35**, 158 (1918).
[3] *J. Phys. Radium*, **5**, 84 s (1924).
[4] *Trans. Faraday Soc.*, **15**, 68 (1920).
[5] W. B. and J. K. Hardy, *Phil. Mag.*, **38**, 32 (1919); W. B. Hardy, *ibid.*, **40**, 201 (1920); Hardy and Doubleday, *Proc. Roy. Soc.* A, **100**, 550 (1922); **101**, 487 (1922); **104**, 25 (1923); Doubleday, *J.C.S.* (1922), 2875; Hardy and Bircumshaw, *Proc. Roy. Soc.* A, **108**, 1 (1925); Hardy, *Phil. Trans.* A, **230**, 1 (1931); Hardy and Nottage, *Proc. Roy. Soc.* A, **138**, 259 (1932). See also Hardy's *Collected Papers* (Cambridge, 1936).
[6] *J. Phys. Radium*, **10**, 32 (1929); *Z. Physik*, **64**, 191 (1930).
[7] *Trans. Faraday Soc.*, **32**, 607 (1936).

the hydrocarbon chain. Four different series were very thoroughly examined, the normal hydrocarbons, primary alcohols, acids, and the optically active secondary alcohols (ethyl carbinols) $C_nH_{2n+1}CH(C_2H_5)OH$. Except for anomalies, when the chains were very short, and one anomalous result in the carbinol series, the coefficients of friction were diminished linearly as the chain length was increased. The effect of the lubricant could be represented by the equation

$$\mu = \mu_0 - d - c(n-1) \tag{7}$$

in which μ_0 is the friction of the clean, unlubricated face, d the change in friction caused by the end groups X and CH_3 in the compound $CH_3(CH_2)_nX$, and c that caused by each CH_2 group in the chain. Table XIII shows the results obtained: d, the contribution of the end groups, is nearly independent of the solid face used: c is accurately the same for different solid faces, but varies with the different homologous series.

TABLE XIII

Lubricant

Surfaces	*Hydrocarbon*			*Alcohol*		*Acid*		*Carbinol*	
	μ_0	c	d	c	d	c	d	c	d
Glass . .	0·94	0·021	0·15	0·023	0·26	0·059	0·19	0·027	0·39
Mild steel D .	0·79	0·021	0·23	0·023	0·33	0·060	(0·18)	0·027	0·37
'50 ton alloy' steel A . .	0·88	0·022	0·24	0·023	0·35	0·060	0·22		
Medium carbon steel B . .	0·83	0·022	0·23	0·023	0·33	0·060	0·19		
Nickel chrome steel C . .	0·93	0·022	0·23	0·023	0·33	0·060	0·23		
Phosphorbronze E . . .	0·94	0·022	0·22	0·023	0·34	0·060	0·24		

When two different solid faces were used the friction of the lubricated metal was the arithmetic mean of the friction observed with the two materials used together; the value of μ_0, in equation (7), for A sliding on B, is $\frac{1}{2}(\mu_0^A+\mu_0^B)$, where μ_0^A, μ_0^B are the values of μ_0 for A sliding on A and B on B, respectively.

Thus each solid face makes a definite quantitative contribution to the friction, irrespective of what the other solid face may be, or what lubricant is present. At one time Hardy attempted to explain this on the theory that the influence of the attraction of the solid face extended for long distances, but more recent analysis of the occurrences during sliding indicates that the process is very complex, and that the coefficient of friction is not, as a rule, a quantity capable of simple interpretation in terms of the properties of *continuous* surface films, and of the underlying solid.

The coefficient of friction, as ordinarily measured, is shown clearly by the discovery of the 'stick-slip' motion to be an average value of a rapidly fluctuating quantity. It probably depends very much on the conditions under which it is measured. Bowden and Leben[1] find a very different relationship between chain length and friction from that obtained by Hardy, using slow kinetic friction. In their experiments the acids, alcohols, and paraffins of the straight chain paraffin series all tended to a constant value of the coefficient of friction, when the molecular weight exceeded a certain value. For the acids this constant value was very nearly 0·1, reached at a chain length of about 8 carbons; the alcohols gave closely similar figures; while the paraffins attained a constant value of about 0·14 when the chain length reached 13 or 14 carbons. With substances in the same series and of shorter chain length the friction was higher, falling gradually but not accurately linearly with increasing molecular weight. The acids alone gave (in the liquid state) continuous sliding, and these only gave it when the chain length was over 5 carbons. 'Stick-slip' sliding was found with the alcohols and the hydrocarbons when liquid, but continuous sliding when solid. Mixtures of mineral oil and 1 per cent. fatty acid showed continuous sliding and a slightly higher coefficient of friction than the fatty acids alone, indicating that the boundary film was mainly composed of the acid. The effect of heating was interesting; an oil of complex constitution which gave continuous sliding at room temperature developed stick-slips on moderate heating; on cooling continuous sliding was restored. The good boundary lubricant in this oil was probably desorbed on raising the temperature. A case was noted of a mineral oil,[2] which at room temperature gave stick-slip motion, oxidized on prolonged use at a fairly high temperature so far that a substance giving continuous sliding appeared. On still further heating and rubbing the friction increased greatly and stick-slip motion reappeared. Some improvement in the lubricating power of mineral oils after moderate use is sometimes claimed in practice; the deterioration of all oils after prolonged use at high temperatures is well known.

8. The role of the various factors in lubrication. Even with boundary lubrication the values obtained under different conditions by different workers vary so much that it seems, at present, useless to attempt to account for the coefficient of friction as a function of the chemical constitution of the lubricant. Still more, the measurements of coefficient of friction by so many friction-testing machines, in which the lubrication is often mainly 'complete' but 'boundary' during a small part of the time, are little if any guide as to the value of the lubricants in practice. Viscosity, not less than a certain minimum, is well established on theoretical and experimental grounds as a necessity for complete lubrication; and a considerable adhesion of at least one constituent of the lubricant to the surface is a necessity for good boundary lubrication. The principal function of boundary lubricants is to cover the surfaces with an adherent film, which reduces the intensity of adhesion between the projections on

[1] *Phil. Trans.* A, **239**, 1 (1940).
[2] Bowden, Leben, and Tabor, *Trans. Faraday Soc.* (1939), 900.

one surface to the other surface to as low a value as possible. It is at present not certain how far different organic compounds differ in their power of reducing this adhesion, because all measurements appear to be complicated by the fact that the adsorbed films of lubricants may be rubbed off during the measurement of friction or during its analysis by photographic methods such as those which led to the discovery of the 'stick-slip' motion; and the extent to which the areas of real contact, where there is very high pressure, remain covered by a film of lubricant is unknown.

Bowden and Leben[1] find that, with a really good boundary lubricant such as stearic acid, one monolayer gives, *for the first slide only* over a fixed track, the minimum coefficient of friction; subsequent slides give a rapidly increasing friction. A film 3 molecules thick (deposited by the multilayer method) retains the minimum friction ($\mu = 0{\cdot}1$) for 8 or 9 runs over the track; 9 films for nearly 20 runs, and 50 films for over 50 runs. Cholesterol, a much poorer lubricant, gave ultimately the same coefficient of friction, but several films were needed to do this. After many runs the friction attains the value for unlubricated surfaces. Even under the best conditions there seems usually to be a little tearing of the surfaces, showing that some removal or breakdown of the films takes place; but this is very much less if the sliding is continuous than if it is 'stick-slip'. Complete and permanent covering of the surfaces by a strongly adherent film seems the primary essential for good boundary lubrication, and *permanent* covering cannot be attained without a considerable reservoir of the boundary lubricant in the oil, to replace losses by wear. The removal by wear may be partly due to heating, and the poorer qualities of the lower members of the aliphatic series as lubricants may be due mainly to their lower boiling-points. It is possible that flexibility in the molecules in the surface film may aid friction; perhaps more probable that a tendency to be oriented perpendicular to the surface, with considerable length in the molecules, may cause such distant separation of the metallic surfaces that there is no longer any appreciable attraction between parts of the film-covered surfaces in contact, except the weak attraction between the methyl groups at the end of the hydrocarbon chains in the boundary film. If a method could be found of measuring the resistance to sliding, under conditions where it was certain that the whole surface was covered and remained covered by a complete boundary film, it might be possible to draw conclusions as to the effect of the chemical constitution of the molecules in the films on the real friction of the film-covered surfaces. Coefficients of friction, as hitherto measured, seem the resultant of too many different factors to be easily interpreted.

The lubricating qualities of solid graphite are very considerable, both when dry and also in addition to oil; a colloidal suspension of graphite in oil is now used for a great variety of lubricating purposes. The structure of graphite is parallel sheets of rings of six carbon atoms, extending

[1] *Phil. Trans.* A, **239**, 13 (1940).

indefinitely in the two dimensions of the sheets; and these sheets are very strong, being held together by covalent linkages everywhere. The sheets do not adhere to each other at all strongly, however; they lie about 3·4 A. apart, and consequently graphite can be very easily split parallel to these sheets; it occurs in the form of thin flakes. These flakes have a tendency to stick to metal surfaces, and are oriented parallel to the metal faces. Probably the flakes of graphite are large enough to cover most of the projections on the metal surfaces completely, and extend some distance down the sides of them; the adhesion to the metal may be large, over an area much greater than that of the projections. Seizure would then occur, even if no other lubricant is present, between the flakes of graphite adhering to the surface, instead of between the metal projections. Owing to the small adhesion between the sheets of atoms in the graphite flakes the bridges between the surfaces formed by seizure usually pull apart in the graphite, and the chance of damaging the metal surfaces is very much reduced.

Finch, Quarrell, and Williams[1] have shown that rubbing cast iron, of the quality used for the cylinders of internal combustion engines, brings graphite to the surface so that the graphite structure predominates in the electron diffraction photographs. This should provide a certain amount of lubrication for the surface of the iron.

[1] *Trans. Faraday Soc.* (1935), 1078.

CHAPTER VII*

SOLID SURFACES: FINE STRUCTURE, ADSORPTION AND CATALYSIS

1. Heterogeneity of solid surfaces. It has been mentioned that, owing to the lack of mobility of the particles of solids, solid surfaces are likely to be very complex in structure, owing to the atoms staying where they are placed when the surface is formed. Even in a comparatively simple material such as a metal, there are many possible types of position and linkage of the surface atoms, which confer different chemical properties in different regions. If the metal is wholly crystalline, and of the simplest possible form—the single crystal—there are many different types of surface on it; the different faces, edges, and corners will all be different. Hausser and Scholz have shown that a spherical single crystal of copper gives most beautiful etch figures,[1] very complicated, which shows how the surface atoms differ in properties in different regions. Most surfaces are more complex; they are not single crystals, but often aggregates of small crystals and broken pieces in all possible orientations, with some amorphous material in the interstices; and pieces of crystals may be present as projections, or may overhang pits.

Among amorphous states in metals, two are known:[2] the hard, compact state obtained by polishing or cold working, and the open, much looser structure obtained by rapid evaporation or condensation, or by stirring up the surface atoms by means of chemical reactions occurring at the surface. A particularly striking instance of this is the action of ammonia on tubes of copper and other metals, at 800°. In a short time, the metal becomes spongy, increasing to many times its original volume; and the copper tube quickly becomes completely blocked. Such partially amorphous arrangements also appear, to a lesser extent, at the surface of the platinum gauze used for the catalytic oxidation of ammonia;[3] and Langmuir[4] has found that the structure of platinum changes, with an increase in adsorptive and catalytic power, when hydrogen and oxygen are caused to combine at its surface.

If metals, with their simple composition, can show all this complication, the possibilities of variety of surface structure from atom to atom must be far greater on other materials; and when charcoal, which is formed from a great variety of the most complicated organic compounds by expulsion of hydrogen, oxygen, and nitrogen, is considered, it must obviously have untold possibilities in the way of cavities and elevations.

* See also Appendix.

[1] Cf. Desch, *J. Inst. Metals*, **39**, 1 (1928); Tammann and Sartorius, *Z. anorg. Chem.*, **175**, 97 (1928).

[2] Beilby, *Aggregation and Flow in Solids*, sect. III; *J.C.S.* (1901), 1245.

[3] Cf. Rideal and Taylor, *Catalysis in Theory and Practice*, 2nd ed., p. 177 (1926).

[4] *J.A.C.S.* (1918), 1361.

The heterogeneity of solid surfaces is shown also by many phenomena of adsorption, and catalysis. About fifteen years ago it began to be realized that all parts of a solid surface have not the same power of adsorbing, or of catalysing heterogeneous reactions. There is now universal agreement that, particularly in regard to catalytic power, most solid surfaces consist of patches of widely different activity, ordinary surface reactions on solids probably going on mainly at localized 'active patches' on the surface, which form a small part only of the whole surface. Evidence from thermionic emission (Chap. VIII, § 4) also indicates the heterogeneity of solid surfaces.

The evidence from the action of poisons on solid catalysts is particularly direct. Armstrong and Hilditch[1] pointed out that the amount of poison necessary to suppress catalytic activity entirely is often far less than that required to combine with the whole of the surface, and suggested that the catalytic surface contains active patches, the greater part of the surface being relatively or totally inactive. Vavon and Husson[2] found that there are, on platinum black, at least three different levels of catalytic activity: a clean catalyst will hydrogenate propyl ketone; after poisoning with a small amount of carbon disulphide, propyl ketone cannot be reduced, but piperonal is hydrogenated; a further addition of carbon disulphide prevents the reduction of piperonal, but leaves the power of reducing nitrobenzene. Earlier observations pointed in the same direction; Vavon[3] had noticed that platinum black, which had lost its power of hydrogenating the nucleus of limonene, could still reduce the double bond in the side chain.

Maxted[4] and others have found that, judged on any one of a number of catalytic reactions, the activity of platinum black decreases linearly with the amount of a poison added, up to a critical concentration of the poison, when the activity is usually diminished to about one-quarter of that of the clean catalyst; if further quantities of poison are now added, the activity decreases much more slowly. These observations are quantitative, and are considered to throw some doubt on whether Vavon and Husson's qualitative work really proves the presence of as many as three different kinds of catalysing patches on platinum; but they do not deal with precisely the same reactions. A more exact re-examination of these reactions seems desirable; but it is difficult to see how there can be less than two or three different kinds of surface, while there may be more.

That some degree of irregularity in a surface is often necessary for catalytic activity was early shown by Palmer,[5] who found that electrolytically deposited copper is inactive in dehydrogenating alcohols to aldehydes, whereas the copper formed by reduction of the oxides was active. Constable[6] has extended this work, showing that a polished surface

[1] *Trans. Faraday Soc.*, **17**, 670 (1922). [2] *Compt. Rend.*, **175**, 277 (1922).
[3] *Bull. Soc. Chim.*, **15**, 282 (1914).
[4] *J.C.S.* (1921), 225; (1922), 1760; (1928), 1600; (1933), 502; (1934), 26, 672; (1935), 393, 1190. [5] *Proc. Roy. Soc.* A, **98**, 13 (1920). [6] *Ibid.*, **110**, 283 (1925).

of copper foil, and copper mirrors, reduced slowly from aqueous solutions of the salts, are inactive; commercial copper gauze is practically inactive, but copper produced by rapid condensation of vapour, or in Beilby's open formation, by the action of ammonia at high temperatures, or formed by rapid decomposition of various copper compounds, is always active. It would seem that the copper is only catalytically active, if it is not arranged in a regular space-lattice, or closely packed as in the amorphous polished layer.

A paper by Taylor[1] may be said to mark the period when the importance of active patches, probably containing atoms with their affinities only slightly satisfied, received widespread recognition. The view that a heterogeneous structure of the surface is advantageous for catalysis receives further support from the fact that almost all catalytic surfaces lose much, or all, of their activity on heating. Usually there is considerable loss of catalytic or adsorptive power, at temperatures far below that at which visible sintering of the surface occurs.[2] The preservation of a heterogeneous, active surface is much assisted by depositing the catalyst on some refractory support, which no doubt acts by fixing the atoms more firmly, so that they are less liable to move under moderate thermal agitation.[3] Constable says: 'The essential feature necessary to the production of copper catalytically active . . . is the sudden liberation of free copper atoms under conditions in which the kinetic energy of the atoms . . . is insufficient to cause collapse of the active structure.' Many chemical changes are active enough to cause rearrangement of the surface structure. In some of these the catalytic activity increases with use, up to a maximum, because new active centres are being formed by movement of the atoms. Any change in the surface arrangement, which tends to greater regularity, diminishes catalytic power as a rule; and a disintegrating action increases the catalytic power, both by increasing the total extent of the surface, and by increasing the number of active patches.

It has at times been suggested that the atoms in the active patches are so loosely held that their energy approaches that of a gaseous atom; indeed Armstrong and Hilditch[4] at one time suggested that the nickel atom actually operative in the well-known hydrogenation catalyses is completely liberated from the solid surface at the moment when the reaction takes place. It is more probable, however, according to Constable,[5] and H. S. Taylor,[6] that the active patches are much more solid affairs than this; otherwise they would hardly be as resistant to the action of heat as they actually are.

Studies of adsorption show very great variations in the energy of

[1] *Proc. Roy. Soc.* A, **108**, 105 (1925).

[2] See '3rd Report on Contact Catalysis', *J. Physical Chem.*, **28**, 911 (1925); Smith and others, *J.C.S.* (1921), 1683; (1923), 2088; Langmuir, *J.A.C.S.* (1919), 191.

[3] Cf. Armstrong and Hilditch, *Proc. Roy. Soc.* A, **108**, 115 (1925).

[4] *Ibid.*, **108**, 111 (1925).

[5] *Proc. Camb. Phil. Soc.*, **24**, 291 (1928).

[6] Alexander's *Colloid Chemistry*, **3**, 109 (1931).

adsorption of gases by different parts of the surface. The heat evolved by adsorption of the *first* small portions of a gas on a solid is often much higher than that evolved as the surface becomes more nearly saturated. Thus Garner and Blench[1] found that oxygen on charcoal evolves anything up to 220,000 calories per mole for the first portions adsorbed, and much smaller amounts for later portions. These large heats of adsorption are found at higher temperatures only, where the oxygen combines covalently with the surface atoms of carbon (see below for the different types of adsorption). They are much greater than the heat of combustion of solid charcoal, and more than half that (about 280,000 calories) estimated for gaseous carbon.[2] Dew and Taylor[3] find that the 'differential heat of adsorption' dq/dm (where q is the heat of adsorption and m the amount of gas adsorbed of ammonia) falls from 16,010 to 8,110 calories per mole, as the surface is progressively saturated; Beebe[4] finds similar results (32,800 to 8,900 calories) for carbon monoxide on copper. Kistiakowsky and others[5] found for oxygen on platinum, 161,000 calories for the first portions, falling to 104,000 for later portions; this specimen of platinum black was very active catalytically. For hydrogen on tungsten, Roberts[6] finds a diminution in heat from 34,200 to 17,500 calories as successive amounts are adsorbed. Even vapours, e.g. carbon disulphide on charcoal, show a similar effect.[7]

More puzzling results were found with hydrogen on copper, giving apparently a low heat of adsorption for the first portions, rising to a maximum, and then falling off later with still more gas adsorbed.[8] In a later paper, however, there are measurements of the heat of adsorption of hydrogen on platinum without this maximum, only a steady decrease of the heat being observed as fresh portions of gas were added.[9] Garner and others[10] found a similar maximum with oxygen on charcoal but later traced it to experimental error.

There is some evidence also of *qualitative* difference in adsorbing power for different gases, between various parts of a solid surface. Thus Pease[11] found that traces of mercury diminished the adsorption of all gases by copper, but of some very much more than of others, as if some gases tended to be adsorbed much more than others on those regions to which the mercury was attached. At 400 mm. pressure, for instance, the adsorption of ethylene was diminished by about 20 per cent., that of carbon

[1] *J.C.S.* (1924), 1288.

[2] Grüneisen, *Verh. Deut. Phys. Ges.*, **14**, 324 (1912); cf. Vaughan and Kistiakowsky, *Physical Rev.*, **40**, 457 (1932).

[3] *J. Physical Chem.*, **31**, 277 (1927).

[4] *Ibid.*, **30**, 1538 (1926).

[5] *Ibid.*, **34**, 799 (1930); see also reviews by Kruyt and Moddermann, *Chemical Reviews*, **7**, 254 (1930); Gregg, *Adsorption of Gases on Solids*, chap. iii (Methuen, 1934).

[6] *Proc. Roy. Soc.* A, **152**, 453 (1935).

[7] Allmand and Lizius, *Proc. Roy. Soc.* A, **134**, 554 (1931).

[8] Flosdorf and Kistiakowsky, *J. Physical Chem.*, **34**, 1907 (1930).

[9] *J. Physical Chem.*, **34**, 799 (1930).

[10] *Trans. Faraday Soc.*, **22**, 461 (1926); *J.C.S.* (1931), 837.

[11] *J.A.C.S.* (1923), 2296.

monoxide by about 50 per cent., and that of hydrogen by about 95 per cent. of its value on the clean surface, by the same amount of mercury. The catalytic power (for the hydrogenation of ethylene) was reduced to less than one two-hundredth part of its original amount. Thus a much greater proportion of the surface can absorb ethylene or carbon monoxide than hydrogen, and the catalytically active part appears to be minute in extent compared with the whole surface. Moreover, minute amounts of carbon monoxide, smaller than the total quantity of hydrogen which can be adsorbed (this is much less than the total amount of carbon monoxide), destroyed the catalytic power, showing that the large area which adsorbs carbon monoxide includes also the catalytically active portions. Pease and Stewart[1] showed that the catalytic activity of a certain copper catalyst, for hydrogenating ethylene, was reduced to only 11 per cent. of its normal activity by adsorption of carbon monoxide, in quantity only one-hundredth of the total amount of this gas which could be adsorbed by the copper. Thus 89 per cent. of the total catalytic activity, for the hydrogenation, appears to reside in only 1 per cent. of the total surface available for adsorption. Very much larger amounts of carbon monoxide were required to destroy the remainder of the catalytic activity, however, so that this activity is not entirely confined to the most active patches.

A chance observation by Beebe[2] may indicate that different substances seek out different regions of the surface for their adsorption, when not enough is present to cover the whole surface; i.e. that what is an 'active adsorbing patch' for one gas need not necessarily be also an active patch for another. In studying the heat of adsorption of carbon monoxide on copper he found that a certain sample gave almost exactly the same initial heats of adsorption before, and after, accidental poisoning which cut down its total adsorbing power by 39 per cent., as if the poisoning substance, whose nature was unfortunately unknown, had been adsorbed on parts of the surface with comparatively small affinity for the carbon monoxide.

In rare cases it is possible for the whole surface to be catalytically active; thus in his classical studies of the catalysis of the oxidation of carbon monoxide by platinum, Langmuir[3] found that practically every carbon monoxide molecule which struck an oxygen atom adsorbed on the platinum surface combined with it to form carbon dioxide.

As a rule, a surface which has a high heat of adsorption is more active catalytically than one with a low heat of adsorption.[4]

2. Composite Surfaces: promoter action. The presence of two or more solid substances enormously multiplies the possibility of variety in the types of surface, and in fact the addition of a second substance, often called a 'promoter', to a catalyst is very often found to increase its adsorptive capacity, and still more its catalytic activity. 'Promoters',

[1] *J.A.C.S.* (1925), 1235. [2] *J. Physical Chem.*, **30**, 1538 (1926).
[3] *Trans. Faraday Soc.*, **17**, 621 (1922).
[4] Cf. Kistiakowsky and others, *J. Physical Chem.*, **34**, 799 (1930).

usually in the form of additions of refractory substances to catalytically active solids, have very great industrial importance. Their number is legion; occasionally they may have some catalytic activity of their own, but more usually they have none. The use of refractory supports for metallic catalysts, as economizers and diluents of expensive materials, is probably as old as the technical practice of surface catalysis; the platinum used for catalysing the oxidation of sulphur dioxide was usually supported on asbestos. The view that an inert refractory support may actually increase the catalytic activity of a given amount of a solid catalyst, in addition to spreading it to a greater area and preserving it against deterioration by heat, appears first in the patent literature about 1913. Scientific studies of promoter action began to appear about 1920; and an enormous number of observations are now on record. As several writers have given accounts[1] in detail, only a few striking cases of promoter action will be mentioned, and an attempt made to indicate some ways in which promoters may act.

Among the more important catalysts are *metals*, which may be promoted by other metals, or by oxides; and *oxides*, which are usually rendered more effective by mixing with other oxides. It is usual to distinguish between 'supported' catalysts, generally metals in a finely divided condition on the surface of silicate minerals, and 'promoted' catalysts, where an oxide, or occasionally some other compound, is mixed with the metal; the mixture being sometimes also supported on an inert refractory support. The distinction is not, however, absolutely sharp.

For metals promoting other metals, an interesting case was studied by Hurst and Rideal.[2] In the combustion of mixtures of hydrogen and carbon monoxide, using copper as the basic catalyst the ratio of the gases burnt depends on the temperature, and also on the amount of small additions of palladium made to the copper. The proportion of carbon monoxide burnt is increased by addition of palladium, a maximum proportion of carbon monoxide being burnt when 0·2 per cent. of palladium is present. With further amounts of palladium, the ratio $CO : H_2$ burnt falls off slowly until, with 5 per cent. palladium, it is nearly the same as with pure copper. This effect of palladium is ascribed to the introduction of a new type of surface, the line of contact between palladium and copper, though the proof that this is the cause of promotion is perhaps not complete. Mittasch and others,[3] in elaborate studies of the promotion of various metal catalysts, particularly molybdenum, for the synthesis or decomposition of ammonia, concluded that the formation of intermetallic compounds

[1] Rideal and Taylor, *Catalysis in Theory and Practice*, chap. v (1926); R. H. Griffith, *The Mechanism of Contact Catalysis*, chap. iii, Oxford (1936); Reports of the Committee on Contact Catalysis, *Ind. Eng. Chem.*, **14**, 326, 444, 545, 642 (1922); *J. Physical Chem.* (1923), 800; (1924), 897; (1926), 145; (1927), 1121; (1928), 1601; (1930), 2129; (1932), 1969; Mittasch, *Ber.*, **59**, 13 (1926); Mittasch and Frankenburger, *Z. Elektrochem.*, **35**, 920 (1929).

[2] *J.C.S.* (1924), 685, 694.

[3] *Z. physikal. Chem.* (*Bodenstein Festb.*), 574 (1931); *Z. Elektrochem.*, **36**, 569, 690 (1930).

is an important, if not a necessary, part of the mechanism of promotion of this reaction. Compound formation would produce new types of surface, with atomic spacings different from the original, and also new linear boundaries between regions of different composition on the surface.

Oxides, not easily reduced, are more commonly used than metals for the promotion of metallic catalysts. Iron, the most usual catalyst for ammonia synthesis by the high pressure processes, is quite a good catalyst alone for a short time; but it rapidly loses its activity. Addition, however, of a small amount of alumina, or magnesia, renders the activity permanent.[1] The alumina is sometimes supposed to operate by preserving a structure of the magnetite, Fe_3O_4, type, through formation of a spinel, FeO, Al_2O_3, isomorphous with magnetite. Iron catalysts are more effective if made from magnetite than from other oxides. Alkalis, which appear to concentrate on the surface even if present in very small amount, are also useful.[2]

Such additions of oxides to metals may also act by preventing sintering, which may easily occur with finely divided metals, far below their melting-point. Sintering is likely to destroy the structure of groups of atoms possessing unusually high potential energy, which the active patches probably have. Besides this selective destruction of the patches which are most efficient for catalysis, any extensive sintering will diminish the total area available for catalysis; and as most reactions catalysed by surfaces are exothermic, the necessity of some protection against sintering is easy to see.[3] On the other hand, as some gases disintegrate metals at high temperatures, slowly, or render them spongy (e.g. platinum in the oxidation of ammonia), there may sometimes be no necessity for the presence of refractory additions to the metals.

Two other interesting studies of the promotion of metallic catalysts by inert supports are those of Medsforth[4] on nickel, and of Griffith and others on molybdenum catalysts. Medsforth found that the hydrogenating activity of nickel, for carbon monoxide or dioxide, was increased nearly twelvefold by addition of suitable oxides, the amounts of different oxides required to produce the maximum rates of reaction varying very much, being roughly 5 per cent. of ceria, 10 per cent. of thoria, and 20 per cent. of ceria, calculated on the amount of nickel present. Griffith[5] finds an extremely sharp peak in the activity for decomposition of hydrocarbons at high temperatures and low pressures, by molybdenum promoted by a variety of oxides. If these oxides cannot be reduced easily (e.g. oxides of Si, Al, Na, Ba, Th, Ce), the sharp maximum of activity occurs at about 4·4 atoms per cent. of the metal in the promoting oxide. But if the oxide is easily reduced (e.g. Pb, Fe, Cu), there is a similar sharp maximum, but at just half the above atomic concentration. This very remarkable peak

[1] Applebey, *Proc. Roy. Soc.* A, **127**, 256 (1930).

[2] Emmett and Brunauer, *J.A.C.S.* (1937), 310.

[3] Cf. Pease and Stewart, *J.A.C.S.* (1927), 2783; Almquist, *ibid.* (1926), 2820.

[4] *J.C.S.* (1923), 1452.

[5] *Proc. Roy. Soc.* A, **148**, 186 (1936); *Nature*, **137**, 538 (1936); *The Mechanism of Contact Catalysis*, pp. 74 ff. (1936).

has been found for other reactions also, including the adsorption of hexane, cyclohexane, and benzene, molecules of differing size, which seems to show that the reason why the activity is so much greater at a particular promoter concentration is *not* that this is a surface pattern of dimensions exactly fitting the adsorbed molecules. For the high pressure hydrogenation of tar, there is a still more curious *minimum* of activity with silicon-promoted molybdenum at the same concentration. But for the conversion of phenol to benzene, there is a very marked peak at about 16 atoms per cent., a trifle less for silicon and a trifle less for aluminium. The significance of these very sharp maxima at particular concentrations of promoter is not yet clear, and should abundantly repay further investigation.

Griffith suggests that the degree of reduction of the metal may be important, this being in part determined by the temperature of the reaction, and that valency bonds between the different metal atoms (it is not quite clear how this differs from intermetallic compound formation) may be formed. In view of the well known effects, in metallurgy, which small amounts of one metal, or non-metal, exert on the microscopic structure of another, it might be worth conducting metallographic investigations in parallel with the investigation of catalytic activity, to find out how far the effects are due to changes in size and in form of the crystals, or to the appearance of a new phase in the solid metal.

A fairly early study by Russell and Taylor[1] of nickel catalysts supported on pumice showed the great importance both of avoiding sintering, and of increasing the proportion of the metal present as active patches. Nickel catalysts are most active, if reduced from the oxide at the lowest possible temperature; at higher temperatures the highly unsaturated atoms in the active patches seem to acquire the mobility necessary to move close to other unsaturated metal atoms and partially saturate each other. Adding 10 per cent. thoria to nickel catalysts already supported on pumice produced a tenfold increase in catalytic activity for hydrogenation, although the amount of either hydrogen or carbon dioxide adsorbed was increased only by 20 per cent. This proves that the thoria increases the *quality* of the surface, for catalytic purposes, much more than it does its total extent; and that patches active for adsorption are often different from patches most active for catalysis; adsorption is of course necessary for surface catalysis, but the quality of the adsorption is even more important than its total amount.

Thus refractory promoters for metallic catalysts may act either by diluting the metal, extending its surface and bringing a much larger proportion of the metal atoms into direct contact with the gas than could be the case if the metal were its own support; they can also act by stabilizing catalytically active groups of metal atoms, diminishing the probability of sintering; and often also they actually induce the formation of additional active centres. Precisely how each promoter acts, we are a long way from understanding at present; but data are gradually accumulating, and it is now probable that both special structures of metallic atoms only, and also special combinations of different kinds of atoms on the surface,

[1] *J. Physical Chem.*, **29**, 1325 (1925).

which may involve linear interfaces or boundaries between different types of atoms on the surface, are important.

Oxides may promote oxide catalysts, and produce an enormous change, not only quantitatively, but qualitatively, in their catalytic activities. A fairly simple case is the catalytic effect of rare earth oxides on gaseous combustion. A gas mantle consists mainly of thoria, but if 1 per cent. of ceria is added, its light-emitting power is considerably increased; and Swan[1] has shown that the same mixture of oxides is the most efficient for catalysing the combustion of hydrogen, suggesting that the reason for the enhanced emission of light is that the temperature is higher.

Research on the important, and difficult, problem of removing small quantities of carbon monoxide from the air has shown that this can be best effected, by catalytic oxidation at room temperature, by mixtures of oxides, which are far more effective than any of the oxides singly.[2] While neither manganese dioxide, silver oxide, nor copper oxide will oxidize carbon monoxide rapidly at room temperature, mixtures of manganese dioxide and copper oxide (60/40) will do so; silver oxide also much accelerates the oxidation by manganese dioxide. It is stated that 1 per cent. of potash is beneficial, but larger amounts retard the oxidation. Not all oxides accelerate; thus cobalt oxide retards oxidation. Various mixtures of manganese dioxide and other oxides as promoters are sold as 'Hopcalite'.

For hydrogenation reactions, particularly the synthesis of methanol from carbon monoxide and hydrogen, oxide catalysts are of immense technical importance. Here the choice of catalyst makes large qualitative, as well as quantitative, differences.[3] While Sabatier found that nickel hydrogenates this gas to methane, Fischer[4] obtained a most complicated mixture of alcohols, ketones, and acids, using iron and alkalis as catalyst; and a suitable choice of oxides produces practically pure methanol. Zinc oxide is most frequently used, and it is generally promoted with chromium oxide. The addition of a little alkali to this oxide mixture promotes the production of higher alcohols. Ferric oxide is said to convert the mixture of carbon monoxide and hydrogen mainly into methane and liquid hydrocarbons; but if a little sulphur is added to the iron oxide, methanol is formed instead.

In few cases has an attempt been made to work out the mechanism of these oxide promoters, the researches having been generally done merely for the purpose of improving the yield of some desired product. Taylor and Williamson's work (see § 10) has, however, shown that the addition of chromic oxide to manganous oxide has two definite effects;[5] it greatly

[1] *J.C.S.* (1924), 780.

[2] Lamb, Bray, Frazer, *J. Ind. Eng. Chem.*, **12**, 213 (1920); Whitesell and Frazer, *J.A.C.S.* (1923), 2841; Benton, *J.A.C.S.* (1923), 887; Neumann and others, *Z. Elektrochem.*, **37**, 121 (1931).

[3] Mittasch, *Z. Elektrochem.*, **36**, 578 (1930); Natta, *Giorn. Chim. Ind. Appl.*, **12**, 13 (1930); Morgan, Bone, *Proc. Roy. Soc.* A, **127**, 244, 254 (1930); Frohlich and others, *Ind. Eng. Chem.* (1929), 1052; (1930), 1051; Huffmann and Dodge, *Ind. Eng. Chem.* (1929), 1056.

[4] *Ber.*, **56**, 2429 (1923), and elsewhere.

[5] Cf. also Taylor and Strother, *J.A.C.S.* (1934), 586.

increases the van der Waals type of adsorption, and also lowers the apparent activation energy, thus increasing the rate of adsorption in the 'chemisorbed' form. The first effect may, as the molecules in the van der Waals adsorbed layers are often mobile, make it possible for the molecules to approach the active patches very quickly; the latter effect may be equivalent to increasing the ease with which molecules can be adsorbed so that they react, and possibly the number of catalytically active patches also. Conversely, molybdenum oxide impairs the efficiency of ZnO catalysts by increasing the activation energy for chemisorption.[1]

As a general rule, the presence of 'active patches' does not alter the X-ray diffraction pattern of a metal. This may be only because the patches on the surface, are of insufficient thickness to give an X-ray pattern of their own—it does not prove that their structure is identical with the normal space-lattice of a metal. Electron diffraction, which reveals the structure of much smaller thicknesses of solids than X-rays, indicates that possibly there may be a difference in structure between catalytically active and inactive platinum.[2] It also shows that the structure of metals on supports of other metals, or of other materials, may not be the same as the normal structure of these metals alone[3]; and thus promoters and supports for metals may influence their catalytic power by altering the spacing of the atoms in the metal on the surface.

It has often been suggested that promotion may arise from an alteration in the spacing of the atoms on the surface of the catalyst through the presence of the promoter. This would naturally alter the extent to which the adsorbed molecules are deformed, and consequently their activation. Frohlich and others[4] attempted to correlate the change in the lattice dimensions of brass, as the percentages of zinc and copper change, with its power to catalyse the synthesis of methanol from carbon monoxide and hydrogen, or the reverse decomposition. A very rough parallelism between the atomic spacings and the methanol decomposing to carbon monoxide was found; but in this instance the change in spacing is rather small, only just over 1 per cent. The idea seems to be worth further test, but this should be combined with metallographic or other investigation of major changes of phase in the surface.

The different theories of promoter action are not, as a rule, mutually exclusive; several of the mechanisms suggested may simultaneously be operating to aid the catalysis.

3. Linear, one-dimensional interfaces. Perhaps the most interesting theory of promoter action is that the linear boundary on the surface between two surfaces of different composition is the seat of the catalysis, i.e. the active patch. There is abundant evidence that such linear interfaces often possess unusual reactive powers. They are undoubtedly

[1] Taylor and Ogden, *Trans. Faraday Soc.*, **30**, 1178 (1934).

[2] Finch, Thomson, and others, *Proc. Roy. Soc.* A, **141**, 414 (1933).

[3] Thomson, *ibid.*, **133**, 1 (1931); Finch and others, *Trans. Faraday Soc.*, **31**, 26 (1935).

[4] *Ind. Eng. Chem.* (1928), 694, 1327; (1929), 109.

important for very many heterogeneous reactions in solids. Many years ago, Wright, Luff, and Rennie[1] showed that reduction of copper oxide by hydrogen can actually be seen to proceed at the boundary where the copper and the unreduced copper oxide adjoin. The oxide and the metal have different colours; and the reduction commences by the formation of a red speck, which spreads rapidly over the whole mass, 'the reduction reminding one of the slow deflagration of touch paper'. Pease and Taylor[2] confirmed that this reaction is autocatalytic, water vapour retarding the formation of the initial patches of copper. Nickel oxide is probably reduced in a similar manner.[3] Langmuir[4] pointed out that the relative stability of atoms at the regions of a surface forming the boundary between two phases, and in the middle of surfaces of one kind only, determine whether or no the reaction proceeds at a one-dimensional boundary. Thus in the dissociation of calcium carbonate, which has already some carbon dioxide, there will be regions of the surface consisting of oxide, and others of carbonate. If the undissociated molecules of carbonate are less stable at the edges of the patches of carbonate surface than in the centre, further decomposition will take place at the edges of the carbonate, and the patches of lime will be few in number and large in extent. This results in the formation of two solid phases. If, however, the molecules at the edge of the bare patch are more stable than those elsewhere on the surface, there will be a tendency to the formation of extremely numerous and small patches of oxide, and finally a mixture of the two constituents in patches of molecular dimensions will result; i.e. a solid solution. Hence the question whether two separate phases or a solid solution are formed will be decided by the relative stability of the atoms at the one-dimensional boundaries, and in the homogeneous regions, on the surface. The majority of heterogeneous decompositions, and some other reactions, proceed with the formation of two solid phases;[5] but a few, such as the dissociation of ferric oxide Fe_2O_3 into magnetic oxide Fe_3O_4 and oxygen, give solid solutions.[6]

One result of a dissociation occurring most easily at the boundary between the two solid phases is that it is often difficult to start dissociation, or the reverse process of recombination, when the solid surface consists entirely of one or the other constituent. Faraday[7] found that hydrated sodium sulphate and some other salts do not commence to effloresce until the surface is scratched, thus starting a one-dimensional interface on the surface by mechanical means, from which the loss of water could occur

[1] *J.C.S.* (1878), 1; (1879), 475. [2] *J.A.C.S.* (1921), 2179.

[3] Hughes and Bevan, *Proc. Roy. Soc.* A, **117**, 107 (1927).

[4] *J.A.C.S.* (1916), 2263.

[5] e.g. Silver oxalate, Macdonald and Hinshelwood, *J.C.S.* (1925), 2764; silver carbonate, Spencer and Topley, *ibid.* (1929), 2633; potassium permanganate, Hinshelwood and Bowen, *Phil. Mag.*, **40**, 569 (1920); *Z. physikal. Chem.*, **101**, 504 (1921); cf. also Rideal, *Surface Chemistry*, 2nd ed., 180 (1930).

[6] Sosman and Hostetter, *J.A.C.S.* (1916), 807.

[7] *Experimental Researches in Electricity*, footnote to § 656 (1833).

most easily. The rate of dissociation or recombination would be, among other things, proportional to the length of the boundary on the surface, between the hydrated and dehydrated salts; it would go on very slowly at the extremes either of complete hydration or complete desiccation. As an instance of slow hydration, it may be mentioned that if lime, or plaster of Paris, are too strongly heated or 'over-burnt', they are very slow in taking up the first traces of water, because water does not easily condense except close to regions where the hydration has already begun.

The presence of one of these one-dimensional interfaces may be detected by the reaction being very slow at the commencement and increasing as the length of the interface grows; it is 'autocatalytic' in nature. Lewis[1] showed that the decomposition of silver oxide proceeds more rapidly as the amount of silver increases, and similar phenomena are often observed in studies of dissociation, as might be expected. The decomposition of potassium chlorate also is autocatalytic, and is accelerated by deliberate addition of the solid decomposition product, potassium chloride.[2] The well-known action of manganese dioxide, and other oxides, in facilitating the decomposition of potassium chlorate is probably another instance of the effect of the boundary between solid phases; and Kendall and Fuchs[3] have shown that the decomposition of various oxides by heat is very much affected, and generally aided, by the presence of other oxides as impurities. Rideal and Taylor[4] discuss this question further, and many additional instances may be found on reference to their book.

Such interfaces are of widespread importance; their avoidance may be very important in the preservation of explosives,[5] where impurities, including those formed by slow decomposition, often accelerate decomposition; their presence may be one of the reasons why impure chemicals are often less stable than pure ones.

Pietsch, Kotowski, and Behrend[6] examined microscopically the course of various reactions of solid crystals with solutions, giving rise to colours, such as H_2S reacting with copper sulphate; dimethyl glyoxime with nickel sulphate; ferric chloride with acetate. In all cases the reaction commenced at the edges of the crystals, spreading thence along the surface, the linear interface reacting more rapidly than the rest of the solid surface.

Schwab and Pietsch[7] find that radioactive lead is much more strongly adsorbed on the edges of crocosite, or lead sulphide crystals, than elsewhere, and can be made visible there. The literature of such 'topochemical' reactions, occurring in localized regions of surfaces, is now fairly extensive.[8]

[1] *Z. physikal. Chem.*, **52**, 310 (1905).

[2] Otto and Fry, *J.A.C.S.* (1924), 269.

[3] *J.A.C.S.* (1921), 2017.

[4] *Catalysis in Theory and Practice*, 2nd ed., 109 (1926).

[5] Cf. Hinshelwood, *J.C.S.* (1921), 721; Hinshelwood and Bowen, *Proc. Roy. Soc.* A, **99**, 203 (1921).

[6] *Z. physikal. Chem.* B, **5**, 1 (1929).

[7] *Z. physikal. Chem.* B, **2**, 262 (1929); cf. *ibid.*, **13**, 13 (1931).

[8] Cf. Kohlschütter, *Kolloid-Z.*, **42**, 254 (1927); *Z. Elektrochem.*, **38**, 345 (1932); *Angew. Chem.*, **47**, 753 (1934); Stäger, *Kolloid-Z.*, **68**, 137 (1934); *Korrosion u. Metallschütz*, **11**, 73 (1935); Feitknecht, *Fortschr. Chem., Phys., Phys. Chem.*, **21**, no. 2 (1930).

Even on a liquid surface, reactions may be catalysed at the boundary of a crystal touching the surface, e.g. the combination of iodine with mercury proceeds very fast at the region where a crystal of mercuric iodide touches the surface,[1] and slowly elsewhere, although the iodine may be covering nearly all the mercury surface.

An early instance where a linear interface was found of importance for catalysis is recorded by Antropoff;[2] the decomposition of hydrogen peroxide by mercury, a reaction which shows periodic variations of rate, occurring at a speed proportional to the *length* of the boundary of a visible skin of oxide on the mercury, and takes place at this boundary.

Antropoff and Germann[3] found that the presence of very small amounts of alkali metals, at the surface of metallic calcium, very much accelerates its combination with nitrogen: these metals apparently act by removing, locally, a layer of oxygen which usually inhibits the combination of calcium with nitrogen.

The remarkable effect of a minute trace of sulphur on the surface of a silver bromide grain, referred to in § 16, indicates that the instability of a one-dimensional interface may be fundamental to the speed of the modern photographic plate.

Schwab and Pietsch[4] have developed a theory of the kinetics of contact catalysis based on the assumption that the active patches are located at such interfaces, using the term 'adlineation' for adsorption there; but though their assumption seems a very probable one, at any rate for many cases of promoter action, it is scarcely possible to test it by comparison of rates of reaction with a theoretically derived equation: there are too many adjustable constants, and other factors. One of these is the rate of surface diffusion to the active linear interfaces, or other active patches, which as many writers have pointed out, may be very considerable.[5]

Such surface diffusion provides a mechanism whereby the active patches, covering but a small fraction of the surface, may be supplied with molecules of a reacting gas very much more rapidly than they could be supplied by direct hits from the vapour phase; surface diffusion (see Chap. VI, § 4) may bring molecules up to any kind of active patch.

4. Surface cracks. Most solid substances have very numerous small cracks in their surfaces.[6] The first evidence for this comes from a comparison of the actual strength of crystals with that deduced from theoretical considerations. In the case of the ionic lattice of sodium chloride the theoretical strength calculated from consideration of the electrostatic forces between the ions is of the order 200 kg. per sq. mm.; actually dry crystals of rock salt can be broken at 0·4 kg. per sq. mm. If strained in air the deformation of rock salt is very small, before it breaks. It has long been known, to those who work in salt mines, that rock salt can be bent

[1] Adhikari and Feldman, *Z. physikal. Chem.*, **131**, 347 (1928).

[2] *Z. physikal. Chem.*, **62**, 548, 567 (1908); cf. Bredig and Stark, *ibid.*, B, **2**, 282 (1929).

[3] *Z. physikal. Chem.* A, **137**, 209 (1928).

[4] *Z. physikal. Chem.* B, **1**, 385 (1928); **12**, 427 (1931); *Z. Elektrochem.*, **35**, 135, 573 (1929).

[5] Cf. H. S. Taylor, *Trans. Faraday Soc.*, **28**, 135 (1932).

[6] Cf. Schmidt and Boas, *Kristallplastizität*, p. 271 (1935).

and twisted if immersed in warm water, without breaking.[1] Joffé found[2] that the tensile strength of this crystal may be increased sometimes to over two-thirds of the theoretical, if the crystal is immersed in water; later workers agree that a considerable increase in strength takes place in water, though they mostly failed to find quite such large a increase as Joffé. Joffé's explanation was that the water dissolved away the surface of the crystal so that a new surface, unbroken by cracks, appeared; and concluded from the loss of strength taking place more or less rapidly after drying, that a surface soon develops cracks, which weaken the crystal by intensifying the stress at their ends.

A. A. Griffith[3] showed in 1920 that very recently drawn threads of glass and silica have approximately the theoretical tensile strength (deduced from the surface tension of the just molten materials) but that the strength diminishes very much after some hours. The diminution in strength was attributed to the development of cracks in the material. The loss of strength might be due to either surface, or internal, cracks, and Smekal has argued in many papers[4] that the primary cracks are internal, and that such surface cracks as are found are incidental to the existence of internal cracks. That a mosaic structure does exist in the interior of most solids is nearly certain;[5] but the fact that the strength of rock salt increases so much on immersion in water, indicates that the main loss of strength is due to surface cracks, which probably develop a short time after the surface is formed. The plasticity of rock salt may continue some little time after the crystal is removed from the water.

Recently Andrade and others have found two methods of rendering these cracks visible. The first[6] is to sputter thin metallic films on the surface; after heating the film, the metal tends to accumulate in thin lines, which re-appear in the same place no matter how carefully the surface is cleaned, provided it is not disturbed by polishing. The lines presumably indicate the surface cracks; they generally run in groups of parallel lines, and different groups frequently cross at right angles. If the surface is re-polished, the original cracks disappear, others often appearing, but in different places. Such lines were found on various glasses and on one of the two varieties of diamond. Mica, which shows the theoretical strength,[7] gave no such lines on heating metallic films sputtered on to it.

[1] Cf. Schmidt and Boas, *Kristallplastizität*, 271 (1935).

[2] *Z. Physik*, **31**, 576 (1925); **35**, 442 (1926); *Trans. Faraday Soc.*, **24**, 65 (1928); *Physics of Crystals*, 56 ff. (1928); *Internat. Conf. on Physics*, II, 72 (Physical Soc., 1934).

[3] *Phil. Trans.* A, **221**, 163.

[4] Including *Z. tech. Physik*, **7**, 535 (1926); **8**, 561 (1927); **15**, 405 (1934). *Ann. Physik*, **83**, 1202 (1927). *Z. Physik*, **55**, 289 (1929). *Physikal. Z.*, **32**, 581 (1931); **33**, 204 (1932); **34**, 633 (1933). *Metallwirtsch*, **7**, 776 (1928). *Internat. Conf. on Physics*, II, 93 (1934).

[5] Cf. also Desch, *Chemistry of Solids* (Cornell Univ. Press, 1934), chap. vi; Zwicky, *Proc. Nat. Acad. Sci.*, **15**, 253, 816 (1929); **17**, 524 (1931).

[6] Andrade and Martindale, *Phil. Trans.* A, **235**, 69 (1935); Andrade, *Science Progress* (1936), 593.

[7] Cf. Orowan, *Z. Physik*, **82**, 235 (1933).

The second method of developing surface cracks is to expose the surface to hot sodium vapour.[1] With various kinds of glass, this treatment produces visible markings (Fig. 45). It is interesting that neither the metallic films nor the sodium vapour show scratches or drawing marks; etching with hydrofluoric acid, on the other hand, shows scratches, but does not show the 'Griffith' cracks,[2] as Andrade has called them.

The cause of these cracks may perhaps be that the natural packing, at any rate of a heteropolar crystal (one composed of ions such as Na and Cl) in bulk is some 5 per cent. greater than the natural packing, under the known electrostatic forces, of the atoms in a surface layer.[3] The attempt on the part of the atoms in a newly formed surface to adjust themselves from the more widely separated packing of the interior to the closer packing of a surface would probably produce considerable tensions and cracks in the surface layer.

5. Measurement of the area of solid surfaces. The measurement of the real area of a solid surface is obviously fundamental to a study of its properties, but is not at all easy. Even the definition of what is meant by the real area presents some difficulties; if the surfaces are irregular, and some of the cracks in it narrow, all depends on the fineness of the measuring device employed, whether or no it can penetrate into the finest cracks.

The method which seems theoretically most nearly sound is that of Bowden and Rideal.[4] These authors measured the quantity of electricity which had to be passed in order to build up a definite overvoltage on a metal surface. There is reason to believe that this quantity, i.e. the number of ions per square centimetre for each millivolt of overpotential is independent or nearly so of the nature of the metal; therefore the true area of the metal surface is proportional to the quantity of electricity needed to build up a given overpotential. It was first assumed that the real area of a mercury surface was equal to the apparent area; with this assumption the real area of various smooth or polished metals appeared

[1] *Proc. Roy. Soc.* A, **159**, 346 (1937).

[2] If these cracks are a phenomenon with which a person's name should be associated, it seems inappropriate to call them 'Smekal' cracks, as many recent writers have done. Griffith's paper anticipated Smekal's rather numerous publications by several years, and gave the essentials of the theory of the weakening of a solid structure by cracks. It was probably Joffé, however, who first saw clearly that the main loss of strength is due to *surface*, as opposed to interior, cracks. The recognition of surface cracks goes back, however, at least as far as Boyle; in his *Experiments and Considerations about the Porosity of Bodies* (1684), p. 103, he mentions that Italian goldsmiths 'have a way of imbuing Fragments of Rock-Crystal ... with divers Colours', indicating that in his opinion the colours penetrate into minute surface cracks. I am indebted to Professor Partington for this reference. Earlier writers refer to penetration of solid bodies (cf. Partington, *Chemistry and Industry*, **13**, 490 (1935)); but it seems doubtful if they distinguish between penetration into cracks, and solution, or penetration through intermolecular interstices.

[3] Lennard-Jones and Dent, *Proc. Roy. Soc.* A, **121**, 247 (1928).

[4] *Proc. Roy. Soc.* A, **120**, 80 (1928).

FIG. 45 *a*. Pyrex tube showing transverse cracks

FIG. 45 *b*. Optically polished glass showing orthogonal system of cracks

to vary from 2·1 to 9 times the apparent area. There now seems reason to believe, however, that the real area of their mercury surfaces was considerably *less* than (of the order one-third of) the apparent area, owing to contamination (see Chap. VIII, § 6), so that many of the polished metals may have had a real area almost the same as the apparent. Scratched metals, and still more platinum black, had an area many times the apparent. This electrolytic method will probably include the area of all cracks whose width exceeds twice the thickness of the electrical double layer.

Measurements of the rate of evaporation into a vacuum, or of dissolution in a solvent, have been proposed for the evaluation of the real area. These are not likely to include the surface of even fairly wide cracks, however, as molecules evaporating off the surface of one side will probably condense on the opposite side of a crack; and the rate of diffusion in solution along cracks is so slow that the amount dissolved in these will probably not contribute much to the apparent rate of diffusion.

A method depending on the simultaneous measurement of the *thickness* of an oxide film (or other film formed by the reaction of the solid with a gas), and of the amount of material lost from the interior of a solid to form this film, was used by J. S. Dunn[1] and by Constable.[2] The thickness of the film was determined by observing the 'temper' colours of the metal wire being oxidized; the loss of material from the inside by measuring the decrease in electrical conductivity. The method is applicable only to surfaces of solids of fairly simple form; and it has been criticized by Evans and Bannister,[3] and by Wilkins,[4] on the grounds that there is risk that the film on the surface may contain metal as well as oxide. It is not always easy to obtain a uniform thickness of film, and the method cannot detect fine cracks or irregularities not larger than the thickness of the oxide film.

In the case of powders, if the particles are of fairly simple form, the surface area (excluding submicroscopic cracks) can be estimated from microscopic measurement of the size of the particles.[5] Powders, or porous solids composed of aggregations of small particles, can have the particle size approximately estimated by the width, and imperfection of definition, of the lines in an X-ray diffraction photograph.[6] This method has been used by Levi and others[7] for finely divided metal such as platinum black; the particles were usually extremely small, of the same order of size as the particles in a colloidal sol of the metal. For the platinum group, the size of crystalline particles was estimated as from 20 to 120 A. across only.

Using this method, the influence of particle size on the decomposition of hydrogen peroxide was studied; it was found that the rate of decomposition increased with increase in surface area up to about

[1] *Proc. Roy. Soc.* A, **111**, 209 (1926). [2] *Ibid.*, **119**, 196 (1928).
[3] *Ibid.*, **125**, 370 (1929). [4] *J.C.S.* (1930), 1304.
[5] E. J. Dunn, *Ind. Eng. Chem.* (*Anal.*), **2**, 59 (1930); Kenrick, *J.A.C.S.* (1940), 2838. [6] Cf. Bragg, *X-rays and Crystal Structure*, 4th ed., 132 (1924).
[7] *Giorn. Chem. Ind. Appl.*, **7**, 410 (1925); *Atti R. Accad. Lincei*, **3**, 91, 215 (1926).

300,000 sq. cm. per gm., but did not increase with further subdivision of the catalyst.[1]

Mark[2] has discussed the theory of the determination of particle size by X-ray diffraction, which has some uncertainties. It seems possible that the adsorption of a monomolecular layer of a salt of a heavy metal on the surface of the particles may assist the estimate of particle size, by introducing a set of surfaces of high scattering power for the rays, which coincide with the surface of the particles. This method has been successfully employed to intensify the natural reflections from cellulose fibres.

Perhaps the most generally employed method for estimating the surface area is to determine the amount of one or more substances which can be adsorbed on the solid; this necessitates making some assumption as to the packing in the adsorbed layer, but with the use of a number of different substances these assumptions can be checked to some extent. Those usually made are either that the layer is a closely packed one of the adsorbate, one molecule thick, or (in the case of chemisorbed layers) that there is one (or a small multiple or a simple fraction of one) atom to each surface atom of the solid.

It is unfortunate that the precise nature of the assumptions made is but rarely pointed out by the users of these methods, which renders it unnecessarily difficult to assess the value of the results obtained.

Dyestuffs have been very much employed for this purpose, as they can be easily estimated. Radioactive indicators have also been employed, and also gases.

With the radioactive indicators, the method is as follows: it was used by Paneth and Vorwerk,[3] and by Hahn.[4] The former shook up a very slightly soluble lead salt with a saturated solution of the same salt, containing, besides ordinary lead, a small quantity of a radioactive isotope. During the shaking, there was an interchange of atoms between the surface of the powder and the solution, the radioactive 'lead' atoms (thorium B) sharing in this interchange just like the inactive atoms. Equilibrium was rapidly set up, and finally, of course, the proportion of active to inactive atoms was the same both in the surface and in the solution. Hence the following equation holds:

$$\frac{\text{radioactive lead in surface}}{\text{radioactive lead in solution}} = \frac{\text{total lead in surface}}{\text{total lead in solution}}.$$

Of the four quantities in this equation, the amount of radioactive 'lead' in the powder and the solution can be determined by electrical methods, and the total lead in solution can be found by chemical analysis, so that the total number of lead atoms in the surface can be found by calculation.

One weak point in this method appears to be that it is not certain that it is the *surface* layer only which takes part in the interchange of atoms;

[1] *Gazzetta*, **56**, 424 (1926). [2] *Trans. Faraday Soc.*, **25**, 387 (1929).

[3] *Z. physikal. Chem.*, **101**, 445 (1922).

[4] *Sitzb. Akad. Preuss. Wiss.* (1929), 535.

at true equilibrium, the radioactive material would penetrate throughout the whole of the solid powder. This criticism is less serious than appears at first sight, because a nearly steady state is found to be established in less than a minute, only slow changes going on after this time. It is probably at the end of this initial period that the equilibrium is established as regards the easily accessible surface. Cracks in the solid material, as well as diffusion within the solid, may account for the further slow interchange.

This method gives the number of lead atoms on the surface; and this was converted into square centimetres by *assuming* the density of the surface layer to be identical with that of the lead salt in bulk, and also that the area of the molecules in the surface layer is the same as if they were cubes with the known volume of the molecule.

The method is only directly applicable to solids which have an element with a radioactive isotope. Kolthoff and O'Brien[1] used artificially radioactive bromine for estimating the surface of silver bromide; it is necessary, here, to have an adsorbed layer of dyestuff, to restrict exchange with the interior. In the case of lead salts the areas deduced by the radioactive method are of the same order of magnitude as those found by microscopic examination; the discrepancies may, however, reach 100 or 200 per cent.

The adsorption of gases has been used as an estimate of area; Brunauer and Emmett[2] find that, if the adsorption isotherms relating the amount adsorbed to the pressure for eight different gases and vapours, are extrapolated to zero pressure, and it is assumed that the adsorbed layer is then unimolecular and closely packed, results consistent within 15 per cent. or so are obtained for the surface area of porous iron catalysts. As these isotherms consist of a long, nearly linear, portion, there is no difficulty in the extrapolation and the consistency among the results obtained using different gases indicates that the fundamental assumption as to packing is likely to be nearly correct.

The direct adsorption of organic dye-stuffs, acetone, and brucine was early used by Paneth and others[3] to indicate the surface area. Using a lead sulphate powder, whose area had been estimated by the radioactive method, they found that about 31 per cent. of the surface was covered by the dye Ponceau 2R, *assuming* that the adsorbed layer was packed with cubical molecules in a monomolecular layer, of the density of the solid dye-stuff. We now know enough about the shapes of organic molecules to suspect that the molecules were not cubical; perhaps they were flattened and the whole surface was really covered. Paneth found that (using this assumption as to the area per molecule of the adsorbed layer) the adsorption of dye-stuffs generally gives lower values for the area than the radioactive method, and concluded that the results given by the adsorptive method are minimum values for the possible area of surface.

[1] *J.A.C.S.* (1939), 3409. [2] *J.A.C.S.* (1935), 1754.
[3] *Z. physikal. Chem.*, **101**, 480 (1922); *Ber.*, **57**, 1215, 1221 (1924). Bachmann and Brieger, *Kolloid-Z.*, **39**, 342 (1926).

There is reason to suppose, from Philip's work on charcoals, that the adsorption method also gives results which may vary very much with the size of the molecules, at any rate in the case of solids containing cracks of dimensions not much exceeding those of the molecules (§ 15).

The adsorption of oleic acid from benzene solution, assumed to be unimolecular with an area per molecule of 20 sq. A., i.e. with the molecules closely packed and arranged perpendicular to the surface, is taken by Harkins and Gans[1] as a measure of the area of titania or silica powders.

Another variant of this method has been used by Howell[2] for estimating the surface of cellulose accessible to coloured salt such as cobalt chloride. Filter paper is soaked in solutions of different concentrations, and dried; the amount of coloured salt on the total surface is thus known, the volume of solution taken up being observed. On examining the absorption spectrum of the now coloured cellulose it is found that, for the first portions of salt deposited, the intensity of the colour increases almost linearly up to a certain critical amount deposited and only slowly thereafter; assuming that this critical amount is a layer one molecule thick on the surface, the available surface was found to be about 85 times the apparent surface, as measured microscopically.

Bartell and Fu[3] have ingeniously used a comparison of the heat of wetting with the adhesion tension (Chap. V, § 20); their thermodynamic reasoning seems open to question, but as the work of adhesion probably differs little from the heat of wetting, and is determined by the method of Bartell and Osterhof (Chap. V, § 15) by a method which does not depend on the surface area, the method may give results no more inaccurate than any of the other methods.

6. Effect of the nature of crystal faces on adsorption. One source of uncertainty (practically never mentioned by those using the adsorption method!) is that even on perfectly formed crystals, some faces adsorb very much more than others. This was known to Lehmann,[4] and was extensively studied by Gaubert.[5] In more recent years, Saylor,[6] France,[7] Buckley,[8] Bunn,[9] and Royer[10] have carried the studies farther, especially on the effect of adsorption of 'impurities' in the solution, on the habit of crystals. A crystal will sometimes adsorb one dye on one set of faces, and another on a second set, no adsorption of the first dye occurring on the second set of faces or vice versa. Thus lead nitrate adsorbs methylene blue on the (110) faces, another set of faces adsorbing none of this dye, but easily adsorbing picric acid. If the crystals are grown from a solution

[1] *J.A.C.S.* (1931), 2804. [2] *J.C.S.* (1937), 979.

[3] *7th Colloid Symposium Monograph*, p. 135 (1930).

[4] *Z. physikal. Chem.*, **8**, 552 (1891); *Ann. Physik*, **51**, 73 (1894).

[5] *Recherches sur le Facies des Cristaux*, Hermann (1911); *Bull. Soc. Franc. Min.*, **23**, 211 (1900); **25**, 245 (1902); **28**, 180, 286 (1905); *Compt. Rend.*, **132**, 936 (1906); **147**, 632 (1908); **151**, 1134 (1910); **180**, 378 (1925).

[6] *5th Colloid Symposium Monograph*, p. 49 (1927).

[7] *J. Amer. Ceram. Soc.*, **10**, 579, 871 (1927); **11**, 571 (1928). *7th Colloid Symposium Monograph*, p. 59 (1930).

[8] *Z. Krist.*, **75**, 15; **80**, 238; **81**, 157; **82**, 31, 285; **85**, 58; **88**, 248, 381; **91**, 375 (1930–35). [9] *Proc. Roy. Soc.* A, **141**, 567 (1933).

[10] *Compt. Rend.*, **198**, 185, 585, 1868 (1934).

containing both dyes, one set of faces develops with a blue colour, the other with a yellow. These different adsorptions are of great importance in determining the habit of crystals, for if a substance, coloured or uncoloured, is adsorbed on a set of faces, growth of the crystals perpendicular to these faces is retarded, because deposition on them is slowed down. These faces often appear finally as the only faces of the crystals, for the others have material deposited on them much faster, so that the faces on which deposition is slowest, or does not occur at all, are prolonged parallel to themselves until they finally meet. A very great variety of different cases is recorded in the papers mentioned; one of the simplest is the effect of urea on ammonium chloride. Urea is adsorbed on the cube faces, and causes the ammonium chloride to form cubic crystals; 'oriented overgrowths' (i.e. small crystals adhering in regular orientation to the surface of the original crystal) of urea on ammonium chloride form easily, on the cube faces only. Urea has the opposite effect on sodium chloride, causing octahedral faces to appear and cube faces to disappear. Bunn's very exact work led him to the conclusion that adsorption takes place on those faces of the original crystal which have the same, or very nearly the same, interatomic spacings as one face of the normal crystal of the adsorbed substance. Oriented overgrowth of the second substance is likely to occur with the adhering crystals attached by the plane which has the same spacing as the original crystal. It appears to be advantageous, for both adsorption and oriented overgrowth, if the space lattices of the crystals of the two substances are as different as possible, *except* for the one plane in which their dimensions must be as nearly identical as possible. The same conclusions were re-stated by Royer a few months later.

France suggested that the retardation of growth perpendicular to a face might occur even if the amount of adsorbed impurity was insufficient to form a complete monomolecular layer, and Buckley has expressed the same view. Dyes are often *included in* crystals, presumably when the retardation of growth by adsorbed dyes is insufficient to stop growth completely.

There is often considerable specificity in adsorption, one of two fairly closely related dyestuffs being adsorbed, the other not. This is to be expected on the theory that a close correspondence of atomic spacings is required. The specificity is of interest as providing a rather simple parallel to the specific adsorptions on complex biological surfaces such as bacterial cell walls or enzymes (see § 17).[1]

In view of these complications, which are of extreme interest in themselves, it would seem that the adsorptive method of measuring the area of irregular solid surfaces must be trusted only as far as the order of magnitude of the surface is concerned; and it would be well to use several different adsorbed substances and to compare the results for area given by each.

[1] For further data on specific adsorption by solids, from solutions, see Chap. III, § 13.

7. Adsorption by solids.[1] Gases are adsorbed on solids by interaction of the unsatisfied fields of force of the surface atoms of the solid, with the fields of force of the molecules striking the solid surface from any gas or liquid, in contact with the solid. In this way the free energy or surface tension of the solid surface is diminished, often probably to a small fraction of its original value, though as there are at present no trustworthy methods for measuring the surface tension of solids, the actual amount of lowering can only be estimated, not measured.

Adsorption on solids is nowadays generally classified according to the type of force involved in binding the adsorbed atoms or molecules to the surface atoms of the solid. There is no doubt of the existence of two distinct types of adsorption, the 'molecular' or 'van der Waals' type,[2] in which the forces are the van der Waals forces which produce condensation in liquids; and 'chemisorption',[3] when the adsorbed atoms are held by co-valent forces to the underlying solid. The most obvious distinction between the two types is in the heat of adsorption, which is usually less than 4,000 calories per mole for the molecular adsorption, but much higher, generally at least 10,000, and occasionally up to 200,000 calories per mole for chemisorption. In 'molecular' adsorption, the gas may be easily pumped off unchanged, particularly if the temperature is raised a little. In chemisorption the tenacity with which the adsorbed gases are held varies, but generally a much higher temperature is necessary to remove them. Often too the binding between the adsorbed atoms and the solid is stronger than the cohesion of the solid, so that heating, or other treatment, tears away some of the underlying atoms; thus a large part of the oxygen adsorbed on charcoal can only be removed as oxides of carbon.

[1] The literature on adsorption by solids is so voluminous that a very small selection only can be referred to here. Valuable reviews with reference to most of the important earlier papers have been given in the following: McBain, *The Sorption of Gases and Vapour by Solids* (Routledge, 1932); Hückel, *Adsorption u. Kapillarkondensation* (Leipzig, 1930); Gregg, *Adsorption of Gases by Solids* (Methuen, 1934); Rideal, *Surface Chemistry*, 2nd ed., 182 ff. (Cambridge, 1930); Freundlich, *Kapillarchemie*, I, 148 ff. (Leipzig, 1930). In *Trans. Faraday Soc.*, **28**, **131–447** (**1932**) there is a very valuable symposium of papers.

[2] Sometimes also called 'primary', 'physical', 'reversible', or 'London' adsorption, the last after the man who has perhaps done most in recent years to advance our knowledge of the type of force involved. The naming and particularly the renaming of natural phenomena and forces after investigators might perhaps be indulged with more restraint than is customary nowadays! 'Reversible' is not an appropriate term, since the other type of adsorption, 'chemisorption', is sometimes reversible, in the sense that sometimes, though not always, the gas can be driven off unchanged.

[3] Also called 'secondary', 'irreversible', and, if it takes place slowly at temperatures not too far above room temperatures, 'activated' adsorption. Chemisorption, defined as co-valent combination of the adsorbate with the surface atoms, is very often irreversible, in the sense that the gas originally adsorbed comes off in a different state (e.g. as atoms instead of molecules, or as compounds with the atoms of the substratum). It need not necessarily be irreversible, however.

Adsorption may occur through simple electrostatic forces,[1] e.g. alkali metals on tungsten, and silver or halide ions on silver halides.

In addition, what used to be called adsorption, on or into porous solids full of very small channels, may be partly an actual condensation of liquid in the finest pores of the solid. The condensation of liquid is due to van der Waals forces, and the transition from a layer of adsorbed gas one molecule thick, to one of several molecules thick, and finally to one filling the whole of a fine capillary space, need involve no sudden change in the phenomena. In such spaces the concavity of the meniscus in the fine capillaries produces a lowering of the vapour pressure below that over a plane surface, thus facilitating condensation (Chap. I, § 15). Many solids have such fine pores. Charcoal, being formed by driving off the atoms of hydrogen and oxygen from complex organic structures often having cellulose-like structures, contains pores of all sizes down to those little larger, probably, than the diameter of one or two oxygen atoms. Many of the carbon atoms on the walls of these pores must have free valencies available for chemisorption of gases, including the permanent gases; but van der Waals adsorption is very large indeed with charcoal. Silica gel, various porous clays, zeolites, etc., also adsorb, or rather 'sorb',[2] large amounts of gases in this manner.

van der Waals adsorption is most marked with gases below, or close to, their critical temperatures, and in general the more easily condensable a gas, the more it will be sorbed by porous solids. Thus charcoal sorbs ammonia, carbon dioxide, sulphur dioxide, and the vapours of organic substances much more easily and in much larger amounts than the permanent gases at room temperature; at liquid-air temperatures large amounts of all gases except helium and hydrogen are adsorbed. The close relation between the ease of liquefaction and of this type of adsorption is of course due to the similarity of the forces involved. These attractions appear to be due to the attractions between permanent dipoles, or to the production of temporary dipoles in adjacent molecules, by sympathetic fluctuation of the clouds of electrons; their detailed consideration is outside the scope of this book.[3]

There is little doubt that if the adsorption is of the van der Waals type, the molecules of the adsorbed gases are not dissociated on the surface. It

[1] Cf. Polanyi, *Trans. Faraday Soc.*, **28**, 316 (1932).

[2] McBain's term 'sorption' applies to all cases when a gas or solute is taken up by a solid. *Ad*sorption means strictly the formation of a layer on an impermeable surface; *ab*sorption to penetration, or solution, into the interior. With the zeolites, there are pores of quite regular shape and size, only a few A. across. With charcoal there are irregular pores of similar size, as well as larger ones. Foreign substances, finding their way into these very fine pores may be said to be *ad*sorbed on the walls of the pores, but as they permeate the whole structure of the solid more or less uniformly, they may equally be said to be *ab*sorbed by the solid. McBain avoids this difficulty simply by omission of the prefix.

[3] Cf. London, *Z. physikal. Chem.* B, **11**, 222 (1930); Lennard-Jones, *Trans. Faraday Soc.*, **28**, 333 (1932); Born, *Atomic Physics*, 254, 339 (Blackie, 1935).

is also probable that the molecules are more or less mobile in the adsorbed layer, and can move along the surface. This motion may, however, as Lennard-Jones points out, be a series of 'activated' hops from one place of low potential energy to another, not necessarily an adjacent one, rather than a continuous motion such as exists in the three dimensions of a gas (see Chap. VI, § 4). Although the mobility in 'molecularly' adsorbed layers is much greater, as a rule, than in chemisorbed layers, there is no absolute distinction, for some chemisorbed layers, at any rate, become mobile to some extent on raising the temperature.

When gases are adsorbed by charcoal, an increase in volume occurs. Bangham and others[1] have studied the expansion of rods of charcoal which accompanies adsorption of various fairly easily condensed gases. Particularly interesting is the interpretation which they place on this expansion.

They find, first, that the expansion X is related to the amount adsorbed and the pressure in a manner very similar to the surface pressure in Gibbs's adsorption equation, Chap. III, eq. (7.5)

$$X = kRT \int \Gamma \, d \log_e p$$

or

$$\Gamma = \frac{1}{kRT} \frac{\partial X}{\partial \log_e p},$$

which indicates that the expansion is probably proportional to the surface pressure of the adsorbed gas, and may be directly caused by this surface pressure. Also, the relation between the expansion, and the reciprocal of the amount of gas adsorbed, is closely similar in form to the relation between the surface pressure and the area per molecule in the 'gaseous' adsorbed films on liquids described in Chapter III. They suggest therefore that the adsorbed films resemble gaseous films in structure, the molecules being mobile, and the two-dimensional surface pressure of the moving molecules actually causing the expansion of the charcoal rods, which is assumed to be proportional to the surface pressure in the adsorbed films. Plotting a quantity proportional to the surface pressure against a quantity proportional to the area per molecule, multiplied by the surface pressure, they find in some cases the initial dip in the FA–F curves of Chapter III, due to lateral adhesion between the molecules, and in all cases the rise due to the repulsive forces between molecules, this rise being steeper, the larger the molecules. Within the (rather small) range of temperature used, the expansion was proportional to the absolute temperature, as it should be if the expansion were ultimately due to a 'gaseous' pressure in the adsorbed films.

Whether or not this very remarkable similarity in the curves indicates that the swelling of the charcoal really is brought about by the lateral bombardment pressure of their moving molecules, must be left to the reader to judge; *a priori* the likelihood of the films being sufficiently mobile to do this seems rather small, but no other explanation of the similarity has yet been advanced.

Chemisorption was recognized as one of the two principal types of adsorption, fairly generally, after Langmuir's paper of 1916;[2] although

[1] *Proc. Roy. Soc.* A, **130**, 81 (1930); **138**, 162 (1932); **147**, 152, 175 (1934); *J.C.S.* (1931), 1324.

[2] *J.A.C.S.* (1916), 2269.

it had been known for a long time that gases adsorbed on charcoal could sometimes be pumped off unchanged, easily, but that if oxygen is adsorbed at room temperature, it comes off only with great difficulty, and as oxides of carbon.[1] For a few years prior to 1916 Langmuir had studied the adsorption and reaction of various gases with tungsten filaments, finding that oxygen and hydrogen form layers which are probably monatomic, and from which the gases can only be removed by fairly strong heating (much stronger in the case of oxygen than of hydrogen), when they come away as single atoms, not as molecules.[2] The latent heat of evaporation of oxygen from a fairly sparsely covered tungsten wire is 162,000 calories per mole, actually more than twice the latent heat of dissociation of oxygen into atoms.[3] Thus the adhesion of oxygen to tungsten is very strong indeed. It is comparable with the cohesion of metallic tungsten, or greater, although tungsten is itself one of the hardest of solids. On exposure of a tungsten filament, at much higher temperatures, to oxygen, the molecules of oxygen hitting the surface atoms of oxygen, each attached firmly to an underlying tungsten atom, remove one atom of tungsten with its adhering oxygen as the oxide WO_3.

The chemisorbed layer of atomic oxygen, when complete, will not react with hydrogen, even at temperatures far above those at which hydrogen and oxygen normally combine violently. If the oxygen-coated filament is heated in hydrogen, however, to a temperature at which the oxygen begins to evaporate off slowly, as soon as a few gaps appear in the film, the remaining oxygen is quickly removed by reaction with the hydrogen, and the adsorption and dissociation of hydrogen then proceeds without hindrance, once the hydrogen can reach the tungsten. But a complete monatomic film of oxygen prevents the dissociation of hydrogen.[4]

The reactivity of gases is generally enormously changed by their adsorption in the chemisorbed form. Dissociation into atoms, or at any rate such a weakening of the bond between the atoms as to imply a partial dissociation of di- or polyatomic molecules, generally occurs; and the reactivity of a gas *may* be very much enhanced by this dissociation. In the synthesis of two molecules of ammonia from one of nitrogen and three of hydrogen, the molecule of nitrogen, and at least one of those of hydrogen must be dissociated. Nearly all heterogeneous catalyses depend on the change of reactivity of adsorbed atoms. It would be incorrect, however, to suppose that enhanced reactivity *always* accompanies chemisorption; as we have just seen, the layer of oxygen on tungsten is abnormally inert towards hydrogen. Again, on platinum, a similar layer of oxygen atoms is easily formed. This does react with either hydrogen or carbon monoxide,

[1] Cf. Angus Smith, *Proc. Roy. Soc.*, **12**, 424 (1863); other references in Lowry and Hulett, *J.A.C.S.* (1920), 1408.

[2] Langmuir, *Ind. Eng. Chem.*, **22**, 393 (1930); *Chemical Reviews*. **13**, 150 ff. (1933).

[3] Langmuir and Villars, *J.A.C.S.* (1931), 486.

[4] For a recent study of the dissociation of hydrogen by *clean* tungsten filaments, see Bryce and Roberts, *Proc. Camb. Phil. Soc.*, **32**, 648 (1936).

very readily, giving rise to the catalytic action of platinum in the combination of these gases; but if carbon monoxide is adsorbed on platinum, its reactivity towards oxygen is diminished, and it acts as a catalyst 'poison'.[1]

We picture the chemisorption of some gases on metals thus:

Oxygen on tungsten

```
O        O        O        O        O
‖        ‖        ‖        ‖        ‖
W        W        W        W        W
  >W<       >W<      >W<      >W<
W        W        W        W        W
```

Carbon monoxide on platinum

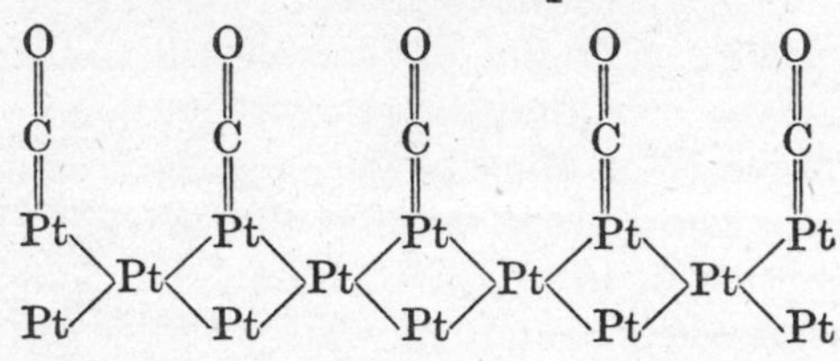

At this date it is probably unnecessary to remind the reader that stoichiometric laws, in the sense of a simple numerical correspondence between the amount of gas combined on a surface, and the amount of underlying material, do not hold, and are not to be expected; yet the absence of such relationships has been occasionally urged as an argument against the chemical nature of the combination involved in 'chemisorption'! There is probably, as a rule, a quite simple relationship between *the number of atoms in the surface, which combine with a given number of adsorbed atoms.*

This mechanism of chemisorption predisposes one to expect that a chemisorbed layer will not exceed one molecule or atom in thickness, the combining capacity of the surface atoms will probably be satisfied by the presence of a single layer of atoms of gas on the surface. As a first approximation this is probably generally true, but there is evidence that it does not provide an exact picture in every case: it does not always appear true that a fully saturated chemisorbed layer consists of a complete, single layer of molecules, or atoms, of the gas adhering to every surface atom of the solid. For hydrogen, Roberts[2] has recently found that there is only one layer adsorbed on tungsten, the amount adsorbed corresponding nearly to one atom of hydrogen for each surface atom of tungsten, actually 1·1 times the apparent number of tungsten atoms in the surface. These figures probably mean that the real surface was about 1·1 times larger than the apparent surface. With caesium adsorbed on tungsten,[3] each caesium atom covers *four* tungsten atoms (they happen to have just double the radius of the tungsten atoms) of the real surface, which was probably

[1] Langmuir, *Trans. Faraday Soc.*, **17**, 607 (1922).
[2] *Proc. Roy. Soc.* A, **152**, 445 (1935).
[3] J. B. Taylor and Langmuir, *Physical Rev.*, **44**, 423 (1933).

1·35 times the apparent surface. A second layer of caesium begins to be formed when the pressure of the caesium vapour approaches saturation.

The behaviour of oxygen on tungsten is most interesting. It was first shown by Langmuir that the first layer of atoms adsorbed forms a film stable up to nearly 2,000° K., and that this film cuts down the thermionic emission from a heated filament to a minute fraction of the value for the clean metal. Roberts has shown[1] that, if this film is formed at about 30° C. on a tungsten wire previously cleaned by flashing at a very high temperature, it contains a few gaps; and in these gaps, oxygen molecules can be adsorbed without dissociation, one of the two atoms adhering to the bare metal atom in the gaps in the first layer; the other projecting above the first layer and forming a very incomplete second layer. The presence of these gaps is due to the fact that the atoms in the first layer are practically immobile at 30° C. As a molecule of oxygen hits the surface it is dissociated into atoms, and the two atoms are adsorbed side by side on adjacent tungsten atoms. As the first film is built up, occasionally molecules from the gas hitting the surface at random will become adsorbed so as to enclose an isolated tungsten atom, not covered by an oxygen atom. Adsorption with dissociation cannot occur here, because there is only room for one of the atoms in the oxygen molecule in contact with the tungsten. Hence dissociation does not occur, but the molecule is adsorbed on one end, with one of the atoms projecting into a second layer. The total amount of oxygen thus adsorbed as molecules is only about one-fifth of that in the first, monatomic, dissociated film; i.e. the gaps in the first film amount to about one-tenth of the available spaces on the surface. The heat of adsorption of the first film is about 130,000 to 160,000 calories per mole; that of the second, about 40,000. The molecules evaporate into a vacuum at about 1,100° K.; but the atomic layer remains up to nearly 1,700° K. In addition to these two definite layers there is van der Waals' adsorption above the monatomic layer, the number of molecules so held varying continuously with the pressure.[2]

An experiment made by shuffling cards showed that the proportion of chance gaps in a monatomic layer formed from a diatomic gas should be nearly equal to the proportion of molecules adsorbed on end. It would appear impossible to form a *complete* monatomic layer from a diatomic gas unless the first layer is slightly mobile.

Definite layers, more than one molecule thick, can however be obtained on metals under certain special conditions. Instances of these are the monatomic layer of caesium on top of a monatomic layer of oxygen, and the similar layers of alternate oxygen and barium atoms, which are of such importance for thermionic emission (Chap. VIII, § 4).

On mica surfaces Bawn's results[3] indicate that a saturated adsorbed layer often contains much less than enough to cover the surface completely.

[1] *Proc. Roy. Soc.* A, **152,** 464 (1935).

[2] Morrison and Roberts, *ibid.*, **173,** 13 (1939).

[3] *J.A.C.S.* (1918), 1361.

The question whether van der Waals adsorption, or any kind of adsorption on glass, ceases when the surface is covered by a layer one molecule or atom thick, does not yet appear to be answered unequivocally. The principal difficulty lies in estimating the surface area of the solid. The recorded observations on adsorption by glass have yielded the most diverse results, ranging from quite small amounts up to quantities equivalent to layers many hundreds of molecules thick, if the surface were not greater than the apparent surface. There is little doubt, however, that the larger amounts adsorbed were obtained with surfaces which were porous. McBain[1] points out that nearly all glass surfaces, especially those which have been cleaned with acid mixtures, are covered by a layer of silica gel of greater or less thickness, rendering it almost spongy in texture from the molecular point of view; and glass is also rather liable to minute surface cracks.

Brunauer and Emmett,[2] however, take the view that, on porous iron catalysts, the first effect of van der Waals adsorption is to cover the surface with a layer one molecule thick. In the case of several permanent gases, and also of carbon dioxide and butane, if the adsorption isotherms are measured not too far above the boiling-point of the gases, the first layer is complete at 50 mm. pressure or less. If the pressure is raised up to atmospheric, further quantities are adsorbed, and there appears a nearly linear relation between the pressure, and the amount adsorbed in excess of the first monomolecular layer; but the increase of adsorption, as the pressure is raised above that at which the first layer is complete, is much more gradual than the increase with pressure, at low pressures, before the surface is completely covered.[3]

The evidence is indirect, but fairly convincing; it rests mainly on the fact that if the linear part of the adsorption isotherms, corresponding to the building up of layers beyond the first, is extrapolated back to zero pressure, and the area of the surface calculated on the assumption that the extrapolated amount of gas adsorbed is in a closely packed monolayer on the surface, consistent results are obtained with all the gases for the area of the surface.

8. Experimental measurement of adsorption. The direct way of measuring adsorption is to measure the volume of gas, or (in the case of solutions) the amount of solute, which disappears from the gas (or solution) when it is brought into contact with the adsorbing solid surface. This method has the inaccuracies common to all measurements in which the small difference between two large quantities has to be measured; and in order to render this type of measurement more easy, a very large proportion of the measurements on adsorption have been made on porous solids, which adsorb comparatively large volumes. This inevitably brings with

[1] *Sorption of Gases by Solids* (1932), chap. vii.

[2] *J.A.C.S.* (1935), 1754; (1937) 310.

[3] For a recent theory of polymolecular adsorbed layers, with references to older theories, see Bradley, *J.C.S.* (1936), 1799.

it the disadvantage that the measurements are difficult to interpret, since there are many types of surface in such solids, and pores of varying size, sometimes down to capillaries not more than a molecule or two across, as with charcoal. Charcoal, inorganic colloids such as silica gel, or chromic or other oxides; finely divided metals reduced from their oxides or other compounds, and silicates, are among the commoner adsorbents.

Freundlich,[1] Rideal,[2] and Hückel[3] have summarized the results of adsorption measurements on porous substances. Very roughly, it may be said that the ease of adsorption is proportional to the ease with which the gases can be liquefied, a fact which has been held to indicate that there is sometimes actual condensation of vapour in the smallest pores. Numerous empirical formulae, of which Freundlich's equation (§ 9) is the best known, have been developed, but none seem to fit the data with any accuracy over a considerable range of pressures.

With the most refined methods of gas analysis, and using high vacuum technique, the amounts adsorbed on small areas can be measured directly. Among recent studies Roberts' measurements[4] on single tungsten wires deserve special mention; a Pirani gauge was employed for measuring the changes in pressure on adsorption, and amounts of the order 10^{-5} c.c. (at N.T.P.) were measured with an accuracy of the order 10 per cent.; in this way adsorption on wires of area not over one square centimetre could be measured. Langmuir's earlier work (see § 13) also used very delicate gas analytical methods.

It is not too much to say that, at the present time, increased delicacy of measurement, with the use of simple surfaces, would be of far greater value than the multiplication of measurements on porous, highly adsorptive powders.

Very careful outgassing of the glass is necessary in this work, since the adsorptive capacity of the glass vessels is usually far greater than that of the surfaces being studied.

The *weight* of gas adsorbed is sometimes measured, and for this purpose various kinds of microbalance have been used. McBain's 'sorption balance' consists of a delicate helical quartz spring,[5] suspending the adsorbing solid; the upper end of the spring is fixed, and the lower end observed with a cathetometer. Bradley[6] has used a balance with a beam, supported in the centre by a fine horizontal quartz fibre; and references to other types of balance are given by McBain.[7]

Methods of detecting adsorbed films, which are of great value as auxiliaries to determinations of the amounts adsorbed, include the measurement of the accommodation coefficient (§ 11), of the thermionic

[1] *Kapillarchemie*, **1**, 143ff. (1920).
[2] *International Critical Tables*, **3**, 249 (1928).
[3] *Adsorption u. Kapillarkondensation*, Leipzig (1928).
[4] *Proc. Roy. Soc.* A, **152**, 445 (1935).
[5] McBain and Bakr, *J.A.C.S.* (1926), 690.
[6] *Trans. Faraday Soc.*, **30**, 587 (1934).
[7] *Sorption of Gases*, p. 19 (1932).

emission (Chap. VIII, § 4), of the elliptical polarization of light reflected from the surface,[1] and of the surface potential;[2] electron diffraction also often reveals the state of the surface.

For the measurement of the heat of adsorption, various types of calorimeter have been described, suitable for measurement of the comparatively large amounts of heat given off by the adsorption on porous solids;[3] Roberts, however, has been successful in measuring the heat evolved from adsorption on a single tungsten wire, by employing the wire as its own calorimeter. Its temperature is raised by the heat evolution, and the rise of temperature is measured by the resistance of the wire.

The heat of adsorption is very frequently deduced indirectly from the decrease in adsorption with temperature, using the Clapeyron equation.[4]

9. The 'adsorption isotherm'. The relation between the amount adsorbed and the pressure in the gas, the 'adsorption isotherm', is a complicated one, and depends on the nature of the solid surface, on its homogeneity or otherwise (and few, if any, solid surfaces are homogeneous), and of course on the forces between gas molecules and solid, which depend on the chemical nature of the gas. For many porous, and some other, solids, a first approximation is given by Freundlich's well-known equation; if x is the amount of gas adsorbed, and p the pressure of the gas,

$$x = kp^{1/n},$$

where k is a constant and n approximately constant and greater than unity. This is the same as the relation between the concentrations of a solute distributed between two bulk phases, when there is association of the molecules in groups n in number in one of the phases. For extensive data illustrating this, Freundlich's book[5] must be consulted. It is an empirical equation, and does not always fit the experimental facts; but is at least as successful as any other single equation.

In 1916 Langmuir[6] considered adsorption as due to the actual condensation of the molecules arriving at the surface from the gas, followed by re-evaporation after a longer or shorter time. Gas molecules reaching the surface may either rebound elastically, with an infinitesimal time of contact, or condense for a finite time. There is evidence, which will be considered later, that many of the molecules do actually condense for a sufficient time to lose the characteristics of motion which they possessed before reaching the surface; and obviously no adsorption could occur if the molecules did not condense at all.

[1] Cf. Frazer, *Physical Rev.*, **34**, 97 (1929); Silvermann, *ibid.*, **36**, 311 (1930); and references in Chap. II, § 9.

[2] Rideal, Whalley, and Jacobs, *Proc. Roy. Soc.* A, **140**, 484 (1933).

[3] See numerous papers from the schools of H. S. Taylor and W. E. Garner; Garner and Veal, *J.C.S.* (1935), 1436; cf. also Ward, *Proc. Roy. Soc.* A, **133**, 506 (1931).

[4] Hückel, *Adsorption u. Kapillarkondensation*, p. 43 (1928); Langmuir and Villars, *J.A.C.S.* (1931), 486.

[5] *Kapillarchemie*, **1**, 154 ff. (1930).

[6] *J.A.C.S.* (1916), 2267; (1918) 1361; *Physical Rev.*, **8**, 149 (1916).

If the adsorbed layer is one molecule thick when complete, and if the attractive forces between the surface and the condensed or adsorbed molecules are considered to be the same everywhere, Langmuir showed that the adsorption isotherm can be calculated from the rate of striking of the gas molecules on the surface, and from the rate at which they evaporate therefrom, once condensed.

Consider unit area of a perfectly homogeneous surface, in contact with a single gas at a pressure p millimetres of mercury; let a fraction θ of the surface be covered with adsorbed gas, and $1-\theta$ be bare. Let the rate at which the adsorbed gas evaporates from the adsorbed layer be $\nu\theta$ molecules per second. The rate at which the gas molecules hit the surface is (cf. Chap. I, § 6) $0{\cdot}0583\frac{p}{\sqrt{(MT)}}\times 6{\cdot}06\times 10^{23} = 3{\cdot}53\times 10^{22}\frac{p}{\sqrt{(MT)}}$ molecules per second, where M is the molecular weight. Call this rate of striking the surface μ, and suppose that a fraction α of the molecules which strike condense, so that the rate of condensation is $\alpha\mu$. As we have supposed that no condensation occurs on the top of an adsorbed layer one molecule thick, the rate of condensation of gas will be proportional to the extent of surface not already covered, and is

$$\alpha\mu(1-\theta).$$

Since, in equilibrium, this must be equal to the rate of evaporation,

$$\alpha\mu(1-\theta) = \nu\theta,$$

$$\alpha\mu = \frac{\nu\theta}{1-\theta}. \tag{1}$$

Let $\alpha\mu = kp$, then $k = \frac{3{\cdot}53\times 10^{22}\alpha}{\sqrt{(MT)}}$; let the number of molecules in a complete adsorbed layer be N_0, and the number adsorbed at pressure p millimetres of mercury η; then $\eta = N_0\theta$. Equation (1) becomes

$$kp\left(1-\frac{\eta}{N_0}\right) = \frac{\nu\eta}{N_0},$$

$$\frac{\eta}{N_0} = \theta = \frac{kp}{\nu+kp} = \frac{1}{1+\nu/kp}. \tag{2}$$

This equation is naturally of the same form as that which expresses the adsorption of a substance from solution, concentration there taking the place of gaseous pressure (see Chap. III, § 4).

The amount adsorbed is thus greater, the smaller ν/kp. High rates of condensation, and low rates of evaporation, promote complete covering of the surface.

Since there are N_0 molecules in a completely covered layer, and the number evaporating per second from such a layer is ν, the fraction evaporating per second is ν/N_0, and the average time elapsing between condensation and re-evaporation, or the average 'life' of a molecule in the adsorbed layer, is N_0/ν.

At very low pressures, when θ, the fraction of the surface covered, is small, equation (1) becomes approximately

$$\theta = \frac{kp}{\nu},$$

so that the amount of adsorption is proportional to the pressure and inversely proportional to the rate of evaporation of the adsorbed film. When adsorption is small, since the rate of evaporation always increases with the temperature, the adsorption decreases with increasing temperature, at constant pressure.

When the adsorption is large, so that the surface is nearly covered, the area of space vacant on the surface is inversely proportional to the pressure, for

$$1-\theta = \frac{\nu}{kp}.$$

The importance of this relation lies chiefly in the fact that many gases are adsorbed on solid catalysts, covering the surface so that the gases which should reach the surface and react there cannot do so; these gases thus act as catalyst poisons. If the amount of such a gaseous poison in the atmosphere is great enough, or its rate of evaporation from the surface small enough, to cause it to cover nearly the whole of the active surface, the amount of space not covered by the poison will be inversely proportional to its partial pressure in the atmosphere, and the rate of the catalysed reaction, being dependent on the rate at which the reacting gases can reach the active surface, will be inversely proportional to the partial pressure of the gaseous poison. Such cases are of very frequent occurrence.[1]

Fowler[2] has pointed out that equation (1) can be deduced from very general statistical considerations based on the states, adsorbed and free, accessible to the molecules in the gas and on the solid surface; and that it is not dependent on any particular mechanism of condensation and re-evaporation.

The Langmuir adsorption isotherm (1) is the ideal case for a perfectly homogeneous solid surface, uniform in all directions, whose substance is impermeable to the gases being adsorbed, when adsorption occurs without dissociation. In all actual cases there arise complications through one or more of these conditions not being fulfilled; the minute cracks mentioned in § 4 may give rise to some slow penetration; crystal edges, and different faces, have different adsorptive powers; and recently it has been shown that even on a perfect crystal face, the extent to which the impinging molecules are condensed or reflected depends very much on the direction in which they hit the atoms in the space-lattice of the surface. Nevertheless it is generally accepted that the Langmuir equation forms a good basis for discussion of the adsorption of gases on solids. It may be generalized to cover the case of a composite surface consisting of numerous different types of homogeneous surface each having different constants α and ν.

[1] Cf. Hinshelwood, *Kinetics of Chemical Change in Gaseous Systems*, chap. viii (1932).

[2] *Proc. Camb. Phil. Soc.*, **31**, 260 (1935).

Suppose that, per sq. cm. of surface, there are fractions β_1, β_2, β_3, etc., square centimetres of patches of different, uniform quality, on which the proportions α_1, α_2, α_3, of the total number μ of molecules striking the surface, condense (the relation between the pressure p and the number of molecules striking will be as before); let the adsorptions be η_1, η_2, η_3, per square cm. and the saturation capacity of each patch be $(N_0)_1$, $(N_0)_2$, $(N_0)_3$, etc., per sq. cm. The adsorptions on each patch will be given by equation (2). Then the total adsorption on the composite surface is

$$H = \beta_1\eta_1+\beta_2\eta_2+\beta_3\eta_3+...$$

$$= \frac{\beta_1\alpha_1\mu(N_0)_1}{\nu_1+\alpha_1\mu}+\frac{\beta_2\alpha_2\mu(N_0)_2}{\nu_2+\alpha_2\mu}+.... \quad (3)$$

The utility of equation (3) is, however, not great, as it contains four undetermined constants for each of an unknown number of different types of surface, and even so it takes no account of the possibility that certain types of surface, e.g. those near the bottom of a surface crack, may be difficult of access to the gas molecules; nor of Frisch and Stern's discoveries regarding the large variations of the factor α with the direction in which the molecules impinge (see below).

Further, Fowler,[1] and Roberts,[2] have shown that in the (extremely frequent) cases where adsorption of a diatomic gas occurs as single atoms on the solid, the theoretical relation between the fraction θ covered, and the pressure, should be of the form

$$\sqrt{(Ap)} = \frac{\theta}{1-\theta}. \quad (4)$$

Purely theoretical considerations do not help much farther in considering the adsorption isotherms, and it is best here to return to experimental data.

On mica surfaces, Langmuir,[3] and more recently Bawn,[4] have shown that the simple Langmuir isotherm (1) fits the data fairly well for the adsorption of several gases. At saturation the amount adsorbed was never more than enough to cover the whole surface with a monomolecular layer, and was sometimes a good deal less than this.

A close study of adsorption isothermals in recent years has shown the almost astonishing fact that they are sometimes not continuous curves, but consist of a series of steps, short curves, each more or less of the shape indicated by equation (1), separated by sharp discontinuities. This was first noticed by Allmand and his colleagues, particularly Chaplin and Burrage.[5] Fig. 46 shows the isothermal for carbon tetrachloride on charcoal; the amount adsorbed being plotted horizontally and the pressure vertically. There are a great many discontinuities; and the curves were reversible, i.e. it was found possible to obtain the same discontinuities by

[1] *Proc. Camb. Phil. Soc.*, **31**, 262 (1935).
[2] *Ibid.*, **32**, 155 (1936).
[3] *J.A.C.S.* (1918), 1361.
[4] *Ibid.* (1932), 72.
[5] *Proc. Roy. Soc.* A, **129**, 235, 252 (1930); **130**, 210, 610 (1930); **134**, 554 (1931). *J. Physical Chem.*, **34**, 2202 (1930); **35**, 1692 (1931); **36**, 2272 (1932). *Trans. Faraday Soc.*, **28**, 218 (1932).

either adsorbing more gas, or removing some of the adsorbed gas. Similar results were obtained with several different vapours, including carbon dioxide; Benton and White[1] have found similar discontinuities with hydrogen and other gases adsorbed on metals, so that the effect is probably not confined to very porous adsorbents.

To find these discontinuities a very large number of points on the

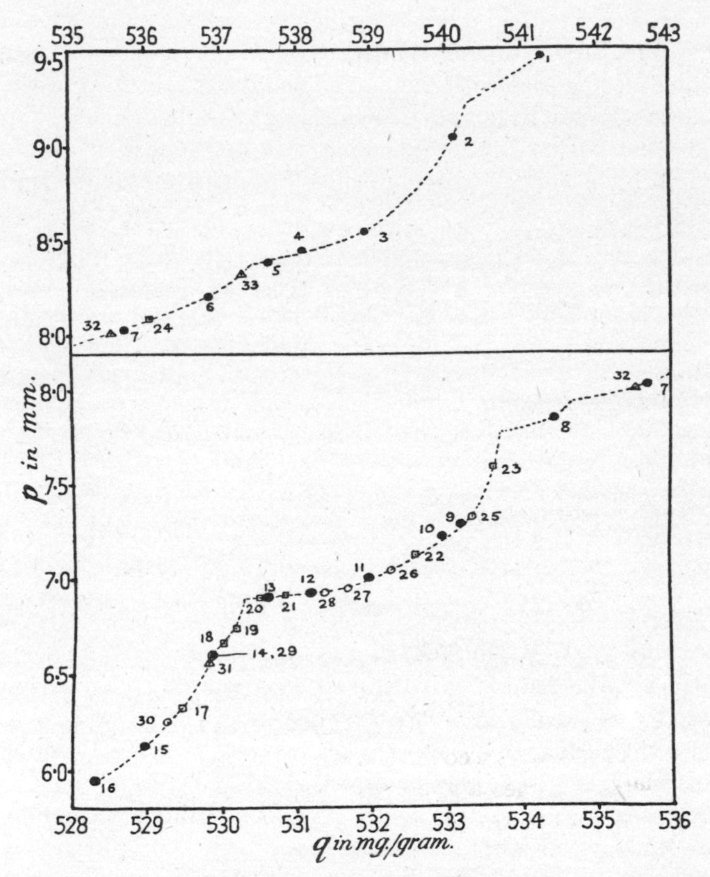

FIG. 46. CCl_4 on charcoal.

isotherms must be determined experimentally; Allmand and Burrage found it necessary to make about three separate measurements for each millimetre rise in pressure; and the reason why previous workers had not noticed them is probably merely that they had not made observations nearly close enough together. In the case of charcoal particularly, reversibility of the isotherms depends on the complete displacement of previously adsorbed oxygen; if this is not done, there is a steady 'drift' of the pressure as the oxygen is slowly displaced, and the adsorption and

[1] *J.A.C.S.* (1930) 2330; (1931) 2807, 3301; *Trans. Faraday Soc.*, **28**, 213 (1932).

desorption curves are not identical. Different vapours vary in the ease with which they displace adsorbed oxygen; carbon disulphide does this very easily, carbon tetrachloride less rapidly, and water only with difficulty.

The cause of the discontinuities must be some kind of heterogeneity of the surface; it is tempting to ascribe them to the separate terms of equation (3), the amount adsorbed taking a sudden turn upwards as the pressure reaches a critical point, at which adsorption commences on a new type of surface. Benton and White suggest that the successive steps are due to the differing ease with which molecules evaporate from the surface, according to whether or not they are adjacent to other adsorbed molecules. It would seem perhaps more probable that differences in different parts of the underlying surface are the cause, but both may contribute to the final effect.

A warning should perhaps be given against too hasty acceptance of the results of a few adsorption experiments only; in the case of charcoal especially, the careful work of Allmand's school has shown that very frequently what may appear to be adsorption is largely the displacement of another previously adsorbed gas from a solid surface; prolonged alternation of adsorption and desorption was necessary to obtain reproducible results with organic vapours on charcoal, probably because of the difficulty of removing previously adsorbed oxygen. Again, Foster[1] has shown that the actual experimental method may make an enormous difference to the shape of the isothermals found; by one method, silica gels showed very marked discontinuities; by another, smooth curves.

The previous treatment of the surface has a very great influence on the results.

10. 'Activated' adsorption. About 1930 H. S. Taylor[2] suggested that, just as an activation energy is necessary to bring about co-valent combination of atoms, so the process of chemisorption requires an activation energy; and that the existence of this activation energy may explain a number of at first sight curious relations between the temperature at which adsorption takes place, and the speed of adsorption, or its amount, or the nature of the adsorbed layer. In particular, it was considered that one and the same gas could often be adsorbed on one solid at two different temperatures in the two forms of van der Waals adsorption and chemisorption. Owing to the much smaller activation energy of the former it took place at very low temperatures; as the temperature rose, owing to the small heat of adsorption, at somewhat higher temperatures the gas was removed more or less completely. At still higher temperatures adsorption recommenced, but in a different form, as chemisorption, the molecules having now attained the considerable energy of activation required to combine by co-valent forces with the surface.

The conception that chemisorption requires an activation energy is

[1] *Proc. Roy. Soc.* A, **150**, 77 (1935); *Trans. Faraday Soc.*, **32**, 1559 (1936).

[2] *J.A.C.S.* (1930), 5298; (1931), 578; *Chem. Reviews*, **9**, 1 (1931); *Trans. Faraday Soc.*, **28**, 131 (1932).

quite natural;[1] most chemical reactions require this. Polanyi[2] points out that free valencies at a surface would not attract molecules, until these have jumped over a potential barrier of more or less height; therefore only those molecules which have a certain energy may be expected to combine chemically with the surface. On the other hand Polanyi[3] also pointed out that reactions in which free atoms take part, either as reactants or as end-products of the reaction, generally have a very small true activation energy, that is an activation energy in excess of any energy needed to supply the heat absorbed in an endothermic reaction, such as a dissociation of hydrogen on a surface. If this is correct there need not be any appreciable energy of activation for a chemisorption involving dissociation into atoms on the surface. How far the experimental evidence supports the view that the actual phenomena, particularly the *rate* of adsorption, are controlled by this activation energy, has provoked a great deal of dispute. Even now, no clear conclusion has been reached, and the size of the energy barrier, if any, which hinders adsorption, does not seem accurately known in most cases.

It now appears clear, however, that the rate of adsorption upon metal surfaces, and charcoal also, and the activation energy of adsorption (if this is the rate-determining factor) depends very much upon the cleanliness of the surfaces, previously adsorbed films slowing down the rate considerably. The very detailed work of Taylor and his school on oxide catalysts, which are porous, at present forms the main support for the theory that the rate of activation either of the adsorbed molecules, or of the surface molecules of the solid with which they combine, is the rate-determining step in the adsorption.

A great many adsorptions apparently occur slowly. One of the earliest known cases was that of oxygen on charcoal; at room temperature adsorption may continue for a very long time.[4] Adsorption on metals may also be slow; but this has recently, in the case of hydrogen on tungsten, been shown to depend on the presence of a previously adsorbed film of oxygen; if the tungsten is really clean, hydrogen is adsorbed very rapidly even at liquid-air temperatures.[5] On the surface of oxides, particularly those of zinc, chromium, or manganese, adsorption may take place slowly.

The evidence to which the greatest weight was originally attached, in support of the theory that the activation energy is responsible for slow adsorption, was in outline as follows. In a number of cases adsorption is considerable at very low temperatures, diminishing at first with rising

[1] Some part of the dispute as to the reality of 'activated adsorption' seems to arise from the use of that term nearly synonymously with 'chemisorption'. No one now doubts the existence of chemisorption; what is in dispute is the amount of activation energy required for this, and how far it accounts for observed effects, particularly the effect of temperature on the speed, nature, and total amount, of adsorption.

[2] *Trans. Faraday Soc.*, **28**, 318 (1932).

[3] *Z. Elektrochem.*, **35**, 562 (1929).

[4] de Saussure, *Gilbert's Ann.*, **47**, 113 (1814); cf. Lowry and Hulett, *J.A.C.S.* (1920), 1408.

[5] Roberts, *Proc. Roy. Soc.* A, **152**, 462, 480 (1935).

temperature; then it increases considerably, finally decreasing again as the temperature is still further raised. The isobars determined by Benton

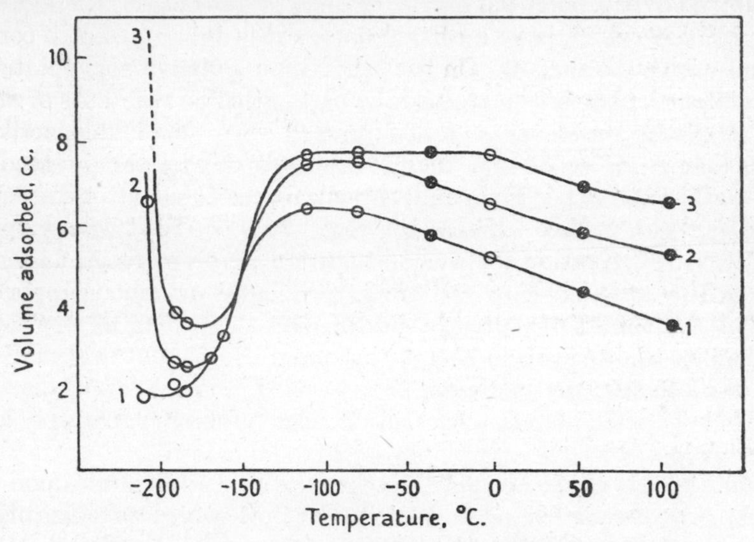

FIG. 47 A. Hydrogen on nickel.
(1) 25 mm.; (2) 200 mm.; (3) 600 mm. pressure.

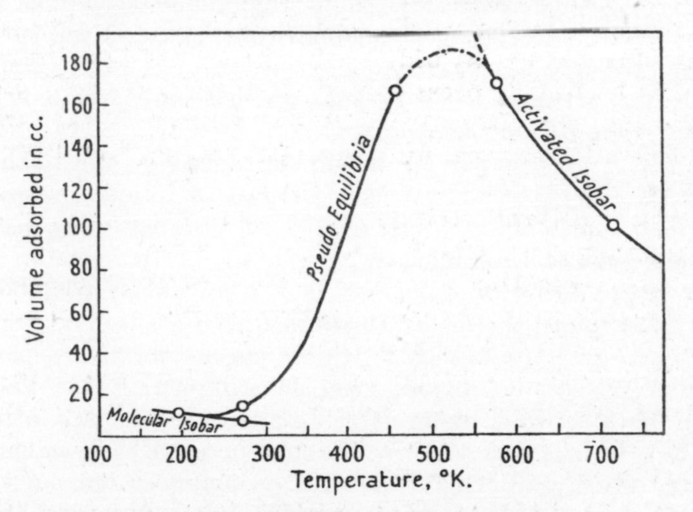

FIG. 47 B. Hydrogen on $MnO—Cr_2O_3$.

and White[1] for nickel, and by Taylor and Williamson[2] for mixed manganous and chromic oxides, are shown in Fig. 47.

With the nickel, at -190 to $-180°$ C., adsorption took place almost instantaneously, and was probably van der Waals; at higher temperatures it was slow. Above $-100°$ it was all 'activated'. Rather similar

[1] *J.A.C.S.* (1930), 2332. [2] *Ibid.* (1931), 2178.

results were obtained for the adsorption of hydrogen on copper,[1] the high temperature adsorption (supposed activated) being marked at and above −80° C.

The manganous-chromic oxides gave a small amount of low temperature adsorption, which decreased slowly up to a temperature of about 0° C.; from 0° to 250° C. the adsorption increased, and at 520° K., say 250° C., the adsorption was a maximum, and was practically all activated. The low temperature, van der Waals adsorption, had a heat of adsorption about 1,900 calories; the high temperature, activated adsorption shows a heat of about 20,000 calories per mole. The energy of activation, deduced from the rates of adsorption at different temperatures by means of the Arrhenius equation, increased from 6,000 to 10,000 calories per mole as the surface gradually became covered. This *increase* in the *energy of activation*, as the surface becomes covered, should be contrasted with the *decrease* in the *heat of adsorption*.

Manganous oxide alone showed no van der Waals, but strong activated adsorption above 100° C., for which the activation energy rose from 12,000 to 20,000 calories as the surface became covered.

Chromic oxide gel has been the subject of very extensive studies.[2] It shows considerable van der Waals adsorption, together with 'activated' adsorption which appears to vary in kind and amount according to the temperature. Even at liquid-air temperatures there is evidence that *some* of the hydrogen adsorbed is dissociated, for the oxide can catalyse the formation of deuterium hydride from a mixture of hydrogen and deuterium,[3] which can only occur through dissociation of the hydrogen and deuterium molecules. It appears that different parts of the surface have different activation energies for adsorption, ranging from low values up to 21,700 calories per mole.

With these important catalytic oxides and their mixtures the catalytic activity generally runs parallel with the activation energy for the chemisorption, which probably indicates that the slowest, rate-determining stage in catalysis on these surfaces is the adsorption. The zinc-chromic oxide mixture has the lowest activation energy for hydrogen of 1,000 calories; MnO,Cr_2O_3 has 6,000; ZnO alone 11,000; Cr_2O_3, 19,000; and MnO, 20,000 calories per mole. Here we have a measurable effect of promoter action, which alters not only the rate of activated adsorption, but also the amount of van der Waals adsorption, which is probably not relevant for catalysis, except possibly as being a preliminary to 'chemisorption'.

Other cases where evidence is found of activated adsorption include hydrogen on zinc oxide,[4] and water on zinc oxide and alumina;[5] also

[1] Benton, *Trans. Faraday Soc.*, **28**, 209 (1932).

[2] See esp. Howard, *Trans. Faraday Soc.*, **30**, 278 (1934); Howard and Taylor, *J.A.C.S.* (1934), 2259; Burwell and Taylor, *J.A.C.S.* (1936), 697.

[3] Gould, Bleakney, and Taylor, *J. Chem. Physics*, **2**, 362 (1934).

[4] Taylor and Sickman, *J.A.C.S.* (1932), 602.

[5] Taylor and Gould, *J.A.C.S.* (1934), 1685.

hydrocarbons on manganese chromite.[1] Garner and Kingman's results[2] on mixed zinc and chromium oxides were somewhat complicated, indicating van der Waals and two kinds of activated adsorption. The reduction of the zinc oxide by the hydrogen is a complicating factor in these cases.[3] Oxygen, hydrogen, and carbon monoxide behave similarly on a variety of solids. Carbon dioxide appears to undergo activated adsorption on silver, on which a layer of oxygen has been previously adsorbed.[4] Bawn's results[5] for carbon monoxide on mica show a slow process; but this is most probably due to the slow attainment of thermal equilibrium in a high vacuum.[6]

At one time Taylor considered[7] that if adsorption on a solid surface would catalyse the interconversion of ortho and para hydrogen, it was an indication that chemisorption with dissociation into atoms occurred; the temperature at which such interconversion took place would (if this were true) have been some indication of the activation energy for chemisorption. No doubt chemisorption does promote this 'spin isomerization'; but it is now known that adsorption of the van der Waals type can result in speedy attainment of the equilibrium mixture of ortho and para hydrogen, provided that the surfaces are of some paramagnetic substance; the close proximity to a paramagnetic surface can catalyse the interconversion,[8] without dissociation of the adsorbed molecules.

The power to catalyse certain other reactions, in which dissociation of the molecules of hydrogen or of some other gas must occur at some stage of the reaction, is more certain evidence of chemisorption. One instance, the 'exchange' reaction in which HD, deuterium hydride, is formed from a mixture of hydrogen and deuterium, has already been mentioned. Another is the immensely important synthesis of ammonia; the reaction

$$N_2+3H_2 = 2NH_3$$

requires the dissociation of both the hydrogen and the nitrogen molecules. While the reaction on a commercial iron catalyst is complicated by the very high pressures used, and by the presence of promoters, Emmett and Brunauer have found a general correlation between the rate of activated adsorption of nitrogen at 300° to 450°, and the catalytic activity at 400° and 1 atmosphere, though the correlation with synthesis at high pressures is not so good. Chemisorption of nitrogen on iron does not occur rapidly at room temperature, a fact which may account for the difficulty of synthesizing ammonia except at a fairly high temperature.

The 'exchange' reaction of deuterium with the hydrogens in ammonia is an excellent test for chemisorption of hydrogen; Taylor and Jungers[9]

[1] Turkevich and Taylor, *J.A.C.S.* (1934), 2254.

[2] *Nature*, **126**, 352 (1930); *Trans. Faraday Soc.*, **27**, 322, 654 (1931); **28**, 261 (1932).

[3] Garner and Veal, *J.C.S.* (1935), 1487.

[4] Drake and Benton, *J.A.C.S.* (1934), 506.

[5] *J.A.C.S.* (1932), 72.

[6] Garner (private communication, 1937).

[7] *J.A.C.S.* (1931), 1614; *Trans. Faraday Soc.*, **28**, 247 (1932).

[8] Taylor and Diamond, *J.A.C.S.* (1935), 1251.

[9] *J.A.C.S.* (1935), 660.

have found that it does not occur on fused quartz surfaces, even at 300° C.; but it does occur at room temperature on an iron catalyst, active for ammonia synthesis.

There is a large group of workers who consider that the slow phenomena, and also the very large increase in adsorption shown in Fig. 47, when the temperature rises to a certain point, is due not to the slowness of activation energy of the actual adsorption process at low temperatures, but to slow diffusion (itself often an activated process) along the surface to areas inaccessible at low temperatures. Ward was the first to take this view;[1] and more recently it has been adopted by Garner and his pupils,[2] and by Bradley.[3]

If this is correct, then the large increase in adsorption at a certain point of the rise of temperature shown in Fig. 47 must be due to the opening up of large new areas, inaccessible at lower temperatures. The slow take up of hydrogen on a tungsten wire covered by a single layer only of oxygen atoms, observed by Roberts, seems rather difficult to explain on the theory of a diffusion process; the distances to be travelled are exceedingly small.

The suggestions made by Allmand, Burrage, and Chaplin,[4] that the slow take up of gas might be due to displacement of previously adsorbed gas of another kind, seems to be negatived by the consistent results on the rate of adsorption of hydrogen by chromic oxide gel. Howard, in many successive experiments involving adsorption and desorption, found that this rate remained finite and constant. Moreover, it is usually impossible to find the gas supposed to be displaced in the gas phase; if it is oxygen, it should appear as oxygen or as water, but it certainly is not generally there. The work of Howard shows that chromic oxide can be made so as to retain very constant properties over considerable periods.

Clarke, Kassel, and Storch[5] interpret the slow adsorption on chromic oxide gel as in part a diffusion of an already adsorbed layer to 'secondary' centres of adsorption; but Burwell and Taylor criticize the whole diffusion hypothesis, partly on the grounds that the temperature coefficient of the rate of adsorption is not that to be expected for diffusion.[6] It may not, however, be easy to distinguish between the gross characteristics of an activated diffusion along the surface, and of an activated adsorption; indeed it seems just admissible to consider the former as a localized form of the latter.

Further research may throw light on the mechanism of these complex phenomena; and this light is perhaps more likely to come from experiments conducted on surfaces of simple form and known composition than on the porous, complex masses of catalyst that are so frequently employed; the risk of some considerable part of the slow adsorption being due to slow penetration is too great.

[1] *Trans. Faraday Soc.*, **28**, 399, 445 (1932); *Proc. Roy. Soc.* A, **133**, 506 (1931); cf. Wilkins, *ibid.*, **128**, 407 (1930).

[2] Esp. Garner and Maggs, *Trans. Faraday Soc.*, **32**, 1744 (1936).

[3] *Trans. Faraday Soc.*, **30**, 587 (1934).

[4] *Ibid.* **28**, 192, 223 (1932); **29**, 677 (1933).

[5] *J.A.C.S.* (1937), 736.

[6] *Ibid.*, 697.

11. Details of the interaction of gas molecules with solid surfaces. When gas molecules hit a solid surface, they may be either reflected, or captured by the surface field of force and condense, to evaporate again later. In Langmuir's adsorption theory the factor α expresses the fraction of the impinging molecules which do condense on the surface. In recent years much information as to the manner of reflection or condensation has been obtained experimentally by the use of molecular rays, and theoretically by wave mechanics. Molecular rays are beams of molecules on which a particular direction has been imposed by slits, moving in a vacuum so high that there are practically no collisions between molecules, and the direction of the beams is maintained for long distances.

When molecular rays hit a solid surface, one of three things may happen. They may be 'specularly' reflected, i.e. leave the surface again at an angle equal to the angle of incidence, just like rays of light on a plane polished surface; they may be 'diffracted', and the discovery of this diffraction by Stern and his colleagues constituted a convincing proof of the correctness of de Broglie's wave theory of matter as applied to molecules; or, they may condense on the surface, and if condensation occurs, the molecules may either become fixed on the surface at once, or move along the surface, still held by its attractive field of force.

An ingenious, but very difficult, experiment by Clausing[1] afforded direct evidence that molecules hitting a surface may remain there some time before re-evaporating. A beam of atoms was passed through a small hole on to a disk which could be made to rotate and move past the hole at a high speed. When the disk was at rest, the atoms striking the disk re-evaporated and were symmetrically deposited round the hole through which they had come. When the disk was rotated, the atoms evaporating from the disk were found to have moved some distance to one side of the hole. The experiment could not easily, however, be made quantitative, owing to the difficulty of distinguishing between the effects due to the lateral momentum imparted to the atoms which had spent any time on the disk, long enough to come into equilibrium with it, and those due to the distance actually travelled while adhering to the disk.

The nature of the interaction between the surface and the beams of molecules can be studied by examining the distribution of intensity in different directions of the molecular rays leaving the surface. A good account of the experimental methods, with the results obtained up to 1930, is given in Fraser's *Molecular Rays*.[2] If condensation occurs, for a sufficient time to reach thermal equilibrium with the surface, the surface behaves like one emitting molecules uniformly, and the distribution of the molecules leaving the surface obeys a cosine law similar to that given by light emitted uniformly from a surface, or reflected diffusely from a perfectly matt surface.[3] A particularly clear case of complete condensation was found by J. B. Taylor,[4] with beams of atoms of the alkali metals hitting crystal faces of the alkali halides. The distribution of intensity

[1] *Physica*, **8**, 289 (1928).

[2] Cambridge, 1930.

[3] Cf. Wood, *Physical Optics* (1923), p. 42.

[4] *Physical Rev.*, **35**, 375 (1930).

in the molecules leaving the surface obeyed exactly the law for uniform emission in all directions from the surface, and it was claimed that if even 0·01 per cent. of the molecules had been reflected instead of condensed, the fact could have been detected.

Scattering, even to an extent simulating the results of condensation and re-emission, may, however, result from the surface being rough or matt, and since the molecules or atoms, and their corresponding waves, are of the order 1 A. across, a very high degree of planeness is required to obtain specular reflection. Unless the surface is extremely even, e.g. that of a cleavage plane of a well-formed crystal, the absence of much specular reflection does not prove that most of the atoms are condensed. Taylor's experiments were done on sufficiently good surfaces to show that the scattering was really due to complete condensation. But a mechanically polished surface has inequalities of the order 10^{-5} cm. in height; and even a good crystal is uneven on account of the thermal vibrations of the atoms. It is well known in optics that some degree of specular reflection can be obtained from a matt surface, provided that the light falls on it at a small angle to the surface; the essential condition is that the height of the inequalities, projected on the direction of the rays, should be less than the wave-length of the light. de Broglie's theory requires that the wave-length should be $\lambda = h/(mv)$, where m and v are the mass and velocity of the molecules. One would not, therefore, expect to find good specular reflection from a mechanically polished surface except when the impinging rays make a very small angle, of the order a few minutes of arc only, with the surface. On natural crystal surfaces, specular reflection should be most easily obtained if (*a*) the angle made by the beams with the surface is not too large, and (*b*) the wave-length of the molecules is large, which is favoured by a low temperature and velocity of the molecules, and by a small mass. Estermann and Stern[1] showed conclusively that specular reflection is greater, the smaller the angle made by the beams with the surface, and the lower the temperature, the effect of angle being very marked. The ease of specular reflection does not vary inversely as the mass of the atoms or molecules, but in general the lighter atoms are more easily reflected than the heavier. Johnson[2] and Kerschbaum[3] have obtained some reflection of hydrogen atoms; Stern and his collaborators find reflection best with helium and fairly good with hydrogen molecules, while neon, carbon dioxide, and argon give little or no reflection.[4] On the other hand Ellett and others[5] find that mercury, sodium, and cadmium are reflected. Josephy confirmed this[6] and called the reflection of these heavier atoms 'diffuse' reflection; he considered it as a kind of 'bouncing

[1] *Z. Physik*, **61**, 95 (1930).
[2] *J. Franklin Inst.*, **206**, 301; **207**, 629, 639; **210**, 135; **212**, 507 (1928–31).
[3] *Ann. Physik*, **2**, 201 (1929).
[4] Knauer and Stern, *Z. Physik*, **53**, 785 (1929).
[5] *Physical Rev.*, **31**, 643; **34**, 493; **36**, 893; **38**, 977 (1928–31).
[6] *Z. Physik*, **80**, 755 (1933).

off' of the heavy atoms according to classical mechanics. This choice of the concepts of classical mechanics only when the predictions of wave mechanics are not verified seems dubious.

A much more satisfactory verification of the wave nature of molecular rays was provided when Estermann and Stern[1] obtained good diffraction of these rays, by the grating formed by the surface atoms of a simple heteropolar crystal such as lithium fluoride. If the direction of the impinging rays is parallel to the *diagonal* of the unit cube of the crystal, i.e. to the direction in which the lines of *similarly charged* ions run in the crystal lattice, diffraction is found. The peaks of intensity in the diffracted beams are not quite sharp, as they would be with monochromatic X-rays or electrons of uniform velocity, but the curves relating intensity to the angle of diffraction rise gradually to a maximum and are generally similar to the curves for a Maxwellian distribution of velocity. This is because the wave-length of the molecules in the beams is, according to de Broglie's formula, inversely proportional to their velocity, and the velocity is not uniform in the beams but is distributed according to Maxwell's law, about a most probable value.

In some cases the number of the molecules diffracted regularly, and reflected, reached a high proportion of the total number of impinging molecules, indicating that but few of the molecules condensed for long enough to lose their original direction.

Still more careful experiments by Frisch and Stern[2] have revealed what is perhaps the most remarkable feature of the whole of the interaction between the moving molecules and the solid surface, namely that, if the impinging molecules have a particular relation between the components of momentum perpendicular to the surface, and parallel to it along one of the diagonals, reflection and diffraction do not occur but the molecules are captured by the surface field of attractive force. This was noticed as two dips or 'saddles' on the normal Maxwellian curves giving the distribution of intensity in the diffracted rays. The recent calculations of Lennard-Jones and Devonshire[3] have shown that this is to be expected on the wave-mechanical theory of the interaction of the periodic field of the surface with that of the helium atoms striking it. If p_z is the component of momentum perpendicular to the surface, and p_y that parallel to it and along a diagonal of the space lattice, the impinging atom is captured by the surface field of the solid, without loss of energy, if

$$p_z^2 - 2p_y = C.$$

The constant C may have either of two values, from which it is calculated that the adsorbed helium atoms can be held on lithium fluoride in one of two states, having energies of adsorption of 57 and 129 calories per mole. For helium and sodium fluoride the corresponding energies were 80 and 193.

[1] *Z. Physik*, **61**, 95 (1930); Stern, *Naturwiss.*, **17**, 391 (1929).
[2] *Z. Physik*, **84**, 430, 443 (1933).
[3] *Nature*, **137**, 1069 (1936); *Proc. Roy. Soc.* A, **156**, 37 (1936); **158**, 253 (1937).

Thus selective adsorption occurs with certain directions of approach of the molecules to the surface. Further calculations indicate, however, that the helium atoms are mobile on the surface, migrating along it freely. After travelling a distance of the order 10^{-5} cm., they will probably evaporate in the same direction as if they had been simply reflected in the first instance. If this had occurred everywhere in the experiments of Frisch and Stern, no dips in the curves would have been noticed, and the phenomenon of selective adsorption would not have been discovered experimentally. But the re-evaporation in specified directions will not occur unless the crystal surface is both perfect and clean; if the migrating helium atoms hit, while on the surface, another adsorbed atom, or an imperfection in the crystal, they will change direction and energy, and the reflected or diffracted beams will be absent, or nearly absent, from those directions in which the selective adsorption has occurred.

The fraction of the atoms or molecules condensing may vary from unity to a very small fraction. The exchange of heat between a gas and a solid is controlled by the fraction of gas molecules which condense, i.e. remain long enough to come into thermal equilibrium with the solid. Much work has been done on the 'accommodation coefficient', defined as α' in the equation

$$T'_G - T_G = \alpha'(T_S - T_G),$$

where T_S is the temperature of the solid, T_G the temperature of the gas before, and T'_G that corresponding to the average kinetic energy of the gas molecules leaving the surface. α' is a measure of the extent to which the gas leaving the surface accommodates itself to the temperature of the surface.

The existence of such a coefficient was recognized by Maxwell;[1] numerous measurements under a variety of conditions have been made by Soddy and Berry,[2] Knudsen,[3] Langmuir,[4] Blodgett and Langmuir,[5] Michels,[6] Compton and Lamar,[7] Archer,[8] Gregory,[9] Alty,[10] and others.

Values from unity down to 0·1 or less were found; it was recognized by Knudsen that the coefficient tended to be larger if the surfaces were rough, a fact simply explained by many molecules making more than one collision with the surface, through rebounding and hitting another part at a different angle to the general plane of the surface. It was clear, especially from the work of Blodgett and Langmuir, that adsorbed surface films greatly affect the value of the coefficient. It is probable that the only values of accommodation coefficients for really clean metal surfaces are those obtained by Roberts,[11] with helium and neon, the solid surface being

[1] *Phil. Trans.*, **170**, 231 (1879).
[2] *Proc. Roy. Soc.* A, **83**, 254; **84**, 576 (1910–11).
[3] *Ann. Physik*, **34**, 593 (1911); **46**, 641 (1915); **6**, 129 (1930).
[4] *J.A.C.S.* (1915), 419.
[5] *Physical Rev.*, **40**, 78 (1932).
[6] *Ibid.*, **40**, 472 (1932).
[7] *Ibid.*, **44**, 338 (1933).
[8] *Phil. Mag.*, **19**, 901 (1935).
[9] *Proc. Roy. Soc.*, A, **149**, 52 (1935).
[10] *Proc. Roy. Soc.* A, **131**, 554 (1931); **149**, 104 (1935); **161**, 69 (1937).
[11] *Ibid.* **129**, 146; **135**, 192; **142**, 518 (1930–33).

generally tungsten. He showed that these gases show very small coefficients, in the case of helium about 0·06 at room temperature and 0·025 at 79° K, when the surface is really clean, but that adsorbed films raise it very considerably. For neon, the coefficient was 0·08 at liquid air temperature, *falling* slightly to 0·07 at room temperature. Values up to 0·6 might be obtained if the wire was covered with adsorbed films. In general much higher results are obtained with film-covered surfaces than with clean.

Maxwell originally assumed, for simplicity, that the molecules either condensed completely, coming into thermal equilibrium with the solid, or were reflected without losing or gaining any energy. If this is so the accommodation coefficient α' is equal to the fraction α of the molecules which condense in Langmuir's adsorption theory. The reflection or diffraction of molecules probably does take place without loss of energy, and the reason why the presence of adsorbed films so much increases the coefficient may be that adsorbed atoms interfere with the regularity of the surface spacing of atoms, which is necessary for diffraction. Many papers have appeared on the theory of interchange of energy between gas molecules and solids, and Devonshire[1] has been able to calculate the values of accommodation coefficients found by Roberts, using for the heats of adsorption on tungsten, 60 calories for helium and 493 for neon, per mole.

12. Activation in heterogeneous reactions. No attempt will be made here to classify further the enormous variety of reactions which can be catalysed by solid surfaces, and space permits only an outline of the possible mechanisms available for the acceleration of chemical reaction at surfaces. In addition to the references given in this chapter,[2] the reader may consult, for periodical accounts of recent work, the reports of the Committee on Contact Catalysis in the *Journal of Physical Chemistry* (1923–32). Schwab gave a clear summary[3] of the literature up to 1928; and the discussion[4] of the Bunsen-Gesellschaft in 1929 contains many interesting papers. Hinshelwood's *Kinetics of Chemical Change in Gaseous Systems*, Chapters VIII and IX of the third edition, gives a concise account of many points. In recent years quantum mechanics has thrown much light on the mechanism of activation of molecules at surfaces.

That some degree of adsorption of the reacting molecules is a necessary preliminary to heterogeneous catalysis is almost obvious, and has been accepted since the time of Faraday,[5] or even earlier. Through the last century two principal lines of thought are discernible; first, that adsorption results in an increased concentration of the reacting molecules at, or near, the surface, so that the velocity of reaction is increased by the law of mass action; second, that intermediate compounds might be formed at the surface of the solid.

Neither of these views has survived in the original form, though the

[1] *Ibid.*, **158**, 269 (1937) (refers to earlier theoretical papers).
[2] See refs., p. 237.
[3] *Ergeb. exact. Naturwiss.*, **7**, 276 (1928).
[4] *Z. Elektrochem.*, **35**, 527.
[5] *Experimental Researches in Electricity*, § 630 (1833); vol. i, p. 184.

modern views contain something corresponding to both points of view. With the disappearance, in the last two decades or so, of the belief that the transition layer between a solid and a gas, and adsorbed layers, are rather diffuse, with a density falling gradually from that of the solid to that of the gas, the idea of a simple concentration near the surface increasing the velocity of reaction has also disappeared. The intermediate compound theory has been replaced by the knowledge that chemisorbed layers, in which the adsorbed atoms are combined by valency forces to the surface, play an important part in surface catalysis.

A very interesting paper by Mendeléeff,[1] in 1886, foreshadowed in qualitative terms some of the most recent developments of the quantum theory of activation of adsorbed molecules. Recognizing that all molecules are in a state of motion or oscillation, the suggestion was made that these motions would be altered by contact of molecules with the surface of a solid, and that the strain thereby set up might frequently so alter the 'equilibrium' of the molecules as to induce various reactions which would not otherwise occur with appreciable speed; in modern terminology the distortion of the adsorbed molecule might bring it nearer to a reactive, or excited state, which depends on the configurations occurring during vibration.

The problem of catalysis is co-extensive with that of chemical reaction in general, and involves consideration of the nature of the resistance to instantaneous occurrence of reactions.[2] Arrhenius' theory, now universally accepted, requires that at any moment only a fraction of the molecules are in a reactive state, and that a certain energy of activation is required to bring them into this state. Increasing temperature aids this, since a larger proportion of the molecules acquire the requisite energy, through the increased energy of motion. The increased energy may be that of translational, or vibrational, motion. In considering activation for chemical reaction, the vibrational energy has recently received much attention, particularly in connexion with what is called the 'transition' state. Consider two diatomic molecules AB and CD, capable of exchanging partners thus

$$AB+CD = AC+BD.$$

The distances between the atoms[3] in each molecule will vary periodically, as the molecules vibrate, and consequently each molecule vibrates through states of different potential energy. These different states have different reactivities, which are probably determined largely by quite simple geometrical considerations. Exchange of partners can only occur

[1] *J. Russ. Phys. Chem. Soc.*, **18**, 8; *Ber.*, **19**, 456.

[2] Polanyi (*Z. Electrochem.*, **35**, 562 (1929)) defines a reaction as free from resistance if no energy has to be supplied to the molecule to bring them into a reactive state, in the case of an exothermic reaction; and if only energy equal to the heat of reaction has to be supplied, in endothermic reactions.

[3] Other coordinates of the molecules may be treated similarly. The theory of transition states has been treated by Evans and Polanyi, *Trans. Faraday Soc.*, **31**, 875 (1935), and refs. therein; cf. also *Faraday Society Discussion*, Sept. 1937.

when the two molecules are in close contact. During this contact the distances apart of A from B, and of C from D, will be constantly varying, and may pass, periodically, through states when, owing to the close proximity of the molecules, A is close to C and B close to D. The theory of the transition state supposes that, as the molecules vibrate, they pass through a state in which A is at a distance where it is equally attracted by B and by C, and similarly D is equally attracted by B and by C. Any vibration which stops short of this 'transition state' will pass back again to the original two molecules AB and CD; any vibration which goes beyond this state will pass over into AC and BD, the potential energy falling in each case. The transition state, where the four atoms are poised at distances apart such that A is equally inclined to move nearer to, and into combination with, B or with C, has the maximum potential energy of all possible states of the four atoms; and the energy of activation for the interchange of partners is the amount by which the energy of this transition state, or 'activated complex', exceeds the normal energy of the original two molecules.

Clearly the chance of attaining the transition state depends on many factors; on the geometry of the molecules, on the amount of potential energy which must be added to them in the course of their vibrations, to bring them to the transition state; also on the manner in which the molecules are oriented when close to each other and on the time during which they are in contact.

During a collision between two molecules in gases, which probably lasts only some 10^{-13} seconds, a time not long in comparison with the period of molecular vibrations, the chance of the transition state being reached during any given collision is small. When, however, the two molecules are adsorbed side by side on a solid surface they may be held for periods very much longer, so that the chance of the vibrations passing through the transition state, in which reaction takes place, is very much increased. This was pointed out by Born and Franck[1] and Born and Weisskopf,[2] and may account in a general way for the prevalence of reactions at solid surfaces. It may be said to be the modern counterpart of the old view that the acceleration of reactions at surfaces is due to increased concentration of the reacting molecules at the surfaces; it is now said that the chance of reaching a reactive state in two molecules simultaneously increases with the square of the time during which they are in contact, so that the function of the surface is to hold them close together for a time sufficient for them to make up their minds to react!

Catalysis by solid surfaces is often very specific, however. The molecular architecture of the active patches is certainly a very important factor in catalysis. This may be accounted for by deformation of the molecules caused by the adsorption.[3] Suppose, for instance, that the

[1] *Nachr. Ges. Wiss. Göttingen* (*Math. Phys.*) (1930), 77.

[2] *Z. physikal. Chem.* B, **12**, 206 (1931).

[3] Cf. London, *Z. Elektrochem.*, **35**, 552 (1929); Polanyi, *ibid.*, **35**, 561; Polanyi

molecule AB is adsorbed on a surface whose atomic spacing is greater than the normal spacing between A and B. The adsorption will tend to stretch the molecule, and probably bring it near to the reactive state. A great deal will depend on the particular geometry of the atoms in the molecules undergoing reaction, and in the solid surface. With suitable stretching, and bringing into proximity of the atoms of the two molecules, the adsorption on the solid surface may, by itself, bring the four atoms A, B, C, D into, or nearly into, the transition state.

The idea that adsorption on a solid surface may alter the reactivity of molecules by straining or deformation has quite frequently been suggested; in addition to the paper of Mendeléeff mentioned above, Raschig,[1] Constable (§ 14), Quastel (§ 17), Bodenstein,[2] Zelinsky,[3] Burk,[4] and others have drawn attention to its probable importance. In the modern theory the straining may be regarded as lessening the thermal energy of vibration required to bring the molecules into a reactive condition, and partly takes the place of the old theory of an intermediate compound. The transition state *is* a kind of unstable intermediate addition compound.

Polanyi represents the reaction thus: suppose that there are four valencies proceeding from four atoms of the solid surface, and the reacting atoms A, B, C, D are attracted, perhaps chemisorbed, to these four atoms of the surface. We have a surface intermediate compound involving all four atoms, in which the spacings may differ widely from those of the unstrained forms of AB and CD. With suitable disposition of the atoms and the forces adsorbing them, the reaction may proceed very easily, particularly if the end products AC and BD are not strongly adsorbed on the surface, and so evaporate as soon as they are formed.

In its extreme form the straining of the adsorbed molecules may be so pronounced that these are practically dissociated into atoms on the surface, the valency forces between the surface atoms of the solid taking the place of the normal binding between the atoms when in the gas.[5] There is a good deal of experimental evidence that many gases are dissociated into atoms on metal surfaces. We have seen above that hydrogen and oxygen are dissociated on tungsten and may come off as free atoms if the metal is sufficiently heated. Gauger,[6] from a study of the ionization potentials of hydrogen in contact with nickel, concluded that it is the atomic hydrogen which is active in the catalytic hydrogenations produced by this metal; Wolfenden[7] criticized Gauger's methods but arrived at substantially the same conclusion, that much of the hydrogen is present as atoms at the surface. Kistiakowski[8] found, by similar methods, the same state of individual atoms for nitrogen and hydrogen adsorbed on a number of

and Eyring, *Z. physikal. Chem.* B, **12**, 279 (1931); Ekstein and Polanyi, *ibid.*, **15**, 340 (1932).

[1] *Z. angew. Chem.*, 1748, 2083 (1906).

[2] *Annalen*, **440**, 183 (1924).

[3] *Ber.*, **58**, 2755 (1925).

[4] *J. Physical Chem.*, **30**, 1134 (1926).

[5] Cf. Polanyi, *Z. Elektrochem.*, **27**, 142 (1921).

[6] *J.A.C.S.* (1924), 674.

[7] *Proc. Roy. Soc.* A, **110**, 464 (1926).

[8] *J. Physical Chem.*, **30**, 1356 (1926).

metals. The 'straining' of the molecules, which results in dissociation, is presumably not merely a geometrical strain, but also involves a deep disturbance of the interactions between the valency electrons.

Very numerous attempts[1] have been made to trace a connexion between the electrical properties of metals, particularly in respect of their power, real or supposed, to ionize atoms or molecules adsorbed on their surfaces: but few, if any, of these seemed satisfactory, until very recently.

Lennard-Jones and Goodwin[2] have, however, shown that the adsorbed atoms can be activated by collisions with the free electrons in the underlying metal; there is no reason to expect a simple connexion between activation and the thermionic work function.

A solid surface may also aid a reaction by providing a means of carrying away the energy liberated in a reaction. Such reactions as the combination of two hydrogen atoms, which produces about 102,700 calories per mole, cannot take place unless there is some means of disposing of the enormous quantities of energy developed in the complex first formed when the atoms unite. Born and Franck[3] calculated that, although an unstable 'quasi-molecule' is formed during the collision and combination of two atoms such as hydrogen or bromine in a gas, this molecule is so 'supercharged' with energy that it is unstable and cannot persist unless it finds means of disposing of its superfluous energy, in a time of the same order (10^{-13} seconds) as that requisite for the actual collision. If the highly energized 'quasi molecule' collides with a third body, e.g. another atom or molecule, not necessarily of the same gas, or with a solid surface, the hydrogen molecule reverts to a lower state of energy and is stable. It is found experimentally that a very small fraction of the collisions between bromine or hydrogen atoms in a dilute gas result in combination, a 'three body' collision being necessary in the gas phase. Solid surfaces greatly accelerate the combination; but here there must also be specific factors, as well as the ability to remove the energy, since different solid surfaces differ in their catalytic power for the recombination of hydrogen atoms.[4]

Orientation at surfaces may influence the speed of reaction by changing the accessibility of reacting groups in the molecules adsorbed on the surface, to the molecules which react with them. We have already seen (Chap. II, § 30) how the orientation of molecules of long chain fatty acids containing double bonds in the middle of the chains alters the rate at which these double bonds can be oxidized by permanganate in the underlying water. Kruyt[5] discusses the influence of charcoal as an adsorbent on various reactions, including hydrolyses and addition and substutition reactions by halogens in organic compounds. The reactions may either be retarded, or accelerated, by the presence of the adsorbent. There is no reason to expect that orientation alone will, in general, accelerate chemical reaction; and presumably if the presence of an adsorbent

[1] Refs. in Schwab, *Ergeb. exact. Naturwiss.*, **7**, 305–6 (1928); cf. also Nyrop, *The Catalytic Action of Surfaces* (Copenhagen, 1937). [2] *Proc. Roy. Soc.* A, **163**, 101 (1937).

[3] *Ann. Physik*, **76**, 225 (1925); *Z. Physik*, **31**, 411 (1925); cf. Bodenstein, *Z. Elektrochem.*, **35**, 537 (1929). [4] Bonhoeffer, *Z. physikal. Chem.*, **113**, 119 (1924).

[5] *Z. Elektrochem.*, **35**, 539 (1929).

in a solution retards a reaction, the reaction must be proceeding very slowly on the surface of the adsorbent, and also such large amounts of the reacting substances must have been taken up by the solid, that their concentration in the homogeneous phases has been seriously diminished.

In order to illustrate the extreme complexity and universal importance of solid surfaces, a few typical instances will be selected with which to complete this chapter.

13. The reactions of gases at very low pressures on heated metallic filaments. In 1909 Langmuir commenced a research on the fate of the residual gases in an electric lamp bulb containing a heated tungsten wire.[1] This research, conducted with extreme skill, with full use of a difficult high-vacuum technique, has not only given us the economical 'gas-filled' lamp, but has also laid the foundation of modern knowledge of gas reactions which occur at surfaces, and of the technique by which the adventures of the molecules undergoing these reactions may be followed. Brilliant as the results were, there is still much to be done in following out some of the reactions which Langmuir studied, and there are many other reactions awaiting investigation by these most powerful methods. Any one who will take the trouble to master the technique may be sure of a profitable field of research.

The gases were maintained at very low pressures, usually less than 0·01 mm. of mercury, and pressures were read down to 10^{-8} or 10^{-9} mm. If the glass was not very thoroughly baked out, or if there were greased stopcocks in the system, water and hydrocarbon vapours were given off, and great quantities of gas, amounting sometimes to 7,000 times the volume of the filament, appeared through the decomposition of these vapours. A gas analysis apparatus was therefore devised, by means of which, without stopcocks, a complete analysis could be made of a quantity of gas which would fill a cubic millimetre at atmospheric pressure. Great attention was paid to the number of molecules hitting the filament in a given time, and also to the rate at which molecules leaving the filament carried away heat energy to the walls of the bulb, which could be ascertained by measuring the rate of loss of heat from the filament by conduction through the gas.

The pressures in the bulb were so low that the gas molecules, leaving the filament at a high temperature, rarely struck other gas molecules on the way to the walls, so that the gas in the bulb was practically at the same temperature as the walls, not as the filament. Thus the products of the reaction at very high temperatures were very quickly cooled, this desirable state of quick cooling being attained by this method more efficiently than by almost any other technique used for research on reactions at high temperatures. Hydrogen reacted with the filament, being dissociated into atoms. The first indication of this was that the rate of loss

[1] *J.A.C.S.*: (*a*) (1912), 860; (*b*) (1912), 1310; (*c*) (1913), 105; (*d*) (1913), 931; (*e*) (1914), 1708; (*f*) (1915), 417; (*g*) (1915), 1139; (*h*) (1916), 1145; (*i*) (1916), 2267; (*j*) (1918). 1361 *k*) (1919), 167. *Physical Rev.*: (*l*) **2**, 450 (1913); (*m*) **8**, 149 (1916).

of heat from a tungsten wire heated in hydrogen was greater than that calculated from the simple kinetic theory of conduction of heat through gases, above 2,100° K. At 3,300° K., indeed, the heat loss was four or five times that anticipated. The dissociation of hydrogen on the surface,[1] followed by the evaporation of the free hydrogen atoms from the filament, absorbs a great deal of heat; and when the atoms recombine on the walls, and elsewhere in the bulb, the part of this heat which is due to the dissociation of the hydrogen is recovered. Thus the gas carries more heat, in the form of chemical energy of the free flying hydrogen atoms, than could possibly be carried by the undissociated molecules of hydrogen, simply by reasc ι of their energy motion.

These free hydrogen atoms mostly travel straight to the walls of the bulb, and stick there (*b*), if the walls are cooled with liquid air. If the bulb is allowed to warm up, and heated slightly above room temperature, some, but only a small fraction, of the hydrogen atoms come off; these combine as molecular hydrogen and cannot be recondensed. The rest of the atomic hydrogen remains on the walls and does not evaporate off. It is extremely reactive, however; if oxygen is introduced, it combines instantly with some of the adsorbed atomic hydrogen in the cold, forming water; and the remainder of the hydrogen atoms are so disturbed by this reaction that they evaporate off, recombining and appearing as molecular hydrogen. Thus the atomic hydrogen is held in three different ways on the walls, part easily volatilized, part firmly held but free to combine with oxygen, and part held until mechanically (or thermally)[2] displaced by a reaction occurring in their immediate vicinity.

The only limit to the amount of hydrogen which could be dissociated by a filament was set by the capacity of the surface of the bulb to adsorb the free atoms. When this surface was covered, the bulb and filament appeared to be incapable of dissociating any more hydrogen. The fresh atoms hitting the completely covered walls combined with the atoms adsorbed, reconstituting the molecular hydrogen.

Reactions could be accomplished by the flying hydrogen atoms, which are practically unknown elsewhere. Thus, in the cold, a layer of phosphorus on the walls of the bulb was converted into phosphine (*b*); and tungstic oxide on the walls was reduced to metallic tungsten.[3]

A quantitative estimate (90,000 calories per gramme molecule) was made of the heat of dissociation of the hydrogen into atoms (*f*), from the enhanced conductivity of the gas; this is in fair agreement with the estimates of Richardson and Davidson,[4] and Beutler[5] (102,700 calories).

[1] In the earlier papers the dissociation was supposed to occur in the interior of the filament, but later (*h*) Langmuir proved that it must take place at the surface

[2] Here the words 'mechanically' and 'thermally' mean the same thing, being concerned with random blows on molecules.

[3] For other properties of free hydrogen atoms see Taylor and Marshall, *J. Physical Chem.*, **29**, 1140 (1925); Taylor, *J.A.C.S.* (1926), 2840; Bonhoeffer, *Z. physikal. Chem.*, **113**, 199 (1924).

[4] *Proc. Roy. Soc.* A, **123**, 466 (1929).

[5] *Z. physikal. Chem.* B, **29**, 315 (1935).

Oxygen and tungsten reacted in a totally different manner. A minute pressure of oxygen formed an adsorbed film over the whole surface of the filament. The presence of this film was shown in three different ways: it was found to diminish the thermionic emission of electrons from the heated wire at 1,500° K.; it was found to inhibit the dissociation of hydrogen at the surface of the wire; and it was shown by quantitative studies that the rate of reaction of the filament covered by adsorbed oxygen, with further supplies of the gas, was so great as to require the presence of a monatomic film of adsorbed oxygen, already combined with the surface of the filament (*g*, p. 1150).

The effect on the dissociation of hydrogen and on the emission of electrons was produced at extremely low pressures of oxygen, about 10^{-8} mm. of mercury, showing that the combination between the metal and the adsorbed layer of gas is extremely firm; that the layer is monatomic was shown, as described previously, by the fact that the thermionic emission and hydrogen dissociation recommenced *instantly*, when the temperature was raised to a value at which the adsorbed film began to be removed; this proved that the least removal of the screen of oxygen adsorbed left a clean surface, which could scarcely occur unless the layer were one atom thick; if it were thicker, the removal of the screen and return of the properties of the clean metal surface would return in stages, not suddenly.

If an excess of oxygen is present, this adsorbed film reacts with more oxygen, forming the trioxide, WO_3. At 800° K. a visible film of the oxide remains on the filament. Above 1,200° it begins to distil off, and condenses on the bulb. By the formation of the trioxide, and its removal by evaporation, a considerable amount of oxygen can be 'cleaned up' by the heated filament, which of course loses in weight. The rate at which the filament combines with the gas is proportional to the pressure of oxygen, and the fraction of the oxygen molecules hitting the surface, which are transformed, increases from 0·0011 at 1,270° K. to about 0·5 at 3,300° K.

The fact that this adsorbed oxygen layer does not evaporate of itself, unless undermined by the combination with fresh oxygen, shows that it is not the usual trioxide, but fits the theory that the adsorbed layer is a monatomic layer of oxygen atoms, combined on the outside of the surface atoms of the metal.

The fact that only a proportion of the surface atoms of tungsten with one adsorbed oxygen on each, actually combine with the molecules of oxygen hitting them, to form the trioxide, shows that either the surface atoms of the solid (covered by the adsorbed film), or the gaseous oxygen, or both, need activation before combination can occur. It is probably not the gaseous oxygen which is activated, for Langmuir showed that the temperature of the gas, between 90° K. and 630° K., had no effect on the rate of reaction; there would surely be more activated molecules in the hotter gas. As the proportion of gaseous molecules which react to form trioxide increases with the temperature of the filament, it is clearly the surface atoms of tungsten, with their combined oxygen, which receive activation; this may well be an ordinary thermal activation by collision, though there is as yet no evidence of its nature.

At extremely low pressures, in the absence of a large excess of oxygen, the single atoms of oxygen could apparently distil off the filament, just like the hydrogen atoms. They could condense on the walls of the bulb, and when there, oxidize any metallic tungsten which had previously been distilled on to the glass (*g*, p. 1153).

The main difference between the action of hydrogen and oxygen on the filament appears to be that the attachment of the single oxygen atoms to the filament is far stronger; this might have been expected from the greater chemical affinity of tungsten for oxygen than for hydrogen. Also, with oxygen, there is the complication that further supplies of the gas can detach the surface atoms of metal from the mass, carrying their load of one adsorbed (or combined) oxygen atom, and form the trioxide. This also must be an effect of the strong tendency of oxygen to combine with the metal.

Nitrogen reacted with the tungsten in yet a third way, forming the nitride WN_2. The rate at which the reaction took place depended not on the pressure of the nitrogen, but on the vapour pressure of the heated tungsten wire (*d*, *g*). Every tungsten atom, in the vapour, which struck a nitrogen atom, was found to react; the reaction between nitrogen and tungsten is thus not a surface reaction at all, but a homogeneous reaction occurring in the vapour. Under certain circumstances, however, when the nitrogen gas is ionized by a stream of electrons, the positive nitrogen ions may be attracted to the filament and, striking it with high velocity, form the nitride at the surface of the filament (*g*, p. 1166). This and similar reactions, accelerated by the ionization of the gaseous molecules, deserve a further investigation.

Molybdenum and nitrogen also react, and here again the reaction takes place between evaporated atoms of the metal and gaseous nitrogen molecules (*k*). Not every collision, however, but only a small proportion of them, results in the formation of a permanently stable nitride. When the evaporating molybdenum atoms were moving at low speeds, i.e. were coming from a comparatively cool filament, more collisions produced combination than when the atoms were moving faster. Langmuir suggested that every collision was really effective in producing some sort of combination, but that most of the combinations produced were so unstable that they broke up as soon as they hit the bulb. The reader should consult the original paper for details of this interesting, if somewhat speculative, theory.

A preliminary study of other reactions revealed a very great variety in the possibilities of reaction (see especially *g*; *i*, p. 2273). Molybdenum and carbon monoxide reacted just like tungsten and nitrogen. Many decompositions take place at the surface of heated filaments; e.g. tungsten will decompose ammonia, carbon dioxide, and cyanogen. Sometimes the products of decomposition undergo further reaction, carbon dioxide for instance producing oxidation of the tungsten to the trioxide, but there is no considerable covering of the metal surface by a stable adsorbed layer of oxygen atoms. When water vapour is decomposed an adsorbed oxygen layer is, however, formed. Carbon monoxide attacks tungsten filaments, and when the gas molecules are at a sufficiently low temperature, it forms an adsorbed, apparently monomolecular film on the surface, which distils off as the compound WCO, each carbon monoxide molecule detaching one tungsten atom. If, however, the gas molecules are hot enough (above room temperature) the formation of this film is either very incomplete or does not occur at all, and the reaction between the gas and the filament proceeds much more slowly.

Impurities in the interior of the filament can sometimes diffuse to the surface, and form there a surface film apparently just like those formed by combination with a gas. Thus thorium (*i*, p. 2280) diffuses to the surface between 2,000 and 2,500° K., forming a film which enormously *increases* the thermionic emission of electrons. This film grows till it is one thorium atom thick, and then ceases to grow. For further information as to the effect of layers of foreign atoms on electron emission, see Chap. VIII, § 4.

14. Some properties of metallic surfaces. The catalytic properties of platinum are well known. It acts as a hydrogenating agent, an almost unlimited number of hydrogenations being effected by its aid. Here the effective catalyst does not appear to be simply platinum, but a complex of platinum and oxygen. Willstätter and Waldschmidt-Leitz[1] discovered that some oxygen must always be present, and that frequent shaking with oxygen is of assistance in maintaining the activity of the catalyst. R. Adams and his collaborators[2] have found that platinum oxide, simply prepared, is a catalyst for hydrogenation nearly, if not quite, equal to a good platinum black. Evidently the effective agent is a mixture of platinum and its oxide, which may be prepared either by partial reduction of the oxide or by shaking the black metal with oxygen. This raises the question whether the hydrogenations supposed to be effected by the metal are not really due to the boundary atoms, at the place where the oxide and metal meet on the surface. Interesting, if as yet unexplained, cases of promoter action occur in these hydrogenations; the platinum oxide catalyst is comparatively ineffectual in reducing the aldehyde group CHO, unless small amounts of either zinc or iron salts are present; these additions do not, however, accelerate the hydrogenation of the ethylenic double linkage, but rather tend to retard it. It is tempting to suppose that the zinc or iron forms, on the surface of the solid, patches containing platinum, oxygen, and iron or zinc, and that these patches can adsorb and activate

[1] *Ber.*, **54**, 113 (1921).

[2] *J.A.C.S.* (1922), 1397; (1923), 1071, 2171, 3029; (1924), 1675, 1684; (1925), 1047, 1098, 1147, 1712, 3061; (1926), 477; (1927), 1093, 1099, 2101; (1928), 1970, 2260.

the aldehyde group. Such a mechanism would be similar to that found by Rideal and Wright for the oxidations effected by charcoal (§ 9). Probably platinum, being a simpler surface than charcoal, would be a more suitable one on which to investigate this type of promoter action quantitatively.

Platinum is also an excellent catalyst for performing oxidations. This property is used on an enormous scale in the preparation of sulphuric acid by the oxidation of sulphur dioxide, and of nitrates by the oxidation of ammonia. Also, like most other metals, platinum assists the decomposition of many organic compounds by heat.

It seems that platinum, like copper, does not catalyse hydrogenations unless its surface is irregular; thus Gauger[1] found that platinum and nickel distilled on to the surface of glass wool are inactive in hydrogenating ethylene, and the presence of oxygen or water vapour did not initiate catalytic activity in these films.

No more complete study of a single catalysed reaction has ever been published than that of Palmer and Constable,[2] extending over eight years, on the dehydrogenation of alcohols by heated copper surfaces. Aldehydes are formed from primary and ketones from secondary alcohols by this reaction. The work has resulted in a considerable increase in our knowledge of the mode of formation and properties of the active centres on the surface of copper, and much of it may be applicable also to other metallic catalysts. The reactions are

$$R\cdot CH_2OH \rightarrow R\cdot CHO + H_2,$$
$$R\cdot CHOH\cdot R' \rightarrow R\cdot CO\cdot R' + H_2.$$

As has been mentioned in § 1, smooth surfaces of copper, including those deposited electrolytically, reduced copper mirrors, and polished surfaces were quite inactive (*a*, *i*); a minute trace of activity only was occasionally detected in commercial copper gauze, but copper prepared by thermal decomposition of either cupric or cuprous oxides, or copper salts of mono- and dibasic fatty acids, by condensation on china-clay rods[3] from the vapour (in nitrogen, to prevent oxidation), or by stirring up the atoms of copper into open formation by heating in ammonia at 820°, was active (*i*).

[1] *J.A.C.S.* (1925), 2278.

[2] Palmer,	(*a*) *Proc. Roy. Soc.* A,	**98,** 13 (1920).
	(*b*) *ibid.*	**99,** 412 (1921).
	(*c*) *ibid.*	**101,** 175 (1922).
Palmer and Constable,	(*d*) *ibid.*	**106,** 250 (1924).
	(*e*) *ibid.*	**107,** 255 (1925).
Constable,	(*f*, *g*) *ibid.*	**107,** 270, 279 (1925).
	(*h*) *ibid.*	**108,** 355 (1925).
	(*i*) *ibid.*	**110,** 283 (1926).
	(*j*) *ibid.*	**113,** 254 (1926).

Cf. also Constable, *Proc. Camb. Phil. Soc.*, **22,** 738 (1925); **23,** 172, 432 (1926); **23,** 593, 832 (1927); **24,** 56, 291, 307 (1928); *J.C.S.* (1927), 1578, 2995.

[3] Condensation of the vapour on *glass* does not appear to have been tried; it would be interesting to find whether copper differs from platinum and nickel by its films condensed on glass being catalytically active.

The copper catalysts preserved their activity up to temperatures of 400° for some hours (except for a poisoning effect traced to the products of reaction, which was not appreciable below 280°), so that it is clear that the active centres are not appreciably destroyed by thermal agitation and mobility of the atoms, below this temperature. Above 400°, sintering occurs, with permanent loss of activity.

A rather remarkable fact was that the activity of the catalysts, produced by decomposition *at a given temperature*, was always practically the same, no matter whether one of the oxides, the formate, or a longer chain salt was used as the compound to be decomposed. The longest chain salt used was the valerate, which has five carbon atoms in the molecule; so that the spacing apart of the copper atoms in the original salt is clearly a matter of little or no importance to the activity of the catalyst resulting from its decomposition (*i*). The temperature of decomposition was, however, very important to the activity, which varied in a most complicated way as this temperature was altered (*d*). There were more than threefold variations in the activity, and the curve showed no fewer than three maxima and minima of activity, as the temperature of reduction was raised from 200° to 420°.

The inevitable conclusion from these last two observations seems to be that the peculiar structure of the active patches of copper atoms is built up *after*, not before, the decomposition has occurred, and that it is the result of sudden freezing of the liberated copper atoms, within a time which is probably extremely short, following their liberation as the compound decomposes. The temperature of decomposition controls the amount of mobility possessed by these atoms after liberation, and the structures formed seem to be controlled by the cohesive forces between the copper atoms, binding them into different formations which are determined by a delicately adjusted balance between the motions of the copper atoms, the time during which they remain mobile, and the possible space-lattice structures and orientations which the atoms can assume.

The surface will certainly contain crystal fragments of copper, and perhaps also some amorphous material,[1] in all possible orientations. The activating power of the various parts of the surface may well depend on the spacing of the surface atoms of copper, on which the alcohol molecules are adsorbed, and on the amount of distortion (electrical or mechanical) imposed on the adsorbed molecules as they are made to fit the surface of the crystalline fragments in their various orientations. This distortion probably lowers the additional amount of energy, or the heat of activation, required to activate the adsorbed molecules. Though the heat of activation on any particular active patch could not be determined, the

[1] X-ray studies of active catalysts, in powder form or on supports, always seem to give the usual diffraction pattern of the fully crystalline material. This is not, however, evidence against the inclusion of *some* amorphous material among crystalline fragments, nor against the distortion of the normal crystal lattice at the surface, since the X-ray patterns are produced by layers much thicker than the surface layer.

mean heat of activation in the adsorbed layer was found to be of the order 21,000 calories per gramme molecule,[1] which is of course far lower than the heat of activation of an isolated, unadsorbed molecule for this reaction.

On these conclusions and suppositions a quantitative theory of the distribution of active centres, and of the rate of the reaction, was developed (*h*). From considerations of probability it was concluded that the number of regions on the surface, capable of reducing the heat of activation of adsorbed molecules to a given amount ϵ, is likely to be proportional to $e^{h\epsilon}$, where h is a constant. It was concluded that the area of the active centres formed a quite small fraction, one-thousandth or less, of the whole surface.

Some insight into the nature of the adsorption and perhaps also of the mechanism of the reaction was gained from other considerations. The rate of reaction was the same for all the primary alcohols studied, containing the group CH_2OH (*e*). These included various lengths of hydrocarbon chain, from ethyl alcohol with two carbons to isoamyl with five; the presence of a branched chain at the end of the molecule remote from the CH_2OH group did not affect the rate of reaction. But the secondary alcohol, isopropyl, which contains the group CHOH, reacted five times as fast as those with CH_2OH. These results make it extremely probable that the alcohol is adsorbed in a monomolecular layer, with the oxygenated group anchoring the molecules to the copper atoms; and also indicate that the activating action of the copper is exerted on the end group, CH_2OH or CHOH. Constable considers that the copper activates, and displaces, the hydrogen on the hydroxyl group. The displacement of this may then so disturb the rest of the end group, by leaving the oxygen with a free valency, that a second hydrogen spontaneously, or with the minimum of activation, leaves the carbon atom in the end group, and the two come off together as molecule hydrogen. This seems probable enough, but is difficult to prove; if it is true, the activating power of copper for this reaction resembles somewhat the activations mentioned in § 6, in which hydrogen is dissociated into two free atoms on the surface, the alcohol being first decomposed by the copper into one free hydrogen atom and an unstable residue, which promptly loses a second atom.

The pressure of the reacting vapours had no appreciable influence on the rate of the reaction, between 100 and 1,400 mm. of mercury (*g*). Therefore the monomolecular adsorbed layer of alcohol is almost certainly tightly packed with molecules, at all the pressures employed.

Finally, the behaviour of the unsaturated allyl alcohol, which can undergo two reactions on the surface of copper, was studied (*j*). It can be

[1] Calculated in the ordinary way from measurements of the temperature coefficient of reaction velocity. There is evidence that the adsorbed layer is completely saturated with alcohol molecules, throughout the temperature range; and this is, as Hinshelwood has shown, the necessary condition for the true heat of activation in the adsorbed layer being equal to the apparent heat of activation for the whole system (*Kinetics*, etc., p. 355).

dehydrogenated to allyl aldehyde or acrolein, and can be isomerized to propionic aldehyde:

$$CH_2{=}CH \cdot CH_2OH \rightarrow CH_3 \cdot CH_2 \cdot CHO$$
$$\searrow CH_2{=}CH \cdot CHO + H_2.$$

The dehydrogenation took place at exactly the same rate as that of the saturated alcohols just described; the active centres seem to be the same, therefore, and to act on the CH_2OH group. The isomeric change to propionic aldehyde might, from the above equation, seem to be first a dehydrogenation to acrolein, followed by a hydrogenation to propionic aldehyde.[1] But since the isomeric change has a much lower heat of activation than the dehydrogenation, it cannot occur in two stages, of which the dehydrogenation is the first; it would appear to be a simple migration of the two hydrogen atoms from the CH_2OH group up the chain to the double bond.

By varying the method of preparation of the catalyst, the relative rates of the two reactions could be much altered; partial sintering of the copper seems to aid the isomeric change. Clearly, then, different active patches are involved in the two reactions.

Metals can perform innumerable catalyses, and for a qualitative extension of this section the reader should consult Sabatier's *Catalysis in Organic Chemistry* (translated by Reid, 1922). There is unlimited scope for an extension of quantitative studies on their surfaces, with accurate methods for tracing out the fate, if possible, of individual molecules at all stages, from the moment when they first hit the surface to the moment when they leave it, having undergone the reaction. And when some progress has been made with this problem, there will remain the still more complicated task of dealing similarly with 'promoted' catalysts, or mixed surfaces of several different constituents.

15. The surface of charcoal. Charcoal is a most complex surface. It can adsorb oxygen in at least three different forms, one of which can only be removed as oxides, at very high temperatures; another can be removed as oxides by evacuation at ordinary temperatures, and another can be pumped off as oxygen. The last is probably adsorbed as molecular oxygen; it cannot exist above 200°. The two other types of adsorption probably have the oxygen combined to the carbon by primary valency, just as in the oxides of carbon, but the oxides are not removed until something occurs to break the carbon to carbon linkage which still binds the CO group to the mass. These facts point to some of the surface atoms of carbon being linked less firmly than others to the mass. Blench and Garner[2] measured the heat of adsorption of oxygen on charcoal and found it greater for the first portions adsorbed than for later adsorptions, when the surface was partly saturated. At temperatures about 450°, the heat of adsorption exceeded 200,000 calories per gramme molecule, which is

[1] The hydrogenating power of copper is well known.
[2] *J.C.S.* (1924), 1288.

more than twice the heat of combustion of solid charcoal, though the heat of combustion of gaseous carbon has been estimated as 280,000 calories.[1] In burning solid carbon, the carbon to carbon bonds are broken, and this absorbs much energy; it would appear that some of the surface atoms are held much more loosely than others. The results for the heat of adsorption varied greatly at different temperatures, indicating that changes were very easily made in the surface.

Charcoal is also an excellent catalyst for many reactions, particularly oxidations, halogenations, and isomerizations. Hydrochloric acid can be prepared from its elements by passing over charcoal; phosgene also from chlorine and carbon monoxide; the *ortho-para* hydrogen interconversion is very much accelerated by charcoal; oximes, and sulphoxides,[2] are readily converted into their stereoisomers, and other isomerizations catalysed; and amino-acids can be deaminated. Charcoal also catalyses the formation of carbon dioxide and hydrogen from carbon monoxide and steam. In this last reaction, H. S. Taylor and Neville[3] have shown that a little ferric oxide is an excellent promoter; apparently the carbon-ferric oxide (or carbon-iron) complex surface activates this reaction. It is interesting to find that, when carbon monoxide is formed by passage of carbon dioxide over heated carbon, a reaction which goes on at the surface of the solid carbon, ferric oxide is not a promoter. The reaction proceeds only slowly in the presence of iron oxide, but if potassium carbonate is added, the reaction is rapid.

In a detailed study of the catalytic oxidation of organic compounds by charcoal, Rideal and Wright[4] have made it clear that for this reaction there are several different types of surface involved. By finding the amount of various substances which had to be adsorbed, either to cover the whole surface, or to destroy an oxidation proceeding at a particular rate, they estimated the areas concerned in each case. These estimates could not be made very accurate, owing to lack of knowledge of the spacing in the adsorbed layers (different substances gave rather different results for the area), but they clearly show the existence of four or five different types of surface. A small fraction of the surface of pure sugar charcoal was oxidizable; this was of the order 0·5 per cent. of the whole. About 40 per cent. was catalytically active with a rather low degree of activity, for the oxidation of oxalic and other acids; the remainder was inactive. These were the only types of surface distinguished on pure sugar charcoal. If nitrogen was added to the charcoal, by carbonizing the sugar with urea, little change in the catalytically active fraction, or in its activity, occurred, though the total surface was increased. If iron was added, by carbonizing with ferric chloride, the bulk of the surface was as before, but a new surface some fifty times more active, and about 0·2 per cent. of the whole

[1] Grüneisen, *Verh. Deut. Phys. Ges.*, **14**, 324 (1912).
[2] T. W. J. Taylor and others, *J.C.S.* (1934), 980; (1935), 974.
[3] *J.A.C.S.* (1921), 2055.
[4] *J.C.S.* (1925), 1347; (1926), 1813, 3182; (1927), 2323.

area, appeared. This adsorbed potassium cyanide specifically, and so was detected; no doubt it contained carbon and iron. Adding iron *and* nitrogen gave a surface about 6 per cent. of which had an activity and specific adsorbing power the same as the active carbon-iron surface of the preceding; there was also about a further 5 per cent. of a still more active surface, with many hundred times the oxidative activity of the pure sugar-charcoal surface; this probably contained carbon, iron, and nitrogen.

Blood charcoal was found to have about 1 per cent. of the carbon-iron surface of fiftyfold activity, but apparently none of the still more active iron-carbon-nitrogen surface, which is somewhat surprising, as there is plenty of nitrogen in this charcoal. It was estimated, from the percentage of iron in this charcoal, that there was about one iron atom to every six atoms of carbon in the most active patches of the blood charcoal. This ratio of six to one suggested that the iron atom may promote the catalytic activity by reason of a combination of the 'co-ordinated' kind; but this is scarcely proved as yet.

It is generally accepted that the oxidative power of charcoal is due to the chemisorbed layer of oxygen on its surface.[1] This oxygen layer appears to be important also in other ways; T. W. J. Taylor's studies on the interconversion of stereoisomeric oximes and sulphoxides show that oxygen is necessary for this reaction. The mechanism appears to be an exchange of the active, adsorbed oxygens on the surface of the carbon, with the molecules of the substances undergoing isomerization in solution. The nature of the layers adsorbed on charcoal influences, naturally, its behaviour as an electrode, and the kind of ions which it sends into solution.[2]

The adsorptive power of charcoal is very much influenced by its admixture with small amounts of foreign substances during carbonization, by the temperature of carbonization, and by the gases present in this operation. Although there is a great deal of empirical information on this 'activation' of charcoal, our knowledge of the atomic arrangements on the surface still seems scanty. The action of oxygen influences the properties of the final charcoal, both by reason of the altered surface, and also probably because the size of the pores in the charcoal depends very much on the extent to which oxygen has acted on the material.[3] If the attack by oxygen is sufficient the charcoal acquires the power of adsorbing substances of larger molecular weight than it could originally, presumably because the pores are widened by actual removal of material from the smaller pores, e.g. naphthalene sulphonic acid and methylene blue were not appreciably adsorbed until a certain stage in the oxidation by air had been reached. This inaccessibility of some parts of the surface, in some charcoals, to substances used to determine the surface area by adsorption, renders the results of such determinations uncertain.

[1] Cf. A. King, *J.C.S.* (1933), 842; (1934), 22; (1936), 1688.

[2] Cf. Frumkin, *Ber.*, **60**, 1816 (1927); *Kolloid-Z.*, **51**, 123 (1930); A. King, *J.C.S.* (1935), 889.

[3] Cf. S. H. Bell and J. C. Philip, *J.C.S.* (1934), 1164; A. King, *J.C.S.* (1924), 1975.

16. The surface of the silver bromide grain in a photographic emulsion. Sheppard and the research staff of the Eastman Kodak Company[1] have brought to light a very interesting case of the effect of a small local change in a solid surface. In searching for the constituent of gelatine which is responsible for the increased sensitivity to light acquired by silver halides in the presence of gelatine, and is the basis of the efficiency of the photographic dry plate, it was found that the sensitivity was not due to any ordinary known constituents of gelatine, but to the presence of minute, accidental amounts of either organic isothiocyanates, or thioureas. Probably the sensitizing substance present in most samples of gelatine is allyl isothiocyanate, $C_3H_5N:C:S$. This substance and a few similar substances, which must, however, contain the C:S group, reacts with the surface of the silver halide grains, forming local patches of silver sulphide. At these patches the stability of the silver halide is reduced, and there is evidence that the light quanta absorbed by the grains of silver halide, probably anywhere on their surface,[2] produce decomposition to silver atoms only at the specks of sulphide. Thus the sulphide specks start centres of reduced silver atoms which are developable by the usual developers. The proportion of the sulphur-containing compound in the gelatine is about one part in 300,000; much more than this produces fog, the bromide grains being rendered too unstable.

This production of a peculiar degree of instability in the silver bromide, close to the atoms of sulphur in the sulphide, seems closely analogous to the other cases of 'promoter' action, and the effects of a one-dimensional interface in a solid surface, which were considered in § 3. It may be an effect of the same nature as the increased ease of decomposition of the calcium carbonate group, when this has calcium oxide groups adjacent to it. There is some evidence that the silver sulphide crystal lattice is rather more easily disorientated than the silver bromide, but since silver sulphide is, alone, not particularly sensitive to light, it seems certain that the sensitizing action of the sulphide speck must be due to a boundary action between the sulphide and the bromide.[3]

[1] *3rd Colloid Symposium Monograph*, p. 76 (1925).

[2] Cf. Webb, *J. Optical Soc. of America*, **26**, 367 (1936).

[3] This discovery of the nature of the sensitizing action of gelatine is one of the most striking—and much too little known—romances of modern applied Chemistry. The search for the sensitizing constituent of gelatine, with no knowledge of its nature or amount, and scarcely any guide beyond the facts that the silver bromide grains appeared to have local centres of peculiar sensitivity scattered at random on their surface, and that the sensitivity of the grains was much reduced by treatment with oxidizing agents, presented an exceptionally difficult problem. It had long been known that different brands, and even different batches, of gelatine differed greatly in sensitizing power; that the sensitizing power was due to some chemical substance rather than to a physical condition was indicated by the fact that an extract could be made from an active gelatine which, on adding to a relatively inactive gelatine, produced a substance of high sensitizing power. A search among the ordinary decomposition products of gelatine, amino-acids, and related substances, including the purine bases and creatine, etc., was fruitless in revealing the active constituent. At

17. The surface of bacteria; enzyme action. Although the surfaces of bacteria are not strictly solid, yet the reactions which occur on them, and also on enzymes, have so much in common with those catalysed by the solid surfaces we have been considering, that a brief account of some very suggestive work by Quastel and his colleagues seems appropriate.[1] The reactions investigated were the hydrogenation and dehydrogenation of simple organic compounds, in the presence of methylene blue, or its leuco-base, and the bacteria, which were generally *B. coli*. The bacteria were used in the resting state, i.e. not proliferating; and sometimes were even 'dead', in the sense that they could not be induced to start growing and proliferating again on nutrient media. A typical reaction was the dehydrogenation of succinic acid to fumaric, and the reverse reaction of hydrogenating fumaric acid to succinic.

$$HOOC\cdot CH_2\cdot CH_2\cdot COOH \rightleftarrows HOOC\cdot CH{=}CH\cdot COOH + 2H.$$

The action of the bacteria was to activate the simple organic compound (called the substrate),[2] so that it could accept or donate hydrogen; if the reaction was a dehydrogenation, the coloured methylene blue took up the hydrogen donated by the activated substrate, becoming colourless; and with a hydrogenation, the colourless leuco-base gave up hydrogen to the substrate, becoming coloured. In this way the methylene blue was an indicator of the progress of the reaction; it does not itself require activation, and so indicates whether or no the substrate has been activated by the bacteria. The rate of change of colour in the methylene blue is also an indication of the degree of activation, or of the number of molecules of substrate that are activated by a given amount of bacteria. It was shown that the methylene blue underwent the reaction mainly at the external surface of the bacteria (*a*), and it was shown to be very probable that the activations actually studied also occurred mainly at this site, although other cell interfaces may play some part, and no doubt can promote reactions of a similar kind.

one time the activity seemed to become concentrated in a fraction allied to cholesterol, and the active substance was thought to be allied to the sterols, perhaps indeed to be calciferol itself; but the hope that the substance giving sensitivity to the photographic plate might prove to be identical with the vitamin which is believed to be essential for the proper growth of bones, had to be abandoned when one day the smell of garlic was detected during the heating of an active emulsion. This clue of smell soon led to the trial of mustard oils and thioureas as sensitizing agents, and to the proof that these simple compounds, containing the C:S group, sensitize the grains. Similar derivatives of selenium and tellurium were found to be perhaps even more effectual. It is rather paradoxical that the peculiar virtue of gelatine, which is commonly supposed to be entirely free from sulphur, should lie in its power, through the presence of an accidental sulphur-containing impurity, of transforming a part of the surfaces of grains of silver halide into sulphide.

[1] (*a*) Quastel, *Biochem. J.*, **20**, 166 (1926).
(*b*) Quastel and Wooldridge, *ibid.*, **21**, 148 (1927).
(*c*) Quastel and Wooldridge, *ibid.*, **21**, 1224 (1927).
(*d*) Quastel and Wooldridge, *ibid.*, **22**, 689 (1928).

[2] *Not* to be confused with the use of the word 'substrate' as the underlying substance upon which there is a surface film.

It was shown, by a process of selective poisoning identical in principle with that used on solid catalysts, that the activations occur at specially active patches, and that these patches have specificity, or the power of discriminating between different substrates, through two separate mechanisms; the power of a given patch to adsorb different substrates depends on their chemical constitution, so that only a few substances are adsorbed; and of those substances which are adsorbed, only a small proportion are activated.

The evidence for the existence of numerous separate active patches was as follows. A number of general poisons were discovered, including 5 per cent. sodium chloride, toluene, chloroform, and ether. These varied in intensity, so that different amounts were required to produce the same effect on the bacteria; but they all suppressed the activations, and the order in which different activations were suppressed was nearly the same for all these general poisons. The activations could be roughly graded into three classes, according to their resistance to suppression. These were (1) very resistant, formic acid, α-glycerophosphoric acid; (2) moderately resistant, lactic, succinic acids; (3) slightly resistant, all fatty acids except formic, sugars, glycerol, glutaminic acid, and β-glycerophosphoric acid. A small quantity of a general poison suppressed the activation of class (3); larger quantities, or a longer time of action, suppressed classes (2) and (1). The action of the general poisons was usually irreversible, at least no treatment has yet been discovered by which an activation suppressed by a general poison can be restored. This evidence is similar in kind to that of Vavon and Husson (p. 233), where it was shown that at least three different active patches exist on platinum. Copper sulphate (*c*, p. 1238) suppressed the activation of succinic, lactic, and formic acids, and of glucose. Treatment with hydrogen sulphide restored the activation of the last two practically to normal; of lactic acid, to one-third of the normal activity, and of succinic acid, to a slight degree only. Mercuric salts also poisoned the activations, and its effect was similarly removed by hydrogen sulphide. Even the proliferating power of the organisms could be restored by hydrogen sulphide.[1] Potassium permanganate and hydrogen cyanide could have their poisoning action partly removed by after-treatment with sodium hydrosulphite; the action of this reagent, at least in the case of the cyanide poisoning, seems mysterious. Evidence of different chemical affinities in the patches responsible for different activations is given by the fact that the permanganate and cyanide attack most easily the formic acid activation, which is the most resistant to the attack of the general poisons.

Further detailed information as to the properties of different patches was obtained (*d*) by studying the nature of certain poisons, similar in constitution to the substrates themselves. In order to simplify the experi-

[1] Cases might arise, in the sterilization by copper or mercury salts, where this restoring action of hydrogen sulphide would be troublesome. H_2S is not usually suspected of being a revivifying agent!

ments, the activity of the organisms was usually first reduced by treatment with toluene, to an extent which left the activations of succinic and lactic acids still in working order, but eliminated numerous other activations. With such a toluene-treated organism, there appeared to be one class of substances which were adsorbed on the centres which would activate lactic acid, and another class which were adsorbed on the succinic acid centres. This adsorption prevented the activation of the lactic or succinic acids until the adsorbed substances (which were not themselves activated) were displaced by the succinic or lactic acid, which could be activated. The succinic acid centre was poisoned by the following acids:

Adsorbed on succinic acid centre.

$HOOC \cdot CH_2 \cdot COOH$	malonic acid
$HOOC \cdot CH_2 \cdot CH_2 \cdot COOH$	succinic acid
$HOOC \cdot CH_2 \cdot CH_2 \cdot CH_2 \cdot COOH$	glutaric acid
$C_6H_5 \cdot CH_2 \cdot CH_2 \cdot COOH$	phenyl propionic acid
$HOOC \cdot CH_2 \cdot CH(COOH) \cdot CH_2 \cdot COOH$	tricarballylic acid
$HOOC \cdot CH(CH_3) \cdot CH_2 \cdot COOH$	pyrotartaric acid

The lactic acid centre had its activity suppressed by the following:

Adsorbed on lactic acid centre.

$HOOC \cdot COOH$	oxalic acid
$OHC \cdot COOH$	glyoxylic acid
$HOOC \cdot CHOH \cdot COOH$	hydroxymalonic acid
$CH_3 \cdot CHOH \cdot COOH$	lactic acid
$CH_3 \cdot CO \cdot COOH$	pyruvic acid
$C_6H_5 \cdot CHOH \cdot COOH$	mandelic acid

Ethyl malonic acid, $HOOC \cdot CH(C_2H_5) \cdot COOH$, was not adsorbed on either centre.

It appears that the $CHOH \cdot COOH$ group, or the $CO \cdot COOH$ group, promotes adsorption on the lactic acid centre, while the $CH_2 \cdot COOH$ group favours adsorption on the succinic acid centre. An exception was found in mesotartaric acid, $HOOC \cdot CHOH \cdot CHOH \cdot COOH$, which seems to be adsorbed on both centres; and the phenyl propionic acid had some tendency to be adsorbed on the lactic acid centre also.

The distinction between the two classes of compound is not perfectly definite; but exceptions are few.

This class of poisons appears to act simply by competing with the substrate for the space available for adsorption on the active centres. If the concentration of the poison is diminished and that of the substrate increased, the activation is restored. Indeed the poison and the substrate probably compete with one another on approximately equal terms for adsorption. The difference lies in the fact that the active patches on a toluene-treated organism can only activate one (or a few) out of the class of substances which are adsorbed.

This points to two separate factors in the specificity of the activating mechanism. The structure of the active patch must first be one which will adsorb the particular substance to be activated, and second, it must activate the substance, once adsorbed. Emil Fischer's comparison of the action of an enzyme on its substrate, to the highly specific relation between a lock and key, now seems capable of being analysed further; the key must not only be capable of entering the keyhole (adsorption), but it must be capable, once inserted, of operating the mechanism inside (activation).

Quastel's earlier work dealt mainly with activations effected by bacteria in which the cell structure is more or less intact. There is every reason to suppose that enzyme reactions are essentially of the same kind. The characteristic feature of enzymes is probably an active patch of special molecular architecture. If these happen to be situated on a cell wall, or some other membrane within a cell, the reactions are said to be brought about by the cell. But if the active patch happens to be mounted on a soluble protein molecule, produced very likely by disintegration of some cell structure, it will still perform its activations *in vitro*, and will be called a 'soluble enzyme'. Some close resemblances have been found not only in the reactions induced, but in the poisons which suppress these reactions, between the bacteria and the soluble enzyme, capable of activating lactic acid, contained in the clear fluid obtained after autolysis of *B. coli* and centrifuging.[1] These enzymes were tested with the same poisons which act on the lactic acid centre in the toluene-treated organism, and found to behave similarly to the active patches in the cell walls. There was no important qualitative difference between the 'soluble enzyme' and that fully supported on the cell wall, though the soluble enzyme was not quite so active. Thus the specific architecture of the active patch is of far greater importance than its inert support. It has been found by Willstätter that adsorption of a soluble enzyme on a neutral, inactive support will often increase its stability and activity; this recalls the action of refractory supports in increasing or maintaining the activity of simple metallic catalysts.

Further resemblances between the behaviour of soluble enzymes and the surfaces of bacteria are given by Murray,[2] who found that lipase is reversibly poisoned by ketones, in just the same manner as the lactic acid centre in the bacteria is poisoned by hydroxymalonic acid. The action is apparently due mainly to the carbonyl group, but a hydrocarbon group of moderate size appears to increase the poisoning effect; forming the oxime, and thus destroying the carbonyl group, prevents the compound acting as a poison. Myrbäck[3] showed that invertase is prevented from acting by silver salts, but that its activity can be restored by treatment with hydrogen sulphide, just as the activations in the bacteria, which are destroyed by copper salts, are restored.

[1] Stephenson, *Biochem. J.*, **22**, 605 (1928).

[2] *Biochem. J.*, **23**, 292 (1929).

[3] *Z. physiol. Chem.*, **158**, 160 (1926).

Both enzymes and the active centres on the cell interfaces lose their activity on warming, and it is not restored on cooling; thus the special architecture of these patches is destroyed by heat, an action which may be compared to the loss of catalytic activity of metallic catalysts caused by sintering.

Narcotics suppress many activities of living cells; and they also inhibit the action of some enzymes.[1] Their action may be an adsorption on the active patches, or possibly they may, through their solubility in lipoid substances, enter into the structure underlying the active patches and distort these so that they can no longer perform their specific functions.

And finally, a certain amount of information is being obtained as to the growth of these active patches or enzymes; if bacteria are grown in the presence of certain substances, they tend to develop the power of acting on these substances.[2]

In some further papers the action of dyestuffs and some other compounds is studied,[3] both on *B. coli* and on some enzymes. One of the more important constitutional factors, in the case of the dyestuff, is the nature of the ionizable groups, whether basic or acidic; it is sometimes found that the basic dyestuffs are so tightly adsorbed upon the surface of an enzyme as to inhibit its normal activity completely, while acid dyestuffs are without effect. This is not invariably the case, however, and specific features of the structure are often quite important in addition to the nature of the electric charge on those groups which confer acidic or basic properties on the molecules. The oxidative power of *B. coli*, in utilizing gaseous oxygen to oxidize some aliphatic organic compounds, is generally prevented by fairly small concentrations (about 1 in 5,000) of basic dyestuffs (*e*). The enzyme fumarase, which hydrolyses fumaric acid into malic acid, is particularly powerfully inhibited by *acid* dyestuffs of the Congo red series (one part in 100,000 may suppress activity completely); and to some extent, but less, by the *basic* triphenylmethane series. Other basic dyes have some inhibiting activity. If acid and basic dyestuffs are mixed, the mixture has no inhibiting power; this may be due to mutual precipitation of the dyes, so that neither reaches the surface in sufficient concentration to become adsorbed on the active patches, but was thought by Quastel to indicate that the specific activating structure on the fumarase surface is a pair of electric charges, positive and negative, in close proximity (*f*, p. 906). Urease (*g*) is quite unaffected by acidic dyes, but the basic dyes, of the triphenylmethane series particularly, have an exceptionally strong inhibitory effect. A curious observation (*h*) is that the *ortho* and *para* polyhydroxy aromatic compounds, and quinones, are very toxic to urease, but that the toxicity is prevented if compounds with SH groups (thiol compounds) are present, the latter fact suggesting that it is not

[1] Cf. A. J. Clark, *Trans. Faraday Soc.* **33**, 1057, (1937); Adam, *ibid.*, p. 1064.

[2] Cf. Hopkins, *Proc. Roy. Soc.* B, **111**, 281 (1932).

[3] (*e*) Quastel and Wheatley, *Biochem. J.*, **25**, 629 (1931).
(*f*) *Ibid.*, **25**, 898 (1931).
(*g*) *Ibid.*, **26**, 1685 (1932).
(*h*) *Ibid.*, **27**, 1116 (1933).
(*i*) Quastel and Yates, *Enzymologia*, **1**, 60 (1936).

the polyhydroxy compounds, but the corresponding quinones, which really inhibit the action of the enzymes. Traces of these quinones, almost certain to be present in the polyphenols, would be reduced by the SH groups. Compounds containing two hydroxyl groups in the *meta* position did not inhibit the action of urease, perhaps because they do not form quinones. A still more curious observation was that the toxic action of the basic dye, brilliant green, is much greater on a rather crude preparation of urease (from Soya bean) than on a purified enzyme; but the toxic action on the purified enzyme again became nearly as great as on the less pure preparation, if a small amount of an aliphatic long chain oil, containing several unsaturated linkages in the chain, was added. Invertase is also poisoned by some dyestuffs (*i*).

The actions of these poisons can be diminished by using large amounts of the substrate, showing that the poisons and the substrates compete for adsorption on the active patches.

The original view that the mechanism of activation is mainly due to electrostatic fields between the active patches and the specifically fitting adsorbed molecules, appears rather too simple at the present time; the reader should consult the original papers (*a*, *f*) for details. Whatever be the mechanism, an electrical activation of a simple nature, or an elaborate quantum mechanical deformation, it is certainly fairly specific, and its further investigation should yield a rich reward, and be perhaps no more difficult than the investigation of the mechanism of activation by inorganic catalysts. In the case of these more complex catalysts, one has the weapon of a controlled variation of chemical constitution, which is not always readily available for researches on inorganic catalysts.

18. Theoretical estimates of the surface tension of crystals. The surface tensions of some simple crystals of salts, with a cubic lattice, have been calculated, together with numerous other physical properties. In these crystals, the atoms are wholly ionized, and it is assumed that the cohesive forces between them are simple electrostatic forces. The internal structure of the ions is the same as that of the inert gases, and the repulsive forces exerted by these ions on each other, when forced into contact by their mutual attractions (electrostatic), can be elucidated by the help of the properties of these gases. Even the distances apart of the atoms in the lattices can be calculated from a knowledge of these forces, and are found to agree well with the observed dimensions.

The calculations are too intricate to be given here; Lennard-Jones and Taylor[1] found for the free surface energies of certain planes and edges the values given in Table XV.

The surface and edge energies can be fairly compared by dividing by the number of atoms in the units of area or length: the (1, 0, 0) plane of sodium chloride contains one atom (either Na or Cl) in every 7·9 sq. A., and the edge, one in 2·81 A. The results are given in Table XV.

The edge energies are always much the same as the (1, 0, 0) surface energies, although the edge atoms are more exposed; but the (0, 1, 1) surface energies are much higher. (0, 1, 1) planes do not easily appear in

[1] *Proc. Roy. Soc.* A, **109**, 476 (1925).

TABLE XIV

Calculated surface free energies: ergs per sq. cm.

(1, 0, 0) plane

	F	Cl		O	S
Na	304	96	Mg	1,362	357
K	180	76·6	Ca	1,032	356

(0, 1, 1) plane

	F	Cl		O	S
Na	784	350	Mg	3,940	1,730
K	489	260	Ca	2,850	1,440

Edge energy: unit 10^{-6} *ergs per cm.*

	F	Cl		O	S
Na	5·13	3·97	Mg	27·0	20·8
K	3·95	3·06	Ca	20·5	16·8

Born[1] has given values some 50 per cent. higher, but he did not take such detailed consideration of the repulsive forces between atoms.

these crystals; and the high energies per atom are due partly to the high energies per square centimetre, and partly to there being fewer atoms than in the (1, 0, 0) plane.

TABLE XV

Energies per atom: unit 10^{-11} *ergs.*[2]

	Spacing, A.		*Surface*		*Edge*
	obs.	*calc.*	(1, 0, 0)	(0, 1, 1)	
NaCl	2·81	2·85	0·78	4·01	1·13
NaF	2·31	2·30	1·61	5·85	1·18
KCl	3·14	3·13	0·75	3·60	0·96
KF	2·66	2·63	1·24	4·79	1·04
MgO	2·10	2·10	6·01	24·5	5·66
MgS	2·54	2·60	2·42	16·5	5·4
CaO	2·40	2·33	5·61	21·9	4·78
CaS	2·84	2·77	2·73	15·6	4·65

The spacing of an isolated plane of atoms, separated from the body of the crystal, has been calculated to be about 5 per cent. smaller than the same plane in a solid lattice. The surface layer of atoms will tend also to have a smaller spacing, and this may result in the surface layer of a crystal being actually surrounded by something like a skin in tension. Lennard-Jones and Dent[3] give values calculated for the tension of this superficial layer; it is important to note that this superficial tension is not the same quantity as the ordinary surface tension or free energy, which is the

[1] *Atomtheorie der festen Zustandes*, 740 (1923).

[2] At Prof. Lennard-Jones's suggestion, the calculated crystal dimensions have been used instead of those observed, for consistency with the original calculations of surface energy.

[3] *Proc. Roy. Soc.* A, **121**, 247 (1928).

quantity given in the preceding tables. The tables give the surface tension calculated without taking account of the surface contraction; it has been calculated by Miss Dent[1] that this surface contraction will diminish the surface tension by about 20 per cent.

Theoretical calculations such as these appear the only method at present available for determining the surface tension of solids.

[1] *Phil. Mag.*, **8**, 530 (1929).

CHAPTER VIII*

ELECTRICAL PHENOMENA AT INTERFACES

IN this chapter an attempt will be made to deal more systematically with the electrical phenomena taking place at surfaces, some of which have been mentioned earlier in this book.

1. Phase boundary potentials and double layers. When two conducting phases are in contact, a difference of electrical potential is generally established between them. The establishment of this 'phase boundary potential' is intimately associated with the formation of an 'electrical double layer' at the surface, i.e. an unsymmetrical distribution of electrically charged particles near the phase boundary, with an excess of positive charges towards that phase which assumes a positive potential, and of negative charges towards the phase assuming a negative potential.

The two sides, positive and negative, of the electrical double layer may be situated on different sides of the material phase boundary, or on the same side. There are three different ways in which electrical double layers may arise, when two phases are brought into contact, and therefore three different origins for interfacial potential differences.

The first is a difference in the rate of escape of the positively and the negatively charged particles, from one phase into the other. The simplest case is the escape of electrons from a metal, heated to such a temperature that 'thermionic emission' takes place readily, but the metal itself volatilizes to a negligible extent; this occurs with many slightly volatile metals, and the emission of electrons from heated tungsten is of course of immense technical importance. At about 1,500° to 2,000° C., according to the state of the surface, tungsten emits electrons freely, but the positive ions of tungsten, which form the space-lattice of the metal, do not evaporate in appreciable numbers.

Consider such a metal brought into an evacuated enclosure; at first electrons leave the metal freely. Very soon, however, the electrons accumulate in the space outside the metal, giving a 'space charge'; and the space becomes negatively charged. The metal simultaneously becomes charged, owing to the loss of negative electrons from the originally neutral metal. Thus a potential gradient is set up between the metal and the space outside, and this tends to retard the emission of electrons; eventually, when the number of electrons removed from the metal has reached a definite amount, a potential difference between the metal and the space, sufficient to prevent further emission, is set up, the total amount of emission at this point depending on the capacities of the two phases metal and space outside.

When this equilibrium has been established, the distribution of charged particles in the two phases is not uniform. The positively charged metal

* See also Appendix.

attracts electrons towards its surface, and the negative electrons in the space repel the electrons away from the surface in the metal, and so leave an excess of positive ions over electrons, i.e. a net positive charge, near the surface of the metal. This concentration of electrically charged particles of opposite sign, in this instance on the two sides of the interface, constitutes the electrical double layer.

The forces which produce this concentration of charged particles near the interface are electrostatic, and vary as the inverse square of the distance between oppositely charged particles. Compared with the forces of attraction (usually of the van der Waals type) between uncharged particles,[1] these are long range forces. Consequently, the electrical double layers are generally diffuse, and extend to much greater thicknesses than the materially inhomogeneous transition layer between two phases.

The electrode potentials obtained when metals dip into aqueous, or non-aqueous, solutions; the potential differences between two electrolytes in contact; the 'membrane' potentials across membranes which permit the passage of one ion more easily than another, are all cases in which the potential differences and double layers result from differences in the escaping tendency between the positively and negatively charged components. In all these cases the electrical double layers are generally diffuse, the density of the charge decreasing gradually away from the interface, and the positive and negative sides are on opposite sides of the material interface.

There are, however, two other ways in which interfacial potential differences and double layers may arise; and in these cases the double layer is usually found mainly on one side only of the material interface. One of these is when neither the positively nor the negatively charged components can leave one phase in appreciable amounts, but the particles of one sign tend to be adsorbed more than those of the other sign at the surface. Cases of this were mentioned in Chap. III, § 10, where the tendency of some anions to be adsorbed more than cations, at an air-water surface, produced a double layer wholly in the water, with the negative side nearer the air than the positive. This causes the water to assume a positive potential relatively to the air. Interfacial potentials arising from this source may conveniently be termed 'adsorption potentials'. Although the amount of charged components actually escaping from the phase is negligible for adsorption potentials, they may still be regarded as due to a difference in escaping *tendency* between the charged components of opposite sign; that component which has the greater escaping tendency being more strongly adsorbed, and giving the sign to the outer half of the double layer.

The third possible origin for double layers is an orientation of neutral

[1] The terms uncharged particles, or components, will be used to describe particles, or components of a system, which have no excess or deficiency of electrons over the number required for electrical neutrality; charged particles or components have an excess or deficiency of one or more electrons.

molecules, which contain, however, electrical dipoles, at the surface. Most molecules contain such dipoles, and their presence is one of the principal reasons for the orientation of molecules at surfaces. An oriented row of dipoles at a surface is a double layer, and is not diffuse; it may, however, induce secondary diffuse double layers extending into the phases on either side of the interface, by attracting mobile charged particles.

Owing to the almost universal existence of dipoles in the molecules of one or both of the phases in contact, such potential differences probably exist with almost every possible pair of phases. Freundlich has called them 'lyoelectric' potentials. There is no means of measuring them, but the *change* in a phase boundary potential due to the introduction of a surface film composed of neutral, oriented molecules containing dipoles, can be measured (the 'surface potential' of Chaps. II and III). As neutral molecules may be brought to the surface by adsorption, a part of a lyoelectric potential may be due to adsorption, and is sometimes called an 'adsorption' potential; but so far as the different components of a surface potential can be distinguished, the term 'adsorption' potential will be reserved in this book for potentials arising from unequal adsorption of oppositely charged ions, and 'lyoelectric' potential for those caused by the orientation of molecules containing dipoles.

It seems probable that electrification by friction, the oldest known method of electrifying bodies, is caused by the sudden separation of the two halves of the double layers set up on contact, when the contact is broken. Helmholtz took this view,[1] and though there has been some little controversy over it,[2] the view still seems the most probable. Ballo-electricity, or waterfall electricity,[3] produced when a mass of water breaks up into small drops, is also probably due to the charge produced when double layers form at the surface of drops. It is closely connected with the electrokinetic or ζ potential (§ 8).

2. Definition of the potential difference between two phases. There is some difficulty in precisely defining the term 'potential difference', when the two points at which the potential is considered lie in phases of different composition. At a point in space where there is no appreciable amount of matter, the electrostatic potential is measured by the work required to bring unit positive charge up from infinity, and this definition presents no difficulty. But when the unit charge, in its journey from the region of zero potential, has to pass through a phase boundary, or a region where the density of matter is varying, the electrical potential is not so easily defined. This is because the charged particles generally have 'chemical',[4] as well as electrostatic, properties, and work has to be done

[1] *Ann. Physik*, **7**, 337 (1879).

[2] Cf. Richards, *Physical Rev.*, **22**, 122 (1923); Macky, *Proc. Roy. Soc.* A, **119**, 107 (1928). Shaw, *ibid.*, **94**, 16; **111**, 339; **118**, 97, 108; **128**, 474, 487; *Phil. Mag.*, **9**, 577 (1917–1930).

[3] Cf. Lenard, *Ann. Physik*, **46**, 584 (1892); Freundlich, *Kapillarchemie*, **1**, 395 (1930).

[4] For convenience, the word 'chemical' will often be used to denote those forces between atoms and ions which are not purely electrostatic, and do not obey Cou-

by or against the 'chemical' forces acting on the particle, as it moves across a region where the nature or density of the matter is changing.

It is unfortunate that different writers use the term 'potential', in reference to the electrical state of a phase, in very different ways, not always specifying what is really meant. Often the potential just outside the phase, in empty or nearly empty space, is meant; this is definite. Sometimes, however, the supposed potential inside the phase seems to be intended, without any clear definition of this being given.

The electrostatic potential of a phase is defined as the potential of the space just outside it, for a phase α let this be V^{α}. The 'Volta' potential difference between two phases is the difference in electrostatic potential between two points just outside the phases. The electrostatic potentials, and therefore the Volta potential, are determined by the amount of charge on the phase and its electrostatic capacity.

The term 'just outside' leaves something to be desired as a definition. Although our knowledge of the forces on an electron or ion being removed from a neutral phase, possessing no net electric charge of either sign, is incomplete, it is probably true that they are due partly to an electrical double layer in the surface, and partly to an 'image' force, the attraction between the charged particle just after it has left the phase, and the charges induced in the phase as a result of the presence of the charged particle outside, i.e. the resultant attraction produced by the displacement of the various charged particles in the phase. This image force is of longer range than the other forces; its value is $e^2/4r^2$, where e is the charge on the particle, and r its distance from the surface[1]; and it falls to a negligibly small value at about 10^{-3} cm. from the surface.[2] The Volta potential is the potential at a distance of about 10^{-3} cm. from the surface. There is no appreciable indefiniteness in this, provided that there is no other charged conductor within a distance of the first, comparable with 10^{-3} cm., since the potential alters but slowly in free space, in the absence of other charged conductors close at hand.

The Volta potential difference between two phases α and β is $V^{\alpha}-V^{\beta}$; it is sometimes called the external contact potential, more commonly simply the *contact potential*.

The internal potential, ϕ, must next be mentioned; it symbolizes the supposed electrical potential *inside* a phase. The difference between the

lomb's inverse square law. There is, of course, no fundamental difference in origin between these chemical forces, which are due largely to permanent or induced dipoles in the molecules, and the pure electrostatic forces due to an excess or deficiency of electrons in the charged particles. Both are electrical in the last analysis. But the 'chemical' group of forces are of short range, obeying an inverse sixth power law approximately; the electrostatic forces are of long range; further, an external electrostatic field acts on charged particles through their susceptibility to electrostatic forces, but does not react with a 'chemical' field of force.

[1] Provided that the phase is a conductor. The image force on a dielectric of constant D is $\frac{D-1}{D+1}\cdot\frac{e^2}{4r^2}$.

[2] Cf. Schottky and Rothe, *Wien-Harms Handb. d. Experimentalphysik*, **13**, pt. 2, 145 ff. (1928).

internal potentials for two phases is called the 'Galvani' potential, $\phi^\alpha - \phi^\beta$. It is unfortunately an indefinite quantity, being the sum of the electrostatic potential outside a phase, and the *electrostatic* part of the work required to take electrons from the interior, through the double layer at the surface and past the range of the image forces, to the point outside at which the electrostatic potential is measured. There is no known means of distinguishing between the 'electrostatic' part of the work of extraction of an electron, and the 'chemical' part, due to the difference in chemical environment of the electrons in the interior of the phase and outside. Owing to their indefiniteness,[1] the internal potential and the Galvani potential difference are unsatisfactory quantities to use; but they are so frequently either referred to explicitly, or indicated vaguely as the electrical potential inside the metal,[2] or the potential difference between two phases, that they must be mentioned here.

If ψ^α is written for the electrostatic part of the work of extraction of electrons, in volts, from α, then

$$\phi^\alpha = V^\alpha + \psi^\alpha, \tag{1}$$

but both ϕ^α and ψ^α are indefinite.

A much more important quantity, because it is a definite and measurable potential (apart from an arbitrary additive constant common to all thermodynamic potentials) is the 'electrochemical' potential $\bar{\mu}_i^\alpha$, of a specified constituent i in the phase α.[3] It is the quantity which corresponds, in analytical thermodynamics, for a charged component, to the 'chemical potential', μ_k, of an uncharged component k, and is a measure of the escaping tendency of the charged component i from the phase α. If G is the Gibbs free energy, $E + PV - TS$, E being the total energy of the phase and S its entropy, then according to the usual definition of chemical potential,

$$\bar{\mu}_i^\alpha = \left(\frac{\partial G}{\partial n_i^\alpha}\right)_{T, P, n_j}, \tag{2}$$

n_i^α being the total number of moles of i in the phase; the suffix n_j indicates that the composition of the phase remains unaltered except in respect of i. Thus $\bar{\mu}_i^\alpha \, dn_i^\alpha$ is the reversible work that must be done to introduce dn_i^α moles of i into α, at constant temperature and pressure, no other components being introduced or removed.

Like other thermodynamic quantities the electrochemical potential is usually expressed in ergs per *mole*. We shall use electrical units (volts generally) for the other potentials, V, ϕ, ψ, and χ, the total work of

[1] For another discussion of the various kinds of potential, see Lange, *Wien-Harms Handb. d. Experimentalphysik*, **12**, pt. 2, 267 ff. (1933).

[2] Many writers on electrochemistry, perhaps most, refer to the electrical potential of a phase, particularly of an electrode, as if it was common knowledge what this means. This seems scarcely satisfactory, but as most electrochemical phenomena are concerned with the sum of two or more phase boundary potentials, the indefiniteness does not usually matter, in the final discussion of electromotive forces.

[3] Cf. Guggenheim, *Modern Thermodynamics* (1933), esp. chap. x.

extraction of electrons from the phase to outside space. In units of work per mole, the electrical units must be multiplied by $z_i \mathfrak{F}$, z_i being the valency of the component considered, and $\mathfrak{F}$ the Faraday, 9,650 absolute electromagnetic units (96,500 coulombs).

The electrochemical potential refers to a specified charged component, an ion, or an electron. The relation between the electrochemical potential of electrons within the phase α, and the electrostatic potential V^α, is undetermined unless an arbitrary zero is fixed for the thermodynamic quantity, the electrochemical potential. If we fix as zero for the electrochemical potential, that of electrons in a gas, in which the charges are separated by distances so great that forces between them are negligible, the work done in bringing up δn moles of electrons to the point just outside the phase α is $-V^\alpha \mathfrak{F}\, \delta n$, and the work done in taking the electrons from this point into the metal is $-\chi^\alpha \delta n$, where χ^α is the thermionic work function, or work required to extract electrons, measured in electrical units. Adopting this convention as to the zero, we have

$$\bar{\mu}_\epsilon^\alpha = -\mathfrak{F}(V^\alpha + \chi^\alpha), \tag{3}$$

but it would be more usual to add an arbitrary constant, $\bar{\mu}_\epsilon^0$, to the right-hand side of (3), thus

$$\bar{\mu}_\epsilon^\alpha = -\mathfrak{F}(V^\alpha + \chi^\alpha) - \bar{\mu}_\epsilon^0. \tag{3.1}$$

The practice of using, when speaking of charged components, a separate symbol, $\bar{\mu}$, and name, electrochemical potential, for the quantity formally identical with the chemical potential of an uncharged component, is of fairly recent origin,[1] but has considerable advantages. There is an important difference between the escaping tendencies of charged, and of uncharged, components; that of uncharged components is independent of any uniform electric field that may be imposed on the system, but the escaping tendency of a charged component depends on the electrical potential and is influenced by an external potential gradient. Very often the electrochemical potential is formally written in two parts, an electrical term, and a 'chemical' term, thus

$$\bar{\mu}_i^\alpha = \mu_i^\alpha + z_i \mathfrak{F} \phi^\alpha, \tag{4}$$

ϕ^α being as before the internal, but undefined, electric potential in the phase α. z_i is the valency, negative for negatively charged components. This division of the electrochemical potential into two parts has been discussed, particularly by Guggenheim, and it is very doubtful if there is any real possibility of making the division definite. It is well known that there exists no means of measuring the single *electrical* potential difference between the interiors of two phases in contact, and the difficulty of even *defining* this was recognized by Gibbs,[2] who wrote in 1899: 'the consideration of the electrical potential in the electrolyte, and especially of the difference of potential in electrolyte and electrode, involves the consideration of quantities of which we have no apparent means of physical measurement, while the difference of potential in pieces of metal of the same kind attached to the electrodes is exactly one of the things which we can and do measure.'

The condition for equilibrium between two phases α and β, in respect

[1] Cf. Brönsted, *Z. physikal. Chem.* A, **143**, 301 (1929); Guggenheim, *J. Physical Chem.*, **33**, 842 (1929); **34**, 1540 (1930).
[2] *Works*, **1**, 429.

of the charged component i, is that the electrochemical potentials should be equal:

$$\bar{\mu}_i^\alpha = \bar{\mu}_i^\beta, \tag{5}$$

or

$$\mu_i^\alpha + z_i \mathfrak{F}\phi^\alpha = \mu_i^\beta + z_i \mathfrak{F}\phi^\beta, \tag{5.1}$$

$$\phi^\alpha - \phi^\beta = \frac{\mu_i^\beta - \mu_i^\alpha}{z_i \mathfrak{F}}. \tag{5.2}$$

Equation (5.2) formally defines the Galvani potential difference between two phases. But there is in general no means of determining the chemical potentials μ_i^α and μ_i^β, and the Galvani potential difference between the phases is not usually definable. If the phases are of practically identical composition, α and α' differing only in the exceedingly small amount of one or more charged components required to give the two phases different potentials, then $\Delta\phi$ has a meaning; there is not, however, equilibrium, and

$$\Delta\phi = \phi^\alpha - \phi^{\alpha'} = \frac{\bar{\mu}_i^\alpha - \bar{\mu}_i^{\alpha'}}{z\mathfrak{F}}.$$

This case is of great practical importance, as the real terminals of any galvanic cell are of the same metal, in which there is a difference of potential set up by the difference in escaping tendencies of the charged components across the phase boundaries present in the interior of the cell.

If two regions are not identical in composition, but can both be treated as ideal solutions in the same solvent, we can write for the case when the electrochemical potentials are equal

$$\phi^\alpha - \phi^\beta = \frac{\mu_i^\beta - \mu_i^\alpha}{z_i \mathfrak{F}} = \frac{RT}{z_i \mathfrak{F}} \log \frac{N_i^\beta}{N_i^\alpha}, \tag{5.3}$$

N_i being the mole fraction of i in the phase indicated.

(5.3) gives the 'membrane potential' between two ideal solutions of different strengths in the same solvent, separated by a membrane permeable to the component i only.

The electrons inside a metal are distributed among a number of energy levels, the number in each level being determined by the Fermi-Dirac statistics; these levels are represented diagrammatically in Fig. 48. For determining the escaping tendency of the electrons from the metal, the only important level is the uppermost, as we shall see in the next paragraph.

In studies on electron diffraction, however, yet another 'potential' is considered, called the 'mean inner potential'. The metal may be considered as a potential box, the distance of the uppermost level below the potential just outside the metal, V, the electrostatic potential already referred to, being equal to χ, the thermionic work function. The lowest level (at low temperatures) is, according to the new statistics, a distance below the upper equal to $[\mu]$, where

$$[\mu] = \frac{h^2}{8m}\left(\frac{3n}{\pi}\right)^{\frac{2}{3}}, \tag{6}$$[1]

[1] Cf. Sommerfeld, *Z. Physik*, **47**, 1 (1928); Nordheim, *ibid.*, **46**, 833 (1928); *Physikal. Z.*, **30**, 177 (1929); *Proc. Roy. Soc.* A, **121**, 626 (1928); Fowler, *Proc. Roy. Soc.* A, **117**, 549 (1928); **122**, 36 (1929); Fowler and Nordheim, *ibid.*, **119**, 173 (1928).

and the 'inner potential' of the metal is

$$\Phi = [\mu]+\chi. \tag{7}$$

Φ is found by observations of the refraction of electrons at the surface of solids;[1] recent measurements[2] of the inner potential in this way give values from 7 to 13 volts for various non-metallic crystals; metals gave the following values, aluminium 17, nickel 16·5, silver, gold 14, copper 13, lead 11, zirconium 10 volts, with an uncertainty of one or two volts at least.

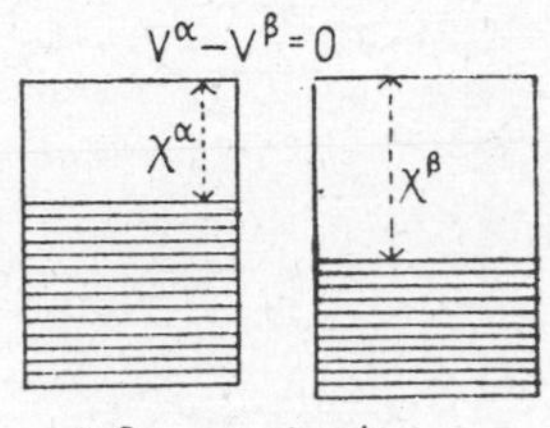

The inner potential, referring as it does to an energy level of the electrons far below the uppermost, is of no importance for the escaping tendency of electrons or ions, and therefore not for phase boundary potentials either. It need not be further considered here.

To sum up, there are two potentials which are definite; V, the electrostatic potential in empty, or nearly empty, space just outside the phase; and $\bar{\mu}_i$ the thermodynamic electrochemical potential of a charged component i. Both of these quantities contain an arbitrary constant, the zero from which the potentials are measured, but differences of either the electrostatic potential or of the electrochemical potential, between two phases, are definite. The thermionic work function, χ, the work required to extract electrons from the highest energy level within the phase, to a state of rest just outside the phase, is also definite; and the relation between the three definite quantities $\bar{\mu}_\epsilon$, V, and χ is given by (3.1), where $\bar{\mu}_\epsilon^0$ is the electrochemical potential of electrons very widely separated from all other charges. The internal electric potential ϕ, and other expressions relating to the electrical part of the potential inside a phase containing dense matter, are undefined, and so are the differences of these quantities between two phases of different composition. This indefiniteness arises from the impossibility of separating the electrostatic part of the forces between particles, from the 'chemical', or more complex interactions between electrons and atomic nuclei, when both types of force are present.

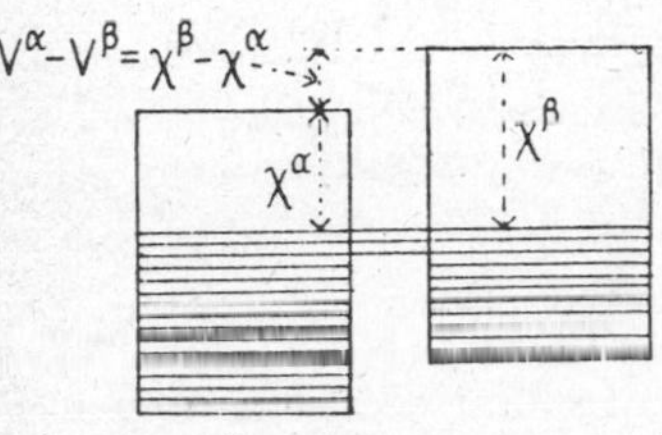

FIG. 48.

Hence, in speaking of phase boundary potentials, we are wise to refer to the Volta potentials, $V^\alpha - V^\beta$; except in the case when the two phases are of identical composition materially, such as the two terminal copper wires of an electrolytic cell. Here it may safely be assumed that, what-

[1] Davisson and Germer, *Physical Rev.*, **30**, 705 (1927); *Proc. Nat. Acad. Sci.*, **14**, 619 (1928). Bethe, *Ann. Physik*, **87**, 55 (1928); Eckart, *Proc. Nat. Acad. Sci.*, **13**, 460 (1927).

[2] Rupp, *Ann. Physik*, **1**, 801 (1929); **5**, 453 (1930); Farnsworth, *Physical Rev.*, **40**, 684 (1932). Tillman, *Phil. Mag.*, **18**, 656 (1934); Laschkarew, *Trans. Faraday Soc.*, **31**, 1081 (1935).

ever be the division into chemical and electrostatic forces, it will be the same for both phases, so that the difference of internal potential, the 'Galvani' potential difference, has the same value as the Volta potential difference.

3. Thermionic work function: contact potential. Representing two different metals α and β, initially separate and each at zero electrostatic potential, by the diagram in Fig. 48 *a*, in which the ordinates are the energy levels of electrons, we see that the energy level of the electrons in α is higher than that in β by the difference between the thermionic work functions, $\chi^{\beta}-\chi^{\alpha}$. On connecting the two metals, as in Fig. 48 *b*, the difference in energy levels causes electrons to flow from the metal having the smaller value of χ, to that with the greater. The flow continues until the energy levels are equalized, thus raising the energy level of an electron just outside β relative to that of one just outside α by $\chi^{\beta}-\chi^{\alpha}$; as the electrons carry a negative charge the electrostatic potential of α becomes positive to that of β. This difference in electrostatic potential caused by the difference in escaping tendency of the metals, due to the difference in the amounts of work required to extract electrons from the metals, is the *contact potential*

$$V^{\alpha}-V^{\beta} = \chi^{\beta}-\chi^{\alpha}. \tag{8}$$

There is a small correction to equation (8), for the Peltier electromotive force between the metals,[1] which arises from differences in the concentrations of electrons in the upper levels of the two metals, when not at absolute zero; its value is of the order 10^{-2} volts, and may be neglected for most purposes.

The existence of a contact potential between two different metals was recognized over a century ago by Volta, who ascribed the origin of the electromotive force of galvanic cells to it. This point of view receded somewhat into the background in the later decades of last century, but is now re-established, as will be seen in § 5. It is not very easy to demonstrate the existence of this contact potential; and its actual value depends very much on the cleanliness of the surface; indeed without very careful cleaning of the surface, and removal of surface films, which requires a high standard of vacuum technique, the true value for the clean metal can scarcely be obtained at all.

There are three principal methods for measuring the contact potential, i.e. the difference of electrostatic potential between two points in space, each just outside one of the metals. Volta,[2] and later Kelvin,[3] used a condenser method, depending on the fact that if the distance between the plates of a condenser is altered, when they are at different potentials, current flows from one and to the other. The two metals are made the plates of an adjustable condenser, and are put into contact; they then assume a potential difference equal to the Volta potential. After breaking the contact, the distance between the plates is altered, when current

[1] Cf. J. Rice, *Commentary on Gibbs' Works* (1937).

[2] *Ann. Chim. Phys.*, **40**, 225 (1801).

[3] *Phil. Mag.*, **46**, 91 (1898).

detectable by an electrometer flows to or from the plates. If now the plates are put into contact, not directly, but with a potentiometer intervening, it is possible to adjust the potential applied to the plates, by the potentiometer, so that no current flows when the distance between the plates is varied. The potential which has to be applied by the potentiometer to achieve this is equal and opposite to the contact potential.

A very sensitive modification of this method has been described by Zisman;[1] one of the plates is made to vibrate rapidly parallel to itself, thus periodically altering the distance between the plates. The oscillating current thus caused to flow to and from the plate is amplified and operates a loud speaker. A potentiometer is used to vary the potential applied to the plates, until the sound vanishes, and the value of the applied potential is then the contact potential.

Another method for measuring Volta potentials is to ionize the air between the plates, and adjust the potential applied to them until no current passes across the air gap. This method appears to have been used first by Righi[2] (with ultra-violet rays as a source of ionization), later by Perrin and many later workers, using radium salts;[3] Greinacher,[4] and Anderson and Morrison,[5] pointed out that errors frequently arose if sources capable of ionizing the air in other parts of the apparatus than directly between the plates; and it is well to use either a carefully shielded source of β or γ rays; or a radioactive source such as polonium, which gives off only α rays which have a range of a few centimetres only. This method is that used for the determination of the 'surface potentials' of insoluble films as described in Chapter II.

There are also numerous methods depending on the measurement of the potential differences which must be applied to various parts of a thermionic valve in order to prevent, or otherwise modify, the flow of electrons from the hot filament; these have been briefly summarized by Oatley[6] in a recent paper; this author describes a new method based on the measurement of the magnetic field requisite to prevent the passage of electrons from a straight hot filament, placed axially inside a cylinder, to the cylinder.

Table XVI gives recent values of the thermionic work functions for several clean metals; and also (for discussion later) the accepted values of the standard electrode potential of the metal in contact with an 'activity molar' aqueous solution of one of its salts, where the concentration is such that the activity coefficient multiplied by the molarity is unity.

For details of theories as to the nature of the forces retaining electrons within metals, and the manner in which these vary with the distance from the material surface, the reader must consult treatises on thermionic

[1] *Rev. Sci. Inst.*, **3**, 367 (1932).
[2] *J. Phys. Rad.*, **7**, 153 (1888).
[3] Cf. refs. quoted by Lange, *Wien-Harms Handb. d. Experimentalphysik*, **12**, pt. 2, 308 (1933); or Whalley and Rideal, *Proc. Roy. Soc.* A, **140**, 484 (1933).
[4] *Ann. Physik*, **16**, 708 (1905).
[5] *Phil. Mag.*, **24**, 302 (1912).
[6] *Proc. Roy. Soc.* A, **155**, 218 (1936).

emission.[1] In the case of clean metals, there are at least two principal forces; the 'image' forces, due to the attraction between the electron just escaping from the surface and its electrical image, or resultant of the

TABLE XVI

Thermionic work functions, χ, and standard electrode potentials E_H on the hydrogen scale, for clean metals.*

Metal	χ	E_H	$\chi - E_H$
	Volts		
Lithium	2·28	−2·96	5·2
Sodium	2·46	−2·71	5·2
Potassium	2·24	−2·92	5·2
Rubidium	2·16	−2·92	5·1
Caesium	1·81	..	..
Calcium	2·24	−2·76	5·0
Barium	2·1	−1·57	3·7
Magnesium	2·42	−1·6	4·0
Zinc	3·5	−0·76	4·3
Thorium	3·38	..	..
Copper	4·3	+0·34	4·0
Silver	4·7	+0·80	3·9
Gold	4·9	+1·36	3·5
Tungsten	4·54	..	..
Molybdenum	4·3	..	..
Mercury	4·5	+0·80	..
Iron	4·7	−0·44	5·1
Cobalt	4·25	−0·29	4·6
Nickel	5·0	−0·23	5·2
Platinum	6·3	..	..
Palladium	5·0	..	..
Rhodium	c. 5·0	..	..
Osmium	4·7	..	..

* The work functions have been taken from various treatises on thermionic emission; the electrode potentials from *International Critical Tables*, and Glasstone's *Electrochemistry of Solutions*. The *methods* of determining the work function can be found in most books on thermionic emission, and need not be indicated here.

charges induced in the metal by displacement of electrons in the metal; and the forces necessary to pass the potential barrier caused by a natural electrical double layer in the surface. The image force becomes negligible at a distance of about 10^{-4} cm. from the surface; its value is $\epsilon^2/4x^2$, where x is the distance from the surface and ϵ the charge on the electron. If such a law of force held right up to contact with the surface, the image force would become infinite just at the point of emergence from the metal, so

[1] e.g. Reimann, *Thermionic Emission* (Chapman & Hall, 1934); Schottky and Rothe, *Wien-Harms Handb. d. Experimentalphysik*, **13**, 2 (1928); de Boer, *Electron Emission and Adsorption Phenomena* (Cambridge, 1935); Dushman, *Rev. Mod. Physics*, **2**, 381 (1930); Compton and Langmuir, *ibid.*, **2**, 136 (1930); T. J. Jones, *Thermionic Emission* (Methuen, 1935).

that the work of extraction of electrons would be infinite. The reason why this is not so is that, owing to the discrete atomic structure of the metal, the force cannot be regarded as a simple image force when the electron is within a few atomic diameters of the surface.

Compton and Langmuir consider that the law of force $F(x)$ between the electron and the surface is of the form shown in Fig. 49; the dotted line shows the course of a law of force on the image theory alone. At a certain distance from the surface the attraction on the electron becomes less than that required by the simple image force, reaches a maximum, and then gradually falls to zero as the interior of the metal is approached.

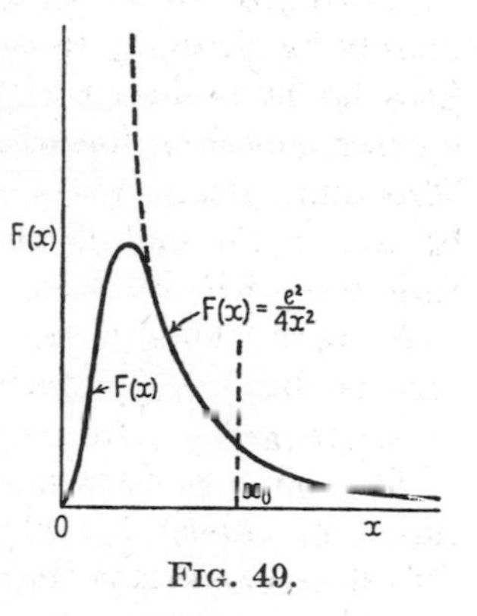

FIG. 49.

The double layer at the surface is sometimes regarded[1,2] as arising from the electrons having a greater tendency to escape than the positive ions; they are, therefore, considered to be slightly farther out, and the double layer might be regarded as a kind of 'adsorption potential' due to adsorption of free electrons from the interior of the metal at the surface. These conceptions are somewhat crude, however, and the point where the force due to the double layer can be replaced by an 'image' force does not yet seem clearly defined.

When surface films of foreign substances are present, the distribution of electrons and positively charged particles on the surface depends on the relative affinity of the positive ions of the metal, and the atoms in the surface film, for electrons, and in general an additional double layer is produced by the surface film. If this has the negative side outwards, it increases the work of extraction of electrons; if the positive side is outwards, the work of extraction is decreased.

4. Influence of surface films on the work function and contact potentials. Richardson[3] early recognized that the contact potential, and the emission of electrons, are profoundly influenced by the presence of surface films, and saw the necessity of using the best possible vacua in the study of these quantities. The most commonly occurring gas films decrease the emission, increasing the work function; thus a monatomic layer of oxygen on tungsten was shown by Langmuir[4] to reduce the emission to less than one hundred-thousandth of its value for the clean metal surface, at 1,500° K., a temperature at which the monatomic layer of oxygen is quite stable on the metal.

Other gases containing oxygen have a similar effect, probably because

[1] Cf. Brillouin, *Statistiques Quantiques*, **2**, 229 (1930).
[2] Frenkel, *Phil. Mag.*, **33**, 297 (1917); *Z. Physik*, **51**, 232 (1928).
[3] *Phil. Trans.*, **201**, 497 (1903).
[4] *Physical Rev.*, **2**, 402, 450 (1913); *Physikal. Z.*, **15**, 516 (1914).

they are decomposed by the hot tungsten, giving a monatomic layer of oxygen on the surface.

Rideal, Whalley, and Jacobs[1] find marked effects of oxygen on the contact potentials of gold and platinum; iodine also has a similar effect on several metals, and on the contact potential between cuprous iodide and the vapour phase.

Hydrogen, however, often increases the emission; it may sometimes act merely by cleaning up traces of oxygen on the surface, but Suhrmann and Csesch[2] have shown that, when chemisorbed in the atomic form, it increases emission, lowering the work function by two or even more volts. This diminution in the work function by hydrogen only occurs in the case of the noble metals such as platinum; hydrogen increases the work function with the less noble metals such as aluminium. It is, indeed, only by extremely careful out-gassing that the correct value of 6·3 volts can be obtained for platinum.[3]

Argon and mercury vapour appear to have no effect on the emission.

The more reactive metals, which have themselves a low work function, have an enormous effect in reducing the work function of tungsten. Of these, the most important are caesium, barium, and thorium. They act best in a layer one atom thick; but they have a very considerable effect even with incomplete monatomic layers. The effect of thorium was discovered through the accidental presence of this element in certain tungsten wires; thoria had been incorporated to assist the drawing process of the wires and the thorium was subsequently liberated and diffused slowly to the surface of the filament. Such thorium coated wires can be operated at a temperature of about 1,900° K., some 500° lower than that necessary for pure tungsten filaments, and at this temperature the thorium evaporates so slowly that the filaments last for thousands of hours. The energy required to operate the thoriated filament is less than one-third of that required for a pure tungsten filament, on account of the lower temperature.[4]

Caesium increases the electron emission even more than thorium,[5] but its adhesion to a *clean* tungsten surface is not so good, although (owing to the fact that the caesium atoms lose their valency electrons to the tungsten, because the ionizing potential of caesium is less than the work function of tungsten) the adhesion is surprisingly high for so volatile a metal. If the temperature is so high that the caesium does not adhere, every atom which touches the tungsten comes off as a positive ion.

The adhesion of caesium to tungsten may be improved, and at the same time the work function still further diminished, if the tungsten is first covered with a layer of oxygen one atom thick. The behaviour of barium

[1] *Proc. Roy. Soc.* A, **140**, 484 (1933). [2] *Z. physikal. Chem.* B, **28**, 215 (1935).

[3] Dubridge, *Physical Rev.*, **31**, 236; **32**, 961 (1928).

[4] Langmuir and Rogers, *U.S. Patents*, 1,244,216, (1917); Langmuir, *Physical Rev.*, **22**, 357 (1923).

[5] Langmuir and Kingdon, *Science*, **57**, 58 (1923); *Proc. Roy. Soc.* A, **107**, 61 (1925).

on tungsten is generally similar to that of caesium, and layers of this metal, with or without an intermediate layer of oxygen, have been extensively studied by Ryde and Harris,[1] several alternating layers of metal and oxygen being obtainable.

The improvement in emission with any of these atomic layers begins when quite a small proportion of the surface is covered, increasing to a maximum at a point which is usually considered to correspond to the complete covering of the surface by a layer one atom thick; some authorities, however, hold that the maximum emission is reached before the surface is completely covered.[2] The variation of the emission with the potential field applied leads to the conclusion that all parts of the surface are not equal in emitting power, with metals covered by these layers, and that the surface consists of patches of differing nature;[3] a conclusion not unlikely in view of the well-known heterogeneity of solid surfaces.

Approximate values for the work function of tungsten covered by different types of layer are as follows.

Work functions of tungsten covered by layers one or two atoms thick.

Surface	χ (*volts*)
Clean W	4·54
W–O	9·23
W–Th (half covered)*	3·20
W–Th	2·63
W–Cs	1·6
W–O–Cs	0·71
W–Ba	1·56
W–O–Ba	1·34

* Cf. Brattain and Becker, *Physical Rev.*, **43**, 428 (1933).

These layers on the surface of metals have very great technical importance; some papers by Langmuir and his colleagues[4] may also be consulted.

The effect of these atomic layers of foreign atoms adhering to the surface is undoubtedly due to an alteration in the strength of the double layer at the surface of the metal. If positive ions of a metal identical with the underlying metal are deposited on its surface, and the deficiency in electrons made up by supply through a wire, which is essentially what occurs in electrodeposition of a metal on the same metal, the free electrons flow out to the new surface layers, and the strength of the double layer at the surface is not altered by the new surface layer. But if the metal deposited on the surface has a smaller affinity for electrons than the

[1] Cf. Reimann, *Thermionic Emission*, 159 ff. (1934).

[2] Cf. Taylor and Langmuir, *Physical Rev.*, **44**, 423 (1933).

[3] Langmuir, *Gen. Elec. Rev.*, **23**, 504 (1920); cf. Compton and Langmuir, *Rev. Mod. Physics*, **2**, 150 ff. (1930).

[4] *Ind. Eng. Chem.*, **22**, 390 (1930); *Gen. Elec. Rev.* (1935), 402; *J.A.C.S.* (1931), 486; (1932), 1252; *Physical Rev.*, **40**, 463 (1932); **43**, 224 (1933); **44**, 423 (1933).

underlying metal, it will tend to lose its valency electrons to the lower layers, and a double layer, positive outwards, will be set up. This imposes a potential positive outwards, equal to the strength of the double layer, and thus lowers the work function.

In some cases the difference in affinity for electrons of the atoms of the surface layer and of the underlying metal is so great that every atom of the metal forming the surface layer becomes ionized on hitting the surface, and if it evaporates, does so as an ion.[1] In such cases the adhesion of the surface metal to the underlying metal is much assisted by the electrostatic attraction between the ionized surface atoms and the oppositely charged layer just below. It is not, however, necessary for adsorption of an electropositive metal that the valency electrons should leave it completely; a tendency to go over to the underlying atoms without passing completely out of the sphere of the surface atom produces a double layer positive outwards. The energy relationships which determine whether the valency electrons are completely or only partially removed into the tungsten has been discussed by de Boer,[2] and by Gurney.[3] It is, however, certain that a low ionization potential of the first valency electron, in the metal being adsorbed, does assist adsorption, and a high work function of the underlying metal does so also. Caesium is much less adsorbed on thoriated tungsten filaments than on clean tungsten.

Adsorbed layers of positive ions on metals are frequently termed 'adions', and the changes in the double layers caused by adsorption the 'polarization' of the surface.

Oxygen on tungsten is strongly negatively charged; the work function is increased by nearly 5 volts through its presence.

The ionized layers on the surface are fairly mobile; e.g. caesium, or barium, diffuse slowly along a heated metal surface, if deposited in a non-uniform manner, until the distribution is uniform all over the surface.[4] Also it appears that inversion of multiple layers may occasionally take place; thus Ryde and Harris[5] found that if a layer of barium on tungsten is exposed to oxygen, its emission first drops to a low value; but if such a filament, on which the coating is presumably W—Ba—O, reading from inside outwards, is heated for some time, the emission recovers and indeed improves up to the value characteristic of a W—O—Ba layer. The layers of barium and oxygen apparently change places without any appreciable loss of barium from the surface.

5. Contact of metals with electrolytes: electrode potentials. Metals consist of a space lattice of fixed, positively charged ions, and electrons free to move. Electrolytes contain no free electrons, but ions

[1] Langmuir and Kingdon, *Proc. Roy. Soc.* A, **107**, 61 (1925).

[2] *Electron Emission and Adsorption* (1935), p. 58.

[3] *Physical Rev.*, **47**, 479 (1935).

[4] Cf. Becker, *Trans. Am. Electrochem. Soc.*, **55**, 153 (1929); Langmuir and Taylor, *Physical Rev.*, **40**, 463 (1932); (Chap. VI, § 4).

[5] Cf. Reimann, *Thermionic Emission*, p. 169.

in a state of association with solvent molecules; in the case of aqueous electrolytes the ions are more or less hydrated. When a metal dips into an electrolyte the charged particles passing across the phase boundary are generally the positive metallic ions. The mechanism whereby the potential difference, between a metal such as copper, and a solution containing copper ions, is set up, is the passage of copper ions from the metal to the solution, or vice versa,[1] the phase boundary acting as a membrane permeable to positively charged ions only.

A metal can only pass into solution in water as positively charged, more or less hydrated ions. Consider the case of a copper electrode dipping into a solution containing copper ions. If the metal is insulated, electrons cannot pass to or from it. Positive ions are deposited on the metal from the solution, and leave the metal for the solution. If, initially, the rate of deposition of ions from the solution is less than the rate of passage from the metal into solution, the metal acquires a negative charge, and the solution a positive charge; the process of dissolution of the metal continues until a double layer of such strength is set up that the energy level of the hydrated ions in solution is raised, and that of the positive ions in the metal lowered, until these levels are equalized, and then ceases; in thermodynamic language, until the electrochemical potentials of the ions, in the metal and in the solution, become equal. The double layer consists, of course, of an accumulation of positive ions in the solution near the surface of the metal, and of electrons near the surface, inside the metal.

If the rate of deposition of ions is initially greater than their rate of passage from metal into solution, the metal becomes positively charged, a double layer being formed by attraction of anions to the surface on the water side and a repulsion of electrons from the surface on the metal side.

The process is essentially similar to that of the establishment of the contact potential between two metals in a vacuum; the equalization in the two phases of the energy levels (or electrochemical potentials), of the ion passing the phase boundary, establishes a definite difference in the electrostatic potentials of the metal and the electrolyte. The main difference from the case of simple contact potentials is that the energy level of the ion in solution is very largely determined by the energy of hydration.

The mechanism of the solution of the metal as ions has been discussed

[1] In some cases the phase boundary between metal and solution is passed by electrons; these electrons are not free in the solution, but bound to ions. The best-known cases are the oxidation-reduction electrodes, in which electrons passing from metal to solution alter the valency of ions in the solution; others are the equilibrium between non-metals, such as the halogens, and their anions in solution, established by the supply of electrons through a platinum or iridium wire in contact with the unionized halogen and the aqueous solution. Cf. chlorine electrodes (Glasstone, *Electrochemistry of Solutions*, 2nd ed., 337 (1937)), and iodine electrodes (Küster and Crotigno, *Z. anorg. Chem.*, **23**, 87 (1899)).

by Heyrowsky,[1] Rideal,[2] Butler,[3] Glasstone,[4] Gurney,[5] Fowler,[6] Uhara,[7] Belton,[8] and others. Gurney's discussion in his *Ions in Solution* is much the most comprehensive and illuminating.

If the difference in energy level between a free ion and one bound to the surface of the metal is Y, and the difference in level between a free ion and a hydrated one is W, then the difference in energy level between the hydrated ion, and the ion at the surface of the metal is $W-Y$. The energy level of the ions in solution depends, however, on the concentration of these ions; this produces the well-known effect of concentration on electromotive force. Gurney gives[9] the strength of the double layer, i.e. the difference in electrostatic potential set up between metal α and electrolyte s, as

$$V^{\alpha}-V^{s} = \frac{Y-W_0}{z\epsilon}+\frac{kT}{z\epsilon}\log_e fc. \tag{9}$$

z is the valency of the ion passing the boundary; ϵ the charge on the electron, k the gas constant per molecule, c the concentration and f the activity coefficient of the ion; W_0 is the energy of hydration of the ion in infinitely dilute solution.

(9) is of the same form as the usual equation showing the change of electrode potential with concentration,

$$V^{\alpha}-V^{s} = V_0+\frac{RT}{n\mathfrak{F}}\log_e fc, \tag{9.1}$$

but we now have a rational light on the meaning of the term V_0.

For the available methods for estimating Y and W_0, and some preliminary results, Chapter XIV of Gurney's book should be consulted.

The old conception of 'solution pressure' of a metal can now be replaced by this difference in energy levels between the positive ions in the metal and in the solution. In the metal the ions are held by chemical forces to the other positively charged ions, and by electrostatic forces to the electrons; or perhaps it would be more correct to say that the electrons neutralize the electrostatic forces of repulsion which would otherwise tend to drive the positive ions apart. In the solution, they are bound to solvent molecules. It is therefore the pull on the ions caused by the difference in energy levels in the solution, and in the metal, that tends to drag the metal ions into solution.

In the light of modern knowledge as to the structure of metals, the term 'solution pressure', suggesting a vigorous kinetic agitation of the metallic ions in the metal, is rather inapt, and might as well be dropped, since the metallic ions are fixed. If any constituent of the metal can be said to have a pressure, it is the electrons rather than the metallic ions, for in the upper energy levels at least, these are in motion.

[1] *Proc. Roy. Soc.* A, **102**, 608 (1923).
[2] *Trans. Faraday Soc.*, **19**, 667 (1924).
[3] *Ibid.*, **19**, 729 (1924).
[4] *Electrochemistry of Solutions*, 2nd ed., 361 (1937).
[5] *Proc. Roy. Soc.* A, **136**, 378 (1932); *Ions in Solution* (Cambridge, 1936).
[6] *Trans. Faraday Soc.*, **28**, 368 (1932).
[7] *Phil. Mag.*, **21**, 958 (1936).
[8] *Ibid.*, **21**, 1140 (1936).
[9] *Ions in Solution*, p. 87.

A single electrode potential, if defined as the difference in electrostatic potential between the spaces just outside the metal and the solution, is definite, but it cannot be measured by merely connecting up the phases with wires, and adjusting a potentiometer, until no current flows; for this connexion introduces more than one phase boundary. Practically all electrolytic cells consist of at least three phase boundaries; and the terminals at which the electromotive force of the cell is measured are, finally, of the same metal. There may, of course, be any greater number of phase boundaries. A simple type of cell consists of two metals, M^α and M^β, dipping into a solution S containing the ions of each metal.

$$\begin{array}{ccccccc} V^\alpha & & V^S & & V^\beta & & V^{\alpha'} \\ M^\alpha & | & \text{Solution} & | & M^\beta & | & M^{\alpha'} \end{array} \tag{C. 1}$$

Let the terminals of the cell be of the same metal, M^α, as one of the electrodes. The electrostatic potentials, when the cell has reached equilibrium with the terminals disconnected from each other, are indicated above the phases; there are three phase boundary potentials concerned in producing the final difference of potential, $V^\alpha - V^{\alpha'}$, between the terminals. These are $V^\alpha - V^S$, $-(V^\beta - V^S)$, and the metal-metal contact potential $V^\beta - V^{\alpha'}$; their algebraic sum is the difference in electrostatic potential of the terminal wires. It is the electromotive force of the whole cell, and can, of course, be measured with a potentiometer.

If M^α is copper and M^β zinc, the equations giving the Volta potential differences at the three phase boundaries are

$$V^{\mathrm{Cu}} - V^S = \frac{1}{2\epsilon}\{Y_{\mathrm{Cu}} - W_{0\,\mathrm{Cu}} + kT\log_e f_{\mathrm{Cu}}\,c_{\mathrm{Cu}}\} \tag{9.2}$$

$$V^S - V^{\mathrm{Zn}} = \frac{1}{2\epsilon}\{-(Y_{\mathrm{Zn}} - W_{0\,\mathrm{Zn}}) - kT\log_e f_{\mathrm{Zn}}\,c_{\mathrm{Zn}}\} \tag{9.3}$$

$$V^{\mathrm{Zn}} - V^{\mathrm{Cu}'} = \chi^{\mathrm{Cu}} - \chi^{\mathrm{Zn}} \tag{9.4}$$

and the e.m.f. of the cell, from left to right outside the cell, is the sum of these, i.e.

$$\mathfrak{E} = \chi^{\mathrm{Cu}} - \chi^{\mathrm{Zn}} + \frac{1}{2\epsilon}\left\{(Y_{\mathrm{Cu}} - W_{0\,\mathrm{Cu}}) - (Y_{\mathrm{Zn}} - W_{0\,\mathrm{Zn}}) + kT\log_e\frac{f_{\mathrm{Cu}}\,c_{\mathrm{Cu}}}{f_{\mathrm{Zn}}\,c_{\mathrm{Zn}}}\right\}. \tag{9.5}$$

Guggenheim has expressed[1] the electromotive force of the cell (C. 1) in terms of the thermodynamic 'electrochemical potentials'. The final result is

$$\mathfrak{E} = \frac{1}{2\mathfrak{F}}\left\{\mu^{\mathrm{Zn}}_{\mathrm{Zn}} - \mu^{\mathrm{Cu}}_{\mathrm{Cu}} + \bar{\mu}^0_{\mathrm{Cu}''} - \bar{\mu}^0_{\mathrm{Zn}''} + RT\log_e\frac{f_{\mathrm{Cu}''}\,c_{\mathrm{Cu}''}}{f_{\mathrm{Zn}''}\,c_{\mathrm{Zn}''}}\right\}, \tag{10}$$

where $\bar{\mu}^0_{\mathrm{Cu}''}$, $\bar{\mu}^0_{\mathrm{Zn}''}$ are the electrochemical potentials of the ions in solution, at unit activity, and $\mu^{\mathrm{Zn}}_{\mathrm{Zn}}$, $\mu^{\mathrm{Cu}}_{\mathrm{Cu}}$ are the chemical potentials of neutral zinc and copper in the metals. These are related to the electrochemical potentials of the ions and electrons in the metal thus:

$$\mu^{\mathrm{Zn}}_{\mathrm{Zn}} = \bar{\mu}^{\mathrm{Zn}}_{\mathrm{Zn}''} + 2\bar{\mu}^{\mathrm{Zn}}_{\epsilon} \tag{11}$$

[1] *Modern Thermodynamics*, pp. 144 ff.

so that

$$\mathfrak{E} = \frac{1}{\mathfrak{F}}(\bar{\mu}_{\epsilon}^{\mathrm{Zn}} - \bar{\mu}_{\epsilon}^{\mathrm{Cu}}) + \frac{1}{2\mathfrak{F}}\left\{\bar{\mu}_{\mathrm{Zn}''}^{\mathrm{Zn}} - \bar{\mu}_{\mathrm{Cu}''}^{\mathrm{Cu}} + \bar{\mu}_{\mathrm{Cu}''}^{0} - \bar{\mu}_{\mathrm{Zn}''}^{0} + RT\log_e \frac{f_{\mathrm{Cu}}\,c_{\mathrm{Cu}}}{f_{\mathrm{Zn}}\,c_{\mathrm{Zn}}}\right\}. \quad (10.5)$$

Comparing (9.5) with (10.5), we see the correlation of the quantities χ, and $Y - W_0$, with the thermodynamic potentials (escaping tendencies) of the ions and electrons. The signs are naturally opposite (the arbitrary zeros of measurements do not appear), and the appearance of R and $\mathfrak{F}$ in (10.5) instead of k and ϵ is due to the thermodynamic quantities being measured in moles instead of molecules.

In most books on electrochemistry, when writing a cell such as the above, only the two metal-electrolyte junctions are mentioned, the final metal to metal junction being taken for granted. The 'standard electrode potentials' of electrochemistry include one such metal to metal junction implicitly. On the 'hydrogen scale' these are the electromotive forces of cells consisting of a standard half cell, hydrogen and platinum, dipping into a solution with hydrogen ion at unit activity, and a half cell of the metal in question dipping into a solution of its ions, of unit activity, after correcting for liquid-liquid junction potentials. The cell

$$\mathrm{Pt} \mid \mathrm{Zn} \mid \mathrm{ZnSO_4} \mid \mathrm{H_2SO_4} \mid \mathrm{H_2Pt} \quad \text{(C. 2)}$$

both solutions having the cation at unit activity, has an e.m.f. of $-0{\cdot}76$ volts. It is written here in an unusual way, with platinum terminals at each end of the cell, to show that a platinum-zinc contact potential, as well as the zinc-zinc sulphate potential, is included in the so-called single electrode potential of zinc. In tabulating electrode potentials on the hydrogen scale the contribution of the activity normal hydrogen electrode is arbitrarily taken as zero; and the sum of the two phase boundary potentials, platinum-metal,[1] and metal-solution, is what is written as the electrode potential of that metal.

Langmuir,[2] in considering the importance of contact potentials for electrolytic cells, pointed out in 1916 that there is a general parallelism between the thermionic work function and the standard electrode potentials. This is shown in Table XVI, where the last column gives the difference between the electrode potential, on the normal hydrogen scale, and the work function. This difference varies much less than the values of either the work function, or the electrode potentials, separately.

It follows that the contact potential between the two metals (difference between the work functions) is the principal factor determining the e.m.f. of galvanic cells consisting of two metals; it is generally decidedly larger than the difference between the two electrode-electrolyte potentials, $V^{\alpha} - V^{S}$, and $V^{\beta} - V^{S}$.

The discussion just given applies to cells in which the terminals are not

[1] If the terminal metals are made, as they usually will be, of a metal other than platinum, no difference is made to this argument; if of copper, a platinum-copper contact potential is added to the right-hand end of this chain of phases, and a copper-zinc one is substituted for a platinum-zinc one at the left-hand end. The difference between the copper-zinc and the copper-platinum contact potentials is equal to the zinc-platinum contact potential, so that the e.m.f. of the cell is unaffected. It is always the platinum-metal contact potential that is included.

[2] *Trans. Am. Electrochem. Soc.*, **29**, 176 (1916).

connected to each other. If now the terminals are connected, electrons will flow from one to the other; in the cell (C. 1) above, if V^{α} is a higher electrostatic potential than $V^{\alpha'}$, electrons will flow from the right-hand terminal to the left, outside the cell. This flow of current immediately upsets the equilibrium of all the double layers in the cell. Electrons flow from M^{β} to $M^{\alpha'}$, positive ions of M^{β} leave the metal, which has now become an anode, for the solution; and positive ions of M^{α} are deposited on the left hand electrode. All these flows of charged particles across the phase boundaries are attempts, generally vain, to restore the equilibrium state of the double layers at these boundaries. If the terminals remain connected, the metal which is the anode, M^{β}, dissolves until it is all dissolved, provided that the quantity of the solution is sufficient to accommodate the additional ions of M^{β} without reversing the direction of the e.m.f. of the cell, and also to provide the equivalent number of ions of M^{α} for deposition on the left-hand electrode. It should be noted that the process of solution at the anode is a slipping away of the positive ions from the surface, in amount equivalent to the electrons removed from M^{β} into $M^{\alpha'}$, and consequently removed also from the negative side of the double layer at the boundary between M^{β} and the solution. The dissolution of the metal takes place by a curious mechanism; both positive ions and electrons are removed, in equivalent amounts for each atom of metal which dissolves; but the metal ions pass into the solution by one side of the electrode, the electrons passing away at a quite different place. This could not occur unless the electrons were mobile in the metal!

Thus the driving force of the galvanic cell is the algebraic sum of the escaping tendencies of the charged components across the various phase boundaries in the cell. The source of the *energy* delivered by the cell to an external circuit is to be found in the means by which an attempt is made to restore the double layers at the phase boundaries; in the above case it is the replacement of M^{α} by M^{β} in the solution. For some decades there was a controversy as to the correctness of the view that the contact potentials between dry metals are the main source of the e.m.f. in cells, one school maintaining that the energy obviously came from the replacement of one metal by the other in the solution, and consequently that the properties of the dry metals could not be of great importance to the e.m.f.

This controversy was reviewed by Langmuir in the paper cited above, and Gurney's account in Chapter XVI of his book is illuminating. It is clear, however, that there is no real difficulty; the contact potential between the dry metals is often the principal term in the sum of phase boundary potentials which make up the e.m.f. of the cell.

The function of the electrolyte is to introduce two metal-liquid phase boundary potentials, whose magnitudes are such that their algebraic sum is *not* equal and opposite to the contact potential between the dry metals M^{β} and $M^{\alpha'}$. Provided that this condition is fulfilled, the potential of M^{α} will not be the same as that of $M^{\alpha'}$, and the cell will have an e.m.f. If the electrolyte were not present, and instead a simple circuit of the dry metals, M^{α}, M^{β}, and $M^{\alpha'}$, the last being the same metal as the first, were substituted, there would be no e.m.f., because the contact potentials at the two junctions of dissimilar metals would be equal and opposite, provided of course that these were at the same temperature.

The mechanism of establishment of the phase boundary potential at gas electrodes, and at oxidation-reduction electrodes, should also be mentioned. At a hydrogen electrode there is molecular hydrogen, which can only pass into solution as positively charged, single, hydrated ions. To establish a reversible equilibrium between the ions in solution, and the molecules of hydrogen, there must be a wire which can remove the electrons from the atoms of the hydrogen, as these pass into solution, to an external circuit; and if the electrode is to cope with anything greater than very small currents and rates of solution, without large deviations from the reversible value of the electrode potential, the metal of the wire should possess considerable power of catalysing the dissociation of hydrogen molecules into atoms, or the recombination of atoms into molecules. Platinum black, with its high adsorptive power (chemisorption) for hydrogen and its large surface, admirably serves this purpose. Cases where the electrode potential is very easily altered by the passage of small amounts of current will be mentioned in § 6.

The case of chlorine or other halogen electrodes is similar, except that these elements ionize into anions, after dissociation, so that electrons must be supplied by the metallic wire, not withdrawn by it, when the gas passes into solution as ions.

An oxidation-reduction ('redox') electrode is a wire of a noble metal dipping into a solution containing some substance capable of existing as ions in two states of valency, e.g. a mixture of ferric and ferrous salts. It is reversible if the solution contains appreciable amounts of both ferrous and ferric salts. The reduction of ferric to ferrous ions involves the capture of one electron, and this is supplied by a wire of some noble metal, which must itself have no tendency to pass into solution. Applying a negative potential to a platinum wire dipping into a solution containing ferrous and ferric ions tends to drive electrons into the solution and to reduce the ion from the ferric to the ferrous state (cathodic reduction); conversely, the richer the mixture of cations is in the more highly oxidized ferric ions, the greater is the pull on electrons, by the solution, from the electrode; and the electrode becomes more positive to the solution, setting up a double layer with an excess of anions near the electrode in the solution, and a deficiency of electrons near the surface in the metal.

As electrons are extracted from, or returned to, the metal in these types of electrodes, the thermionic work function of the electrode material is of importance to the *single* potential difference between the metal and the solution. But this does not provide a means of estimating the magnitude of the work of extraction of electrons, since as was pointed out by Butler, Hugh, and Hey,[1]

[1] *Trans. Faraday Soc.*, **22**, 24 (1926).

it is always exactly balanced in the contact potential difference between the metal used for the terminal of the cell and the noble metal conveying the electrons to the solution. In the cells

$$\mathrm{Cu}\overset{*}{\Big|}\mathrm{Pt}\overset{*}{\Big|}\begin{matrix}\mathrm{Fe}^{\cdot\cdot}\\ \mathrm{Fe}^{\cdot\cdot\cdot}\end{matrix},\ \mathrm{Cl'}\Big|\mathrm{K^{\cdot}\,Cl'}\,|\,\mathrm{HgCl}\,|\,\mathrm{Hg}\,|\,\mathrm{Cu}, \qquad \text{(C. 3)}$$

$$\mathrm{Pt}\overset{*}{\Big|}\begin{matrix}\mathrm{Fe}^{\cdot\cdot}\\ \mathrm{Fe}^{\cdot\cdot\cdot}\end{matrix},\ \mathrm{Cl'}\Big|\mathrm{H^{\cdot}Cl'}\overset{*}{\Big|}\mathrm{H_2},\ \mathrm{Pt}, \qquad \text{(C. 4)}$$

at the two interfaces marked by an asterisk the work of extraction of electrons from platinum enters into the e.m.f., with opposite sign, so that the algebraic sum cancels; in (C. 3) the second interface is that between copper and platinum; in (C. 4), it is that between the platinum of the hydrogen electrode and the solution.

The thermionic work function, however, sets a limit to the metals which can be used as electrodes for oxidation-reduction purposes; it must be fairly high, or electrons will come out spontaneously without supply from an external source, and then the metal itself dissolves, the positive ions leaving the positively charged metal easily. Many metals will serve for reducing systems, but for solutions with a high oxidizing potential, such as permanganate with a little manganous salt, it is doubtful whether any metal sufficiently noble exists to measure the oxidation-reduction potential.

6. Irreversible electrode phenomena: polarization and over-potential. Most of the electrode reactions mentioned in the preceding paragraph are nearly reversible; that is, the electrode when dipped into the electrolyte immediately assumes a definite potential difference from the solution, which is but slightly affected by small currents passing across the electrode. Should the potential of the electrode be raised slightly above the equilibrium reversible value, the current flows from the electrode to the solution; if the potential falls slightly, the current flows in the opposite direction. For a perfectly reversible electrode, an infinitesimal departure of the potential from the equilibrium value should cause a considerable current to flow in one or the other direction.

There are many cases, however, where quite small currents passing in either direction produce large changes in the potential difference between electrode and electrolyte; so much so, indeed, that the small currents accidentally passing across the phase boundary in the ordinary course of e.m.f. measurements by means of a potentiometer cause changes of potential of several tenths of a volt, and the potential appears not to be reproducible. There is probably no absolutely sharp division between reversible and irreversible electrode phenomena, for no electrode can suffer large currents to pass without some change in potential, and even with the so-called irreversible electrodes there is probably no mathematical discontinuity of potential as the current changes from very small positive to very small negative values. But with those electrodes ordinarily called 'reversible', currents of a milliampere or so can pass in either direction without much affecting the potential; with 'irreversible' electrodes, currents of a microampere or so may quickly produce, and maintain, potentials several tenths of a volt different from the reversible value.

As always, the changes in potential are associated with changes in the strength of the double layers at the interfaces. It is evident that, in the case of reversible electrodes, the strength of the double layer corresponding to the equilibrium potential difference is not easily altered by currents passing; in the case of irreversible electrodes, it is very easily altered. The immediate effect of currents passing is to bring ions up to, or remove them from, the side of the double layer in the electrolyte; in order to restore the equilibrium potential these ions must be discharged, or supplied from the metal, according to the direction of the current. A reversible electrode therefore is one which has the power of rectifying changes in the concentrations of the ions, in the side of the double layer situated in the electrolyte, *rapidly*, by discharge of ions at the electrode, or by supply of fresh ions from the electrode; with an irreversible electrode, the natural rate of supply or removal of ions, by transfer of electricity across the phase boundary between electrode and electrolyte, is too slow to cope with any but very small currents. The 'polarizability' of an electrode therefore depends largely, or entirely, on the rate at which ions, or electrons, can pass the phase boundary.

In the case of a metal dipping into solutions containing its own ions, the electrodes are reversible and can usually carry fairly large currents without serious polarization. The mechanism of transfer of electricity is so simple, either a deposition of ions (accompanied by dehydration), or a mere slipping away of ions (with hydration), from the surface, that it is not surprising that there is not usually serious delay at this point. Oxidation-reduction electrodes are also generally reversible, provided that there is a reasonable concentration of both the ions, of higher and of lower valency, in the solution. There appears here to be little hindrance to the passage of electrons across the phase boundary, or to the changes in hydration, if any, which accompany a change from one state of valency to another of the ions in solution.

With the 'gas electrodes', i.e. those which supply, or remove, the electrons required to facilitate the passage of gases (nearly always diatomic), from the molecular state into single ions in solution, cases of irreversibility to a marked degree are extremely common. In the best studied cases of this polarization, more frequently called 'overpotential' or 'overvoltage'[1] nowadays, it is indubitable that the nature of the surface of the metallic electrode is of predominant importance. Thus when hydrogen is being

[1] The literature on overpotential and irreversible electrode phenomena is very extensive; the reader may consult Kremann, *Wien-Harms Handb. d. Experimental-physik*, **12**, pt. 2, pp. 161–262 (1933); Faraday Society Discussion, Nov. 1923 (*Trans. Faraday Soc.*, **19**, 748 (1924)); Newman, *Electrolytic Conduction* (1930), pp. 276 ff.; Glasstone, *Electrochemistry of Solutions* (1937), 407 ff.; Baars, *Ber. Ges. Förd. Naturwiss. Marburg*, **63**, 213 (1928), for reviews and references to other papers not cited here. Frumkin's recent booklet, *Couche Double, Électrocapillarité, Surtension* (Actualités Sci. et Ind., 1936) is excellent.

liberated by electrolysis, at a platinized platinum cathode of very large surface, the electrode is found to be reversible—if this were not so, the hydrogen electrode would be an exceedingly troublesome piece of apparatus, instead of a very simple one. If the electrode is of *smooth* platinum the rise of potential with ordinary currents is quite considerable; and to produce gas bubbles the potential must be appreciably above that required to evolve gás from the platinized electrode. If, however, the electrode is of lead, or still more of mercury, the potential necessary to produce bubbles of gas is from 0·4 to 0·7 volts above the reversible value for platinized platinum, and the electrode is quite irreversible. Further, the results published (and these are multitudinous) by different observers vary to a degree far exceeding the error of measurement of potential, indicating that there are probably several factors determining the amount of overpotential, not adequately controlled in the experimental work.

The term overpotential has been used in two ways: the earlier workers, Helmholtz,[1] Pirani,[2] Roskowski,[3] Nernst,[4] Caspari,[5] focused attention on the minimum overpotential required to produce visible bubbles of gas. This we may term the '*minimum*' overpotential, although it is not the smallest overpotential that can be obtained. Nowadays the overpotential is generally measured at a specified current density; it is the difference between the potential actually observed when a known current is passing, and the reversible potential.

Although some workers take a different view, it appears that the actual appearance of bubbles is an incident in the phenomena taking place at the electrode, of no exceptional theoretical significance, however important it may be practically. The element which later appears as gas must be liberated at a rate proportional to the current passing; whether or not it appears as visible bubbles must depend, among other factors, on the solubility of the gas in the liquid, on its rate of diffusion in solution away from the electrode, on the degree of stirring, purposely or accidentally present, near the electrode, and also perhaps on the contact angle of the electrolyte against the electrode.[6] These are not relevant to the important theoretical question, of the mechanism of discharge of the ions at the electrode.

Details of the methods of measurement of overpotential need not be given here; one of the simplest arrangements is to measure the e.m.f. of a cell consisting of one reversible electrode and the irreversible electrode being studied; and to have an auxiliary electrode in series with a galvanometer and the irreversible electrode, through which known currents can be passed across the irreversible electrode in either direction. A number of the earlier workers feared to use this simple arrangement, on account of the disturbance of potential caused by the passage of the polarizing current from the auxiliary electrode; they therefore arranged that the polarizing current should be cut off by a specially designed commutator, which arranged also for measurement of the e.m.f. at a

[1] *Ann. Physik*, **34**, 735 (1888).
[2] *Ibid.*, **21**, 64 (1884).
[3] *Z. physikal. Chem.*, **15**, 26 (1894).
[4] *Ber.*, **30**, 1547 (1897).
[5] *Z. physikal. Chem.*, **30**, 89 (1899).
[6] Cf. Möller, *Z. physikal. Chem.*, **65**, 626 (1909); *Ann. Physik*, **25**, 725; **27**, 665 (1908).

very short time interval after the polarizing current was cut off. Unfortunately, in many cases, the overpotential decays so very rapidly after cutting off the polarizing current, that much greater errors appear to have been introduced, than avoided, by this technique.[1] In the case of the smaller polarizing currents, of the order of a microampere, which are usually the most interesting theoretically, the errors introduced by potential fall in the path of the polarizing current are negligibly small, so that it would appear best to keep the current flowing during measurement.

For theoretical purposes, it is the current density, rather than the total current passing, that is important; therefore an estimate of the true area of the surface is required. This presents some difficulty, though there is now reason to believe (Chap. VII, § 5) that a well-polished metal surface has a true area not far different from its apparent area.

The amount, and the nature, of the gases present in the electrolyte, is of very great importance in overpotential measurement; it is also very important to eliminate from the electrolyte metallic ions which also occur in the electrode, as these would set up a secondary reaction at the electrode, and carry current across themselves, impairing the polarization. A high degree of polarization cannot possibly be obtained if there is, in the electrolyte, an ion of the same metal used for the electrodes. The most dangerous dissolved gas, if hydrogen overpotentials are being measured, is oxygen; very small traces of oxygen in solution increase the time required to build up a given overpotential very much indeed; and the rate of decay of overpotential is much accelerated, after the current is shut off, by dissolved oxygen. Probably much of the lack of concordance between different workers' results might have been avoided if all had used really stringent precautions to exclude dissolved oxygen and other impurities in the electrolytes. The refinement of technique required is, however, so great, that very few workers' results can be considered as free from objection on this score.

In work on minimum overpotentials the currents required to produce visible bubbles are sufficiently large to swamp a good deal of the disturbance caused by ordinary amounts of impurities. The first systematic measurements on the minimum overpotential of a number of metals were due to Caspari, who also coined the term 'überspannung', translated as 'overpotential'. Many others have continued his measurements; though there are considerable discordances in the quantitative values of the overpotential, most workers agree as to the order in which different metals are to be placed. The results of Thiel and his collaborators,[2] which are unusually complete, include the following values for the minimum overpotential of hydrogen, in volts: Pt, Pd, zero; Au, 0·016; Ag, 0·097; Ni, 0·137; W, 0·157; Cu, 0·19; Sb, 0·233; Al, 0·296; graphite, 0·335; Mn, 0·37; Cd, 0·392; Pb, 0·402; Zn, 0·482; Hg, 0·570; Tl, 0·570. Other workers find definite overpotentials for polished platinum.

The manner in which the overpotential depends on the intensity of the current passing has been studied by numerous investigators. The only point on which there seems to be universal agreement is that an equation,

[1] Cf. Knobel, *J.A.C.S.* (1924), 2613.

[2] *Z. anorg. Chem.*, **83**, 329 (1913); **132**, 15 (1923).

first found empirically by Tafel[1] in 1905, holds good approximately over a wide range of current density, I:

$$E_s = a + b\log_{10} I, \tag{11}$$

which might with greater mathematical propriety be written

$$E_s = a' + b\log_{10}\frac{I}{I_0}, \tag{11.1}$$

I_0 being the unit in which the current density is measured. a and b are constants. Equation (11) was first established for currents of the order 10^{-3} amperes per sq. cm., but has recently been shown to hold good[2] down to 10^{-7}. From its mathematical form, however, it cannot hold good down to indefinitely small currents, for the overpotential never becomes negative. For extremely small currents it seems likely that the relation between E_0 and I approximates to a linear one.

The actual range of validity of (11) probably depends on the impurities, including dissolved gases, in the solution; naturally the rate of decay of overpotential becomes increasingly important, the smaller the current which builds up the overpotential. Butler and Armstrong[3] found a linear relation for hydrogen overpotential on platinum, when I is 10^{-6} or 10^{-7} amperes per sq. cm. Erdey-Gruz and Volmer[4] found small overpotentials for the deposition of metals on metals, and a linear relation often up to quite large currents. There is here, however, nothing analogous to the recombination of hydrogen atoms in the adsorbed layer, the rate of which probably plays an important part in determining the overpotential. It seems that a current-potential relation of the form of (11) holds when the block in discharge is serious, and a linear relation when there is only a small block.

If the currents exceed 10^{-3} amperes per sq. cm., the potential-current relation becomes more complex.[5]

The value of the first constant a in equation (11) depends on the unit of current chosen, and workers have usually not troubled to record it explicitly. If we make the approximate assumption that bubble evolution occurs at equal current densities for all metals, then the differences between the values of a for the different metals are the differences in the minimum overpotential for bubble formation (see above, p. 324).

Much more attention has been paid, recently, to the absolute value of b. Measured in volts, Baars[6] gives the following values among others

Smooth platinum	0·085
Copper	0·105
Silver	0·120
Gold	0·123
Mercury	0·147
Lead	0·200

the overpotential being measured in volts.

Bowden finds that the value of b changes with platinum, according to the

[1] *Z. physikal. Chem.*, **50**, 641. [2] Bowden, *Proc. Roy. Soc.* A, **126**, 107 (1929).
[3] *Trans. Faraday Soc.*, **28**, 380 (1932); cf. *Proc. Roy. Soc.* A, **157**, 423 (1936).
[4] *Z. physikal. Chem.*, **157**, 165 (1931). [5] Cf. data in *Int. Critical Tables*, **6**, 339.
[6] *Ber. Ges. Förd. Naturwiss. Marburg*, **63**, 213 (1928).

condition of the surface, steadily increasing from 0·08, with a fresh, strongly heated surface and brief electrolysis, to 0·11 after an hour's electrolysis, and up to nearly 0·2 after prolonged electrolysis at the cathode. Such changes cannot be due merely to changes in current density consequent on increase of the real area of the electrode; the low value for freshly heated platinum may possibly be connected with the presence of a film of oxide.

For pure mercury, silver, and nickel surfaces, Bowden found b about 0·11 or 0·12; but for composite surfaces consisting of mercury with a platinum film, or silver with a contamination of mercury, or a mercury surface which had been electrolysed for a long time and had probably become dirty, b was about twice this. The overpotential thus tends to increase with contamination.

The value of b is practically independent of p_H on the acid side of neutrality; Bowden found that on the alkaline side it tended to increase, with increasing alkalinity; and increasing the current density also had a tendency to increase the value of b, if not many hydrogen ions were present. This is ascribed to the hydrogen ions being present in insufficient numbers to diffuse to the surface so that the slowest stage of discharge is now transferred from the group of reactions occurring *at the surface*, to the diffusion process of hydrogen ions up to the surface. It should be mentioned, however, that earlier experimenters are not in full agreement with Bowden on the facts here.[1]

Within the accuracy of experiment, b increases proportionately to the absolute temperature.

Closely connected with the rate of passage of current at a steady overpotential is the rate of decay of overpotential after the current has been suddenly cut off. Apart from the observation of Bowden and Rideal that the rate of decay is enormously accelerated by dissolved oxygen, the data seem insufficient for generalization. Baars gave the equation for decay, $E_s = a - b \log t$, b being the same constant as the b in Tafel's equation; but his own data do not bear this out very exactly; Bowden and Rideal gave the equation

$$\frac{dE_s}{dt} = k_1 e^{-k_2 E_s}.$$

Further exact work seems to be required.

It seems extremely probable that any electrode evolving a gas is covered more or less completely with an adsorbed, probably monatomic, layer of that gas; and that these films are present to some extent even with reversible electrodes. Their presence has been proved beyond a doubt in the case of oxygen evolution from a platinum anode. Bowden[2] showed that, with polished electrodes, free from oxygen initially, immersed in a hydrogen-saturated and oxygen-free electrolyte, a definite quantity of 3×10^{-3} coulombs of electricity per apparent sq. cm. had to be passed in order to change the potential from the reversible value for hydrogen to the *reversible* value for *oxygen*; an equal amount had to be passed for the reverse change. Butler and his collaborators also find that anodic platinum is covered[3] by a layer of oxygen, probably monatomic.

[1] Cf. references on p. 115 of *Proc. Roy. Soc.* A, **126**; also Glasstone, *J.C.S.* (1924), 2415.

[2] *Proc. Roy. Soc.* A, **125**, 446 (1929).

[3] *Proc. Roy. Soc.* A, **137**, 604 (1932); **143**, 89 (1933); *J.C.S.* (1934), 743; *Trans. Faraday Soc.*, **32**, 427 (1936).

If the platinum had been anodically oxidized, or treated with oxidizing agents, more electricity had to be passed to bring it to the hydrogen potential, and the potential did not change linearly and continuously from the hydrogen to the oxygen value, as it did in the case mentioned above, but remained arrested for a time which increased with increasing extents of oxidation, at one, or two, definite values. These values Bowden identified with the reversible potentials of a layer of platinum oxide in contact with gaseous hydrogen, or oxygen. Apart from these arrest points, found only with oxidized electrodes, the amount of electricity required to change the potential from the reversible hydrogen to the reversible oxygen value was always 3×10^{-3} coulombs per apparent sq. cm.

Butler does not agree that these arrest points are due to platinum covered by a layer of oxide; the reader should consult the original papers for details. Fortunately there is no dispute as to the presence of the monatomic layer of oxygen on an electrode evolving oxygen, which is the most important point for overpotential theory.

The quantity of electricity passed, 3×10^{-3} coulombs per sq. cm., is of the right order of magnitude to remove a monatomic layer of hydrogen and deposit one of oxygen.

That oxygen is present on a platinum surface exposed to gaseous oxygen is well known; hence the presence of the monatomic layer on the electrode is practically certain. The evidence as to the presence of a layer of hydrogen, on the surface evolving hydrogen, is less complete, but it is probably present.

The 'capacity' of the polarizing double layer which produces the overpotential has received much attention, and the number of ions per sq. cm. in it can now be estimated. Bowden found that, *after* the reversible oxygen or hydrogen potential had been reached in the above experiments, additional but *much smaller* amounts of current had to be passed to produce an overpotential. This and other studies of the amounts of current necessary to produce a given overpotential, starting from an electrode giving the reversible potential, by Bowden and Rideal,[1] Bowden,[2] Baars,[3] Brandes,[4] Volmer and others,[5] have shown conclusively that the overpotential is exactly proportional to the amount of current passed, provided that the conditions are such that the rate of natural decay of the overpotential is quite small compared with the rate of building up. For such experiments oxygen must be absent, as its presence enormously accelerates the decay of overpotential; there must be a means of recording very rapid changes in potential, a string galvanometer or oscillograph being suitable.

According to Bowden, 20×10^{-7} coulombs per *apparent* sq. cm. are required for each 100 mv. of hydrogen overpotential; and 37×10^{-7} coulombs for the same amount of oxygen overpotential, on polished platinum. This indicates a capacity of 20 microfarads per *apparent* sq. cm. for the double layer producing the overpotential at a cathode; and 37 μf.

[1] *Proc. Roy. Soc.* **A, 120,** 59 (1928). [2] *Ibid.*, **125,** 446; **126,** 107 (1929).
[3] *Ber. Ges. Förd. Naturwiss. Marburg*, **63,** 213 (1928).
[4] *Z. physikal. Chem.* **A, 142,** 97 (1929). [5] *Ibid.*, **150,** 203 (1930).

per sq. cm. at an anode, both being of polished platinum. The exact interpretation of these figures depends on the ratio of the real to the apparent area of the electrodes. Bowden and Rideal found that mercury surfaces had a capacity, when acting as cathodes, of about 6 μf. per sq. cm., one-third of the value for smooth platinum. Other metal surfaces had higher capacities, increasing with the roughness of the surface, and culminating in platinum black, whose capacity per unit of apparent area was some 1,800 times that of mercury.

A great part, possibly all, of these differences in the capacity of the double layer, per apparent sq. cm., is due to the real area being greater, and sometimes very much greater, than the apparent area. Bowden and Rideal assumed at first that the value for mercury, viz. 6 μf. per sq. cm., corresponds to that of a surface whose real area is equal to the apparent. There seems good reason to believe, however, that the real area of the mercury surfaces used by them, and by Erdey-Gruz and Kromrey,[1] who also found capacities of the same order of magnitude (except with surfaces rather strongly polarized anodically, which had larger capacities) was *less* than the apparent area, owing to contamination of the mercury. There are three other methods available for determining the capacity of a polarized liquid metal surface. One is to find the second differential coefficient of the electrocapillary curve, $\partial^2\gamma/\partial V^2$, which, as will be seen in § 7, is equal to the capacity of the double layer. Another is to measure the amount of electricity carried away by a known area of freshly formed mercury surface, in a dropping electrode, the mercury being kept at a known potential. Both these methods indicate capacities for a polarized mercury surface which vary, it is true, considerably with the sign and magnitude of the applied potential, but are usually between 20 and 60 μf. per sq. cm.

Alternating currents may be used for determining the capacity of the double layer, and Proskurnin and Frumkin[2] have shown that, if great precautions are taken against contamination of a mercury surface, values from 20 to 80 μf. per sq. cm., agreeing well with those deduced from the electrocapillary curve, were obtained. They also show that, unless the applied potential is sufficient to produce a very considerable density of charge on the surface, contamination with capillary active organic substances lowers the capacity very much. Fig. 50 shows typical results. The capacities are always least with cathodically polarized surfaces.

Recently, using very small currents, Bowden has found capacities of the order 20 μf. per sq. cm. for mercury.[3] The balance of evidence therefore is that a cathodically polarized surface, whose real area is equal to the apparent area, has a capacity of about 20 μf. per sq. cm.; and this is lowered by organic substances. We may perhaps regard the lowering of capacity by adsorbed organic substances as the replacement of a surface

[1] *Z. physikal. Chem.*, A **157**, 213 (1931).

[2] *Trans. Faraday Soc.*, **31**, 110 (1935); cf. also *Acta Physicochim., U.R.S.S.*, **4**, 825 (1936).

[3] Private communication (1936).

layer of high, by one of low, dielectric constant. It would seem that a polished platinum surface has a real area practically the same as its apparent area.

The proportionality between the amount of electricity passed and the overpotential suggests that the overpotential is produced by a double

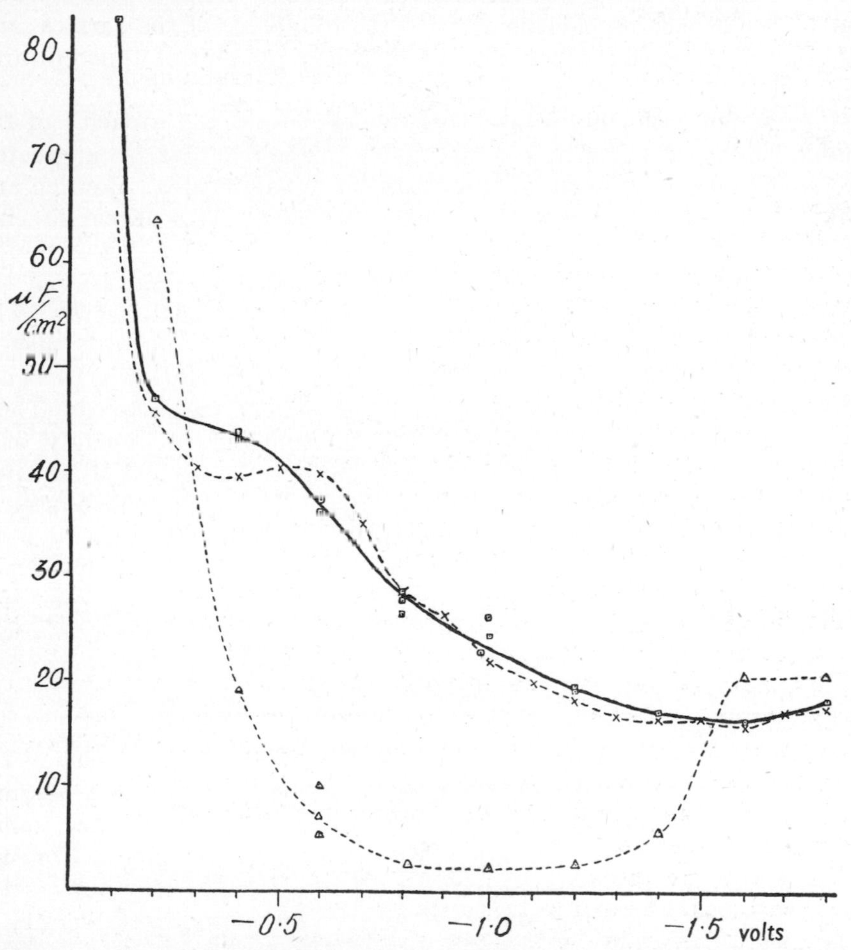

FIG. 50. Capacity of a polarized surface of mercury in normal aqueous sodium sulphate. Full line, observed capacities with clean surface; upper dotted line, calculated from electrocapillary curve. Lower dotted line, observed capacities after contamination with picein.

layer, consisting of hydrogen ions in the aqueous solution, together with their induced images in the metal, electrons drawn nearer to the surface than normal. The amount of hydrogen ion in the water, awaiting discharge, is quite small, very much less than a close-packed monolayer of ions. Taking the capacity as 20 μf. per sq. cm. and assuming that the whole of the charge on the water side of the interface is in the form of hydrogen ions awaiting discharge, the number of these ions must be

$12 \cdot 6 \times 10^{12}$ per sq. cm. for each 100 mv. of overpotential, and the area available for each, with this amount of overpotential, about 800 sq. A. Even with overpotentials as high as a volt, the area per hydrogen atom must be little less than 100 sq. A. The state of the hydrogen ions in the double layer thus resembles a 'gaseous' monomolecular film;[1] this is not surprising, considering the very low cohesion to be expected for hydrogen ions, and the very high electrostatic repulsions between them.

All determinations of the capacity of double layers at *anodes* agree in indicating higher capacities than those of *cathodes*. Anodic mercury often reaches 60 or even 80 μf., and Bowden's value for platinum was 37 μf. per sq. cm. The work required to bring inorganic anions to a surface is in general less than that required to bring up cations; and we have already seen evidence (Chap. III, § 10) of the greater ease of adsorption of anions. As a broad rule, anions are more easily adsorbed than cations, but the specific chemical characteristics of the ions will of course be important.

We have then the following picture of the state of an electrode discharging hydrogen. There is always a film, probably one atom thick and closely packed, of hydrogen adsorbed on the surface. If the electrode is more or less irreversible and is polarized there is, in addition, a layer of hydrogen ions in the solution awaiting discharge; this layer is not closely packed, and the amount of hydrogen ions in it is accurately proportional to the excess of the potential over the reversible potential.

The theory of the mechanism of production of overpotential is not yet clear, but the following considerations seem relevant.

The chief difference between a reversible and an irreversible electrode is that, in the former, the ions are fully discharged and removed as molecules, usually as gas, *at a rate not less than the rate at which the ions are brought up to the electrode.* In the irreversible electrode the ions are not removed at this rate until the potential has reached a value very much in excess of the reversible equilibrium potential; there is a block producing delay in one of the stages between the ions in solution, and the molecular hydrogen or other gas.

The stages are probably as follows, taking hydrogen as an example:

(*a*) movement of the ions up to the electrode;

(*b*) neutralization by the transfer of an electron from the cathode to the ions;

(*c*) dehydration of the ion;

(*d*) adsorption of the hydrogen atoms produced by neutralization and dehydration of the ions on the surface of the electrode;

(*e*) combination of pairs of hydrogen atoms;

(*f*) desorption of hydrogen molecules from the electrode.

[1] These figures are not the same as Bowden and Rideal's estimate of 1/3000 of a monolayer of ions, assuming a diameter for the hydrogen ion of 1 A; but the value for the capacity used here is three times theirs. The difference is not very important; they were the first to show that the layer of ions giving rise to the overpotential is very far from closely packed.

As written above, these processes seem rather numerous, but in all probability (*b*), (*c*), and (*d*) occur simultaneously; and since the energy of adsorption of hydrogen molecules is so much less than that of hydrogen atoms (if indeed hydrogen can be adsorbed as molecules), (*e*) is probably a much slower process than (*f*). Also, at any rate with ordinary current densities, (*a*), the rate of movement of ions up to the surface, need not be smaller near the surface than anywhere else in the solution, so that it is simply part of the resistance of the whole solution to the passage of current and does not form part of the electrode processes. Therefore there are two possible stages at which the delay at the electrode may occur, namely

(*g*) the simultaneous neutralization and dehydration of the ions, and adsorption of the atoms on the electrode, and

(*h*) the combination of the hydrogen atoms to form molecular hydrogen.

At one or other of these stages there is delay, overcome only by an increase in the potential difference across the double layer; in other words by bringing up more ions close to the electrode.

It has often been suggested that the delay may, or does, occur in stage (*g*). Many writers have worked out, in a more or less quantitative manner, the consequences of a slow transfer of electrons from the metal to the hydrated ion. Smits[1] was apparently the first to suggest that this is the bottleneck; Butler,[2] Volmer and Erdey-Gruz and their collaborators,[3] Hammett,[4] and others have treated the matter from the standpoint of ordinary statistical mechanics; Gurney,[5] and Fowler[6] have calculated the rate of passage of electrons across potential barriers of various kinds by quantum mechanical methods; Bell,[7] Topley and Eyring,[8] among others, have applied similar calculations to the separation of the hydrogen isotopes by electrolysis.

Volmer and Erdey-Gruz's treatment supposes that the transfer of electrons requires an energy of activation, which is lowered by application of the overpotential to the electrode. The amount by which this energy of activation was lowered was taken, however, not as $E_s\mathfrak{F}$, but as a fraction $\alpha E_s\mathfrak{F}$. The adjustable factor α was selected so as to bring the theory into agreement with equation (11), taking b as 0·116 (which it frequently, but by no means always, is). It can be shown that the theory leads to an equation

$$E_s = \text{const.} + \frac{2{\cdot}303RT}{\alpha\mathfrak{F}}\log_{10} I, \tag{11.2}$$

and α must be 0·5 if the constant b is to be 0·116.

[1] *Theory of Allotropy* (English tr.), pp. 115 ff. (1922); cf. *Z. physikal. Chem.* A, **172,** 470 (1935).

[2] *Trans. Faraday Soc.*, **19,** 734 (1924); **28,** 379 (1932); and other papers cited above.

[3] *Z. physikal. Chem.* A, **150,** 203 (1930); **162,** 53 (1932); *Physikal. Z. Sowietunion*, **4,** 346 (1933).

[4] *J.A.C.S.* (1924), 7; *Trans. Faraday Soc.*, **29,** 770 (1933).

[5] *Proc. Roy. Soc.* A, **134,** 137 (1931); *Physikal. Z. Sowietunion*, **4,** 360 (1933).

[6] *Trans. Faraday Soc.*, **28,** 375 (1932).

[7] *J. Chem. Physics*, **2,** 164 (1934).

[8] *Ibid.*, **2,** 217 (1934).

Unfortunately this theory takes no account of the value of the first constant a in (11), which is the really important thing about overpotential, as it describes the striking differences between different metals; and the necessity for an adjustable factor α is unfortunate. Practically all theories lead to a relation between E_s and I of the general form of (11), and this is not surprising, if the theories involve an energy of activation, for this (if a Boltzmann law is assumed) must lead to an exponential with the energy, into which E_s enters, in the index. Mere formal agreement with (11) is very far from proving the correctness of any assumptions made in the theories.

The other view, that the recombination of adsorbed atoms is the slowest stage in the process of discharge, has rather different evidence in its favour. The first noticed, and most obvious, fact about overpotential is the very great difference between the overpotentials found with different metals.[1] Bonhoeffer's semiquantitative values for the power of different metals in catalysing the recombination of hydrogen atoms[2] gives an order of catalytic power almost exactly the same as the order of metals in respect of their overpotential for hydrogen, the lowest overpotentials being found with the metals which catalyse the recombination best; the highest with metals possessing little catalytic power. The number of metals was large enough to render the probability of even this qualitative correlation in order of the metals for the two phenomena, very small unless one process is closely connected with the other; and more recent measurements of the catalytic power of five metals by Suhrmann and Csesch[3] confirm the correlation. Bowden found that if anodic and cathodic currents were passed alternately across a platinum electrode, a treatment well known to increase its catalytic activity, there was considerable difficulty in obtaining any overpotential at all. And recently Volmer and Wick[4] find that poisoning of the platinum surfaces by small amounts of arsenic, which is well known to decrease its catalytic activity, enormously increases the overpotential at a given current. Much earlier, Rideal[5] took the view that the catalytic power was closely connected with overpotential.

The qualitative evidence that the delay occurs at the stage of recombination of hydrogen atoms thus appears fairly good. Though he did not specifically claim a general relationship between catalytic power and overpotential, Tafel introduced the idea that the rate of recombination is important implicitly into his equations in 1905,[6] It is interesting that

[1] Readers of Gurney's paper in 1931 have sometimes considered, from the frequent appearance of the thermionic work function in this paper, that the values of overpotential should, on the theory that the block lies at (g), depend on χ. This does not appear to be justified; although electrons have to be extracted from the metal, they do also in a reversible electrode, and in either case the χ's cancel out, as described at the end of § 4, through a second contact potential elsewhere in the circuit. A glance at the figures for overpotential on p. 324 shows no correlation with χ, from Table XVI.

[2] *Z. physikal. Chem.*, **113**, 213 (1924).

[3] *Ibid.*, B, **28**, 234 (1935).

[4] *Ibid.*, A, **172**, 429 (1935).

[5] *J.A.C.S.* (1920), 94.

[6] *Z. physikal. Chem.*, **50**, 649.

he also, *on this assumption*, obtained a theoretical relationship of the form of (11) between current and overpotential.

Assuming that (*a*) the rate of combination between hydrogen atoms in the adsorbed layer is proportional to the square of their concentration, c_H there, and (*b*) the potential difference between electrode and electrolyte is a linear function of the concentration of hydrogen atoms on the surface, in formal analogy with the Nernst solution pressure hypothesis, then

$$\frac{I}{\mathfrak{F}} = -\frac{dc_H}{dt} = kc_H^2, \qquad E_s\mathfrak{F} = RT\log_e c_H + \text{const};$$

hence

$$E_s = \frac{2{\cdot}303RT}{2\mathfrak{F}}\log_{10} I + \frac{2{\cdot}303RT}{2\mathfrak{F}}\log_{10}\frac{1}{\mathfrak{F}k} + \text{const.}$$

$$= a + 0{\cdot}029\log_{10} I \qquad (12)$$

if E_s is measured in volts. *a* is smaller, the more rapidly the atoms combine.

This simple theory can scarcely be expected to be quantitatively correct, since the assumptions made in its derivation treat the adsorbed layer formally like a gaseous phase; nevertheless it does, qualitatively, show how the overpotential increases, the slower the rate of recombination; and though the value of the constant to be compared with *b* of equation (11) is smaller than is ever observed, that is perhaps not surprising in view of the extreme simplifications introduced.

The argument of Volmer and Erdey Gruz, that because values of *b* frequently gather around 0·116, instead of 0·029, Tafel's reasoning must be rejected entirely, appears unconvincing, in view of the fact that they merely substituted for this theory one involving an energy of activation which included an adjustable factor to which they assigned the value 0·5, in order to obtain numerical agreement with 0·116 instead of 0·029 for the constant *b*; and that their theory does not attempt to explain the variation of the first constant *a*. It must be remembered also that *b* has been shown experimentally to have values between 0·085 to 0·20. The constant *a*, and particularly its variation with different metals, appears considerably the more important of the two constants in (11), but it has received much less attention, recently, than *b*. Discussion of energies of activation is fashionable nowadays: but as these energies are of very widespread occurrence the mere demonstration that one of two constants in (11) can be deduced from the assumption (with the aid of a convenient adjustable constant!) of an energy of activation, most certainly does not prove, as has sometimes been argued, that Volmer and Erdey-Gruz's paper established the correctness of the view that the delay causing overpotential is a delay in the transference of the electrons to neutralize the ions.

It is obvious that, if the surface is fully covered by hydrogen atoms, the discharge of ions can only occur either by the appearance of gaps in the adsorbed layer, or by the liberation of molecular hydrogen without the atoms ever being adsorbed on the surface. The energy of activation, or the energy barrier to be crossed, by a hydrated hydrogen ion in passing directly to the molecular state, is certain to be very much greater than that needed for adsorption followed by combination; because first, the pull of the adsorbent on the hydrogen will aid its dehydration during discharge to atomic hydrogen, and second, the recombination of atoms will be facilitated, as always, by the solid surface. Hence the theory that the delay occurs in 'clearing' the adsorbed layer of atoms on the solid surface seems likely to be correct.

It is rather less obvious, however, why an increase in the phase boundary potential (the overpotential) should assist the removal of the adsorbed

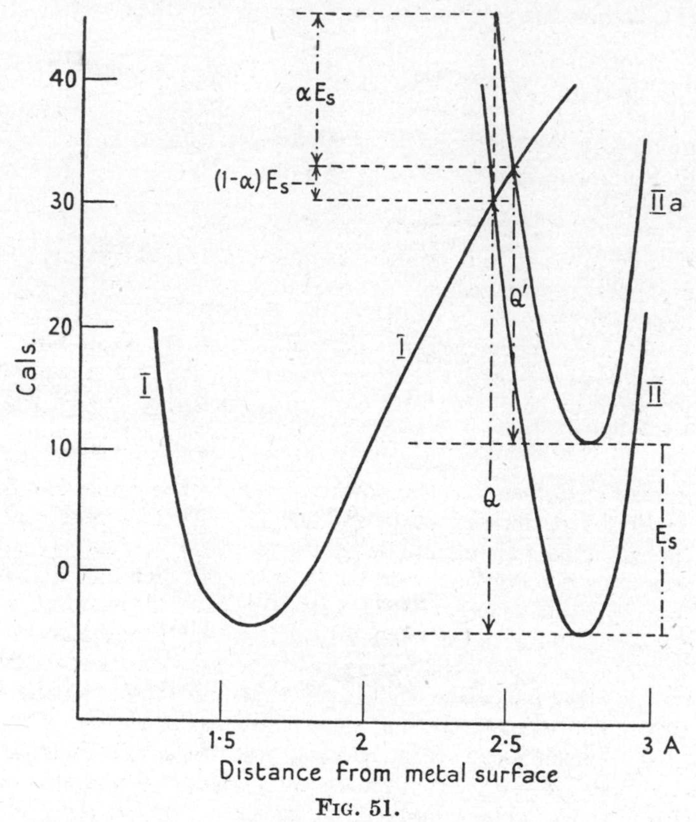

FIG. 51.

layer of hydrogen atoms. Gurney has pointed out[1] that the energy of adsorption depends largely on the free electrons in the metal, for the close approach of these electrons to the atomic nuclei of the adsorbed hydrogen atoms makes a large contribution to the energy of adsorption. It would appear possible that the energy of activation of the adsorbed hydrogen atoms may also depend on the potential energy of the electrons in the metal, i.e. on the potential of the electrode.

The general energy relationships of discharge have been discussed in terms of quantum theory by Horiuti and Polanyi,[2] Horiuti and Okamoto,[3] and Butler.[4] Fig. 51 (redrawn from the first-named authors' paper) shows

[1] Private communication (1936); cf. also Lennard-Jones and Goodwin, *Proc. Roy. Soc.* A, **163**, 101 (1937).
[2] *Acta Physicochim. U.R.S.S.*, **2**, 505 (1935).
[3] *Sci. Papers Inst. Phys. Chem. Res.*, **28**, 231 (1936).
[4] *Proc. Roy. Soc.* A, **157**, 423 (1936).

possible potential energy curves for (I) a hydrogen atom, (II) a hydrated hydrogen ion, at various distances from a metal surface, and (II *a*) a hydrated hydrogen ion when an overpotential E_s is present. Curve (II *a*) is simply curve (II) raised parallel to itself by E_s. The activation energy Q for the transference of an electron from the metal to the hydrated ion is the height of the intersection of curves (I) and (II) above the lowest point of (II). When the whole curve (II) is raised to (II *a*) by the application of the overpotential E_s, the point of intersection is raised only by an amount $(1-\alpha)E_s$, where the factor α depends on the relative inclination of curves (I) and (II) to the vertical, in the region where they intersect. If their inclination to the vertical is identical, then α is 0·5, the value selected by Volmer and Erdey-Gruz. On none of these theories can α be greater than unity.

There seems to be a close relation between this factor α and the index β, in Brönsted's relation[1] $k = cK^{\beta}$ between the dissociation constant K of an acid and its catalytic activity k; this had been suggested by Frumkin;[2] the reader must consult the originals for further elaboration.

Butler considers that the electrode process will be reversible if it can go *via* the adsorbed layer of hydrogen atoms; irreversible if this is blocked and discharge and combination has to proceed without its aid. Horiuti and Okamoto think the rate of combination of hydrogen atoms is always important, while Hammett[3] concluded that it is the rate determining process at low overpotentials, the electron transfer being the slow stage at high overpotentials.

The confusion in theories is considerable, and is not much enlightened by the great variety of mathematical treatment, much of which, as seems all too frequent nowadays, appears to contain conveniently adjustable constants. It is to be hoped, however, that clear discussion on the lines of Gurney's treatment of the reversible electrode mentioned in § 4, is not far distant. At present, it certainly seems as if the rate of recombination of adsorbed hydrogen atoms is important, perhaps of predominating importance. If the transfer of electrons from metals to ions in solution were intrinsically a slow process, the oxidation-reduction electrodes would not be reversible.

Among questions to which more attention might be directed is the following. Why does the state of the surface, which is of vital importance in determining the magnitude of overpotential,[4] apparently play very little part with reversible electrodes? On galena electrodes, combination of the surface with xanthate reduced the anodic overpotential very much.[5] But accidental, or intentionally applied, adsorbed films rarely if ever affect reversible electrodes,[6] as is shown not only by the ease with which reproducible values can be obtained for the potential of almost any reversible electrode, but also by the work of Freundlich and Rona,[7] and Freundlich and Wreschner,[8] on glass and calomel electrodes. Adsorbed films are of vital importance in all electrokinetic phenomena.

1 Cf. *Chem. Reviews*, **5**, 231 (1928). 2 *Z. physikal. Chem.* A, **160**, 116 (1932).
3 *Trans. Faraday Soc.*, **29**, 770 (1933).
4 Cf. Kremann, *Wien-Harms Handb. d. Experimentalphysik*, **12**, pt. 2, 218 (1933).
5 Lintern and Adam, *Trans. Faraday Soc.*, **31**, 564 (1935).
6 Unless possibly they render the electrodes irreversible.
7 *Sitzb. Preuss. Akad. Wiss. Berlin* (1920), 397. 8 *Kolloid-Z.*, **28**, 250 (1921).

The view was once taken that overpotential and polarization is due mainly to an increase in ordinary ohmic electrical resistance at the surface, caused by the presence of a film of gas. For ordinary cases of overpotential this is certainly not the cause; just possibly the resistance to passage of current through the comparatively thick oxide films, which impose 'passivity' on metals such as iron and aluminium, may be important. These films are, of course, of immense interest and practical importance; but they have been so thoroughly dealt with by U. R. Evans[1] that they need not be discussed here.

Hydrogen overpotential is important in connexion with the electrolytic reduction of organic compounds. Tafel[2] found that those compounds which are more difficult to reduce require a cathode with high overpotential. This may, in rather general terms, be ascribed to the greater energy of activation to which the hydrogen has to be raised, before it comes off as gas, if the metal has a high overpotential, but details want working out.

7. The influence of electric charges at a surface on surface tension: the electrocapillary curve. It has long been known that the form of a curved surface of mercury in an aqueous solution depends on its state of electrification;[3] also that complicated motions[4] may occur on a mercury-water surface, when a potential is applied, or current passes.

In general, the repulsion between similar electric charges present at a surface lowers the surface tension; in Chap. II, § 21, we have already seen cases where the development of similar charges, by dissociation, on the end groups of a surface film, increases the surface pressure. In the well-known capillary electrometer, in which a potential difference can be applied across a mercury-water interface, simultaneously with measurement of the surface tension, any changes in the potential difference will alter the density of electrification at the interface, and consequently alter the surface tension.

Such changes in surface tension occur with all polarizable electrodes, but it is usually only with liquid electrodes that the tension can be measured.[5]

[1] *Metallic Corrosion, Passivity and Protection* (Arnold, 1937).

[2] *Z. physikal. Chem.*, **34**, 187 (1900); **50**, 713 (1905). Cf. Glasstone and Hickling, *Electrolytic Oxidations and Reductions*, 185 ff. (Chapman and Hall, 1935); Butler and others, *Trans. Faraday Soc.*, **32**, 435, 989 (1936).

[3] Henry, *Nicholson's J.*, **4**, 224 (1801).

[4] Gerboin, *Ann. Chim. Phys.*, **41**, 196 (1801); and other references quoted by Lippmann.

[5] Krouchkoll (*Ann. Chim. Phys.*, **17**, 162 (1889)) quotes an experiment by Gouy, in which a spiral of very thin gold foil was found to coil more tightly if negatively polarized, less tightly if positively; this may be an effect of change of surface tension of the gold. Krouchkoll also found that metallic wires altered their potential against aqueous solutions on stretching, a phenomenon which may correspond to the change of potential of an insulated dropping electrode, or may be due to a change in structure of the metallic surface. Krouchkoll also found a change in coefficient of friction on electrification of a metal surface (*ibid.*, **17**, 182; cf. Edison, *Comptes Rend.*, **87**, 270 (1878)).

Bangham also finds (private communication 1937) that a charcoal rod immersed in an electrolyte elongates or contracts when the potential difference between it

Lippmann was the first to record an accurate study of the relation between electrical potential and surface tension, in the classical memoir[1] in which the capillary electrometer is described.

In essentials, this consists of a vertical tube *A* (Fig. 52), drawn out to a very fine capillary tube *B*, in which the mercury which fills *A* meets the aqueous solution in a very narrow meniscus. The position of this

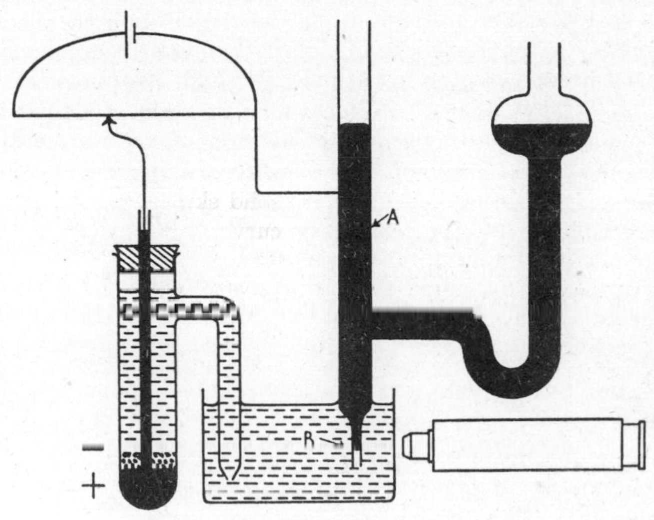

Fig. 52.

meniscus is observed by a microscope, and is kept constant by altering the height of the mercury in *A* by the reservoir. If the fine tube has been first wetted with water, there is usually no difficulty in ensuring zero angle of contact, so that absolute measurements of the surface tension may be made by recording the height of the column of mercury in *A*. The mercury in *A* is connected to the negative end of a potentiometer; the aqueous solution is connected to the other end of the potentiometer by means of a non-polarizable electrode, which in the original experiments was usually just a large surface of mercury at the bottom of the vessel containing the solution. So little current passes (for the small electrode is almost completely polarizable) that a large mercury surface does not polarize to a serious extent. Fig. 52 shows a calomel electrode connecting the solution to the potentiometer. This is the usual form of the capillary electrometer for accurate work; more complicated forms have been described by Koenig,[2] and Hansen and Williams.[3] The relation between interfacial

and the electrolyte is altered; there is a minimum length at a certain potential difference. It was seen in Chap. VII, § 7, how adsorption of gases on dry charcoal causes an interesting elongation, probably proportional to the lowering of surface tension, and this change in length may be due to the influence of the change in potential on the solid-liquid tension.

[1] *Ann. Chim. Phys.*, **5**, 494 (1875); cf. also *Ann. Physik*, **149**, 546 (1873).

[2] *Z. physikal. Chem.*, **154**, 454 (1931). [3] *J. Physical Chem.*, **39**, 439 (1935).

tension and potential can also be traced by the use of other methods of measuring tension; e.g. that of sessile drops,[1] or drop volumes,[2] for which Craxford and McKay have described apparatus capable of giving accurate results.[3]

The proper working of the capillary electrometer depends on the nearness of the approach to perfect polarization of the small electrode; i.e. the current passing must be as small as possible. The residual current passing multiplied by the resistance of the system should be added to the potential applied to the electrometer, but is generally quite negligible, provided that the solutions are not extremely dilute and that the applied potential does not differ from that of the maximum by more than a volt or so.[4] Breakdown of the barrier to the passage of current, at the small mercury surface, occurs when sufficiently high charges accumulate; at this point the discharge of ions results in the formation of bubbles of gas, or sometimes of a semi-solid skin on the surface, making it impossible to follow the electrocapillary curve to potentials indefinitely far from that of the maximum of surface tension.

The final surface tension corresponding to any potential is not always reached instantaneously; the delay may result in a considerable amount of hysteresis in the curves, which was called by Gouy 'electrocapillary viscosity'.

If the relation between the e.m.f. applied to the terminals of the capillary electrometer, and the interfacial tension between mercury and the electrolyte, is plotted with tension as ordinate and the (negative) potential applied to the small mercury meniscus increasing as abscissae, the curve is called the 'electrocapillary' curve.[5]

The usual form of this curve approximates to a parabola with vertex uppermost. As a general rule, in the absence of an applied e.m.f., the mercury has a positive charge. As the cathodic potential on A is increased the charge is first diminished and then neutralized; the surface tension increases while this happens, reaching a maximum when there is no charge on the mercury side of the interface. Further increase of cathodic potential develops a negative charge on the mercury, and the tension again falls. It is usual to speak of the part of the curve when the tension falls with increasing cathodic potential as the 'ascending' branch; the part to the right of the maximum of tension as the 'descending' branch. There is no charge on the mercury at the maximum of tension; on the ascending branch there is a positive charge on the mercury, and on the descending branch a negative charge.[6]

[1] Gouy, *Ann. Physique*, **6**, 5 (1916).

[2] Kučera, *Ann. Physik*, **11**, 529, 698 (1903). [3] *J. Physical Chem.*, **39**, 545 (1935).

[4] Philpot, *Phil. Mag.*, **13**, 775 (1932), has considered this correction carefully.

[5] Valuable reviews on the electrocapillary curve have been written by Frumkin (*Ergeb. exact. Naturwiss.*, **7**, 235 (1928)); *7th Colloid Symposium Monograph*, p. 89 (1930); Freundlich, *Kapillarchemie*, **1**, 402 ff. (1930); Koenig, *Wien-Harms Handb. d. Experimentalphysik*, **12**, pt. 2, 376 ff. (1933). Theoretical treatments by Butler (*Proc. Roy. Soc.* A, **113**, 594 (1927); **122**, 399 (1929)); and Philpot, Craxford, Gatty, and McKay (*Phil. Mag.*, **16**, 849; **17**, 54; **19**, 965; **22**, 359, 402; **23**, 1079; **25**, 1041 (1933–8)) should also be consulted, in addition to papers mentioned in this section.

[6] Proofs of these statements will follow: they are however fairly obvious if it is

These statements as to the sign of the charge carried on the *mercury* may be verified by direct experiment, using an apparatus such as that shown in Fig. 53, due to Varley[1] and to Lippmann. Mercury flows in small drops from the jet at the bottom of the funnel A, collecting in B. If the mercury surface has a positive charge, then electrons flow away from the surface as each drop forms, into the funnel, and current flows through the outer circuit in the direction shown by the arrow; the intensity of the current is equal to the area of new surface formed per second, multiplied by the charge on the mercury surface per unit area. It is found experimentally[2] that the current through the outer circuit is zero if the mercury is polarized by an auxiliary circuit to the same potential as the maximum of the electrocapillary curve; a current passes in the direction of the arrow when the applied potential falls on the ascending branch of the curve, and in the opposite direction when on the descending branch.

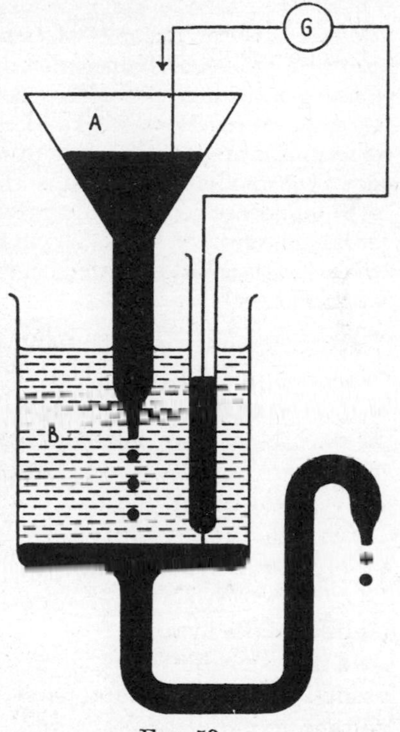

FIG. 53.

Corresponding to the charge on the mercury, ions in the solution will be attracted to the surface of the water; when the mercury is positive (E small), there will be an excess of anions near the surface in the water; when the mercury is uncharged anions and cations will be either absent from the surface layer, or present in equivalent numbers; and when there is an excess of electrons near the surface of the mercury there will be a corresponding excess of cations near the water surface.

These changes in concentration of electrons on the mercury side of the

admitted that the repulsion between similar electric charges causes the lowering of tension. As the charges are not isolated, but carried on ions, in the aqueous side of the interface, one effect of altering the potential is to attract or repel ions from the surface, and the lowering of tension may be in part ascribed to the surface pressure of these ions at the surface, an increase in the two-dimensional osmotic pressure near the surface, through the concentration there of the ions forming part of the double layer.

In cases when the concentration of mercury ions in the solution is high, the mercury may become negatively charged; and only the descending part of the curve be realizable. The capillary electrometer works poorly under these conditions, as the current is carried by the $Hg^{\cdot\cdot}$ ions across the interface, and the polarization is very imperfect.

[1] *Phil. Trans.*, **161**, 129 (1871).

[2] Pellat, *Comptes Rend.*, **104**, 1099 (1887).

interface, and of ions on the water side, affect the surface tension. The repulsion of the electrons lowers the tension, and the concentration of ions in the water also lowers the tension.

If the cations and anions were exactly similar in their effect on the tension, and had either no tendency to be adsorbed, or the ions of each sign were equally adsorbed, we should expect the fall of tension produced by a given departure of the potential E, from that necessary to produce an uncharged surface of mercury, to produce equal decreases in surface tension whether the changes in tension were positive or negative. The curve would then be symmetrical about the maximum. It will be shown below that, if the capacity of the double layer is independent of the applied voltage, that is independent of the nature of the ions or other substances in it, an exact parabola is to be expected for the curve. A few solutions approach the pure parabolic form, but most deviate from it considerably.

Experimental studies of the electrocapillary curve are very numerous. Besides Lippmann, Paschen,[1] Rothmund,[2] S. W. J. Smith,[3] Gouy,[4] Frumkin,[5] Koenig,[6] Butler, Ockrent, and others,[7] Hansen and Williams,[8] and many others have published results. By far the most comprehensive studies are still those of Gouy. A few of the more typical of his results are reproduced in Fig. 54.

Diagram (*a*) shows the results obtained with several inorganic salts, the adsorption of whose anions at the mercury surface increases in the order $Cl' < Br' < CNS' < I' < S''$. The uppermost curve, for potassium hydroxide, is nearly symmetrical. The effects of the adsorption of the anions are a considerable depression of tension on the ascending part of the curve, a small or moderate depression at the maximum, and a shift of the applied voltage required to reach the maximum, to more negative values. The descending part of the curve is not appreciably altered a short distance past the maximum.

On the ascending part of the curve, where the mercury is positively charged, the tendency of the anions to be preferentially adsorbed aids the electrostatic forces in bringing anions to the surface, and the interfacial tension is lowered below that of the curve of the salt showing little adsorption. This persists up to, and in some cases slightly beyond, the maximum; but as soon as the applied voltage is sufficiently negative to charge the mercury negatively, the anions are repelled from the surface, and the cations, which are the same (potassium) in all the curves, are brought to the surface by the electrostatic attraction and reduce the tension in

[1] *Ann. Physik,* **39,** 43; **40,** 36; **41,** 42, 177, 186, 801, 899; **43,** 568 (1890–1).

[2] *Z. physikal. Chem.,* **15,** 1 (1894).

[3] *Phil. Trans.* A, **193,** 47 (1900).

[4] *Ann. Chim. Phys.,* **29,** 145 (1903); **8,** 291 (1906); **9,** 75 (1906). *Ann. Physique,* **6,** 5 (1916); **7,** 129 (1917).

[5] See references elsewhere in this section.

[6] Koenig and Lange, *Z. Elektrochem.,* **35,** 686 (1929); Koenig, *Z. physikal. Chem.* A, **157,** 96 (1931).

[7] *J. Physical Chem.,* **34,** 2286, 2297, 2841; **35,** 3293, 3354 (1931).

[8] *J. Physical Chem.,* **39,** 439 (1935).

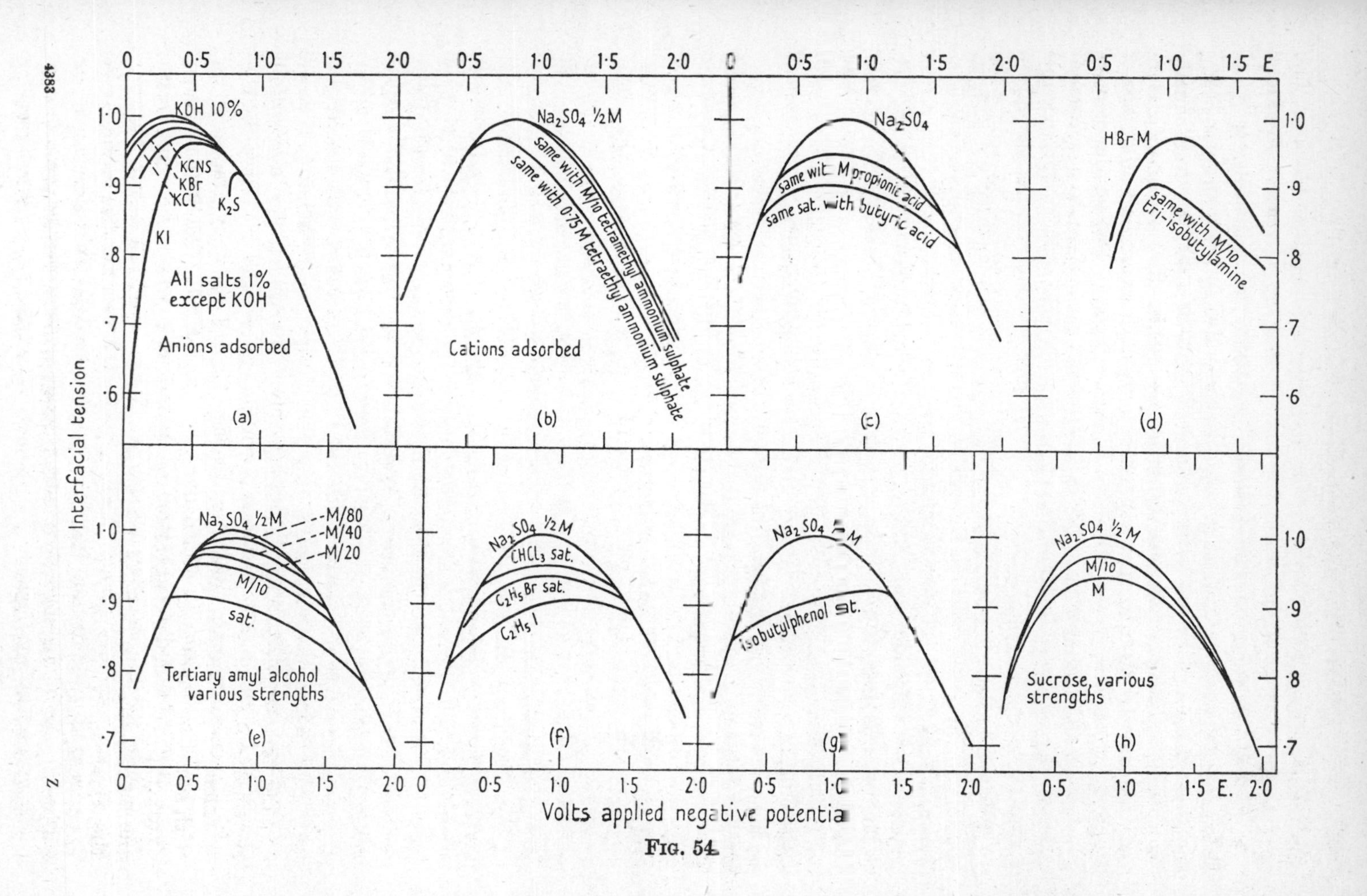
Interfacial tension
KOH 10%
KCNS
KBr
KCl
K2S
KI
All salts 1%
except KOH
Anions adsorbed
(a)
Na2SO4 ½M
same with M/10 tetramethyl ammonium sulphate
same with 0·75 M tetraethyl ammonium sulphate
Cations adsorbed
(b)
Na2SO4
same with M propionic acid
same sat. with butyric acid
(c)
HBr M
same with M/10
tri-isobutylamine
(d)
Na2SO4 ½M
M/80
M/40
M/20
M/10
sat.
Tertiary amyl alcohol
various strengths
(e)
Na2SO4 ½M
CHCl3 sat.
C2H5Br sat.
C2H5I
(f)
Na2SO4 M
isobutylphenol sat.
(g)
Na2SO4 ½M
M/10
M
Sucrose, various
strengths
(h)
E
Volts applied negative potential

FIG. 54.

the same manner as with potassium hydroxide, so that the descending part of the curve is unchanged.

The shift of the maximum towards more negative potentials, as the anions become more easily adsorbed, was accounted for by Gouy substantially as follows. The tendency of the anions to be adsorbed more than the cations produces a double layer wholly within the water, with the negative side towards the mercury; this repels electrons from the surface into the mercury, and consequently a greater negative potential must be applied to the mercury in order to neutralize the positive charge on its surface, than when there is no such 'adsorbed' double layer or 'adsorption potential' within the water.

The adsorption of the anions at the mercury-water interface is not exactly in the same order as the adsorption at an air-water interface (cf. Chap. III, § 10), for the mercury exerts specific attractions on certain ions, notably the sulphide and iodide; the degree of hydration of the ions, which was all-important for the air-liquid adsorption, is here only one of the factors controlling the adsorption. Talmud[1] shows marked lowering of tension and a similar shift of the maximum to the right, with soap solutions, in which of course the anions are strongly adsorbed.

Diagram (*b*) shows similar, but opposite, phenomena with the capillary active cations, tetramethyl and tetraethyl ammonium. The phenomena are reversed; the rising part of the curve is not affected; the falling part, and the maximum, are depressed; and the maximum is shifted to more positive potentials. This is because the adsorption tends to form a double layer in the water, with the positive ions nearer the surface than the negative, and this positive adsorption potential aids in attracting electrons to the mercury surface and neutralizing it, so that the maximum is reached with the application of smaller negative potentials E.

The other curves show the effect of various slightly dissociated, or neutral, organic substances on the curve normally obtained with sodium sulphate, a salt whose electrocapillary curve is nearly parabolic and symmetrical. In every case the maximum is depressed and very considerably flattened, so that the depression extends some way down both the rising and the falling parts of the curve. Sometimes, as with tertiary amyl alcohol, the effect of adsorption of the organic substance is to cut off the top of the parabola by a nearly straight, though rarely horizontal, line, cutting the original curve pretty sharply. Sometimes the adsorption continues a considerable distance down the curves, and the curve for the solution of the organic substance reaches the original very gradually, as with sucrose (diagram *h*). With alanine,[2] $CH_3 \cdot CHNH_2 \cdot COOH$ (not shown here), there is a slight depression of tension everywhere, the curve with the organic substance being almost parallel to, and just below, that for the sodium sulphate alone. This is probably because this amino-acid contains both positive and negative ions (zwitterions) in the molecule, so that each half of the curve is affected; perhaps the molecules are oriented

[1] *Kolloid-Z.*, **48**, 164 (1929). [2] Gouy, *Ann. Chim. Phys.*, **8**, 298 (1906).

with the amino group to the mercury on the falling, and the carboxyl group to the mercury on the rising part of the curves.

The position of the maximum is shifted in most cases either to the right or to the left, even with substances which are electrically neutral. Gouy suggested that this is because the molecules contain dipoles, which are oriented on adsorption at the surface. If the positive end of the dipole is to the mercury the shift is to the left, just as it was when the cations were adsorbed and for a similar reason, namely that the oriented layer of dipoles produces a potential fall in the water near the surface, which (if of this sign) aids the electrons in the mercury to reach the surface. This is the case with most of the organic substances, the alcohols, acids, esters, aldehydes, ketones, amines, many amides; but the halogenated compounds, some aromatic ring compounds including phenols and pyrrol, and some amides, notably biuret and thiourea,[1] have the maximum shifted to the right, indicating that the molecules are oriented in the water surface so that the negative ends are towards the mercury. As the negative end is nearly always towards the polar end of the molecule[2] it is probable that the adsorbed molecules are oriented with the halogens to the mercury; at present it seems mysterious why the phenols and pyrrol should produce an 'adsorption potential' opposite in sign to the alcohols and most amines.

The contact angle between two liquids and air varies,[3] with an applied potential, in a manner very similar to the interfacial tension between mercury and water; this is to be expected, since the angle depends on the three surface tensions meeting at the line of contact, of which the liquid-liquid tension probably varies most as the potential is changed.

Thermodynamics establishes several general relations between the surface tension, applied potential, and concentration. The best known of these states that the slope of the electrocapillary curve, $\partial\gamma/\partial E$, is equal to the quantity of electricity q^{α} on the mercury side of the interface per unit area

$$\left(\frac{\partial\gamma}{\partial E}\right)_{T,P,i,j} = q^{\alpha}. \qquad (13)^{4}$$

E is the (negative) potential applied to the mercury or other liquid metal in A (Fig. 52). An increase in E decreases the potential difference between mercury and the solution, $V^{\alpha}-V^{\beta}$. The suffix α will be used for the metallic phase, β for the electrolyte.

Equation (13) is generally called Lippmann's equation, having been first deduced by him from consideration of the quantity of electricity on

[1] Cf. Frumkin, *Ergebnisse d. exakten Naturwissenschaften*, **7**, 257 (1928).

[2] Not invariably; cf. the surface potential measurements on epi-cholestanol (Chap. II, § 25).

[3] Frumkin and others, *Couche Double, Électrocapillarité, etc.*, pp. 17 ff.; *Physikal. Z. Sovietunion*, **1**, 255 (1932).

[4] The suffixes to the partial differential coefficient indicate that temperature, pressure, and the concentrations of all charged and uncharged components are unchanged when the potential is altered.

the surface, and its variation when the area is changed.[1] The general thermodynamic relations constitute an extension of Gibbs's adsorption theory to systems containing charged components.

Gibbs[2] showed that this equation follows from the general thermodynamics of adsorption, his equation (690) giving explicitly the relation between the amount of charge associated with *all*[3] the adsorbed ions and $\partial\gamma/\partial E$.

The following is adapted from Koenig's discussion[4] of the thermodynamics of systems containing ions as well as uncharged components, in contact with liquid metals.

The general adsorption equation (Chap. III (7))

$$d\gamma = -\eta_s dT - \Gamma_1 d\mu_1 - \Gamma_2 d\mu_2 - ...,$$

which was obtained by considering the increase in energy of a system containing an interface, when the area and amounts of the components are varied, holds

[1] Lippmann's proof was essentially as follows. The interface was supposed to be analogous to a parallel plate condenser with a difference of potential $\Delta\phi$ between the plates; the work required to increase the charge on the plates by dQ is $dQ.\Delta\phi$. Work is also required to increase the area, owing to the surface tension; hence the total reversible work is

$$dG = \gamma dA + \Delta\phi . dQ,$$

whence

$$\left(\frac{\partial G}{\partial A}\right)_{\Delta\phi} = \gamma + \Delta\phi\left(\frac{\partial Q}{\partial A}\right)_{\Delta\phi},$$

$$\left(\frac{\partial G}{\partial(\Delta\phi)}\right)_A = \Delta\phi\left(\frac{\partial Q}{\partial(\Delta\phi)}\right)_A.$$

As dG is a perfect differential,

$$\frac{\partial^2 G}{\partial A \partial(\Delta\phi)} = \left(\frac{\partial\gamma}{\partial(\Delta\phi)}\right) + \left(\frac{\partial Q}{\partial A}\right)_{\Delta\phi} + \Delta\phi\left(\frac{\partial^2 Q}{\partial A \partial(\Delta\phi)}\right) = \Delta\phi\left(\frac{\partial^2 Q}{\partial A \partial(\Delta\phi)}\right).$$

Therefore

$$-\frac{\partial\gamma}{\partial(\Delta\phi)} = \left(\frac{\partial\gamma}{\partial E}\right) = \frac{\partial Q}{\partial A} = q^{\alpha}.$$

[2] *Works*, **1**, 336.

[3] Some writers have discussed the electrocapillary curve as if the adsorption of ions on the water side was confined to mercury ions. (See Warburg, *Ann. Physik*, **41**, 1 (1890); Frumkin, *Z. physikal. Chem.*, **103**, 55 (1923); Schofield, *Phil. Mag.*, **1**, 641 (1926).) But, as pointed out by Koenig, electrocapillary curves are more often than not obtained when no mercury ions are present in the solution; indeed the condition for successful measurement is that there should be no ions common to both phases. The statement often made, that the polarization of the surface is set up by transference of mercury ions from the metal to the water, does not seem correct in general; the double layer can be built up by the attraction or adsorption of any ions that happen to be present in the solution. If the metal is positively charged relatively to the solution, as is usually the case in the absence of externally applied potentials, there is necessarily an excess of mercury ions, i.e. a deficiency of electrons, near the surface of the mercury; but this is in the metal, not in the aqueous solution. Schofield also discusses the 'adsorption', i.e. the excess or deficiency, of electrons on the metal side of the interface, and this seems quite in accordance with the facts; but discussions of the adsorption of mercury ions from solution are generally remote from the facts, though they may lead formally to the correct result for the charge on the surface.

[4] *Wien-Harms Handb. d. Experimentalphysik*, **12**, pt. 2, 380 ff. (1933); *J. Physical Chem.*, **38**, 111, 339 (1934).

good for systems containing charged components (including electrons), and therefore for cases when there are electrical charges at interfaces. When charged components are present, however, the potentials μ must be replaced by the electrochemical potentials, which may be formally split up into a 'chemical' and an 'electrical' term. Thus the general adsorption equation should be written, for systems containing charged components i and uncharged components k,

$$d\gamma = -\eta_s dT - \sum \Gamma_i d\bar{\mu}_i - \sum \Gamma_k d\mu_k. \quad (14)$$

Γ_i and Γ_k denote, as in Chapter III, the amount of the charged component i or uncharged component k present in the actual system, per unit area of interface, in excess of that which would be present in an idealized pair of phases separated by a mathematical plane (the Gibbs surface) up to which the phases continue without any change in composition.

In order to trace the connexion between the amounts adsorbed, Γ_i, and the electric charge on the two sides of the interface, the Gibbs surface will be placed so as to coincide as nearly as possible with the physical interface between the mercury and the water; it will be remembered that the magnitudes of all the quantities Γ depend on the arbitrary position assigned to this Gibbs surface. The proper working of the capillary electrometer depends on its being as nearly as possible perfectly polarizable; no current should pass across the small mercury-water interface. This requires that no charged component shall be present in appreciable concentration on both sides of the interface. In the case of mercury in contact with aqueous potassium chloride, for instance, mercury ions and electrons are present in the metallic phase, and potassium and chlorine ions in the aqueous phase, but the transfer across the physical interface is negligible. If then the Gibbs surface is fixed to coincide with the surface of the mercury, the whole of $\Gamma_{Hg^{\cdot}}$ and $\Gamma_{\epsilon'}$ (for electrons) is on one side and the whole of $\Gamma_{K^{\cdot}}$ and of $\Gamma_{Cl'}$ on the other side of this surface. This non-sharing of the charged components between the phases, which is the basis of the complete polarizability of the capillary electrometer, renders it possible to identify the charges on the mercury and on the water side of the interface, q^{α} and q^{β}, with the surface excesses of the charged components, the Γ_i.

Since the system is electrically neutral as a whole,

$$q^{\alpha}+q^{\beta} = 0, \quad (15)$$

and writing Γ_i^{α} for the surface excess of those charged components which occur in the metallic phase, Γ_i^{β} for those which appear in the aqueous phase,

$$q^{\alpha} = \sum z_i^{\alpha} \mathfrak{F} \Gamma_i^{\alpha}, \quad (16)$$

$$q^{\beta} = \sum z_i^{\beta} \mathfrak{F} \Gamma_i^{\beta}. \quad (17)$$

Dividing the electrochemical potentials formally into their chemical and electrical terms according to (4), and separating the Γ_i into those present in the metallic and the aqueous phases, (14) becomes

$$d\gamma = -\eta_s dT - \sum \Gamma_i^{\alpha} d\mu_i^{\alpha} - \sum \Gamma_i^{\beta} d\mu_i^{\beta} - - \sum z_i \mathfrak{F} \Gamma_i^{\alpha} d\phi^{\alpha} - \sum z_i \mathfrak{F} \Gamma_i^{\beta} d\phi^{\beta} - \sum \Gamma_k d\mu_k, \quad (18)$$

which reduces, using (15), (16), and (17), to

$$d\gamma = -\eta_s dT - \sum \Gamma_i^{\alpha} d\mu_i^{\alpha} - \sum \Gamma_i^{\beta} d\mu_i^{\beta} - \sum \Gamma_k d\mu_k - q^{\alpha} d(\phi^{\alpha}-\phi^{\beta}), \quad (19)$$

ϕ^{α} and ϕ^{β} are the internal electrical potentials of the two phases.

It was emphasized in § 2, that the potentials ϕ are not strictly definable. Nevertheless, as the application of the external potential E does not change the composition of either the metallic phase or the electrolyte, the *imposition* of the (negative) potential E on the mercury does *decrease* the internal potential difference at the phase boundaries by exactly E; writing $\Delta\phi$ for this undefinable potential difference $\phi^{\alpha}-\phi^{\beta}$, we do know that $dE = -d(\Delta\phi)$.

If the composition, i.e. the chemical potentials, and the temperature, are kept constant, (19) reduces at once to the Lippmann equation;

$$-\frac{\partial\gamma}{\partial(\Delta\phi)} = \frac{\partial\gamma}{\partial E} = q^{\alpha}.$$

The relation between the change of tension, at constant applied potential, and the change of potential at constant interfacial tension, for a given change in concentration of any component, in either phase, can be obtained at once from Lippmann's equation, since

$$\left(\frac{\partial\gamma}{\partial c}\right)_E = -\left(\frac{\partial\gamma}{\partial E}\right)_c\left(\frac{\partial E}{\partial c}\right)_\gamma = -q^{\alpha}\left(\frac{\partial E}{\partial c}\right)_\gamma, \tag{20}$$

c is here the concentration of any constituent in either of the phases, and therefore (20) applies to mixtures of liquid metals as well as to aqueous solutions.

The effect of variations in the composition of the aqueous solution can be calculated from (19). For the case of a metal of constant composition in contact with a solution of a uni-univalent electrolyte, in a solvent whose dissociation can be neglected, (19) becomes (T constant)

$$d\gamma = -\Gamma^{\beta}_{+}\,d\bar{\mu}_{+} - \Gamma^{\beta}_{-}\,d\bar{\mu}_{-} - \Gamma^{\beta}_{0}\,d\mu_0 - q^{\alpha}\,d(\Delta\phi),$$

the subscripts $+$, $-$, and 0 referring to cation, anion, and solvent respectively. In sufficiently dilute solutions the term $\Gamma^{\beta}_{0}\,d\mu_0$ can be neglected, so that

$$d\gamma = -\Gamma^{\beta}_{+}\,d\bar{\mu}_{+} - \Gamma^{\beta}_{-}\,d\bar{\mu}_{-} - q^{\alpha}\,d(\Delta\phi). \tag{21}$$

At the maximum of the electrocapillary curve, $q^{\alpha} = 0$, and the ions of opposite sign are adsorbed in equal amounts on the water side of the interface, so that

$$\Gamma^{\beta\max}_{+} = \Gamma^{\beta\max}_{-} = \Gamma^{\beta\max}_{\text{electrolyte}}.$$

Also

$$\bar{\mu}^{\beta}_{+} = \mu^{\beta} - \bar{\mu}^{\beta}_{-}, \tag{22}$$

where μ^{β} is the chemical potential of the electrolyte and (21) becomes

$$\Gamma^{\beta\max}_{\text{electrolyte}} = -\frac{\partial\gamma^{\max}}{\partial\mu^{\beta}} = -\frac{1}{2RT}\,\frac{\partial\gamma^{\max}}{\partial\log f_{\pm}c^{\beta}}, \tag{23}$$

c^{β} being the concentration and $f_{\pm}$ the mean activity coefficient of the dissolved electrolyte.[1]

The further exact application of (22) to the experimental data really requires consideration of the effects of changes in composition on the liquid-liquid junction potential between phase β and the reference electrode. Neglecting any changes at this junction, however, so that dE is still equal to $-d(\Delta\phi)$, and assuming that the solution is ideal, so that $\mu_{+} = \mu_{-} = RT\,d\log c^{\beta}$; and remem-

[1] For (22), and the meaning of $f_{\pm}$, see Guggenheim, *Modern Thermodynamics*, chap. x.

bering that $q^{\alpha} = -q^{\beta} = -\mathfrak{F}(\Gamma^{\beta}_{+} - \Gamma^{\beta}_{-})$ we have for the ascending or descending parts of the curve

$$d\gamma = -(\Gamma^{\beta}_{+} + \Gamma^{\beta}_{-})RT\, d\log c^{\beta} - (\Gamma^{\beta}_{+} - \Gamma^{\beta}_{-})\mathfrak{F}\, dE,$$

whence
$$\Gamma^{\beta}_{+} + \Gamma^{\beta}_{-} = -\frac{1}{RT}\left(\frac{\partial\gamma}{\partial \log c^{\beta}}\right)_{E}. \tag{24}$$

Thus the slope of the γ–$\log c^{\beta}$ curves, *at constant applied potential,* is an approximate measure of the total number of ions adsorbed in the aqueous side of the interface. The difference from the air-liquid interface is that, except in the case of the maximum of the curves, the ions are not adsorbed in equivalent amounts. On the ascending part of the curve anions are in excess; on the descending, cations predominate.

The variation of concentration of neutral components k also yields an equation similar in form to Gibbs's ordinary adsorption equation. If there is only one neutral component besides water, and if the solution is dilute, the adsorption of water can be neglected and (19) becomes

$$\Gamma^{\beta}_{k} = -\frac{1}{RT}\frac{\partial\gamma}{\partial \log f_k c_k}, \tag{25}$$

so that the slope of the γ–$\log f_k c_k$ curve at constant potential measures the adsorption of the organic non-electrolyte in solution, provided that the concentrations and activity coefficients, hence the adsorptions, of any ions in the solution remain unchanged by the presence of the organic substance. The curves of Fig. 54 show that conditions in solutions of both electrolytes and non-electrolytes may be very complex.

Experiments have been done on the electrocapillary curves of amalgams; the most important are by Frumkin and his colleagues.[1] The most noticeable effect of the introduction of less noble metals, such as thallium or cadmium, into mercury, is that the maximum is shifted to the right; i.e. greater negative potentials have to be applied to the mercury surface in order to neutralize its charge, than with pure mercury. The effects of varying the composition of the aqueous solution, with a given amalgam, are very similar to those obtained with pure mercury. The adsorption of the added metal may be calculated by an adaptation of the general equation (19); the reader should consult Frumkin and Gorodetzkaja's paper or Koenig's review.

The easily melted gallium gives curves similar to mercury[2] (though there is more trouble from electrochemical attack by the solutions) and the maximum is roughly 0·35 volts to the right of that obtained under similar conditions for mercury. Consideration of the adsorption of electrolytes by charcoal led Bruns and Frumkin[3] to the conclusion that the potential at which the carbon surface is uncharged is about 0·2 to 0·3 volts more positive than the potential for mercury.

The experimental verification of Lippmann's equation has been carried out in three ways. Pellat[4] showed that in an experiment such as that indicated in Fig. 53, where mercury drops continuously from a fine jet and reunites in a

[1] *Z. physikal. Chem.*, **136,** 451 (1928); *J. Physical Chem.*, **34,** 74 (1930).

[2] Frumkin and others, *Z. physikal. Chem.*, **136,** 215 (1928); *Acta Physicochim. U.R.S.S.*, **4,** 75 (1936).

[3] *Z. physikal. Chem.* A, **141,** 141 (1929).

[4] *Comptes Rend.*, **194,** 1099 (1887).

pool below, no current flows if the potential is maintained at the maximum of the electrocapillary curve, where $(\partial\gamma/\partial E)$ is zero. The current measured, divided by the area of surface formed per second, measures the charge q on the mercury. Frumkin[1] and Schofield[2] measured the amount of current flowing in a similar experiment, finding it to agree well with that calculated from the slope of the electrocapillary curve at various points on the curve. Paschen[3] measured the potential of an *insulated* mass of mercury from which a fine jet issued into the aqueous solution. Under these circumstances the potential alters spontaneously until it reaches that of the maximum of the electrocapillary curve. This would be expected, according to Lippmann's equation, for if the potential is such that there is a charge on the freshly forming mercury surface, electrons must flow to or from the surface where the drops form. Suppose the mercury is initially positive to the solution, electrons (to the amount of q^{α}) will flow into the mercury for each fresh unit of area formed, and consequently the potential of the mercury will become more negative; this process will stop, since the mercury is insulated, as soon as the mercury drops are uncharged. Since this potential is identical with that found at the maximum of the electrocapillary curve, at this maximum the mercury surface is not charged. Smith and Moss found, however, that chemical attack of the mercury, e.g. by dissolved oxygen might produce a different potential in the insulated dropping electrode from that of the electrocapillary maximum.

The capacity C of the double layer per square centimetre, or the rate of change of the charge with the applied potential E, can be found from the electrocapillary curve, for it is equal to the second differential coefficient of the surface tension with respect to the potential. This follows at once from (13), since

$$C = -\frac{\partial q^{\alpha}}{\partial E} = -\frac{\partial^2 \gamma}{\partial E^2}. \tag{26}$$

If the capacity were constant throughout the range of potentials applied, the electrocapillary curves would be parabolas. Although with salts which are but slightly adsorbed, there is a fair approach to the parabolic form, yet rarely if ever is the capacity even approximately constant. Fig. 55, obtained by Gouy in 1903, shows that the capacities at low applied (negative) potentials E are very much higher than at high E; when anions predominate in the surface layer there is a much higher capacity than when cations form this layer. The arbitrary units of the ordinates, used by Gouy, are such that 500 is approximately 20 μf. per sq. cm.

The capacity provides a good test of theories of the constitution of the double layer; on the simple diagrammatic theory (often called the Helmholtz theory) that positive and negative charges face each other in two plane parallel sheets at a fixed distance apart, it should remain constant; on the various theories of the diffuse double layer, it should change in various ways. Philpot[4] has measured the charge on a mercury surface,

[1] *Z. physikal. Chem.*, **103**, 55 (1923). [2] *Phil. Mag.*, **1**, 641 (1926).
[3] *Ann. Physik*, **39**, 43; **40**, 36; **41**, 42, 177, 186, 801, 899; **43**, 568 (1890–2). Cf. Smith and Moss, *Phil. Mag.*, **15**, 478 (1908); Palmaer, *Z. physikal. Chem.*, **59**, 129 (1907); Frumkin and Cirves, *J. Physical Chem.*, **34**, 74 (1930).
[4] *Phil. Mag.*, **13**, 775 (1932).

at various potentials, by a development of the simple experiment of Varley shown in Fig. 53. The current carried by the mercury, and the rate of dropping, were measured, which gives (as with the experiments of Frumkin and of Schofield designed to test the Lippmann equation) the charge on the mercury surface directly. The slope of the curve relating charge to applied potential measures the capacity; the capacity is practically constant, at values of the order 22 μf. per sq. cm., when the mercury

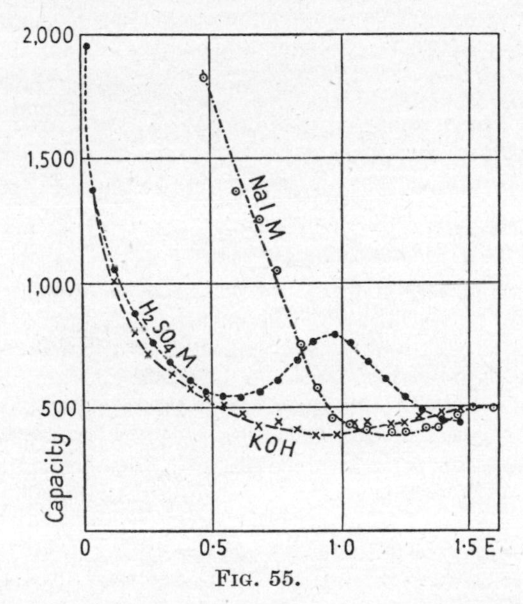

FIG. 55.

surface is fairly strongly negative and the surface layer of the water contains *cations* only; it is again constant with strongly positive mercury and *anions* at the surfacc of the water, at about 45 μf. per sq. cm.; and in the neighbourhood of the maximum of the electrocapillary curve (small charge, and probably both types of ion present in the water surface) the capacity changes. The results are found to be in good agreement with Stern's theory that part of the double layer is fixed through adsorption, and part diffuse; and for the adsorbed part, the capacities were found to be about 55 μf. per sq. cm. for Cl′, and about 23·5 for H˙ and Na˙.

The curves of Fig. 54 show that the lowering of tension by, and therefore the adsorption of, the organic substance, is generally greatest at the applied potential corresponding to the maximum of the curves obtained with the salt solution alone; i.e. when the electrostatic field due to the accumulation of ions at the surface is a minimum. This suggests that the adsorption of the neutral organic substance is strongly influenced by the intensity of the electrostatic field in the double layer produced by the charged components. Frumkin,[1] and Butler,[2] have developed theories which are in very fair agreement with experiment to account for this effect. The more highly polarizable water molecules (which have the higher dielectric constant) tend to be attracted to the surface

[1] *Z. Physik*, **35**, 792 (1926). [2] *Proc. Roy. Soc.* A, **122**, 399 (1929).

in place of the less polarizable organic molecules (with the lower dielectric constant) as the intensity of the field at the surface increases owing to the electrostatic attraction of ions to the surface as the applied potential departs from that of the maximum. The phenomenon is similar to the movement of bodies of high dielectric constant into the strongest parts of an electric field; the work gained by adsorption increases with increasing intensity of the electrostatic field in the surface layer, to a greater extent, the more polarizable the molecule.

Butler's quantitative development of the theory leads to an equation for the lowering of tension $\Delta\gamma$ by the organic substance

$$\Delta\gamma = \Delta\gamma_m e^{-a(E-E_m)^2}, \tag{27}$$

where $\Delta\gamma_m$ is the maximum lowering of tension observed, at an applied potential E_m, and a is a constant depending on the difference of polarizability between the water and the organic molecules. E_m is found experimentally but is theoretically equal to

$$\frac{p_B - p_A}{(\alpha_A - \alpha_B)D},$$

where p_A, p_B are the permanent polarizations of the water and organic molecules (which shift the maximum of the curves according to the orientation of the dipoles) respectively, and α_A and α_B their polarizabilities by the electrostatic field in the double layer. D is the dielectric constant. The depression of the tension by the organic solute should decrease exponentially with a quantity depending on the square of the difference between the applied potential and that at which the adsorption is a maximum. Agreement with experiment is very fair; it is usually better on the descending than on the ascending branch of the curves.

Butler and Ockrent[1] have obtained data with solutions of several organic substances, sometimes containing two adsorbed components; in such cases naturally the more strongly adsorbed component predominates at the surface.

The old question as to whether or not the potential at which the maximum of the electrocapillary curve occurs is that at which the potential difference between the phases is zero, can be answered, as has long been known, in the negative. The maximum of the electrocapillary curve occurs when the *charge* on the mercury surface is *nil*. If it could be definitely known that nothing else besides the charge on the mercury surface, and an equivalent layer of oppositely charged ions attracted to the surface in the water, contributed to the interfacial potential difference, then, and then only, would the potential difference be zero at the maximum of the curve. But double layers contributing to the potential can be formed in the water layer alone, by differential adsorption of oppositely charged ions, or by the orientation of neutral adsorbed molecules containing dipoles, as appears above. Even in the absence of such double layers caused by solutes in the aqueous solution, there is still a doubt whether the water molecules themselves, which are dipoles, are not oriented at the surface sufficiently to give a potential difference. They probably are, and produce a potential difference of unknown magnitude. Hence the problem of determining single potential differences is *not* solved by the use of the electrocapillary curves; and the value of about 0·57 volts for the N/10 calomel cell, obtained by Smith[2] and Palmaer[3] by measuring the potential necessary to bring

[1] Refs. on p. 340.
[2] *Phil. Trans.* A, **193**, 71 (1899).
[3] *Z. physikal. Chem.*, **59**, 129 (1907).

the small mercury surface in the capillary electrometer to its maximum tension when the reversible electrode was the N/10 calomel cell, or by insulated dropping electrodes, is not certain. The best that can be said for such a value for the single potential in the calomel cell is that it is obtained with a number of aqueous solutions in which there is little or no adsorption of ions, but the influence of oriented dipoles of water molecules at the surface cannot be estimated. The difficulty lies partly in the lack of precise definition of the term potential difference (§ 2).

8. Electrokinetic phenomena: ζ potential; structure of the double layer.[1] We have seen that an electrical double layer is set up at almost every phase boundary, and that associated with this double layer there is a change of electrical potential. If two phases, originally uncharged, are brought into contact, one assumes a slight positive and the other an equal negative charge, almost always.

In any system whatever containing matter in two phases with different charges, the application of an electric field causes one phase to travel relatively to the other, the negatively charged phase moving to the positive pole, and the positively charged one to the negative pole. This motion is called 'electrokinetic'. The rate of relative motion of the two phases is proportional to the intensity of the applied field; it also depends on the size and shape of the objects, on the properties of the fluid, and on the structure of the double layer, particularly on a certain potential, which will be described in more detail presently, called the ζ potential.

There is no intrinsic difference between electrokinetic motion, and the motion of any charged particle, such as an ion in solution, in an electric field. This has been recognized by many writers, but McBain and Laing's strong emphasis[2] on the identity of these phenomena is perhaps timely, since some writers have tended to lose sight of the similarity in their studies of this ζ potential. If the charged objects which move in the fluid, under the electric field, are small ions, the motion is called 'electrolytic migration', and is studied as electrochemistry; little attention was paid to the potential difference near to and around the ions until the Debye-Hückel theory, but it has now become very important. If the charged objects are somewhat larger,[3] such as colloidal particles, or particles in suspensions, the phenomenon is called 'cataphoresis'; if the case is one of a comparatively

[1] It is only possible to give a brief survey here of electrokinetic phenomena, mainly as an attempt to show their relation to other phenomena. There are many excellent treatises on the subject. The reader should refer to Freundlich, *Kapillarchemie*, **1**, 335–402 (1930); also to vol. **2** in several places; Svedberg, *Colloid Chemistry*, pp. 218 ff. (1928); H. Abramson, *Electrokinetic Phenomena* (Chem. Catalog Co., 1934; Koenig, *Wien-Harms Handb. d. Experimentalphysik*, **12**, pt. 2, 409 ff. (1933); D. C. Henry, *Ann. Rep.*, **28**, 335 (1931) (a clear discussion with full literature references); E. J. W. Verwey, *Chemical Reviews*, **16**, 363 (1935), for further information and an introduction to the very voluminous literature.

[2] *J. Physical Chem.*, **28**, 673, 706 (1929); *Z. Elektrochem.*, **37**, 651 (1931).

[3] Roughly, the common classification is as 'electrolytic' when the charged particles moving relatively to the fluid are too small to be considered as a separate phase; as 'electrokinetic' when they are sufficiently large.

bulky solid in contact with a fluid, such as a capillary tube containing the fluid, or a porous, solid membrane impregnated with the fluid, it is the fluid which moves, not the solid, and the motion is called 'electric endosmose' or 'electrosmosis'. Finally, there are also the converse effects to endosmose and cataphoresis; the 'streaming potentials', an electric field being set up by forcing the liquid through a capillary tube or porous plug; and the 'Dorn' effect, the production of a potential gradient when suspended particles fall through a liquid. These also are 'electrokinetic' phenomena.

The methods of measuring the velocity of electrokinetic motion are fully described in some of the reviews mentioned above. They include (for cataphoresis) various forms of U-tube in which the motion of the boundary of the suspension is observed, transference methods similar to Hittorf's 'transport number' measurements in electrochemistry, and microscopic cells in which the motion of individual particles is watched, due allowance being made for the motion of the suspending fluid in the opposite direction to the particles. Sumner and Henry's device[1] of fixing a sphere on a fibre and observing its deflexion in a horizontal electric field is very ingenious, and not so frequently mentioned as other methods.

For endosmose a potential difference is applied between the two ends of a capillary tube, or the two sides of a porous plug or membrane, and the rate of motion, or the pressure required to prevent motion, of the liquid, is noted. For 'streaming potentials' the liquid is forced through the tube and the potential difference measured. In every case it is the relative velocity of motion of the two phases in the electric field that is measured, or conversely, the intensity of the field set up when the particles are caused to move.

Though the discovery of electrokinetic phenomena is certainly as old as Reuss's experiments in 1808,[2] when he noted the transport of water through a plug of quartz powder, theories of its relation to the double layer began seriously with Helmholtz in 1879.[3] He presented a simplified conception of the double layer with a plane layer of positive charges on one side of the phase boundary, and a similar plane layer of negative charges on the other side.

If D is the dielectric constant of the parallel plate condenser formed by these two plane layers of opposite charges, r their distance apart, or the 'thickness of the double layer', then the capacity of the double layer per square centimetre is $D/4\pi r$; if σ is the amount of charge in each layer per square centimetre, the potential difference between the two sides of this idealized double layer is $\zeta = 4\pi r\sigma/D$. The force on the charge σ in a field of potential gradient X is $X\sigma$; but the resistance to motion of the layer of liquid at the distance from the solid surface where the outer side of this double layer is situated, is $\eta(\bar{v}/r)$, where η is the viscosity and $\bar{v}$ the velocity with which the liquid moves. At steady motion the driving force and viscous resistance to motion

[1] *Proc. Roy. Soc.* A, **133**, 130 (1931).

[2] For the history, see Abramson, *Electrokinetic Phenomena*, chap. i.

[3] *Ann. Physik*, **7**, 337 (1879).

are equal, hence the velocity of relative motion of the two sides of the double layer, if this layer were of the simple Helmholtz plane parallel type, would be given by

$$\frac{\eta\bar{v}}{r} = X\sigma,$$

or

$$\bar{v} = \frac{\zeta DX}{4\pi\eta}, \tag{28}$$

the 'thickness' of the double layer disappearing when the potential difference across it is substituted. (28) applies to a long thin cylinder, whose sides are parallel to the electric field.

It should be noted that it is assumed that the liquid between the two halves of the double layer has the viscosity and dielectric constant of the liquid in bulk, and the 'potential' is that between two layers of electrification, one of which moves wholly with one phase, the other wholly with the other phase.

Smoluchowski,[1] treating the problem from a much more general point of view, obtained the same equation (28), and all subsequent workers have found an equation similar in form, notwithstanding that it is universally agreed now that the double layer is *not* of the simple, plane parallel type used as an illustration by Helmholtz. All the formulae agree except as to the exact value of the constant. Smoluchowski found 4π; Debye and Hückel[2] 6π for spherical particles; Henry,[3] taking into account the conductivity of the two phases, found for spheres,

$$\bar{v} = \frac{3\kappa}{2\kappa+\kappa'}\,\frac{DX\zeta}{6\pi\eta}, \tag{28.1}$$

which reduces to the 4π form if κ', the conductivity of the solid moving particle is zero, and to the 6π form if it is equal to κ, that of the surrounding liquid.

Debye and Hückel considered that the constant should depend on the shape of the particles; the question appears still undecided theoretically, but a considerable body of experiment[4] indicates that shape has not much effect; and also that, when the size is greater than ultramicroscopic, the size does not affect the mobility either. Kemp,[5] however, finds, experimentally and theoretically, that size is important.

The half of the double layer, on the solid side of the interface, *may* be fairly nearly a plane sheet of charges, though there is no proof that it is so;[6] on the liquid side it certainly is not. On the liquid side, in the case of an electrolyte, the ions take part in the thermal motions of the liquid, and all those ions which are not specifically adsorbed at the surface will be distributed according to a Boltzmann distribution in the liquid, the density of ions being greatest close to the surface and gradually diminishing, with increasing distance, to the average density of ions in the bulk of the solution. The same equation (28) is obtained, with the assumption of a plane parallel double layer, or with any law of variation of density of electrification in the double layers.

[1] *Graetz's Handb. d. Elektrizität u. Magnetismus*, **2**, 366 (1914).

[2] *Physikal. Z.*, **25**, 49 (1924). [3] *Proc. Roy. Soc.* A, **133**, 106 (1931).

[4] Cf. Freundlich and Abramson, *Z. physikal. Chem.* A, **128**, 25 (1927); **133**, 51 (1928); Abramson, *Electrokinetic Phenomena* (1934), 111.

[5] *Trans. Faraday Soc.*, **31**, 1347 (1935).

[6] O. K. Rice (*J. Physical Chem.*, **30**, 1501 (1926)), considers the layer as diffuse on the metal side also.

Why does the particular assumption as to the distribution of electricity in the double layer make so little difference to the relation between the potential and the relative velocity of motion of the two phases? The reason is that, although at any given distance from the material phase boundary the actual potential, and the velocity of motion, vary very much according to the distribution of the double layer, at each point one is always proportional to the other, and the sum of the contributions of each layer of liquid to the total potential difference between the surface of the solid and the fluid beyond the double layer, is proportional to the sum of the different steps in relative velocity, proceeding from one infinitesimal layer to another, outwards in the liquid.[1]

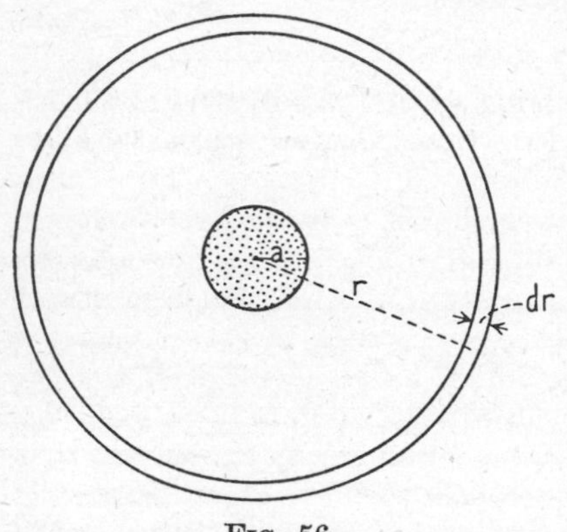

FIG. 56.

This may be clear from Fig. 56. Consider a conducting, solid, spherical particle of radius a, carrying a positive charge q, immersed in a liquid of dielectric constant D. The potential of the sphere is q/Da. Next consider the contribution to the potential difference between the sphere and the liquid made by a spherical shell in the liquid, of radius r and thickness dr; the charge dq on this will be opposite in sign to that on the sphere, and the contribution to the *difference* in potential between the surface of the solid and the liquid will be dq/Dr. The total difference in potential between the surface of the solid and the liquid beyond the outer limits of the double layer will be the sum of the contributions from the sphere and all the shells, i.e.

$$\zeta = \frac{1}{D}\left\{\frac{q}{a} + \int\limits_{r=a}^{r=\infty} \frac{dq}{r}\right\}. \tag{29}$$

If v_1 be the velocity of the particle, by Stokes's law the resistance to motion will be $6\pi\eta a$, which is equal to the electric force on the particle Xq; therefore the central particle moves in one direction with a velocity

$$v_1 = \frac{Xq}{6\pi\eta a}.$$

Let the shell of radius r move in the opposite direction with velocity v_2; the viscous resistance to motion is similarly $6\pi\eta r$, and the force on the shell $X\,dq$; hence

$$v_2 = \frac{X\,dq}{6\pi\eta r},$$

and the relative motion between the central particle and the fluid beyond the double layer will be

$$\bar{v} = \frac{X}{6\pi\eta}\left\{\frac{q}{a} + \int\limits_{r=a}^{r=\infty} \frac{dq}{r}\right\}. \tag{30}$$

[1] Cf. G. S. Hartley, *Trans. Faraday Soc.*, **31**, 45 (1935).

Combining (29) and (30) we have Debye and Hückel's relation between velocity and potential

$$\bar{v} = \frac{\zeta DX}{6\pi\eta}. \tag{28.2}$$

This equation takes no account of any distortion of the field by the particle itself, a factor considered by Henry in deducing (28.1).

Since at present there appears to be no other method of measuring the ζ potential, than the measurement of the velocity of migration in an electric field and the application of one or other of the formulae (28) to (28.2), we have not yet the power of verifying these formulae by experiment.

Some considerations regarding the definition of the ζ potential may be useful, however. It is the difference in electric potential between two points lying wholly in the same fluid phase, one of which is just outside the boundary of the other phase (which is often solid but may be liquid or gas); the other is at a distance from the second phase large enough to be outside the limit of the diffuse electrical double layer. The properties of the fluid are supposed the same, throughout this region, as in bulk. Indeed the ζ potential appears precisely analogous to the electrostatic potential V, as defined in § 2; with the difference that, in the case of the electrostatic potential, the point where V is measured, and the point at an infinite distance taken as the zero of potential, are both in a vacuum; in the case of ζ, the points are both in the fluid medium, one very close to the surface of the second phase, the other at a great distance from it.

The quantity in the ordinary theory of electrolytes which corresponds to the ζ potential in electrokinetics, is the potential due to an ion, at a distance from its centre equal to its radius, i.e. half the distance of closest approach of two ions. In the case of moderately complex charged particles such as the 'ionic micelle' of paraffin chain salts, soaps, etc., the ζ potential is the potential in the water just outside the micelle with its adherent 'gegenions', the small ions of opposite sign which, according to G. S. Hartley, adhere to the micelle and very considerably affect its motion in an electric field.[1]

In the case of larger particles such as those commonly considered in electrokinetics, if ions are adsorbed on the solid (or other) phase sufficiently closely to move with it, the ζ potential is that at the boundary of the adsorbed layer of ions; in every case the zero of potential is here taken as the potential at a distant point in the same fluid.

The relation between the ζ potential and the net *charge* on the particle, or charge per unit area in the case of an extended surface, cannot be found without a specific hypothesis as to the distribution of electricity in the double layer. For the idealized, plane parallel double layer, if r is the thickness of the double layer, then ζ would be $4\pi\sigma r/D$.

The almost universally accepted theory of the structure of the double

[1] *Aqueous Solutions of Paraffin Chain Salts* (Actualités Scientifiques, no. 387, 1936); cf. Adam, *Ann. Rep.* (1936), 103.

layer is now that of Stern,[1] who considers it as in two parts, one, practically entirely fixed to the solid surface, and approximating to Helmholtz's plane parallel double layer, about the thickness of a single ion; the other, diffuse, outside the first part, in which all the ions are free to move, and their density in each plane parallel to the surface is determined by the opposing tendencies of the thermal agitation to distribute the ions equally, and the electrostatic attraction to concentrate the charges of one sign close to the surface. This part of the double layer has a distribution analogous to the distribution of the molecules of a gas in a gravitational field, the electrostatic attraction taking the place of this field. The ζ potential is, to a near approximation, the potential difference between the boundary of the fixed part of the double layer and a point in the liquid far from the surface; i.e. the potential fall in the diffuse part of the double layer.

Earlier theories by Gouy, Chapman, and Herzfeld discussed the double layer as wholly of this diffuse type; but Stern points out that these give far too high values for the capacity of the double layer, partly because in them the ions are supposed mathematically to be able to approach indefinitely close to the solid surface, which is impossible physically owing to the size of the ions. Stern's theory gives a complicated expression for the capacity of the double layer, but accounts reasonably well for the experimental values. Though the layer is largely diffuse in many cases, the capacity is usually of the same order as if the layer were of the plane parallel type, because most of the ions are fairly close to the fixed part of the layer.

Philpot[2] has found that the capacity of a double layer containing only anions on the water side, such as Cl', is more than double that of a layer containing cations, $H^{\cdot}$ or $Na^{\cdot}$; we have already seen evidence that anions are usually more strongly adsorbed than cations; this brings them closer to the other phase, so that the dipole moment formed by each anion with its positive image in the other phase is less than the moment of a cation with its image, so that a given number of ions contribute less to the potential.

Adsorption of ions into the fixed part of the double layer has an enormous influence on the ζ potential; it is possible to reverse the sign of this potential and the direction of motion, by adding suitable ions; the data on this are very extensive and may be found in several of the treatises mentioned. The effectiveness of the ions increases enormously with increase in valency.

The ζ potential is also closely connected with the stability of lyophobic colloids;[3] if it is reduced below a critical value, the dispersed particles coagulate rapidly. Ions of opposite charge to the colloidal particles are easily adsorbed and cause coagulation. The effectiveness of the ions increases enormously with increase in valency according to the well-known

[1] *Z. Elektrochem.*, **30**, 508 (1924). [2] See p. 348.

[3] Freundlich, *Kapillarchemie*, **2**, 125 (1932); *Kolloid-Z.*, **23**, 163 (1918); Kruyt, Alexander's *Colloid Chemistry*, **1**, 306 (1926); Müller, *Kolloid-Beih.*, **26**, 257 (1928).

'Schulze-Hardy' rule.[1] Specific properties of the ions promoting easy adsorption are also important; e.g. with a series of sodium salts of aromatic sulphonic acids, the introduction of an aliphatic side chain decreases the concentration necessary to diminish the ζ potential by a given amount, by a factor of three for each additional CH_2 group in the side chain[2]: this is another case of Traube's rule in adsorption.

The importance of the ζ potential in stabilizing colloids may be visualized thus. When two particles approach sufficiently closely, the van der Waals attractive forces cause them to stick together. If the particles are similarly charged, work has to be done in bringing up one through the electrostatic repulsion of the other, and this depends on the potential round the particle, which in its turn depends on the total charge on the particle, its density, and on the dielectric constant of the fluid surrounding the particles. The charge on the particles, acting through the potential which it produces in the surrounding fluid, hinders the approach of the particles to the critical distance at which they stick together. For 'rapid' coagulation, in which every collision between particles produces adhesion, the critical ζ potential has been much studied; if the potential is higher than this, some coagulation may still occur, for the momentum of the faster moving particles can carry them through the repulsive electrostatic fields within range of the van der Waals attractive forces.

The adsorbed ions aid coagulation by reducing the *net* charge on the central, compact core of the particle, which includes the fixed part of Stern's double layer.

Very approximately, the rule relating the equivalent concentration of the adsorbed, coagulating, ion to its valency z, is that the minimum concentrations for rapid coagulation are, for tri-, di-, and monovalent ions, in the ratio $C:C^2:C^3$. A very simple explanation of this rule can be given as follows.[3] If electrostatic forces are the only forces causing adsorption of the ion of opposite charge to the original colloid particle, the work gained on adsorption of an ion will be $z\epsilon\zeta/D$, since the ion of charge $-z\epsilon$ is brought up to a region of potential ζ. The concentration in the adsorbed layer will bear, approximately, to that in the solution, c, a ratio given by the Boltzmann equation

$$\frac{c_{\text{surface}}}{c} = e^{z\epsilon\zeta/DkT}.$$

Coagulation is, for a given colloid, brought about when the total charge of the adsorbed ions reaches the same value, whatever the valency; hence the concentrations required to coagulate should be proportional to $e^{-z\epsilon\zeta/DkT}$. For a given colloid, ζ, and therefore $e^{\epsilon\zeta/DkT}$, is a given quantity; hence the coagulating concentration c is $1/C^z$, where C is a constant for the particular colloid. The ratios of the concentrations for tri-, di-, and monovalent ions are therefore $C:C^2:C^3$.

In most actual cases, other forces besides simple electrostatic attraction enter into the work of adsorption of the ions, so that this relation is only approximate.

[1] Schulze, *J. prakt. Chem.*, **25**, 431 (1882); W. B. Hardy, *Proc. Roy. Soc.*, **66**, 110 (1900).

[2] Freundlich, *Kapillarchemie*, **1**, 372 (1930).

[3] G. S. Hartley (private communication, 1937).

Up till about 1921, it was often supposed that the ζ potential could be identified with the single potential difference at the phase boundary. Freundlich and his collaborators[1] showed that this is quite impossible, since the variation with concentration, and the influence of adsorbed substances, are entirely different in the two cases; sometimes indeed the two potentials may have different signs. The phase boundary potential, if defined as the Volta potential, is the difference between the energy levels of the charged component, to which the phase boundary is permeable, inside the two phases when these are both at the same electrostatic potential. We have seen that it is difficult, or impossible, to define the phase boundary potential in any other way (see §§ 2 and 3). It includes the work of extraction of the charged component from each phase, and this includes the part of the double layer which according to Stern's theory is fixed. The ζ potential is merely the potential fall in the mobile, diffuse part of the double layer, and is wholly within one phase.

Some writers have urged that the results of electrokinetic measurements should be expressed in terms similar to those usual with electrolytes containing small ions, i.e. of mobilities and valencies, and not as ζ potentials. One difficulty here is that, although the mobility is measured, it is very seldom that the actual magnitude or density of the charge on a colloidal particle or surface is known. The charge on, or valency of, a colloidal particle must depend on its size, and may also depend on its shape. The ζ potential probably depends but little on either.

ζ potentials of a substance in colloidal solution need not be, indeed generally are not, the same as on fair-sized surfaces of the same substance in solid or crystalline form.[2] This is because the orientation of the molecules at the surface is different; e.g. with paraffin chain salts, the ionic micelle has the water-soluble groups pointing outwards, but the crystals have the hydrocarbon ends of the molecules outwards, over the greater part of the surface. The same applies to dyestuffs, and in general the surface properties of colloids, including their potentials, will depend on the means used to form the colloidal solutions.

The relative motion of the two sides of the mobile double layer in electrokinesis transports electricity; consequently the presence of *any* surface in a fluid ought to increase the conductivity of that fluid; this effect is called 'surface conductivity'. When the area of surface is considerable, as with a suspension or colloidal solution, the increase should be appreciable. Smoluchowski predicted this effect, which has been shown to exist by a good many workers,[3] but the theory and its verification by experiment appear at the present time to be in a state of considerable confusion. Some workers, indeed, claim that there is no correlation[4] between the ζ potential and the surface conductivity, which seems improbable. The reader must draw his own conclusions from the litera-

[1] Cf. *Kapillarchemie*, **1**, 356 ff. (1930).

[2] Cf. Hartley, *Trans. Faraday Soc.*, **31**, 67 (1935).

[3] McBain and others, *J.A.C.S.* (1929), 3294; *J. Physical Chem.*, **34**, 1033 (1930); *Proc. Roy. Soc.* A, **125**, 394 (1929). Bull and Gortner, *J. Physical Chem.*, **35**, 309 (1931).

[4] Fairbrother and others, *J.C.S.* (1924), 2495; (1931), 1564. For elaborate mathematical theory see Bikermann, *Z. physikal. Chem.* A, **163**, 378; **171**, 209 (1932–4); *Kolloid-Z.*, **72**, 100 (1935).

ture, but it seems possible that some of the experiments are vitiated by a change in bulk conductivity caused by actual solution of some of the finely divided solids used. Possibly, also, there may be some degree of mobility along the surface in the fixed part of the double layer, as there is in so many adsorbed layers; if this were considerable, it might completely destroy any correlation between surface conductivity and ζ potential.

9. Potential differences between organic liquids and aqueous solutions. Potential differences exist between organic liquids and aqueous solutions, their magnitude depending on the composition of the two liquids. They may be permanent, or transient, or be composed of a permanent and a transient portion. Much work has been done by Beutner, Loeb, and Baur,[1] who have found changes in potential ranging from small values up to as much as 300 mv. when the composition of the aqueous solution is changed.

The e.m.f. of the cell

$$\text{Hg} \mid \text{HgCl} \mid \text{KCl N} \mid \text{O} \mid \text{X aq.} \mid \text{KCl N} \mid \text{HgCl} \mid \text{Hg},$$

where X aq. is an aqueous solution of a salt or of a soluble organic substance, and O is a liquid organic substance immiscible or only slightly miscible with water, depends largely on the boundary potential at the interface X aq. | O, and it is usually assumed that the changes in e.m.f. of the cell when the composition of X aq. is changed are entirely due to the changes in the potential at this interface.

A typical case, one of the earliest investigated, is that of salicylic aldehyde saturated with salicylic acid for the organic substance. If X aq., the variable aqueous solution, is potassium chloride, the e.m.f. changes from +137 mv. to −32 mv. as the salt concentration is increased from N/6,250 to 2·5 N, the e.m.f.'s being established at once and remaining practically constant up to at least two hours. As the concentration of the salt increases, the organic phase, which is acid in reaction, becomes *less positive* to the water.

With the basic organic phase, e.g. *o*-toluidine, the sign of the change of potential was opposite to the above, the organic phase becoming *more positive* to the water with increasing concentration of salt. If the salt was

[1] The principal papers, of which the earlier are usually more interesting, are given below. Those marked P are little more than polemics.

Beutner, Loeb, and others. *Z. Elektrochem.*, **19**, 319, 467 (1913); **24**, 94 (1918) P; **25**, 100 (1919) P; **28**, 483 (1922).

Z. physikal. Chem., **87**, 385 (1914); **104**, 472 (1923) P; *Biochem. Z.*, **41**, 1; **44**, 303 (1912); **51**, 288 (1913); **59**, 195 (1914); **137**, 496 (1923).

Protoplasma, **19**, 370 (1933).

Arch. Exp. Zellforschung, **15**, 217 (1934).

Entstehung elektrischer Ströme in lebenden Geweben (Stuttgart, 1913); *Physical Chemistry of Living Tissues, etc.* (1933), pp. 189 ff.

Baur and others. *Z. Elektrochem.*, **19**, 590 (1913); **24**, 100 (1918) P; **25**, 151 (1919) P; **28**, 421 (1922); **31**, 514 (1925); **32**, 547 (1926).

Z. physikal. Chem., **92**, 81 (1916); **103**, 39 (1922) P; **106**, 157 (1923) P.

Rec. Trav. Chim. Pays-Bas, **42**, 656 (1923).

potassium chloride, the positive change in e.m.f. was somewhat less, for a given increase in concentration, than the negative change in e.m.f. for an equal increase in concentration with the acid organic substance. Potassium thiocyanate, however, produces a larger positive change, with *o*-toluidine, nearly equal in magnitude to the negative change with the acid organic substance. Other acid organic liquids behaved similarly to the salicylic aldehyde-acid mixture.

Cells similarly constructed, but with different salts at the same concentration[1] on either side of the organic phase, sometimes gave quite large potentials, e.g.

M/10 NaCNS | *o*-toluidine | M/10 Na_2SO_4 +0·260 volt.

M/10 NaCNS | salicylic aldehyde | M/10 Na_2SO_4 +0·018 volt.

A large number of comparisons were made with cells of the type,

M/10 NaCl | organic liquid | M/10 aqueous solution of X,

the organic liquids being acidic, basic, or neutral. With all the organic liquids, a positive e.m.f.[2] was obtained in every case where the right hand aqueous solution, X, was the hydrochloride of an organic base; a negative e.m.f., however, if X was the salt of an organic acid. This seems to the author to give a clue as to the nature of these potentials. One would naturally expect that the organic ion would be preferentially adsorbed on the organic liquid; therefore with salts of organic bases, the anions will adhere to the organic liquid, which will be positively charged relative to the aqueous solution X; but with salts of organic acids, the organic liquid will have an adsorbed layer of anions and will therefore be negatively charged, giving the potentials observed above. The specific nature of the organic salts in aqueous solution makes a great deal of difference to the magnitude of the potential differences, but their sign is determined as above.

Beutner gives an extensive table of these potentials[3] obtained with many different in organic salts as the solution X. The lyotropic series of anions, in the salts KCl, KBr, KI, KCNS, gives regularly increasing positive potentials on the aqueous and negative on the organic liquid, indicating that

[1] Here Beutner compares an M/10 solution of a monovalent salt with an M/10 divalent salt. There are, however, evidently large and remarkable effects due to specific qualities of the ions.

[2] The left-hand end of the chains is taken as the positive; if the e.m.f. has a positive sign the terminal on the left was positive, and vice versa. Making the assumptions that the whole effect of the solute X is exerted at the interface with the organic liquid, and that the potential between the organic liquid and M/10 NaCl is zero, a positive sign would mean that the organic liquid is positively charged with respect to the solution X.

[3] *Z. physikal. Chem.*, **87**, 405 (1914). The sign in the table appears in this paper to be the opposite of that which Beutner uses elsewhere, and of that used above, i.e. a minus sign here indicates that the *aqueous* solution is negatively charged relatively to the organic liquid.

the least hydrated anions (e.g. CNS′) are most strongly adsorbed at the interface.[1]

It would appear that many, at least, of these potentials at the interface between organic liquids and water are due to the preferential adsorption of one or the other ion on the organic liquid, setting up a double layer at the interface with the accompanying potential difference between the phases. The potentials are not always permanent. Baur[2] took the precaution of extending his measurements over many days, finding that, as a rule, the potentials slowly decreased. This might be due to a slow diffusion to the surfaces of traces of impurities, partly neutralizing the potentials first set up; but in view of the considerations brought forward by Dean, Gatty, and Rideal (see Appendix), it seems more probably due to ions from the aqueous phase passing into the organic phase, causing compensation of the adsorption potentials initially set up. They show that, if one or more ions can pass the interface and come into equilibrium on both sides thereof, adsorption will not produce a permanent difference of potential between the phases. All *equilibrium* potential differences must be due to changes in the distribution of ions between the two liquids; temporary potential differences may be set up by adsorption, but if ions can pass the interface, the double layer caused by adsorption (either unequal adsorption of oppositely charged ions or adsorption of polar molecules), will be exactly compensated by a new double layer of those ions which have crossed the interface.

For measurements to be practicable it is almost necessary to have some degree of conductivity in the organic liquid, which means that ions can pass, though not necessarily at a rapid rate. Therefore such adsorption potentials as are measurable will probably be transient. Measurements with benzene or paraffins as the organic liquid have not yet been made,[3] on account of the difficulty of their low conductivity. Possibly a modification of the vibrating plate method described on p. 35 might be applied to the measurement of oil-water potentials when the oil has a very low conductivity.

An almost furious controversy raged for several years between Beutner and Baur as to the nature of these potentials. Baur called them 'adsorption potentials', considering that they were due to adsorption of ions. Beutner maintained that they were due to partition of the ions between different phases, treating the systems as concentration cells. Ultimately Baur gave way. It seems quite likely, however, that both were right, according to circumstances; although the final potential when thermodynamic equilibrium is attained is not an adsorption potential, the establishment of this equilibrium probably takes a very long time.

The importance of these potentials as indicating mechanisms whereby

[1] Compare Frumkin's measurements (Chap. III, § 10) on air-water potentials of various salts, when it is found that the least hydrated anions are the most strongly adsorbed.

[2] Especially *Z. physikal. Chem.*, **92**, 81 (1916).

[3] Except a few preliminary ones (see Alexander and Teorell, *Trans. Faraday Soc.* (1939), 732).

the electrical potential differences found in living tissues can be produced has been repeatedly pointed out. Animal and plant membranes give similar potential differences and many measurements on such membranes are described in the papers listed above.[1] The sudden spreading or the destruction of, or indeed any sudden change in, an adsorbed film with a double layer of its own due to dipoles produces (see Appendix) a sudden change in the interfacial potential, which is later slowly neutralized by the diffusion of ions. It seems possible that the action currents accompanying many vital activities are due to such sudden changes in an interfacial film, and their decay to a redistribution of ions to meet the conditions arising from a change in the interfacial film.

10. Influence of electrification on the stability of thick films of air between two liquids. Two jets of water, impinging on each other at an angle, do not always coalesce, but may bounce off again. It is often noticeable also, that drops of water, or other liquids, slide about on the surface of a mass of the same liquid for some time before uniting with it. This is due to a film of air between the two liquid surfaces, which does not easily escape past the edges of the drops, and acts as a buffer preventing the liquids coming into contact. Rayleigh[2] found that a difference of electrical potential between two jets, of the order one volt, immediately produces union of the colliding jets, as also does dust in the liquids. The cushion of air between the jets is no doubt bridged across by dust projecting from the surface, so that union occurs. The action of the potential difference is explicable thus. Any slight protuberance in the surface of either liquid brings it nearer to the other liquid, and if there is a potential difference between the liquids, the attraction between the tip of the protuberance and the other liquid surface is greater here than elsewhere between the liquids; hence the protuberance will tend to grow. Thus the formation of bridges across is assisted by the charge, and the electrification tends to render two surfaces of liquid, separated from each other by a narrow air cushion, unstable.

[1] Cf. also Ettisch, *Z. physikal. Chem.* A, **139**, 516 (1928).

[2] *Proc. Roy. Soc.*, **28**, 406; **29**, 71 (1879); **34**, 130 (1882); *Phil. Mag.*, **48**, 328 (1899).

CHAPTER IX*

THE MEASUREMENT OF SURFACE TENSION

1. Classification of the methods of measuring surface tension. There are static and dynamic methods. The static methods measure the tension of practically stationary surfaces which have been formed for an appreciable time, and depend on one of two principles. The most accurate depend on the pressure difference set up on the two sides of a curved surface possessing surface tension (Chap. I, § 10), and are often only devices for the determination of hydrostatic pressure at a prescribed curvature of the liquid; these include the capillary height method, with its numerous variants, the maximum bubble pressure method, the drop-weight method, and the method of sessile drops. The second principle, less accurate, but very often convenient because of its rapidity, is the formation of a film of the liquid and its extension by means of a support caused to adhere to the liquid temporarily; methods in this class include the detachment of a ring or plate from the surface of any liquid, and the measurement of the tension of soap solutions by extending a film.

The dynamic methods depend on the fact that certain vibrations of a liquid cause periodic extensions and contractions of its surface, which are resisted or assisted by the surface tension. Surface tension therefore forms an important part, or the whole, of the restoring force which is concerned in these vibrations, and may be calculated from observations of their periodicity. Dynamic methods include determination of the wave-length of ripples, of the oscillations of jets issuing from non-circular orifices, and of the oscillations of hanging drops. Dynamic methods may measure a different quantity from the static methods, in the case of solutions, as the surface is constantly being renewed in some of these methods, and may not be old enough for adsorption to have reached equilibrium. In the formation of ripples there is so little interchange of material between the surface and interior, and so little renewal of the surface, that the surface tension measured is the 'static' tension (§ 12).

Unfortunately the dynamic methods do not give, in their present stage of development, a quantitative measure of the time which has elapsed since the formation of the surface before the measurement is effectively taken, and the extent to which adsorption has proceeded is therefore not ascertainable. In the case of solutions showing pronounced adsorption, therefore, the interpretation of the measurements made by dynamic methods can usually only be qualitative.

2. The 'capillary constant'. A quantity which occurs so often that it must be defined at once is the so-called 'capillary constant'. The approximate formula (5) of Chapter I, for the rise of a liquid in

* See also Appendix.

very narrow capillary tubes, may be written, when the contact angle is zero,

$$\frac{2\gamma}{g(D-d)} = rh = a^2, \qquad (1)[1]$$

r being the radius of the tube and h the height to which the liquid rises. The product rh is called the 'capillary constant', or the 'specific cohesion'; it has the dimensions of area and is nearly always expressed in *square millimetres.* This rather oddly defined quantity has been used widely for over a century; it arose because the first law of Capillarity known was that the product of the height of rise and the radius of the capillary tube is approximately constant; and its continued use is due to the fact that the square root, a, of the capillary constant, when introduced into most of the formulae used for calculating surface tension, simplifies them greatly.

3. The capillary height method. The approximate theory of this method was given in Chap. I, § 12. It was shown that the curvature of the meniscus of the liquid in the tube determines the pressure immediately under the meniscus, by the fundamental relation (Chap. I, equation (3)) between the curvature, surface tension, and pressure difference across the surface. The liquid then rises or falls in the tube, until the height of the meniscus is such that the weight of the column of liquid adjusts the pressure inside and outside the tube to equality. When the tube is so narrow that the meniscus may be taken as spherical, then

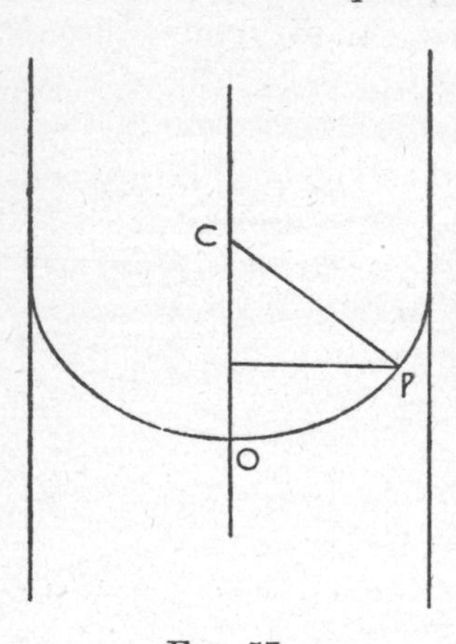

FIG. 57.

$$\gamma \cos\theta = \tfrac{1}{2}grh(D-d), \qquad (2)$$

where θ is the contact angle. In what follows, the contact angle will be taken as zero, since it is only with a zero contact angle that accurate results can be obtained by this method of measuring surface tensions.

When the radius of the tube is appreciable, equation (2) requires correction, because the meniscus is no longer spherical. In Fig. 57, let b be the radius of curvature of the lowest point O of the meniscus (the two radii will be equal at this point, since the tube is cylindrical and the point is on the axis of revolution). The pressure immediately under the centre of the

[1] D is the density of the denser phase, and d that of the lighter, throughout this chapter. If the liquid is taken in contact with air, d is the density of air; if in a vacuum, d is the density of the saturated vapour at the temperature of the experiment. In these cases d may often be neglected without serious loss of accuracy. The equations also apply to interfaces between two liquids in which case d is the density of the lighter liquid.

The symbol D_1 denotes the density below the vertex of a fluid interface, and D_2 that above the vertex.

A few writers, including Rayleigh, have used another 'capillary constant', with the same symbol a^2, half that defined above; this is, however, much the commonest.

meniscus is less than that under a plane surface outside by $2\gamma/b$, so that the height to which the lowest point of the meniscus rises is

$$h = \frac{2\gamma}{bg(D-d)} \tag{3}$$

or, by (1),

$$a^2 = bh. \tag{4}$$

Equations (3) and (4) are accurate for any size of tube; but since the radius of curvature b is very difficult to measure, they cannot be used until a relation between b and the radius of the tube is obtained.

This relation can be obtained from the fundamental equation (Chap. I (4)) for the form of a liquid surface under gravity and surface tension. Unfortunately this equation cannot be solved in finite terms. Approximate solutions have been obtained in several ways which are outside the scope of this book. Sufficient account must, however, be given of the methods of Bashforth and Adams,[1] to enable the reader to use their tables of numerical results, which are the most complete and accurate ever compiled. Some other important approximate formulae will also be given, for applications of the fundamental equation to special cases.

4. Bashforth and Adams's treatment of surfaces of revolution. The solution of the equation is given to four, or five, significant figures, by these authors, for figures of revolution about a vertical axis. Until 1921, however, their results were but little used, and unfortunately their monograph is now out of print and very rare. For the special cases of the capillary height, and maximum bubble pressure methods, Sugden has calculated subsidiary tables; and Dorsey and Porter have done the same for the method of sessile drops.

The fundamental equation for the surface of separation between two fluids is

$$\gamma\left(\frac{1}{R_1}+\frac{1}{R_2}\right) = C+gz(D_1-D_2), \tag{5}$$

where z is the vertical height of a point on the surface, measured from a fixed point, z being positive when measured towards the concave side of the curve. Four cases are important (Fig. 58); in case a, which includes the ordinary form of the meniscus in the maximum bubble pressure and the capillary height methods, the vertex is convex downwards and the denser fluid is below; in b (hanging drops) the vertex is convex downwards and the denser fluid is above; in c (sessile drops) the vertex is concave downwards and the denser fluid is below; in d, the vertex is concave downwards and the denser fluid is above, this is a bubble escaping upwards into a liquid. The figure shows sections of the surface through the axis of revolution, OC.

The equation (5) may be transformed as follows. Taking O as origin, let the vertical and horizontal coordinates of a point P on the curve be z and x. Draw PC normal to the curve, cutting the axis at C; the angle PCO is ϕ.

[1] *An Attempt to test the Theories of Capillary Action* (Cambridge, 1883).

Let the radius of curvature of the surface at P, in the plane of the paper, be ρ; the radius perpendicular to this is PC, since PC is the normal, and C being on the axis of revolution, P remains on the curve when PC rotates about OC and P moves perpendicular to the paper. The principal radii R_1 and R_2 are therefore $\frac{x}{\sin\phi}$ and ρ.

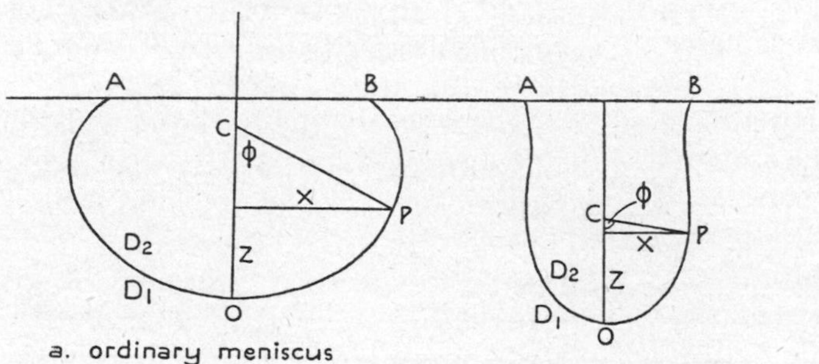

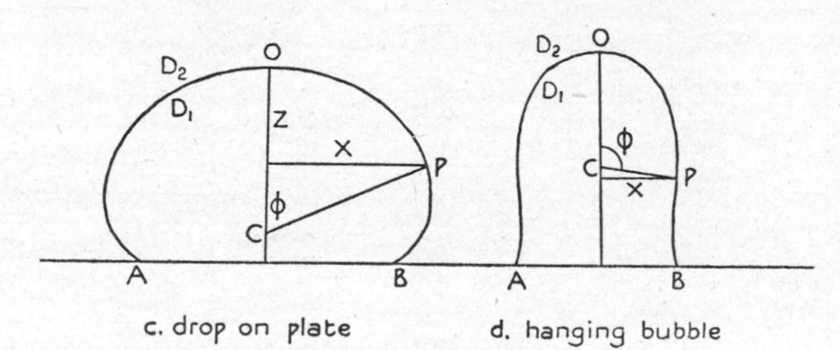

FIG. 58.

Let the radius of curvature at O be b (all the radii are equal at this point); then at O, $z = 0$ and $C = 2\gamma/b$; (5) becomes

$$\gamma\left(\frac{1}{\rho}+\frac{\sin\phi}{x}\right) = \frac{2\gamma}{b}+gz(D_1-D_2)$$

or

$$\frac{1}{\rho/b}+\frac{\sin\phi}{x/b} = 2+\frac{z}{b}(D_1-D_2)\frac{gb^2}{\gamma}.$$

Putting

$$\beta = \frac{gb^2}{\gamma}(D_1-D_2) = \frac{2b^2}{a^2}, \tag{6}$$

where a^2 is the capillary constant defined by

$$a^2 = \frac{2\gamma}{g(D_1-D_2)},$$

$$\frac{1}{\rho/b}+\frac{\sin\phi}{x/b} = 2+\beta\frac{z}{b}. \tag{7}$$

Equation (7) describes the meniscus in a form in which one quantity, b, determines the scale of the meniscus, while one other, β, determines its shape.

Two cases arise, according to the sign of β. β is positive if the fluid above the interface is the lighter, and negative if it is the denser, as it has the same sign as D_1-D_2. Cases a and c have β positive; hence a drop of liquid on a plate has the same shape as the bubble formed downwards or the meniscus at the top of a column of liquid. Cases b and d have β negative, so that the hanging drop, and the bubble escaping upwards, have similar shapes.

Bashforth and Adams's tables give the values of x/b, z/b, and V/b^3 for given values of ϕ and β, both positive and negative. V is the volume included between the horizontal plane at the height z and the apex of the surface.

5. Application to the capillary height method. Sugden[1] has pointed out that, when the contact angle is zero, the ratio r/b of the radius of the tube to the radius of the lowest point of the meniscus is the x/b of Bashforth and Adams's tables. By (6)

$$\frac{r}{a} = \frac{r}{b}\sqrt{\frac{\beta}{2}}, \tag{8}$$

where a is the square root of the capillary constant. A table was constructed giving corresponding values of r/a and r/b, thus: from Bashforth and Adams's table, corresponding values of r/b and β were found for $\phi = 90°$ (zero contact angle); then r/a was found by (8). The range so calculated was from $r/a = 0{\cdot}25$ to $r/a = 2{\cdot}24$. For tubes of smaller diameter, Rayleigh's formula[2]

$$a^2 = rh\left\{1+\frac{1}{3}\frac{r}{h}-0{\cdot}1288\frac{r^2}{h^2}+0{\cdot}1312\frac{r^3}{h^3}\right\} \tag{9}$$

was used; for values of r/a greater than 4·3, a second approximation formula due to Rayleigh was used:

$$\frac{r}{\alpha}-\log_e\frac{\alpha}{h} = 0{\cdot}8381+0{\cdot}2798\frac{\alpha}{r}+\tfrac{1}{2}\log_e\frac{r}{\alpha}, \tag{10}$$

in which $\alpha = \dfrac{a}{\sqrt{2}}$; h is the height of rise. For intermediate values, graphical interpolation was employed.

The first part of the table, which is reproduced by permission from the *Journal of the Chemical Society*, is accurate to the last figure.

The tables are used as follows. A first approximation is made to a, by assuming the height of rise to be that given by the approximate formula $rh = a^2$; the value of r/b corresponding to this value of r/a is looked up, b is found, and so a second approximation to a is obtained from the formula $bh = a^2$; with this value of a a second approximation to r/b and b is read off from the tables, and the process is repeated until a constant value

[1] *J.C.S.* (1921), 1483.

[2] *Proc. Roy. Soc.* A, **92**, 184 (1915).

TABLE XVII

Values of r/b for values of r/a from 0·00 to 2·29

	0·00	0·01	0·02	0·03	0·04	0·05	0·06	0·07	0·08	0·09
0·00	1·0000	9999	9998	9997	9995	9992	9988	9983	9979	9974
0·10	0·9968	9960	9952	9944	9935	9925	9915	9904	9893	9881
0·20	9869	9856	9842	9827	9812	9796	9780	9763	9746	9728
0·30	9710	9691	9672	9652	9631	9610	9589	9567	9545	9522
0·40	9498	9474	9449	9424	9398	9372	9346	9320	9293	9265
0·50	9236	9208	9179	9150	9120	9090	9060	9030	8999	8968
0·60	8936	8905	8873	8840	8807	8774	8741	8708	8674	8640
0·70	8606	8571	8536	8501	8466	8430	8394	8358	8322	8286
0·80	8249	8212	8175	8138	8101	8064	8026	7988	7950	7913
0·90	7875	7837	7798	7759	7721	7683	7644	7606	7568	7529
1·00	7490	7451	7412	7373	7334	7295	7255	7216	7177	7137
1·10	7098	7059	7020	6980	6941	6901	6862	6823	6783	6744
1·20	6704	6665	6625	6586	6547	6508	6469	6431	6393	6354
1·30	6315	6276	6237	6198	6160	6122	6083	6045	6006	5968
1·40	5929	5890	5851	5812	5774	5736	5697	5659	5621	5583
1·50	5545	5508	5471	5435	5398	5362	5326	5289	5252	5216
1·60	5179	5142	5106	5070	5034	4998	4963	4927	4892	4857
1·70	4822	4787	4753	4719	4686	4652	4618	4584	4549	4514
1·80	4480	4446	4413	4380	4347	4315	4283	4250	4217	4184
1·90	4152	4120	4089	4058	4027	3996	3965	3934	3903	3873
2·00	3843	3813	3783	3753	3723	3683	3663	3633	3603	3574
2·10	3546	3517	3489	3461	3432	3403	3375	3348	3321	3294
2·20	3267	3240	3213	3186	3160	3134	3108	3082	3056	3030

TABLE XVIII

Values of r/b for larger values of r/a

	0·0	0·1	0·2	0·3	0·4	0·5	0·6	0·7	0·8	0·9
2·0	0·384	355	327	301	276	252	229	206	185	166
3·0	149	133	119	107	097	088	081	074	067	061
4·0	056	051	047	043	039	035	031	028	025	022
5·0	020	018	017	015	014	012	010	009	008	007
6·0	006	006	005	004	004	003	003	003	002	002

of a is found, which is the true value. The table rarely requires to be used more than twice in this way to obtain the correct value of a. The surface tension is then found from (1).

Water has $a^2 = 14{\cdot}88$ sq. mm. at room temperature; hence the first part of the tables, which are as accurate as those of Bashforth and Adams, apply to tubes of radius up to 8·8 mm. For many organic liquids, which have a^2 often about 5, the accuracy is the same up to about 5 mm. radius. These tubes are of course far wider than those generally used, except for the purpose of a reference surface with which the height in the narrower tube may be compared.

Sugden's tables (up to $r/a = 2{\cdot}2$) are probably the most accurate approximation existent. Rayleigh's formula (9) for small tubes agrees with these tables up to $r/a = 0{\cdot}46$, within one part in two thousand. For larger tubes, the approximation given by (9) becomes rapidly worse; thus at $r/a = 0{\cdot}7$ this formula is about 1 per cent. in error.

Poisson gave the first three terms of Rayleigh's equation (9), in 1831, and Laplace, the first two terms on the right-hand side of equation (10) for wide tubes, in 1805. Bosanquet[1] has calculated the corrections for moderately wide tubes, using a different method of approximation from that of Bashforth and Adams. Porter[2] has given further calculations of the corrections.

6. Experimental details of the capillary height method. The details necessary to obtain results of the highest accuracy are fully discussed by Richards and Coombs,[3] Richards and Carver,[4] and Harkins and Brown,[5] especially the second named.

The measurement of the height of the bottom of the meniscus has theoretically to be made relative to a plane surface of liquid in communication with the capillary tube. It is not always recognized that a very large surface is required, if it is to be sufficiently plane; the cylindrical tubes of 20 mm. diameter often used have a decided capillary rise. Tubes of 40 mm. diameter or more must be used if the surface is to be considered as plane. Richards and Carver have, however, tested Rayleigh's formula (10) for wide tubes, and found it to agree with experiment within a few thousandths of a millimetre for a tube 38 mm. diameter; this formula can be used with fair accuracy down to tubes of 25 mm. diameter, as a correction to the level in the wide tube. The actual measurement of the difference in height between the two levels requires an accurate cathetometer and suitable illumination of the menisci (see Richards and Coombs).

Measurement of the radius of the tube presents great difficulties, since it is practically essential, as the meniscus moves up and down the tube, to have the tube of uniform diameter; glass tubing is usually very uneven. The radius is ascertained usually by measuring the length of a column of mercury moving along the tube; for accurate work often hundreds of feet of tubing must be examined before a single piece is found of sufficient uniformity. Thin-walled 'quill' tubing is often more uniform than thick walled 'capillary' tubing. Irregularities in the thickness of the wall, which may cause optical distortion of the position of the meniscus, must be avoided.

An accurately circular cross-section is not necessary; some workers have laid unnecessary stress on the attainment of this. The height of rise is proportional to the sum of the reciprocals of the principal radii of curvature of the meniscus, which will be nearly equal to the major and minor semi-axes of the tube, r_1 and r_2, if the section is elliptical; the error in the rise is therefore the difference between $\frac{1}{r_1}+\frac{1}{r_2}$ and $\frac{2}{r}$, where r is the mean radius. This is only 0·1 per cent. for 6 per cent. difference between the maximum and minimum radius. Richards and Carver found the error due to ellipticity even less than this, experimentally.

The contact angle between the glass and the liquid must be zero. If the glass is properly cleaned the contact angle is almost always zero with

[1] *Phil. Mag.*, **5**, 296 (1928). [2] *Trans. Faraday Soc.*, **29**, 702, 1307 (1933).
[3] *J.A.C.S.* (1915), 1656. [4] *Ibid.* (1921), 827. [5] *Ibid.* (1919), 503.

water and organic liquids.[1] A simple and probably sufficient test of a zero angle is to photograph a glass rod dipping into the liquid. A more accurate method is to photograph the reflection of an illuminated slit at the junction between the meniscus and the tube; if the reflection from the liquid is continuous with that from the tube, there is no contact angle. Richards and Carver, and Hunten and Maass,[2] have shown the absence of contact angle for a variety of liquids, in this way. A contact angle of $2\frac{1}{2}$ degrees introduces only 0·1 per cent. error.

The contact angle may not, however, be zero if much evaporation takes place at the edge of the liquid, or if the liquid is advancing up the tube. The capillary height should be measured with a falling meniscus.

The capillary height method is the ultimate standard, being at present the most accurate method known both experimentally and in the degree of approximation to which the theory has been carried. It needs to be remembered that the mathematical theory of all the methods for determining surface tension involves approximations, if only in the numerical solution of equations; and it is a regrettable fact that the literature abounds in 'measurements of surface tension' whose results have been calculated by the use of altogether inadequate formulae. Mathematical errors of 10 per cent. and upwards are by no means uncommon, in some methods, although an accuracy of one part in a thousand can be attained with the capillary height method.

The following results obtained by this method provide easily accessible liquids of known surface tension, which may be used as standards for calibrating some of the instruments which will be described.

TABLE XIX

Accurately known surface tensions, in air (20°)

	Harkins and Brown.	Richards and Carver.
Water	72·80	72·73
Benzene	28·88	28·88
Toluene	..	28·43
Chloroform	..	27·14
Ether	..	16·96

The above methods, with a wide reference tube from which to measure the height of rise, require much liquid. Sugden[3] employed a U-tube with two limbs of different diameter, one about twice that of the other, comparing the height of rise in both. The corrections to the simple formula (1) were found from his tables, and the method appears capable of little less accuracy than the highest refinements of the capillary height method, if

[1] Aqueous solutions of many nitrogenous bases with long aliphatic chains are exceptions. The bases appear to be strongly adsorbed by the positively charged nitrogen at the end, the hydrocarbon chains being oriented outwards so that the surface becomes strongly hydrophobic.

[2] *J.A.C.S.* (1929), 156.

[3] *J.C.S.* (1921), 1483.

the tubes are selected with proper care, and their diameters come within the range of the first part of the tables.

7. Variations of the capillary height method. A useful modification is to measure the pressure which must be applied to force the meniscus down till it is level with the plane surface of liquid outside the tube. This is recommended by Ferguson and Dowson,[1] and measurements have been made by Edwards.[2] One great advantage of this method is that the radius of the capillary tube needs to be known only at one point, and can, if necessary, be determined by cutting the tube afterwards and measuring with a microscope. Ferguson and Hakes[3] also measure the pressure needed to force the meniscus down to the lower end of the tube, below the outside water-level.

This method might be very useful as a differential method for comparing the surface tensions of two similar liquids, such as water at different temperatures, and water and dilute solutions, for differences of gaseous pressure can be measured with great accuracy.

Ferguson[4] has also devised two ingenious methods for determining the surface tension of very small amounts (1 or 2 cu. mm.) of liquid. The pressure required to force the meniscus, located at the end of a capillary tube, to a plane form, is measured; it is equal to $2\gamma/r$ for tubes so narrow that the meniscus would naturally be spherical. In one method the tube is vertical; in the other it is horizontal, and in this modification the density of the liquid need not be determined. The contact angle must be zero, as in all variants of the capillary height method.

A method for which very great accuracy is claimed is due to Grinnell Jones and Ray;[5] the apparatus consists as usual of a wide tube (ground and polished to a true cylinder inside) and a narrow one; the liquid is brought to a fixed mark in the narrow tube. The principal novel feature is that the difference in levels of the narrow and wide menisci is found by weighing the total amount of liquid in the apparatus when the liquid in the narrow tube is at the fixed height. As a differential instrument, for comparing two liquids whose tensions differ but little, this apparatus seems very accurate.

Other variants are the rise between two parallel plane surfaces of glass, and the so-called 'hyperbola' method, which measures the rise between two vertical plates inclined at a small angle. If the parallel plates are at a distance b apart, the radius of curvature is infinite in one direction and $\frac{1}{2}b$ in the other. The height of rise is therefore (neglecting any deviation of the meniscus from a cylindrical form)

$$h = \frac{2\gamma}{gb(D-d)}. \tag{11}$$

The 'hyperbola' method has two vertical plates inclined at a small angle ϕ radians to each other, so that their distance apart increases with increasing

[1] *Trans. Faraday Soc.*, **17**, 384 (1922).
[2] *J.C.S.* (1925), 744.
[3] *Proc. Physical Soc.*, **41**, 214 (1929).
[4] *Ibid.*, **36**, 37 (1923); **44**, 511 (1932).
[5] *J.A.C.S.* (1937), 187.

distance from their vertical intersection. If y is the vertical and x the horizontal coordinate of a point on the liquid surface, taking the point where the line of intersection of the two plates cuts the water as origin, then the plates are a distance $x\phi$ apart at a distance x from the junction. When ϕ is small we can use (11) to calculate y, the height of rise, so that

$$\gamma = \tfrac{1}{2}xyg\phi(D-d); \tag{12}$$

xy is constant, thus the surface of the liquid in profile has the form of a rectangular hyperbola.

For the case where ϕ is not very small, Ferguson and Vogel[1] have calculated the corrections to (12); and Grünmach[2] has constructed an instrument with a series of hyperbolas ruled on the plates; the angle ϕ is altered until the surface of liquid coincides with one of them, when the surface tension can be calculated from (12). The method is ingenious but not capable of very high accuracy.

Sentis's method[3] employs a capillary tube with a hanging drop at the bottom of the tube, and the height of the meniscus in the tube above the drop is measured.

8. The maximum bubble pressure method. If a bubble is blown at the bottom of a tube dipping vertically into a liquid, the pressure in the bubble increases at first, as the bubble grows and the radius of curvature diminishes. It was shown in Chap. I, § 13, that when the bubble is small enough to be taken as spherical, the smallest radius of curvature and the maximum pressure occurs when the bubble is a hemisphere; further growth causes diminution of pressure, so that air rushes in and bursts the bubble. At this point the pressure in the bubble is

$$P+P_1 = gh_1(D-d)+\frac{2\gamma}{r}, \tag{13}$$

where $P_1 = gh_1(D-d)$ is the part of the measured pressure required to force the liquid down the tube to the level h_1 of the end of the tube below the plane surface of the liquid, and r is the radius of the tube; in the case of a liquid which wets the tube moderately well, it is the internal radius of the tube, since the liquid covers the lower edge of the tube completely.

This method is independent of the contact angle, provided that it is not so great (above 90°) that the liquid recedes to the outer edge of the tube; if this occurs, r is the outer radius of the tube.

If h is the height of a column of the liquid equivalent to the part of the pressure, P, due to the bubble, (13) reduces to

$$a^2 = rh. \tag{14}$$

This is the same equation as the approximate one for the rise in a capillary tube, as it must be, since the height of rise is a measure of the pressure effect of the curved surface of the meniscus.

[1] *Proc. Physical Soc.*, **38**, 193 (1925).
[2] *Physikal. Z.*, **11**, 980 (1910). *Z. Instrument.*, **30**, 366 (1910); **39**, 195 (1919).
[3] *J. Physique*, **6**, 571 (1887).

For larger tubes the surface cannot be taken as spherical, and the fundamental equation (5) must be applied. Numerous writers have given approximation formulae, of which the best is that of Schrödinger,[1]

$$a^2 = rh\left(1-\frac{2}{3}\frac{r}{h}-\frac{1}{6}\frac{r^2}{h^2}\right). \tag{15}$$

As with the rise in the capillary tube, all such formulae can only be accurate for moderately narrow tubes. A more satisfactory plan has been adopted by Sugden,[2] who applied Bashforth and Adams's tables as follows.

Fig. 59 shows a vertical section of a bubble; comparing it with Fig. 58 a, clearly the radius r is the value of x when ϕ is BCO, and z is the vertical height of the bubble; b is the radius of curvature of the bubble at its apex O.

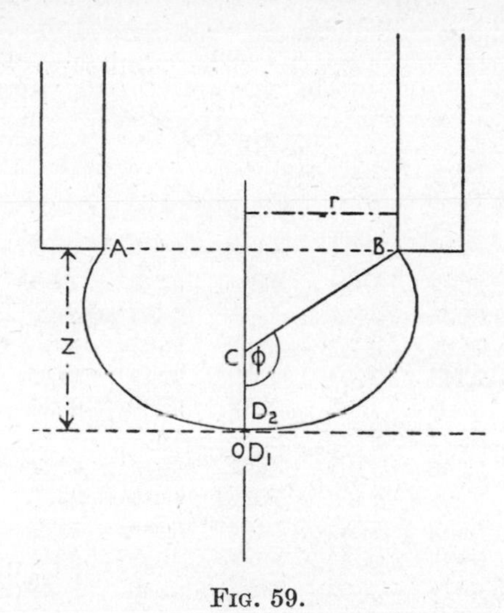

Fig. 59.

The pressure in the bubble at the level AB of the bottom of the tube exceeds that in the liquid outside at the same level by an amount P, where

$$P = \frac{2\gamma}{b}+gz(D-d),$$

and if h is the height of the corresponding column of liquid, $P = gh(D-d)$, therefore, by (1),

$$h = \frac{a^2}{b}+z,$$

or

$$\frac{hr}{a^2} = \frac{r}{b}+\frac{r}{a}\frac{z}{b}\frac{b}{a}. \tag{16}$$

The problem will be solved by finding a quantity X which obeys an equation

$$a^2 = Xh \tag{17}$$

corresponding to (14) but accurate for any size of tube, if X can be found from the tables.

[1] *Ann. Physik*, **46**, 413 (1915). [2] *J.C.S.* (1922), 858; (1924), 27.

From (16), (17), and (6)

$$\frac{r}{X} = \frac{hr}{a^2} = \frac{r}{b} + \frac{r}{a}\frac{z}{b}\sqrt{\frac{\beta}{2}}, \tag{18}$$

and by (6)

$$\frac{r}{b} = \frac{r}{a}\frac{a}{b} = \frac{r}{a}\sqrt{\frac{2}{\beta}}. \tag{19}$$

When the pressure is a maximum, h is a maximum, and, by (17), $1/X$ and r/X will be maxima; hence a maximum value of r/X corresponds to the maximum pressure in the bubble. Only two of the fractions in equations (18) and (19) are independent. Sugden has taken various values of β for each of a series of values r/a, and calculated the corresponding values of r/b from (19). Using Bashforth and Adams's tables, he found the values of ϕ and z/b for these values of r/b and β; thence by (18) the values of r/X were determined. Examination of these showed what are the maximum values of r/X for each value of r/a, and a table was constructed; it is reproduced by permission from the *Journal of the Chemical Society.*

TABLE XX

Minimum values of X/r for values of r/a from 0 to 1·50.

r/a	0·00	0·01	0·02	0·03	0·04	0·05	0·06	0·07	0·08	0·09
0·0	1·0000	9999	9997	9994	9990	9984	9977	9968	9958	9946
0·1	9934	9920	9905	9888	9870	9851	9831	9809	9786	9762
0·2	9737	9710	9682	9653	9623	9592	9560	9527	9492	9456
0·3	9419	9382	9344	9305	9265	9224	9182	9138	9093	9047
0·4	9000	8952	8903	8853	8802	8750	8698	8645	8592	8538
0·5	8484	8429	8374	8319	8263	8207	8151	8094	8037	7979
0·6	7920	7860	7800	7739	7678	7616	7554	7493	7432	7372
0·7	7312	7252	7192	7132	7072	7012	6953	6894	6835	6776
0·8	6718	6660	6603	6547	6492	6438	6385	6333	6281	6230
0·9	6179	6129	6079	6030	5981	5933	5885	5838	5792	5747
1·0	5703	5659	5616	5573	5531	5489	5448	5408	5368	5329
1·1	5290	5251	5213	5176	5139	5103	5067	5032	4997	4962
1·2	4928	4895	4862	4829	4797	4765	4733	4702	4671	4641
1·3	4611	4582	4553	4524	4496	4468	4440	4413	4386	4359
1·4	4333	4307	4281	4256	4231	4206	4181	4157	4133	4109
1·5	4085									

The table is used by first calculating a, assuming the simple equation (14); finding the value of X corresponding to this value of a from the tables, and then obtaining a second approximation to a by using (17). A fresh value for X is found, and hence a calculated more accurately by (17), and the process is repeated until constant values for a are obtained. The values for X/r up to $r/a = 0{\cdot}20$ were calculated from Schrödinger's formula (13). This formula ceases to be accurate within 0·3 per cent., when r/a exceeds 0·3, so that Sugden's tables are the best approximation available.

The experimental arrangements differ according as one or two tubes are employed for forming bubbles. In Jaeger's method[1] a single tube is employed, which is adjustable by means of a micrometer screw, so that the depth of its lower end below the liquid is known; an accurate know-

[1] *Z. anorg. Chem.*, **101**, 1 (1917).

ledge of this is essential, as the pressure due to the depth of the tip below the plane surface of the liquid is added to that due to the bubble. It is difficult to determine this nearer than to 0·1 mm.; and also, if a single tube is used, any curvature of the surface due to capillary rise in the vessel containing the liquid affects the pressure, so that a vessel of well over 3 cm. diameter is necessary.

Sugden has shown that these complications, and the necessity of measuring the depth of the tip below the surface of the liquid, may be avoided by using two tubes of different diameters (Fig. 60), dipping to the same depth in the liquid, the simple apparatus requiring only to be set vertically. Bubbles can be blown on the smaller tube by closing the tap leading to the larger. If P_a and P_b are the pressures recorded on a manometer placed between the side-tube of the bubbler and an aspirator, when bubbles are blown on the small and large tubes, then

$$P_a - P_b = 2\gamma\left(\frac{1}{X_a} - \frac{1}{X_b}\right). \tag{20}$$

Finally, it was found that equation (20) could be replaced, with an accuracy of one part in 1,000, by an empirical formula

$$\gamma = A(P_a - P_b)\left(1 + 0{\cdot}69 r_b \frac{gD}{P_a - P_b}\right), \tag{21}$$

where r_b, the radius of the larger tube, does not exceed 2 mm. The radius of the smaller tube should be about 0·1 mm.

By the use of equation (21) the instrument can be used as a means of comparing surface tensions, the constant A being determined by calibration with benzene. The method may be still further simplified by using a rubber stopper in place of the ground joint, but the two tubes must be fused together so that they preserve the same relative level in the liquid. Two or three cubic centimetres of liquid are all that is required, and the method is reliable to about 0·3 per cent., measurements being taken easily within 15 minutes. The density does not need to be accurately known, as an error of 1 per cent. causes an error of less than one-tenth of this percentage in the surface tension. The factor in the bracket of (21) rarely exceeds 1·05.

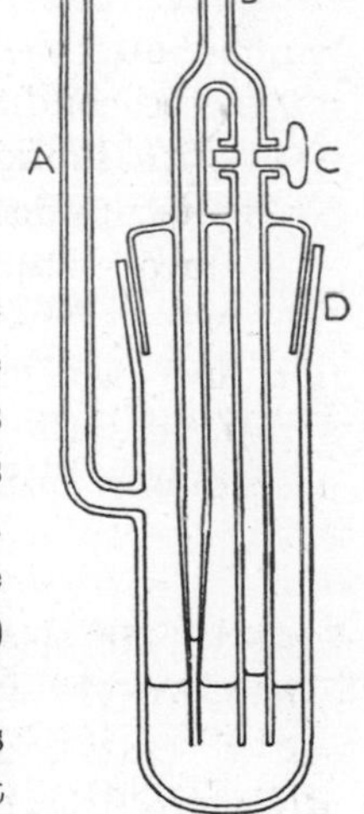

Fig. 60.

Sugden's method appears to combine the advantages of speed, simplicity, and accuracy to a greater extent than any other method; and it has the advantage that a fresh liquid surface is formed for each determination, so that there is little risk of contamination. Theoretically the bubbles must be formed slowly, but in practice no change in the pressure reading occurs if the rate is reduced below about two per second, with pure liquids. If a simple pressure controlling device is used to blow the liquids over, instead of sucking by an aspirator, the bubbles may be formed slowly. The author has used this method for studying the change of tension of certain solutions, with time, for periods up to 10 minutes. It appears suitable for any liquid except such solutions as reach their final surface tension very slowly.

A useful differential method on this principle has been described by Warren.[1] Two equal jets are made, by carefully cutting a fine tube across, and arranged to dip into two beakers containing the solutions whose surface tensions are to be compared; the beakers are mounted on stands whose height is accurately adjustable by micrometer screws. Both tubes are connected to the same source of air under measured pressure, and the heights of the beakers are adjusted until the bubbles come alternately from the two tubes. The maximum pressure in the bubbles is then the same, and the surface tensions can be calculated, after ascertaining the depth of the tips of the two tubes below the surface of the liquids, by equation (13) or preferably by a similar equation in which X is substituted for r in (13) and is found from Sugden's tables.

This method is simple, and should be a very good method of measuring small differences in surface tension produced by small amounts of dissolved substances.

9. The drop-volume method. One of the commonest methods of determining surface tension is by measuring the volume or weight of drops which fall slowly from the tip of a vertical tube; 'stalagmometer' is the generic name for instruments for forming and weighing drops. Although so widely used, the theory of the method is even now far from worked out; and though the correct result can be obtained under carefully regulated conditions, this has only been attained by laborious standardization with liquids whose surface tension has been previously determined by better understood methods.

Accurate study of the relation between the weight of falling drops and the surface tension began with Tate,[2] who concluded that the weight of the drop is proportional to the radius of the tube from which it falls, depending also on the physical and chemical properties of the liquid. A curiously crude formula for the weight of a drop,

$$W = 2\pi r\gamma, \tag{22}$$

based on the theory that the surface tension of the liquid, acting vertically round the rim of the tube, holds the drop up against gravity, is sometimes called 'Tate's law', although Tate did not go so far as to state that the drop weight is proportional to the surface tension.

The formula (22) is very seriously wrong for many reasons, two of which are that the edge of the drop at the tip is very rarely vertical, and that

[1] *Phil. Mag.*, **4**, 358 (1927).

[2] *Phil. Mag.*, **27**, 176 (1864). Tate's opening remark, that 'People generally, and medical men especially, speak of a drop of liquid as if it were some definite quantity', is amusing and possibly still appropriate.

not the whole, but a part only, of the drop falls. In practice the drops are always smaller than $2\pi r\gamma$, usually by about 40 per cent., but sometimes by even more. Perrot[1] gives an account of numerous investigations into the deviations from this formula prior to 1917. No satisfactory corrections of a simple kind can, however, be made.

Guye and Perrot's cinematographic study[2] of the falling of a drop makes it clear why no simple formula exists; the four sketches (Fig. 61) show

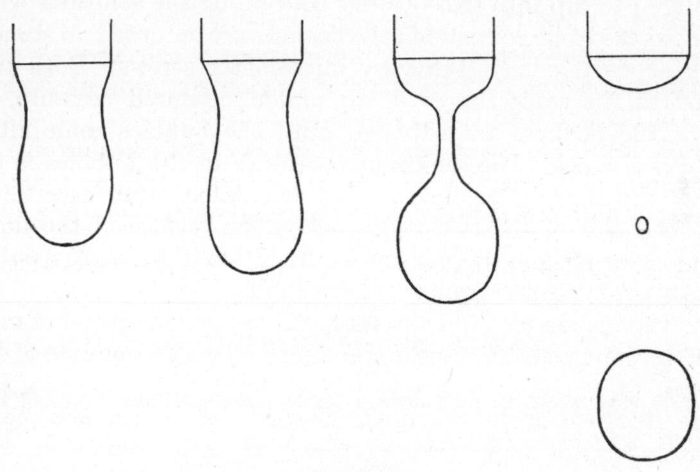

FIG. 61.

successive stages from the time when the drop becomes unstable until it has broken away. A slight waist develops, just before instability sets in; this lengthens and narrows very much, and finally two drops break away, the first large, the second very small, and much liquid remains behind. Of course, the weight of both the large and the small drop are counted as 'one drop' in the drop-weight method.

The full theory of the weight of the falling drop involves two points, the size of the drop at the point where the break-away commences through instability, and the fraction of the total bulk which falls; Lohnstein's work[3] is the most thorough, though it is not complete. For practical purposes the gaps in the theory have been covered by the work of Harkins and Brown,[4] who have carefully measured the weight of drops falling from tubes with tips of different sizes. They find, as was predicted by Lohnstein, that the weight of a drop is a function of r/a, where r is the radius of the tube and a the square root of the capillary constant, so that

$$W = 2\pi r\gamma f\left(\frac{r}{a}\right), \tag{23}$$

where $f(r/a)$ is determined uniquely by the value of r/a. In an actual determination of surface tension, a is unknown; Harkins and Brown point

[1] *J. Chim. Phys.*, **15**, 164 (1917). [2] *Arch. Sci. phys. nat.* (Geneva), **15**, 178 (1903).

[3] *Ann. Physik*, **20**, 237, 606; **21**, 1030 (1906); **22**, 767 (1907).

[4] *J.A.C.S.* (1919), 499.

out that $f(r/a)$ is also a function of $r/V^{\frac{1}{3}}$, where V is the volume of the drop. Hence (23) may be written

$$W = 2\pi r\gamma\psi\left(\frac{r}{V^{\frac{1}{3}}}\right), \tag{24}$$

and the surface tension is given by (24), in terms of r, V, W, and the function ψ.

The functions $f(r/a)$ and $\psi(r/V^{\frac{1}{3}})$ have of course identical numerical values, although f and ψ are not the same, because r/a is different from $r/V^{\frac{1}{3}}$. The values of these functions are given in Harkins and Brown's paper.[1]

The surface tension may be quickly calculated from the weight of a falling drop, formed with the precautions described below, by the following equation and table, which embody the results of Harkins and Brown's measurements. The weight and volume or density of a number of drops are measured, and the radius of the tip from which the drop falls. F is a function of V/r^3, such that $F = \dfrac{1}{2\pi\psi(r/V^{\frac{1}{3}})}$; m is the mass of the drop.

$$\gamma = \frac{mg}{r} \times F. \tag{25}$$

The table is reprinted by permission from *International Critical Tables.*

TABLE XXI[2]

Values of F for drop-weight corrections

V/r^3	F	V/r^3	F	V/r^3	F
5000	0·172	2·3414	0·26350	0·729	0·2517
250	0·198	2·0929	0·26452	0·692	0·2499
58·1	0·215	1·8839	0·26522	0·658	0·2482
24·6	0·2256	1·7062	0·26562	0·626	0·2464
17·7	0·2305	1·5545	0·26566	0·597	0·2445
13·28	0·23522	1·4235	0·26544	0·570	0·2430
10·29	0·23976	1·3096	0·26495	0·541	0·2430
8·190	0·24398	1·2109	0·26407	0·512	0·2441
6·662	0·24786	1·124	0·2632	0·483	0·2460
5·522	0·25135	1·048	0·2617	0·455	0·2491
4·653	0·25419	0·980	0·2602	0·428	0·2526
3·975	0·25661	0·912	0·2585	0·403	0·2559
3·433	0·25874	0·865	0·2570		
2·995	0·26065	0·816	0·2550		
2·637	0·26224	0·771	0·2534		

[1] These functions are an attempt to express the actual weight of the drop in terms of an ideal drop defined by equation (22). This 'ideal drop' does not, however, exist either in practice or in sound theory, and it is better to abandon the term altogether, and to cease the attempt to square the results with this erroneous equation. Some writers have proposed a second 'ideal drop', of half the above size; but this has no more justification than the first.

[2] The experimental error is within 0·1 per cent. when V/r^3 lies between 2·637 and 1·2109. It is within 0·2 per cent. between 10·29 and 0·865.

The experimental details requiring attention are to have the tip of the tube carefully ground and sharp, and to form the drops sufficiently slowly. The drop weight will be too large if the drop is formed too fast, a total time of formation about ten minutes for each drop being requisite. This can be considerably shortened, however, by forming the initial stages of the drop rapidly, permitting the final stages only to proceed very slowly. Harkins and Brown achieve this by fixing the dropping tip in a closed bottle with an outlet tube to which suction can be applied; the liquid is supplied from another bottle by a siphon connected to the tip. The level of the liquid is such that it runs over very slowly by gravity; the final stages of the drop are formed by gravity alone, but the initial stages are formed by suction. In this way the time of formation of each drop can be shortened to one minute without loss of accuracy. Bircumshaw[1] finds that perfect control can be exercised over the formation of the drop by blowing the liquid over. Another device is described by Harkins.[2] The preparation of the tips is described by Harkins and Brown; they may be made of moncl or other metal, or of glass.

The drop-weight method is capable of 0·1 per cent. accuracy in careful hands, provided the correction table is used. It cannot, however, be too forcibly pointed out that the common practice of comparing surface tensions, by dropping different liquids from the same tip and assuming that the surface tensions are proportional to the weights of the drops, is very dangerous. It leads to errors of variable magnitude, which are often as great as 10 per cent. and sometimes even greater. The use of the table is so simple that there is now no excuse for the old plan of simply comparing the weights of drops, and hoping the result will not be far wrong!

A very convenient method of measuring the volume of single drops has been described by Gaddum,[3] using the micrometer syringe, which is probably the best instrument now available for the measurement of volumes of liquid less than 0·5 c.c. The arrangement used by the author, a slight modification of Gaddum's technique, incorporating a convenient method of refilling the syringe, is shown in Fig. 62. The glass tip D, ground according to Harkins's directions, is attached to the end of the micrometer syringe C by a carefully ground joint; B is the piston of the syringe and A the micrometer which propels the piston in the accurately ground cylinder. The tip is fitted by a cork into one side E of a U-tube, which is open to the air through F; the level of the liquid in E is controlled by adjusting the relative heights of the plain tubes H and I, which are connected with the other half, G, of the U-tube by rubber tubing. The syringe is partly filled with the liquid before assembling, air bubbles being expelled; filling is completed by raising the level in E so that the tip dips below the surface, and screwing the micrometer upwards, a rubber band being fixed so that the piston moves up with the micrometer. Thus the surface tensions are determined in a saturated atmosphere. As the

[1] *J.C.S.* (1922), 887. [2] *6th Colloid Symposium Monograph*, p. 34 (1928).
[3] *Proc. Roy. Soc.* B, **109**, 114 (1931).

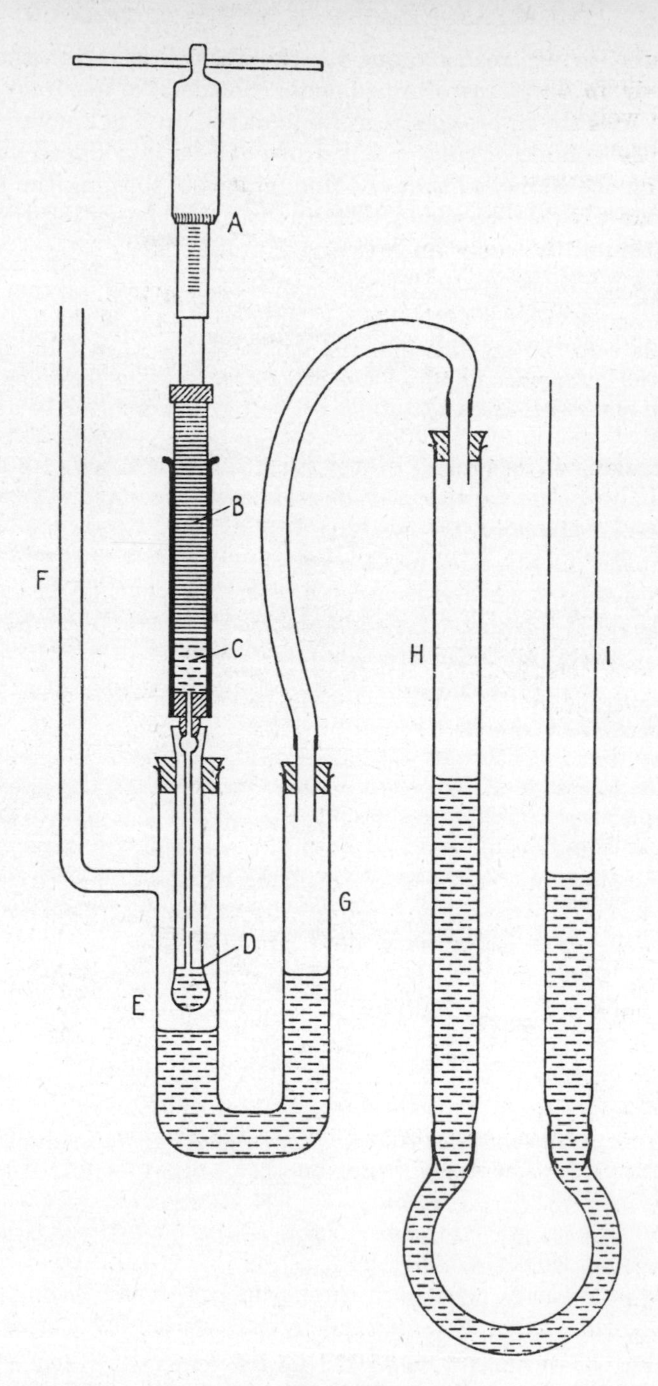

FIG. 62.

micrometer syringe reads to one ten-thousandth of a c.c., the volume of a single drop can be determined with considerable accuracy; and since after one trial the approximate volume of the drop is known, over 95 per cent. of the volume of subsequent drops can be introduced very quickly, by turning the screw, so that the final stages of forming the drop can be carried out with the requisite slowness without extending the total time of formation of the drop much over 1 minute.

If interfacial tensions between two liquids are required, all that is necessary is to float one or two c.c. of the lighter liquid on the top of the heavier liquid in E. In this case the tip dips into the lighter liquid when forming the drops, and into the lower when filling. There is little difficulty in obtaining an accuracy of 0·5 per cent. with this apparatus, and better results might be achieved with great care.

If the making of the ground joint between the tip and the end of the syringe presents difficulty, metal tips may be soldered to the piece of metal which fits the end, and normally carries the hypodermic needle supplied with the instrument. In many cases a simple rubber connexion will be found adequate; it must not be allowed to wobble, or the volume might be altered.

The table has been constructed from the results of most careful, and concordant, measurements on four different liquid-air interfaces. If it is applied to other interfaces, including liquid-liquid junctions, it must be assumed that the functions f, ψ, and F depend only on the value of r/a or V/r^3. The validity of this assumption cannot be fully proved in the present incomplete state of the theory, but the following considerations show that it is a probable one.

Worthington[1] showed, by projecting the outline of hanging drops of different liquids on a screen, that drops of similar shape break away at equal stages of growth. A drop hanging from a circular tube is a figure of revolution about a vertical axis, and can be treated by Bashforth and Adams's methods. The quantity $\beta = 2b^2/a^2$ was found to determine the shape of the surface completely, in equation (7); thus Worthington's observation shows that, whatever the liquid, if β is the same for two drops, the stage at which the drops break away is the same for all liquids. If β is the same for two drops, coming from tips of radii r' and r'', then the conditions for similar shape of the two drops are that

$$\frac{2b'^2}{a'^2} = \frac{2b''^2}{a''^2}.$$

When the drops have similar shape, all corresponding linear dimensions of the two drops will be proportional to one another, so that

$$\frac{b'}{b''} = \frac{a'}{a''} = \frac{r'}{r''} = \frac{V'^{\frac{1}{3}}}{V''^{\frac{1}{3}}},$$

also

$$\frac{r'}{a'} = \frac{r''}{a''} \quad \text{and} \quad \frac{r'}{V'^{\frac{1}{3}}} = \frac{r''}{V''^{\frac{1}{3}}}.$$

Thus taking equal values of r/a or $r/V^{\frac{1}{3}}$ for two liquids is equivalent to ensuring that the drops have similar shapes at the moment of breaking away. The use of the tables therefore amounts to an assumption that the fraction of drops of similar shape, which break away, is the same for all liquids; if the verification

[1] *Proc. Roy. Soc.*, **32**, 362 (1881).

of this for four different liquid-air interfaces is thought an insufficient basis for measuring the surface tension of an unknown liquid, it may be possible to make a direct photographic test, whether the fraction breaking away is normal for that liquid. It seems unlikely that any error can arise except in the case of liquids of high viscosity.

10. Other methods depending directly on the fundamental equation. Direct measurement of the radius of curvature of a surface, by methods similar to those used in determining the radius of curvature of mirrors, has been applied by C. T. R. Wilson[1] and C. V. Boys:[2] simultaneous measurement of the pressure on both sides of the surface gives the surface tension at once by (2). No convenient instrument has been designed for rapid measurement of surface tensions, on this principle, however.

The method of 'sessile' drops or bubbles is of value when changes in surface tension extending over long periods of time have to be measured. Diagrams *a* and *c* of Fig. 58 show the shape of bubbles underneath a plate, or drops on a plate. The theory of the two cases is identical. The usual measurements are of the height h, from the equator (the maximum horizontal diameter) to the vertex O of the drop or bubble, and of the maximum diameter. The height h must be determined with the greatest possible accuracy, as it is usually only 2 or 3 mm., and the surface tension depends on its square, so that errors in measurement of this height are doubled in the final result for the tension. The maximum horizontal diameter of the bubble or drop need not be so accurately measured, as it is required only for correction of the limiting formula relating h and surface tension in bubbles or drops of very large diameter. When the diameter is so large that the curvature at the apex can be neglected, the relation between surface tension and h is

$$h^2 = a^2 = \frac{2\gamma}{g(D-d)}. \tag{26}$$

For drops where this curvature cannot be neglected, Verschaffelt[3] and others have given approximate formulae for the calculation of the surface tension from h and the diameter; Dorsey[4] and Porter[5] have applied Bashforth and Adams's calculations, and Porter's results are given in a form so simple that the surface tension can be calculated in a few minutes from the observations.

The method is independent of the angle of contact between the liquid and the plate, provided that this is not so variable as to distort the bubbles or drop seriously from the form of a figure of revolution about a vertical axis, to which alone the calculations apply. With bubbles under a plate, it is almost necessary to use very slightly concave plates, or it becomes impossible to retain the bubble in position.[6] A measuring microscope with a very good vertical travel is desirable for the measurement of h, and it should also be capable of horizontal

[1] *Proc. Camb. Phil. Soc.*, **14**, 206 (1907).

[2] *J. Soc. Chem. Ind.*, **39**, 58T (1920).

[3] *Proc. K. Akad. Wetensch. Amsterdam*, **21**, 357, 836 (1919).

[4] *J. Washington Acad. Sci.*, **18**, 505 (1928).

[5] *Phil. Mag.*, **15**, 163 (1933).

[6] For experimental details, cf. Gouy, *Ann. de Physique*, **6**, 5 (1916); Burdon, *Trans. Faraday Soc.*, **28**, 866 (1932); Adam and Shute (1938).

motion and measurement, to find the diameter as well.[1] The position of the apex is conveniently found by the shadow when the bubble or drop is illuminated from behind; the equator by placing a slit horizontal on the end of the microscope tube, close to the objective and in the same horizontal line as the axis, and illuminating from behind. The microscope is moved up or down until the reflection of this horizontal slit in the front of the drop or bubble coincides with the horizontal cross wire in the eyepiece of the microscope.

Very great precautions must be taken against accidental contamination of the surface, which cannot be renewed except by removing the bubble or drop, and replacing it by a new one. The method has recently proved useful with metals, and in studying the slow changes of surface tension which take place in solutions of some colloidal electrolytes.

11. The 'ring' and other detachment methods. The surface tension may be determined by measuring the force required to detach objects of various shapes from a liquid surface. As the object is lifted, if it is wetted by the liquid, some of the liquid comes up with it. The form of the volume of liquid lifted depends on the shape of the object, and on the surface tension and density of the liquid. At a certain height the liquid lifted above the normal level of the surface becomes unstable and breaks away. The force that has to be applied to raise the object to this point is equal to the weight of the object plus the weight of the liquid lifted. The method is a very old one; Gay-Lussac used the force required to detach a flat horizontal plate and further work on this method was done by Gallenkamp.[2] In this form the method does not appear very accurate. Wilhelmy[3] used a thin vertical plate; Sondhauss,[4] and Timberg[5] a horizontal ring of thin wire, and Lenard[6] a horizontal straight wire.

The exact calculation of the weight of liquid lifted, in terms of the surface tension and density, is difficult and requires usually special solutions of the fundamental equation of Capillarity, for figures which often are not figures of revolution. The pull may reach a maximum some distance before the object is completely detached; and the measurement of this maximum is considered more satisfactory than that of the pull at the moment of detachment.[7] In most cases, however, the pull is applied by means of a torsion balance, and the upward motion of the object cannot be checked after the maximum pull is past, so that the detachment takes place almost immediately the maximum pull is reached.

The elementary theory, still too often used in calculating the surface tension, states that the pull required to detach the object from the surface is equal to the total perimeter of the wire multiplied by the surface tension. For a thin vertical plate, or a thin horizontal wire, the perimeter would be twice the length. There are, however, end corrections of uncertain magnitude, and accurate results cannot be obtained by the use of this over-simplified theory. As far as the author's experience goes, if elementary theory must be used, Wilhelmy's vertical

[1] Messrs. R. and J. Beck, of London, make an instrument excellently adapted for this purpose.

[2] *Ann. Physik*, **9**, 475 (1902).

[3] *Ibid.*, **119**, 177 (1863).

[4] *Ibid.*, Erg. Bd., **8**, 266 (1878).

[5] *Ibid.*, **30**, 545 (1887).

[6] *Ibid.*, **74**, 381 (1924); cf. also Schwenker, *ibid.*, **11**, 525 (1931).

[7] Cf. Freundlich, *Kapillarchemie*, **1**, p. 25 (1930).

plate method, using long thin coverslips, approaches nearest to accuracy. Zero contact angle is of course of vital importance, but since the angles will always be receding angles, this is quite frequently obtained in practice.

The theory and practice of the method, using horizontal rings of thin platinum wire, has been carried a good deal farther, and it is now claimed that results of 0·25 per cent. accuracy can be obtained. Cantor[1] and Tichanowsky[2] have given approximate formulae, but the most thorough work is that of Harkins and Jordan,[3] and Freud and Freud.[4] These workers have shown, both theoretically and experimentally, that the maximum pull on the ring, i.e. the weight of liquid raised, depends on R^3/V and R/r, besides, of course, on the surface tension and density. R is the mean radius of the ring, and r the radius of the wire of which the ring is composed, V the volume of liquid raised, or the observed pull P divided by the density, $D-d$.

Thus, on the elementary theory,

$$\gamma = \frac{P}{4\pi R}, \tag{27}$$

and to this a correcting factor F has to be applied so that

$$\gamma = \frac{FP}{4\pi R}. \tag{28}$$

F is found to vary, according to the shape and size of the ring, from about 0·75 up to 1·45. Tables are given in Harkins and Jordan's paper. The use of the simple formula (27) may thus give rise to very large errors; on the other hand, as F is sometimes quite near unity, it may on occasion give the correct result. It is therefore not enough to attempt to reassure oneself as to the correctness of the elementary formula (27) by determining the surface tension of some known liquid; given good luck, the right result *may* be obtained!

Instruments with torsion wires for measuring the pull are in very general use on account of their simplicity and convenience; du Nouy[5] and Lottermoser[6] have developed several useful forms of these. Chainomatic balances have also been found useful. Errors may arise if the ring is not exactly in a plane, or if it is not suspended accurately parallel to the surface of the liquid; Harkins and Jordan have investigated the magnitude of these errors. A *large* surface of liquid (over 8 cm. across) is desirable, and evaporation should be minimized by covering with an inverted funnel.

The ring must be completely wet with the liquid, but with platinum rings suspended by platinum stirrups this is usually easily achieved by flaming the rings gently. The method may be used for interfacial tensions also, but here the contact angle must be carefully watched, as zero contact angles with two liquids are more difficult to obtain than with one liquid only. Vibration must be avoided.

The downward pull on a vertical plate, without detachment, gives a very accurate measure of surface tension.[7]

[1] *Ann. Physik*, **47**, 399 (1892). [2] *Physikal. Z.*, **25**, 299 (1924); **26**, 522 (1925).

[3] *6th Colloid Symposium Monograph*, p. 39 (1928); *J.A.C.S.* (1930), 1751.

[4] *J.A.C.S.* (1930), 1772.

[5] *J. Gen. Physiol.*, **1**, 521 (1919); *Surface Equilibria of Colloids*, Chem. Catalog Co. (1926); cf. also Herčík, *Oberflächenspannung in d. Biologie u. Medizin*, Steinkopff (1934).

[6] *Kolloid-Z.*, **66**, 276 (1934); **73**, 155 (1935); *Kolloid-Beih.*, **41**, 74 (1934).

[7] Harkins and Anderson, Chap. II, Appendix.

12. Surface tension by observation of the spreading power of oils. An extremely rapid estimate of the extent to which the surface tension of water is lowered by films of contamination may be obtained by observing whether or not drops of certain oils remain as lenses, or spread out upon the surface. Adam[1] has used solutions of dodecyl alcohol in a non-spreading hydrocarbon, of various strengths; the behaviour of drops of these solutions is first observed on water covered by a monomolecular film under known surface pressure, using the apparatus described in Chap. II, § 6. A change of about 3 dynes per cm. in the lowering of surface tension determines whether or not the drops will spread rapidly on the surface, or not at all; and a change of only 1 dyne makes a noticeable difference to the behaviour of the drop. With a set of a dozen small bottles of these solutions the surface tension of an exposed water surface can be determined in under a minute. Some very recent observations indicate, however, that the method may fail on solutions of strongly adsorbed substances; this requires further investigation.

13. The method of ripples. Waves on the surface of a liquid cause periodic local extensions and contractions of the surface. The theory of these was first fully investigated by Thomson (Lord Kelvin),[2] who gave the formula, for considerable depths of liquid,

$$v^2 = \frac{g\lambda}{2\pi} + \frac{2\pi\gamma}{D\lambda}, \tag{29}$$

or

$$\gamma = \frac{\lambda^3 D}{2\pi\tau^2} - \frac{g\lambda^2 D}{4\pi^2}. \tag{30}$$

λ is the wave-length of the ripples, v their velocity of propagation, and τ their periodic time. If the depth h of the liquid cannot be neglected, the first term in (30) must be multiplied[3] by $\coth(2\pi h/\lambda)$.

Equation (29) shows that the velocity of propagation of waves depends on their wave-length, the first term depending on gravity and the second on the surface tension. The gravity term is unimportant for very short waves, but for long waves it becomes predominant. Table XXII shows the relative importance of surface tension and gravity in propagating waves in water, according to (29).

Either moving or stationary waves may be used; if moving waves are employed, the commonest plan is to view them stroboscopically. As a source of vibrations of steady periodicity, to excite the waves, tuning forks, or electrically oscillating circuits may be used. Rayleigh, Dorsey,[4] Grünmach,[5] Hartridge and Peters,[6] R. C. Brown,[7] and others (referred to in Brown's paper) describe apparatus for producing and observing the ripples.

Although the ripple method is commonly classed as a dynamic method,

[1] *Proc. Roy. Soc.* B, **122,** 134 (1937).
[2] *Phil. Mag.*, **42,** 368 (1871).
[3] Rayleigh, *Phil. Mag.*, **30,** 386 (1890).
[4] *Physical Rev.*, **5,** 170, 213 (1897).
[5] *Verh. deut. physikal. Ges.*, **1,** 13 (1899); *Ann. Physik*, **3,** 660 (1900).
[6] *Proc. Roy. Soc.* A, **101,** 354 (1922).
[7] *Proc. Physical Soc.*, **48,** 312 (1936).

TABLE XXII

Velocity of surface waves on water

Wave-length, cm.	*Velocity, cm. per sec.*	*m.p.h.*	*Percentage of v^2 due to surface tension term*
0	∞	∞	100·0
0·1	67·8	1·52	99·97
0·5	31·5	0·706	92·2
1·0	24·8	0·555	74·5
1·71 (minimum)	23·1	0·517	50·0
2·0	23·2	0·520	42·4
5·0	29·5	0·660	10·5
10·0	40·0	0·896	2·86
100	125	2·80	0·03
1,000	395	8·85	..
10,000	1,250	28·0	..
100,000	3,950	88·5	..

it actually gives the 'static' surface tension; it appears particularly from Brown's results that there is no renewal of the surface, or displacement of adsorbed substances, when the ripples pass along the surface. Working with a solution of a long chain colloidal electrolyte, which was found by the method of sessile bubbles to fall in surface tension very slowly with time, he found that the surface tensions given by the ripple method also fell slowly with time, reaching a final value as low as that given by the static method. Instead of the tensions being higher than those given by the static method, they were (except when the final value was obtained) usually lower, as if the ripples travelling along the surface actually stirred the solution, aiding the solute to come to the surface, and accelerating the fall of tension. Bohr (*loc. cit.* below[2]) briefly refers to sources of error in this method, which tend to make the results too high.

14. Dynamic methods: oscillating jets and drops. If a jet issues from an orifice which is not circular, the surface tension commences to rectify the departure from a circular section in the jet, and the momentum of the liquid causes the jet to become unsymmetrical again after passing through a circular form. Nodes and swellings appear periodically on the jet, when seen from one side, and from their distance apart the surface tension may be calculated. If a spherical drop is deformed, the surface tension tends to restore the spherical form, and oscillations are set up. The theory of both oscillations has been given by Rayleigh,[1] and that of the jets improved by Bohr,[2] who allowed for the viscosity of the liquid. Rayleigh, Bohr, and Stocker[3] have made measurements by the method of oscillating jets. Satterly and Strachan[4] have used stationary waves on a vertical jet.

[1] *Proc. Roy. Soc.*, **29,** 71 (1879).
[2] *Phil. Trans.* A, **209,** 281 (1909); *Proc. Roy. Soc.* A, **84,** 395 (1910).
[3] *Z. physikal. Chem.*, **94,** 149 (1920). [4] *Trans. Roy. Soc. Canada*, **29,** 105 (1935).

Lenard[1] has observed the oscillations of falling drops, and further measurements have been made by his pupils.

15. Measurements on molten metals. The maximum bubble pressure method has proved one of the most satisfactory, but sessile drops, and drop-volumes have also been used with success.[2] The principal difficulty lies in the proneness of metals to form skins of oxides, or other compounds, on their surfaces; and these are sure to reduce the surface tension. Unless work is conducted in a very high vacuum, a freshly formed surface is almost a necessity; if the sessile bubble method is used, the course of formation of a surface layer may, if great precautions are taken, be traced by the alteration in surface tension. Another difficulty lies in the high contact angles formed by liquid metals with almost all non-metallic surfaces, which are due to the very high cohesion of metals compared with their adhesion to other substances.

Bircumshaw has applied the maximum bubble pressure method using two tubes, following Sugden's method fairly closely; Sauerwald used a single tube. Hogness formed drops on the end of a tube pointing upwards, measuring the pressure, the theory being the same as with the bubbles on tubes pointing downwards, as is obvious from Fig. 58, § 4. With the drop-volume method the surface can be quickly renewed, and there is little difficulty in working in a very high vacuum. A point which must be watched is the extent of wetting of the tip on which the drops, or bubbles, are formed by the molten metal. With water and organic liquids, as a rule the tips are completely wet, so that the drops come off from the outer edge of the tip and the bubbles from the inner; with liquid metals, the angle of contact is usually much greater than 90°, so that the drops come off at the inner edge, the radius at the base being equal to the radius of the bore of the tube; bubbles, on the other hand, come off at the outer edge.

16. Methods applicable to interfaces between two liquids. Although theoretically practically all the preceding methods are applicable to liquid-liquid interfaces, the practical difficulties in the application of such methods as the maximum bubble-pressure method, the 'bubbles' being blown of a lighter liquid, would be great. Few methods have yet been developed to a high degree of accuracy. Devices for employing the capillary height method have been described by Harkins and Humphery,[3] Reynolds,[4] Bartell and Miller,[5] Bartell and Mack,[6] and Speakman.[7]

The drop-weight method, in the hands of Harkins and his collaborators (see Harkins and Humphery above) has given a greater number of valuable results than any other method. It is probably the easiest to use, but should at present be checked occasionally by using the capillary-height method. The ring method, with careful attention to complete wetting of the ring by the lower liquid, is also available.

The ripple method has been used by Watson[8] and by Hartridge and Peters for the interface between immiscible liquids. In equation (30)

[1] *Ann. Physik*, **30**, 209 (1887).

[2] See references, Chap. III, § 9, and Chap. IV, § 9.

[3] *J.A.C.S.* (1916), 239.

[4] *J.C.S.* (1921), 460.

[5] *J.A.C.S.* (1928), 1961.

[6] *J.A.C.S.* (1932), 936.

[7] *J.C.S.* (1933), 1449.

[8] *Phys. Rev.*, **12**, 257 (1901).

the density D must be replaced by $D+d$ in the first term and by $D-d$ in the second, when the second fluid has a density d of appreciable magnitude.

17. General review of the different methods. For investigations requiring the highest precision, where time is of secondary importance, the capillary-height method is the best, and Sugden's tables are adequate for reducing the best observations yet made. The verification of the condition that the contact angle is zero is an essential condition of trustworthiness.

For rapid work, requiring an accuracy of about three-tenths per cent., Sugden's modification of the maximum bubble-pressure method is probably the most convenient; very little apparatus is required, and a complete measurement can easily be made in 15 minutes. Two or three cubic centimetres of the liquid are all that is necessary. The drop-weight method (using Harkins's indispensable corrections) is also simple and equally accurate.

Where great economy of material is desirable, Ferguson's methods, or Sentis's, (§ 7) are perhaps the most economical; Sugden's modification of the capillary-height method is also good and accurate.

For examination of slow changes in the tension of an exposed surface the ring method is perhaps the best, and the use of du Noüy's tensimeter, with the corrections of Harkins and Jordan, gives fairly accurate results.

The various dynamic methods give the surface tension of more or less recently formed surfaces, and may yield results different from the static methods, if adsorption occurs, and is incomplete at the moment when the tension is actually measured. One factor in dynamic measurements, which cannot be satisfactorily measured at present, is the time which has elapsed between the formation of the surface from the homogeneous interior liquid, and the actual measurement of the surface tension. If this could be varied, and measured with an accuracy of say 10^{-4} second, a valuable new weapon would be available for investigating the progress of adsorption. Bohr's work on oscillating jets is probably the best on any dynamic method.

A further need is the development, and more extended use, of differential static methods for measuring small differences of surface tension, such as those between a pure solvent and dilute solutions. The existing data in the literature, on the surface tension of solutions, have mostly been obtained by comparing separate measurements of surface tensions of solvent and solution; the greatest care is necessary to obtain accurate results in this way, and indeed the data at present available for determining the state of adsorbed films, by the methods of Chapter IV, are much less accurate than can be obtained with modern methods. Warren's surface-tension balance (p. 376), and the differential development of the capillary-height method suggested on p. 371, seem suitable for obtaining data for an accurate study of adsorption, with little trouble.

Some useful reviews, which include references to other methods not mentioned in this chapter, have been compiled by Ferguson,[1] Dorsey,[2] Bakker,[3] and Lenard;[4] Freundlich's section should also be consulted.[5]

[1] *5th Colloid Report*, p. 1 (1923).

[2] *U.S. Bureau of Standards, Sci. Papers*, **21**, no. 540 (1926).

[3] *Kapillarität u. Oberflächenspannung, Wien-Harms Handb. d. Experimentalphysik*, **6**, ch. 5 (1928).

[4] *Ann. Physik*, **74**, 381 (1924).

[5] *Kapillarchemie*, **1**, 14 (1930).

APPENDIX

SOME RECENT ADVANCES

CONTENTS

CHAPTER II

New technique for measuring surface pressure. Direct measurement of surface tension, by observation of the downward pull on a clean glass plate held vertically in the surface, has been developed by Dervichian[1] and by Harkins and T. F. Anderson[2] so effectively that the method now rivals the ordinary film balance with a horizontal float, both in accuracy and in convenience. The glass plate used has a thickness of about a millimetre, and is hung from one end of the beam of a sensitive balance, which carries a mirror so as to record the depth to which the plate is immersed in the water. The depth at which the plate floats in the water depends on the surface tension, which pulls it downwards, and the weight of water displaced by the plate, which pushes it upwards. The zero is the position of the spot of light reflected from the mirror on the balance beam when the water surface is clean; as the film is compressed, the surface tension decreases and the plate rises in the water. A sensitivity approaching 0·01 dyne per cm. is claimed, and it is stated that this could easily be exceeded by using thinner slides, but this would involve a proportionate sacrifice of the range over which the pressures can be measured with one plate. It is essential that the contact angle of the water with the glass should be zero; this is not usually difficult to attain, provided that the film is progressively compressed, and therefore the plate rises in the water, giving a receding contact angle. If the film is de-compressed, the plate then falls and the angle becomes an advancing one and is usually not zero. This is a drawback to the use of the instrument, since small amounts of collapse with consequent hysteresis of the film are often only detected by de-compressing the film after compressing; it might possibly be overcome by de-compressing slightly more than necessary and then re-compressing slightly. Dervichian has made his instrument record the surface pressure automatically.

Harkins and Anderson have carried out a very careful comparison of the results given on a film, simultaneously, by the ordinary film balance and the vertical plate method, concluding that the film balance may give pressures some 3 per cent. higher than the vertical plate; they consider that the vertical plate is the more trustworthy, and give a careful analysis of possible errors of the ordinary film balance.

One great advantage of the vertical plate is that nothing except the trough, barriers, and vertical plate need be in contact with the water; this greatly facilitates the sometimes important problem of keeping all metals out of contact with the water.

Guastalla[3] describes the measurement of very small surface pressures, by observing the displacement of a fine vaselined silk thread dividing the film-

[1] *J. Phys. Rad.*, **6**, 221, 429 (1935). [2] *J.A.C.S.* (1937), 2189.
[3] *Compt. rend.*, **206**, 993 (1938).

covered from the clean surface; also another instrument[1] depending on the movement imparted to a small carriage slung on vertical threads, by a special float in the surface.

For studying films at an oil-water interface, A. E. Alexander and T. Teorell[2] recommend measurement of the interfacial tension by the force required to detach a metal ring from the interface (Chap. IX, § 11). This method was compared with that used by Askew and Danielli (p. 9), and also with measurement of the pull on a vertical plate. Zero contact angle in the water, a necessary condition for accuracy, appears to be regularly attained at, or before, the moment of detachment of the ring from the interface. An alternative technique is to measure the force required to raise the ring to a definite height in the interface without detachment.

For measurement of the surface potential at an oil-water interface, the polonium electrode can be used, if of very large size, but must be placed in the air just above the thinnest possible layer of the oil. If the polonium electrode is placed in the oil, close to the water surface, no conductivity is obtained, and potential measurements have not been found possible.

Further observations on films at oil-water interfaces. Alexander and Teorell[3] find that proteins spread more easily and completely on these interfaces than at air-water surfaces; and that lecithin (a liquid-expanded film at the air-water surface) is a gaseous film. Sodium cetyl sulphate is also gaseous; but it would form a gaseous adsorbed film at the air-water surface also.

This disruption of lateral adhesion between the hydrocarbon chains was also found by Askew and Danielli. It is to be attributed to the hydrocarbon chains of the interfacial film sharing in the random translatory motions of the oil molecules, to which they are bound by van der Waals' forces. In the case of a film which is liquid-expanded at the air-water surface this means that the term F_0 in Langmuir's equation (6), p. 66, vanishes, i.e. that in the presence of the moving oil molecules the lateral adhesions of the hydrocarbon chains of the film molecules no longer prevent the films expanding indefinitely along the surface.

A hint as to one of many possibly important effects of addition of small amounts of substances to a liquid on one side of a liquid-liquid interface is given by the observation of Alexander and others,[4] that kephalin films at a water-benzene interface increase their surface pressure substantially when calcium ions are added to the water. This is due to more powerful anchorage of the kephalin molecules in the interface, causing additional molecules to crowd in from solution in the benzene. The development of means of studying liquid-liquid interfaces opens a wide and extremely important field.

Surface viscosity. Since 1933, the enhanced viscosity (see p. 19 for the earliest observations) imparted to a surface when a monolayer is

[1] *Compt. rend.*, **208**, 973 (1939).
[2] *Trans. Faraday Soc.* (1939), 727.
[3] *Ibid.* 733.
[4] *Ibid.* (1939) 1200.

present has been studied quantitatively, especially by Joly and Dervichian[1] in France and Harkins and others[2] in America. Two principal experimental methods have been employed, the 'surface slit' viscometer,[3] effectively a two-dimensional capillary tube in the surface, and measurement of the rate of damping of the oscillations of a disk in the surface. A serious complication is that the surface film carries with it some of the underlying liquid, to an appreciable depth, so that the 'viscosity' of the surface film has no complete independence of the viscosity of the underlying liquid. The surface slit viscometer appears preferable to the oscillating disk type, because the instrument, being stationary, does not impart motion to the underlying liquid. Joly has designed an ingenious instrument in which the difference of pressure at the two ends of the long narrow channel, through a barrier in the surface, which constitutes the 'surface slit', is kept constant. It can be shown, assuming the whole of the resistance to passage through the surface slit to reside in the surface viscosity of the monolayer, that the amount passing in unit time should be $Q = \frac{Fd^3}{12\eta l}$, where d is the width and l the length of the slit, η being the coefficient of surface viscosity. While for very narrow slits the quantity passing does vary nearly as the cube of the width of the slit, as the slits become wider, the amount passing increases less rapidly than the cube of the diameter.

There are all degrees of viscosity, plasticity, and rigidity in different monolayers, ranging from the viscosity of water, with a clean surface, through small and moderate simple viscosity, and films showing anomalous viscosity, up to solid films so strong that they can form a bridge across a wide gap capable of withstanding a pressure of several dynes on one side and nothing on the other. The viscosity naturally increases with increasing numbers of film molecules in unit area of the surface, but it also depends, in a way which has not yet been fully worked out, on the orientation of, and the attractive forces between, the film molecules. In general, when a film is compressed until it reaches one of the more closely packed states, not only does the viscosity increase, but departures from simple viscous flow appear, i.e. the viscosity becomes 'anomalous', the coefficient of viscosity decreasing with increasing rate of shear. The condensed films of long-chain alcohols, studied in some detail by Fourt and Harkins,[4] and long known to give a surface pressure-area curve in two parts, close-packed chains above a definite 'kink-point' (Fig. 15, curve III), give normal viscosity at pressures below the kink-point and ano malous viscosity above this point. Joly finds that, with gaseous films,

[1] *J. Phys. Rad.*, **8,** 471; **9,** 345 (1937–8); *Kolloid-Z.*, **89,** 26 (1939); **36,** 285 (1939); *Nature*, **141,** 975 (1938).

[2] *J. Chem. Phys.* (1937), 601; (1938), 53; *J. Physical Chem.* (1938), 897; *J.A.C.S.* (1939), 1188.

[3] Used for semi-quantitative work by Bresler and Talmud, *Physikal. Z. Sowjetunion*, **4,** 864 (1933).

[4] *J. Physical Chem.* (1938), 897.

there is a rather marked increase of viscosity at areas roughly equal to the length of the molecules lying flat. Most gaseous films have long been known to show a faintly marked decrease in compressibility at this area, which is obviously due to the molecules commencing to tilt away from the horizontal position, because there is no longer sufficient room on the surface for all to remain flat. With protein films[1] spread hastily against a considerable and increasing pressure, the viscosity frequently increases with time; there is a very marked increase in viscosity as the pressure increases, ending in the solid or two-dimensional elastic gel state first recorded by Hughes and Rideal (p. 88). If a protein film is spread slowly, care being taken to keep the surface pressure resisting spreading very low, the film has a lower viscosity, which has no tendency to increase.

The different types of surface films. In Chapter II, the following distinct types of film have been recognized: gaseous, liquid-expanded, and condensed. The gaseous films sometimes have such a high degree of lateral adhesion between the molecules that they rather closely resemble the liquid-expanded, without, however, possessing a definite limiting area and therefore not forming a separate phase in the surface from the gaseous; these are the 'vapour-expanded' films. The condensed films fall into two fairly sharply defined groups, those with the chains closely packed and probably vertical, and those here called 'condensed films with close-packed heads', a name which is not wholly satisfactory, since although the constitution of the end groups does determine the area and shape of the pressure-area curves, the chains almost certainly tilt over (though with what regularity of packing is quite unknown) to a close packing.

Dervichian[2] has attempted a revision of this classification and nomenclature. He renames the condensed films with close-packed chains 'solid condensed', the less closely packed condensed films 'mesomorphous', the liquid-expanded simply 'liquid', and calls the transitional region between the condensed and liquid-expanded states the 'expanded mesomorphous' state. Gaseous and vapour states remain as before, the latter term being naturally used for gaseous films with a good deal of lateral adhesion between the molecules. The new nomenclature has several disadvantages, even apart from the confusion incidental to any unnecessary changes in nomenclature. Since the 'close-packed chain' type of condensed film is sometimes liquid, in the accepted sense that the film flows in the surface, the term 'solid condensed' is misleading. In a sense, since there is molecular orientation without complete crystalline structure, all the films, more closely packed than the liquid-expanded, are analogous to the mesomorphous state in three dimensions, so that the use of this name for one particular state of the films seems arbitrary. The transition from the condensed to the liquid-expanded states is probably not a single state, since it is known that the surface has a patchy structure in respect of surface potential, and therefore it seems erroneous to assign this transition a name as if it was a single state. Finally, as there are liquid states other than the liquid-expanded, it seems undesirable to restrict the word liquid to this particular state.

Dervichian claims the discovery of new transformations ('of higher order'), whose presence is indicated by marked changes in the compressibility, surface

[1] *Compt. rend.*, **208**, 975 (1939); *J. Chim. Physique*, **36**, 285 (1939).

[2] Dervichian and Joly, *J. Phys. Rad.*, **10**, 375; Dervichian, *J. Chem. Phys.*, **7**, **931** (1939).

potential, and viscosity, at certain areas. One of these certainly occurs in most gaseous films, near to the area at which the surface would be completely covered by the molecules lying flat, and probably indicates the commencement of forcible tilting of the molecules away from the horizontal position, by the pressure. Another occurs at the 'kink-point' in condensed films where a film with close-packed heads changes, under pressure, into one with close-packed chains, as in curves II to VI of Fig. 15. Both these had been previously recognized from surface pressure measurements alone; the sudden changes in viscosity are a useful confirmation of a change in structure. Others are said to occur at 19·5, 20·5, 22, 23·5, and between 24·5 and 26·5 sq. A. Unfortunately the experimental data presented in support of these points of transformation is so scanty at present that it is difficult to believe in their real existence, and when Dervichian,[1] in reply to a criticism by Harkins and Boyd,[2] states that these areas are 'average' values, without giving the actual values on which the average is based, scepticism seems desirable. An attempt is made to identify these areas with definite tilts of the hydrocarbon chains said to be of frequent occurrence in dry crystals at room temperature, but neither the range of substances studied, nor the experimental accuracy, appear to justify this close correlation; owing to the entanglement of water molecules it is doubtful whether such exact correlation should exist.

A re-examination of the finer points in the structure of condensed films certainly seems called for, however, with an accuracy if possible of 0·5 per cent. or less in the areas, and there is no doubt that Dervichian is right in expecting that the combination of pressure, potential, and viscosity measurements will probably yield important information.

Another slight anomaly requires reinvestigation; in the transition region (Fig. 13) between liquid-expanded and gaseous films there is a slight rounding off of what ought, theoretically, to be a quite sharp intersection on the left between the horizontal straight line of constant surface vapour pressure and the very much steeper liquid-expanded curve. The most probable explanation of this slight apparent increase in the surface vapour pressure, amounting to a very few hundredths of a dyne, at areas between 100 and 50 sq. A., is that the substances in the films were not quite pure. Still purer material should be employed in a further study of this point as well as of the others mentioned above.

Recent work on the relation between film structure and constitution. Stenhagen[3] has examined many disubstituted acetic acids, $\begin{matrix} R_1 \\ R_2 \end{matrix}\!\!>$CH COOH, on dilute acid solutions. In one series (Fig. 26 *b*) the total number of carbon atoms in the saturated chains R_1 and R_2 was 15. The curves, marked 1 : 14 for methyl tetradecyl acetic acid, 7 : 8 for heptyl octyl, and so on, are all of the liquid-expanded type, the limiting areas at room temperature increasing regularly from 54 sq. A. with the 1 : 14 up to 90 for the 7 : 8 acid. Rise of temperature causes a slight increase in area similar to that found in other liquid-expanded films, possibly a little larger. If the length of one chain is kept constant, and the

[1] *J. Chem. Phys.* (1940), 347.
[2] *Ibid.* (1940), 129.
[3] *Trans. Faraday Soc.* (1940), 597.

other lengthened, the area usually diminishes a little, at the lower pressures, but not very regularly. If the total number of carbons in the two chains exceeds 25, the films become rather unstable. Substitution of a saturated ring, containing three to six carbons, in the α position to the carboxyl group, gives a similar film with limiting area about 75 sq. A.

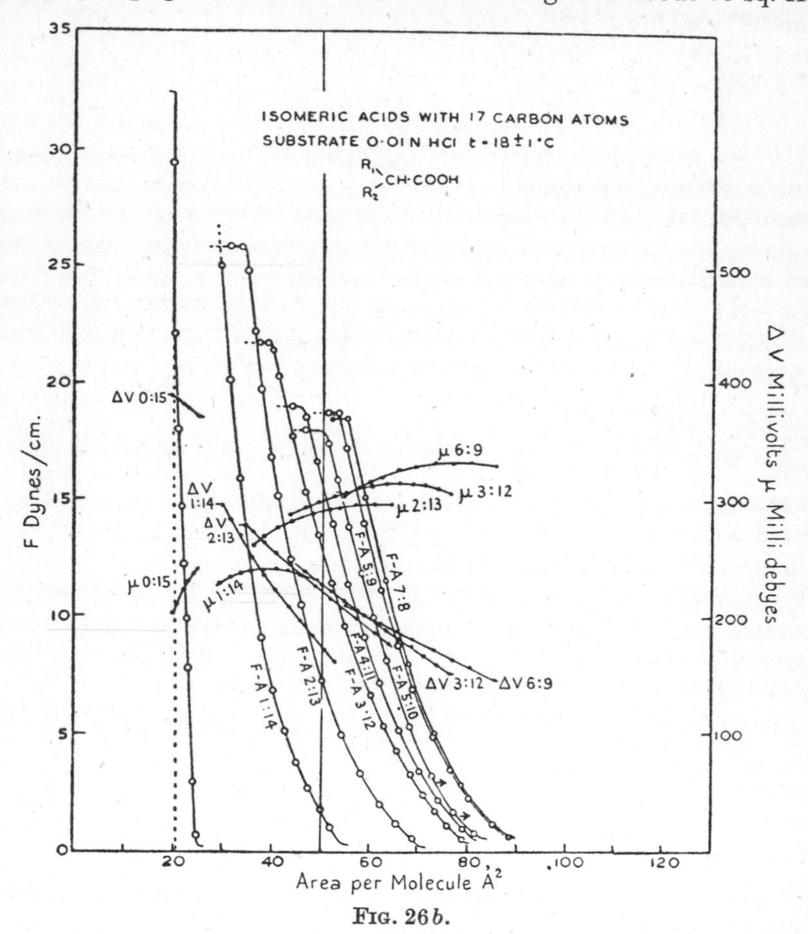

FIG. 26 *b*.

Various sapogenins, complex ring compounds with ring-systems rather similar to the sterols, give films resembling those of sterols.[1] If there is one strongly water-attracting group at the end of the molecule (position 3 in the sterols) the films are condensed with an area usually between 37 and 45 sq. A., varying with the constitution. A second water-attracting group some distance away causes the films to be gaseous.

A careful comparison[2] of films of *cis* and *trans* unsaturated compounds confirms that the cohesion in condensed films of compounds with *trans* chains is considerably greater than with *cis* chains, and shows that the

[1] Askew, Farmer, and Kon, *J.C.S.* (1936), 1399; Noller, *J.A.C.S.* (1938), 1629.
[2] Marsden and Rideal, *J.C.S.* (1938), 1163.

oxidation by permanganate proceeds more rapidly with the *cis* than with the *trans* compounds, in monolayers. These facts are in accord with the information from X-rays, that the *trans* chains pack, in crystals, in a manner much more closely resembling the saturated chains, than do the *cis* chains.

Careful work by Nutting and Harkins[1] shows, confirming some indications in earlier work of the author's, that condensed films of fatty acids and alcohols, with close-packed heads, occupy slightly smaller areas as the chain length is considerably increased. When the chains are closely packed, the area also appears a little smaller with the longer chains, but the data are not so complete.

Incorporation of carcinogenic hydrocarbons in sterol films. An interesting, and possibly very important, interaction between sterols and those hydrocarbons which induce cancer has been reported by Clowes, Davis, and Krahl.[2] Films of sterols appear to be able to incorporate, while retaining stability at 10 dynes per cm., about one molecule of benzpyrene or methyl cholanthrene to five of the sterol; rather larger amounts can be incorporated if the pressure is lower. The benzpyrene occupies an area of about 36 sq. A. in the film, in addition to the normal area of the sterols. From the experiments done so far it appears that only those hydrocarbons which have pronounced carcinogenic activity can be incorporated with sterols in monolayers; phenanthrene, even, is not held in the films. If this hint that the hydrocarbons have a unique specific property of entering surface films of sterols is confirmed by further work, an important clue to a stage in the development of cancer may have been discovered. The hydrocarbons do not, of course, spread on water unless mixed with sterols.

Films of proteins. Intensive study of monolayers of proteins[3] has consolidated the knowledge indicated in § 28, and made important further discoveries. Two new methods for spreading proteins have been devised; instead of putting drops of an aqueous solution straight on to a water surface, Langmuir and Schaefer first spread the protein solution on a thin metal strip, nearly as long as the width of the trough, and then dip this strip slowly into the water; the water rises up the face of the strip and easily carries away the dissolved protein over the surface; spreading is thus from a solution of protein, applied gradually over the whole width of the surface. Ställberg and Teorell dissolve the protein in a 60 per cent. aqueous solution of propyl alcohol, containing 0·5 M sodium acetate; this solution dissolves many proteins apparently without change, and when

[1] *J.A.C.S.* (1939), 1180. [2] *Amer. J. Cancer*, **36**, 98 (1939).

[3] H. Neurath and H. B. Bull, *Chem. Reviews*, **23**, 391 (1938); Langmuir, *Cold Spring Harbour Symp. Quant. Biol.*, **6**, 171 (1939); *Proc. Roy. Soc.* A, **170**, 30 (1939); *Proc. Physical Soc.*, **51**, 592 (1939); Langmuir and Schaefer, *Chem. Reviews*, **24**, 181 (1939); *J.A.C.S.* (1938), 1351, 2803; *Science*, **85**, 76 (1937); Langmuir and Wrinch, *Nature*, **143**, 49 (1939); Langmuir and Waugh, *J.A.C.S.* (1938), 745; (1940), 2771; S. Ställberg and T. Teorell, *Trans. Faraday Soc.* (1939), 1413, 1416; Cockbain and Schulman, *ibid.* (1939), 1266.

applied to a water surface does not penetrate below the surface nearly as much as a purely aqueous solution does. To test the completeness of spreading, Langmuir and Schaefer deposit multilayers (see Chap. V, appendix) on plates and determine the thickness optically; comparison with the amount spread on the water surface gives an approximate indication of the fraction of the amount applied which had spread in the monolayer. It appears probable that the reason why spreading by Gorter's method, in which a drop of the aqueous solution is applied directly to the surface, is most nearly complete at the isoelectric point, is that a good deal of the solution penetrates below the surface and the protein in this must later reach the surface by diffusion upwards. If the molecules of protein already spread at the surface are electrically charged, they hinder diffusion of further molecules from the interior to the surface, and thus delay or prevent the completion of the spreading of those molecules which have at first been carried below the surface.

There is now no doubt that the spreading of proteins to a monolayer is an unfolding from a globular shape to a flat sheet, and that this unfolding is accompanied by an enormous diminution in the solubility of the protein. Svedberg's studies by the ultracentrifuge, and Adair's osmotic pressure measurements, show that the soluble proteins almost always have molecular weights approximately 17,500n, where n is one of the integers 1, 2, 4, 8, 16, 24, 48, 96, 168, 192, 384; thus the units of which the soluble, or 'globular', proteins are composed consist of certain definite numbers of amino-acids. Wrinch's mathematical studies[1] of the possible ways in which internal linkage, to form symmetrical aggregates in three dimensions by means of the 'cyclol' bond,[2] can occur with polypeptide chains indicate that there should be certain preferred numbers of amino-acids in each unit. Though there seems as yet no general agreement as to the correctness of the details of Wrinch's hypothesis as to the mode of aggregation of the polypeptide chains to the soluble globular aggregates, there is little doubt that these aggregates are so constructed that the hydrocarbon groups are buried in the interior, leaving the surface covered by water-soluble groups, the whole aggregate or micelle being therefore very soluble in water. When such an aggregate reaches the surface, there is a strong tendency for the hydrocarbon parts of the protein molecule to cover the surface, and this is accomplished by the unfolding of the whole aggregate to a flat sheet. In this unfolding many of the linkages, probably of the cyclol type, must be broken, but these are probably not very stable and may be expected to break fairly frequently: the effect of the surface is that the cyclol links concerned in the construction of the globular aggre-

[1] *Proc. Roy. Soc.* A, **160,** 59; **161,** 505 (1937).

[2] Formed, as suggested first by F. C. Frank (see Astbury, *Chem. Weekblad*, **33,** 781 (1936)), by a 'lactam-lactim' tautomerism when a —CO— and a —NH— group approach closely, thus

$$>NH + OC< \rightleftharpoons >N-C(OH)<$$

gate do not re-form, because the preference of the hydrocarbon parts of the molecule for the air-water surface prevents the requisite closeness of approach of the —CO— and —NH— groups.

Langmuir considers that, although Wrinch's hypothesis permits the existence of some large and symmetrical plane 'cyclol' structures, the spread proteins have no such regular structure, but have, as Hughes and Rideal suggested (p. 89), the polypeptide chains lying on the surface, with the side chains spread out separately, or dipping into the water, according to the surface pressure. Astbury and others[1] found a fibrous structure in multilayers deposited from monolayers of egg albumin; and when multilayers collapse, they usually form fibrous structures. The spread protein resembles a net hanging, perhaps rather untidily, from the hydrocarbon groups in the surface. It is the presence of these hydrocarbon groups which make it possible to spread the protein at all.

The surface pressure-area curves of most proteins which have so far been spread are generally similar; fairly pure proteins free from appreciable amounts of products of hydrolysis with low molecular weight give coherent films with a limiting area at no compression, usually between 0·6 and 1·5 sq. metres per milligramme. If these films are rapidly compressed and then re-expanded, they return accurately to their original area; if, however, they are maintained for some time at a pressure above 10 or 20 dynes, they contract somewhat, the amount of contraction depending on the time during which the compression is applied.[2] Usually a part of the material in the film is permanently displaced by this compression, but after a certain amount of 'ageing' under pressure the film returns to its area at, say, 1 dyne pressure, even after some contraction has taken place at a high pressure.

Gibbs's adsorption theorem (Chap. III, eq. (7)) shows that the solubility of the substance in a surface film, in equilibrium with the interior, should increase according to the equation

$$\frac{\partial \log_e f_2 N_2}{\partial F} = \frac{1}{RT\Gamma_2}, \tag{1}$$

where f_2 is the activity coefficient, N_2 the mole fraction in the solution, Γ_2 the number of gramme molecules per sq. cm. in the film. Hence

$$\log_{10} f_2 N_2 = \frac{FM_2}{2{\cdot}303RTx_2} + \text{const.}, \tag{2}$$

where x_2 is the amount in the film in grammes per sq. cm. and M_2 the molecular weight. Equation (2) shows that the solubility increases rapidly with increasing surface pressure of the film, *especially if the molecular weight is large*; Langmuir has calculated that the solubility of a protein of molecular weight 35,000 ought to increase no less than one million times for each increase of 1 dyne in the surface pressure; yet most proteins

[1] *Nature*, **142**, 33 (1938).
[2] Langmuir and Waugh, *J.A.C.S.* (1940), 2771.

can be compressed to at least 25 dynes and re-expanded, quickly, to their original area. The enormous difference between the solubility of proteins in the globular and in the spread condition is comparable with, but more marked than, the difference between the extremely soluble ionic micelles of soaps and other paraffin chain salts and their rather insoluble surface films. There is no certainty, however, that the surface films are in real equilibrium with the interior during the comparatively short time of an experiment on a surface film, conducted with due regard to avoidance of the accumulation of accidental surface contamination. Langmuir points out the danger of permitting films to remain on a water-air surface for hours on end, a danger of which the author has always been only too well aware, though it is much less if the surface pressure is kept fairly high during the period of waiting. Those undertaking kinetic studies of reactions in monolayers must provide evidence that accidental contamination has not occurred.

Although the pressure-area relations of different proteins are generally similar, their mechanical properties in the surface are much more characteristic. The viscosity is generally highly anomalous, that is, the coefficient varies greatly with the rate of shear in the surface, and sometimes the films become quite rigid, or 'gelatinize'. Variations in the apparent viscosity coefficient of different proteins under similar conditions of shear and surface pressure may be hundredfold or more.[1] A simple and ingenious qualitative method of showing differences in the mechanical properties of the monolayers is given by Schaefer's 'expansion patterns'.[2] A drop of a slightly oxidized lubricating oil (indicator oil) is allowed to spread in the middle of a protein monolayer, giving the so-called 'external' expansion patterns; also 'internal' expansion patterns are made by the expansion of the oil in the middle of a protein monolayer. The outline of these patterns may be smooth and circular, or smooth but not circular, or may have various degrees of irregularity, mostly quite characteristic of the particular protein, up to a very well-defined star with a few large rays. The irregularities indicate some degree of rigidity in the protein film, with elastic properties varying in different directions in the surface.

Careful observation of the expansion patterns[3] gives evidence of the presence, sometimes, of protein in the solution just below the monolayer. Such material lowers the interfacial tension between the indicator oil and the water, permitting expansion to a greater area, so that the oil layer is thinned where there is protein below it in solution. This appears as a different colour of the oil layer. Protein below the monolayer may be there owing to imperfect spreading, when it is noticed, especially during the spreading of oil against a monolayer, as a thinning of the oil near the advancing edge. Sometimes it is due to displacement of the protein by compression of the monolayer; the amount of material displaced at various

[1] Langmuir, *Cold Spring Harbour Symp. Quant. Biol.*, **6**, 177 (1938).

[2] *J. Physical Chem.* (1938), 1089.

[3] Langmuir and Waugh, *J.A.C.S.* (1940), 2771.

surface pressures can be used as an indication of the molecular weight of the part displaced, and therefore as a test for molecular homogeneity, or partial hydrolysis, of the protein in a monolayer.

It is not easy to displace a true protein, of molecular weight 17,500 or some multiple thereof, by pressure alone; but the studies of Rideal, Schulman, and others[1] on penetration and displacement of films by adsorbed material show that fatty acids, sterols, or paraffin chain salts in the water easily displace protein monolayers from the surface. This is intelligible, since the place of the hydrocarbon groups of the protein at the surface is now taken by the much larger, and therefore more strongly adsorbed, hydrocarbon groups in the displacing molecules.

Whether enzymes retain their specific chemical activities when spread as a monolayer is still doubtful. Pepsin, spread on water and then deposited on a metal plate, clots milk vigorously when the plate is dipped in the milk; the clotting occurs, however, in the interior of the milk, not merely at the surface, and the layer of pepsin is removed from the surface into the interior. This only shows that milk contains some substance which will re-form the enzyme, which may be a globular, soluble protein, very rapidly from a monolayer. The active constituent of pepsin is much more easily spread at a water-air surface than the inactive impurities in a commercial specimen; indeed, the activity of many commercial pepsins may be greatly increased by spreading on water and transferring to a plate.

Urease, spread on water, retains only about 5 per cent. of its original power of liberating ammonia from urea; and this small activity might be due to a little unspread enzyme.

The effect of so-called 'heat denaturation' on the power of proteins to form monolayers is very variable; Neurath's conclusion (p. 90) that heating tends to diminish the tendency to spread is sometimes confirmed; but a denatured albumin, once spread, has if anything a slightly larger area than the original.[2] Langmuir and Waugh show that heat decomposes pepsin rather extensively into substances of lower molecular weight, but with insulin, it not only does not decompose the protein but actually renders it less easily digested by pepsin. The word 'denaturation' seems to cover a great variety of changes, and may we hope that it will soon disappear from the chemists' vocabulary!

On concentrated salt solutions, protein solutions often spread very vigorously, but very thick layers, sometimes 1,000 A. thick or even more, appear to be formed.[3]

Effect of dissolved salts in the water. The effects of minute traces of salts on monolayers, especially of fatty acids (p. 97), have received some further attention,[4] but are by no means fully elucidated. Any substance in solution which can 'cross-link', or combine with several, fatty

[1] Cf. *Proc. Roy. Soc.* B, **122,** 46 (1937).

[2] H. B. Bull, *J. Biol. Chem.*, **125,** 585 (1938); Ställberg, *Trans. Faraday Soc.* (1939), 1416.

[3] Langmuir and Schaefer, *J.A.C.S.* (1938), 2803.

[4] Harkins and T. F. Anderson, *J.A.C.S.* (1937), 2195; Langmuir and Schaefer, *ibid.* (1937), 2400.

chains by their soluble end groups, tends to make the film rigid and usually also to reduce the area, generally to that of close-packed chains. Thus calcium, even in dilute acid solution, reduces the area of stearic acid films to 19·5 sq. A. or even less; sodium polymetaphosphates (Calgon), which have the power of forming large complex ions containing several divalent cations, produce great rigidity in films of barium stearate. The crumpled material formed when films are collapsed on the surface, under high pressure, varies greatly in appearance according to the cations present in the water, and can often be shown to have accumulated almost the whole of extremely small traces of such ions as copper or aluminium. In the case of aluminium, the effects of even 10^{-8} molar concentrations are noticeable. The extremely small quantities of salts needed to change the area and the viscosity make systematic investigation quite difficult, as the quantities normally present even in good specimens of distilled water often have a large effect.

Evaporation through surface films. Sebba and Briscoe[1] describe an instrument called an 'evaporant' for measuring the rate of evaporation of water into dry air passing over a water surface, while permitting simultaneous measurement of the surface pressure. The observed reduction in the rate of evaporation increases with increasing pressure at rates which differ somewhat with different substances. At equal pressures, the resistance to evaporation is greater the longer the hydrocarbon chain. Below 10 dynes the apparent reduction in the rate of evaporation is small; with the normal alcohol of 22 carbons evaporation is 20 per cent. of the rate over water, at 20 dynes, and at 48 dynes is almost nil. With other alcohols and acids the rate is considerably retarded at 40 dynes. To produce serious obstruction to evaporation, the pressure must be considerably higher than that required merely to produce a film with close-packed chains. Cholesterol, despite its closeness of packing, offers no appreciable resistance to evaporation even at 35 dynes; protein films also are without effect.

A curious 'ageing' has been observed; if a film is left on water at a rather low pressure for some time, and then compressed to a pressure at which it would, if it has been rapidly brought to this pressure, have obstructed evaporation seriously, it has a much smaller retarding effect. The effect is attributed to possible association between the polar end groups, but the explanation is not clear.

CHAPTER III

Gibbs's adsorption equation. Guggenheim,[2] developing some considerations put forward by Verschaffelt, has worked out the thermodynamics of surfaces, using a conception of the surface layer which is much more easily visualized physically than that used by Gibbs. Gibbs's surface excess is a very difficult quantity to interpret physically, as it is

[1] *J.C.S.* (1940), 106, 128. [2] *Trans. Faraday Soc.* (1940), 397.

the difference between the total amount of a component in the actual system, and that in a physically impossible system in which the two phases retain their bulk composition right up to the mathematical surface of no thickness, which can be arbitrarily placed.

In the new conception of the surface layer, two mathematical surfaces are drawn, AA' and BB' in Fig. 32 *a*, parallel to the surface. These surfaces may be placed anywhere, but it is preferable to place one just inside each of the homogeneous bulk phases, near to the boundary of the physically inhomogeneous transition region, so that the space enclosed between AA' and BB' corresponds as nearly as possible to the actual inhomogeneous surface layer. The distance between AA' and BB' is τ cm., so that the volume, for an area A, is $V^\sigma = \tau A$. The surface phase is now the whole region included between AA' and BB'. Unlike the Gibbs surface 'phase', it is a definite region of matter, with its own volume, entropy, energy, and other extensive properties; the Gibbs surface phase has no volume. Denoting the extensive properties of the newly defined surface phase thus: volume, V^σ; energy, ϵ^σ; entropy, η^σ; amounts in moles of the various components $n_1^\sigma, n_2^\sigma, n_3^\sigma, \ldots, n_i^\sigma$, all for an area A sq. cm., the thermodynamics can be developed along lines closely similar to those of a bulk phase; and the relation between adsorption and lowering of surface tension has in the general case, the same form as the usual Gibbs's equation (7), except that a term including the volume of the surface phase appears, when variations of pressure are permitted.

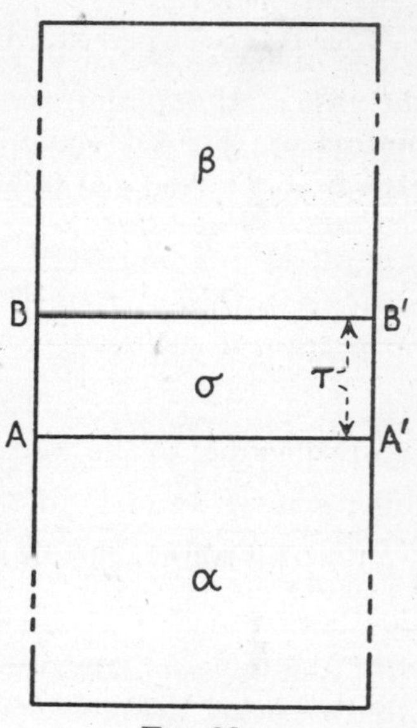

FIG. 32 *a*.

The surface tension is conveniently regarded as the deficiency in hydrostatic pressure across a plane cutting the surface perpendicularly, compared with a plane of similar area wholly in one of the bulk phases; this is the aspect of surface tension used by Bakker (see Chap. I, § 4, p. 4). The work done in increasing the volume in one of the bulk phases by dV is $P\,dV$; that done in increasing the volume of the surface phase by dV^σ, and its area by dA, is $P\,dV^\sigma - \gamma\,dA$, where γ is the surface tension.

The thermodynamic development is similar to Gibbs's theory and may be carried out as follows (cf. § 2). If ϵ^σ is the total internal energy of the surface phase, for an area A, and η^σ its entropy,

$$d\epsilon^\sigma = T\,d\eta^\sigma + \gamma\,dA - P\,dV^\sigma + \sum \mu_i\,dn_i^\sigma. \tag{22}$$

Integrating, without change of composition,

$$\epsilon^\sigma = T\eta^\sigma + \gamma A - PV^\sigma + \sum \mu_i\,n_i^\sigma. \tag{23}$$

Differentiating (23) and comparing with (22),[1]

$$A\,d\gamma = -\eta^\sigma\,dT + V^\sigma\,dP - \sum n_i^\sigma\,d\mu_i^\sigma, \tag{24}$$

and for unit area,

$$d\gamma = -\eta_\sigma\,dT + \tau\,dP - \sum \Gamma_i^\sigma\,d\mu_i^\sigma, \tag{25}$$

where $A\eta_\sigma = \eta^\sigma$.

This corresponds to equation (3), and differs from it only in the appearance of the term $\tau\,dP$.

For changes at constant temperature and pressure,

$$d\gamma = -\sum \Gamma_i^\sigma\,d\mu_i^\sigma. \tag{25.1}$$

The Helmholtz free energy F^σ, and the Gibbs free energy G^σ, of the surface phase may be defined thus:

$$F^\sigma = \epsilon^\sigma - T\eta^\sigma, \tag{26}$$

$$G^\sigma = \epsilon^\sigma - T\eta^\sigma + PV^\sigma - \gamma A. \tag{27}$$

From (23) and (27),

$$G^\sigma = \sum \mu_i n_i^\sigma, \tag{28}$$

corresponding to the well-known equation for a bulk phase, α,

$$G^\alpha = \sum \mu_i n_i^\alpha.$$

For two components only, at constant temperature and pressure,

$$d\gamma = -\Gamma_1^\sigma\,d\mu_1 - \Gamma_2^\sigma\,d\mu_2. \tag{25.2}$$

$d\mu_1$ and $d\mu_2$ are, however, connected by the Gibbs-Duhem equation, N_1 and N_2 being the mole fractions in the liquid phase α,

$$N_1\,d\mu_1 + N_2\,d\mu_2 = 0, \tag{29}$$

hence

$$-d\gamma = \left(\Gamma_2^\sigma - \frac{N_2}{N_1}\Gamma_1^\sigma\right)d\mu_2, \tag{25.3}$$

$$N_2\left(\frac{\Gamma_2^\sigma}{N_2} - \frac{\Gamma_1^\sigma}{N_1}\right) = -\left(\frac{\partial\gamma}{\partial\mu_2}\right)_{T,P} = -\frac{\partial\gamma}{RT\,\partial\log f_2 N_2}, \tag{25.4}$$

f_2 being the activity coefficient of the solute species 2. Comparing (25.3) with (7.2), we see that the Gibbs surface excess $\Gamma_2^{(1)}$, obtained when Gibbs's single dividing surface is placed so as to make Γ_1 vanish, is related to the Γ^σ thus:

$$\Gamma_2^{(1)} = N_2\left(\frac{\Gamma_2^\sigma}{N_2} - \frac{\Gamma_1^\sigma}{N_1}\right). \tag{30}$$

We may now define *positive* adsorption of the solute 2, one of two components, as occurring when $\dfrac{\Gamma_2^\sigma}{N_2} > \dfrac{\Gamma_1^\sigma}{N_1}$, or $\dfrac{\Gamma_2^\sigma}{\Gamma_1^\sigma} > \dfrac{N_2}{N_1}$; negative adsorption if

[1] A simple alternative method of deducing equations similar to (23) and (24) from one similar to (22) is given in Guggenheim's paper (p. 400); it brings out very clearly the fact that an extension of the surface, without change in the intensity factors, is the essential part of this, not always fully understood, mathematical operation.

$\frac{\Gamma_2^\sigma}{\Gamma_1^\sigma} < \frac{N_2}{N_1}$. This is in agreement with the common definition of positive or negative adsorption, according as $\Gamma_2^{(1)}$ is positive or negative. By (7.4) or (25.4), adsorption is 'positive' if $\frac{\partial \gamma}{\partial \log f_2 N_2}$ is negative, and vice versa. Since the activity coefficient f_2 is always positive, a fall in surface tension with increasing concentration indicates positive adsorption; a rise, negative adsorption, of the solute 2.

While the numerical values of the Γ^σ naturally depend on the exact positions assigned to the surfaces AA' and BB', the quantities $N_i\left(\frac{\Gamma_i^\sigma}{N_i} - \frac{\Gamma_1^\sigma}{N_1}\right)$ can be shown to be independent of these positions. Therefore the choice of the positions of AA' and BB' does not affect the sign of the adsorption.

In § 4, $\Gamma_2^{(1)}$ is taken as an approximation to the total amount of the solute in the surface layer. This is, by (30), only true if Γ_2^σ is much larger than $\frac{N_2}{N_1}\Gamma_1^\sigma$, that is, if the solute is strongly adsorbed and the solution is dilute; it is a close approximation in the cases chosen.

McBain[1] has drawn attention to the existence of a number of cases in which strongly surface active substances first lower the tension of water considerably, but as the concentration increases further, the surface tension either becomes nearly constant or shows a slight increase. The cases for which the evidence is most conclusive are aqueous solutions of soaps or other paraffin chain salts and of some dyestuffs. The minimum surface tension often occurs in quite dilute solution, e.g. with dodecyl sodium sulphate[2] it is about 0·006 N; the exact concentration of the minimum, however, depends on the purity of the water used as solvent.

If the solution could be treated as a two-component one, then a constant surface tension would indicate no adsorption, i.e. that the ratio of molecules of solvent and solute is the same in the surface layer as in the interior; a surface tension rising with concentration would indicate that, in the surface layer, the solvent was present in a somewhat larger proportion than in the interior. This would not be, as is sometimes supposed, incompatible with the considerable lowering of surface tension; it is possible that the inhomogeneous surface phase is more than one molecule thick, with the solute molecules oriented in the outer part so that their hydrophobic parts cover a large part of the surface; just below this there may be more water molecules, per solute molecule, than are found in the interior, perhaps in close association with the electrolytically dissociated end groups of the adsorbed solute molecules. It is not quite clear why the hydration of the solute should be greater in the surface phase than in the interior, but it may be due to the formation of ionic micelles in the interior, which may be less hydrated than the single ions, of which the

[1] *Reports on Progress in Physics, Physical Society*, **5**, 30 (1939).
[2] Lottermoser and Stoll, *Kolloid-Z.*, **63**, 49 (1933).

adsorbed layer is composed. Some degree of lowering of surface tension would be expected if *any* molecules with a hydrophobic portion reached the surface, since their field of attractive force is less than that of water, and this could occur with the surface phase less rich in solute molecules than the interior, though one would not expect any great lowering of tension unless the more hydrophobic solute were concentrated to some extent in the outermost layer of the surface phase. It may be significant that the surface-tension minimum in the paraffin chain salts occurs at the same order of concentration as that at which the ionic micelles are formed in quantity in the interior, and that the precise concentration depends on the presence of small amounts of other substances as impurities in the water.

It is very doubtful, however, if these solutions can be treated as two component systems; they contain water and at least two ions, of which the adsorption is not the same; and soaps, unless rather strongly alkaline, contain free fatty acid which is much more strongly adsorbed than the anion of the fatty acid. The course of a surface tension-concentration curve in a solution with several components may be complicated; it seems possible that a rise of tension with increasing concentration may be due to a moderately surface active ion, present in large amount, displacing a more surface active component, present in smaller amount, from the surface.

There seems no reason for calling the validity of Gibbs's equation in question; but it is necessary to consider carefully the meaning of $\Gamma_2^{(1)}$, even if the solution is one which may legitimately be taken as having only two components. But these solutions must usually *when changes in surface area are taken into account*, be taken as having three or even more components. If one constituent (e.g. undissociated molecules) is adsorbed more than another (e.g. ions) their ratio will vary with change of surface area. An additional variable is thus introduced, and the number of components, that is the fewest constituents out of which the system can be constructed, will be increased.

Neither does it appear correct to suggest that Gibbs's general equation (7), or the corresponding (25.1) of Guggenheim's theory, is incomplete and requires additional terms representing the electrical charges at the surface. These charges are always carried on ions, each species of which has a term $\Gamma\, d\mu$. It is true that the potential (usually called the electrochemical potential) of these ions depends on the electrostatic potential of the phase in which they occur, so that their adsorption and consequently the charge on the surface depends on the electrostatic potential difference across the surface; but this is all included in equations (7) or (25), as indicated in Chapter VIII, pp. 344 ff.

Gibby and Argument,[1] continuing measurements of the adsorption of dyestuffs at liquid interfaces, by a method similar to that used first by Donnan (see p. 113), find that very often the adsorption is considerable at very low concentrations, but decreases at somewhat higher, though still fairly low, concentrations. The experimentally measured adsorption does not usually decrease nearly so much as that calculated from the

[1] *J.C.S.* (1940), 596.

simple form of Gibbs's equation (7.7), but this only confirms that (7.7) is a very rough approximation, probably partly because it neglects to take account of activity coefficients, and partly because of the objections stated above to the use of (7.4) for calculating the excess of the solute 2 in the surface phase, in a system which may contain several components.

New technique for the experimental measurement of the amount adsorbed is described by McBain, G. F. Mills, and T. F. Ford.[1] The surface is reduced to a small fraction of its original area, the adsorbed material being displaced into the interior, and its amount estimated interferometrically. The results with hydrocinnamic and dodecyl sulphonic acids confirm Gibbs's equation fairly well, but the method does not yet appear consistent enough to give more than the order of magnitude of the adsorption.

Guggenheim shows that the change in surface tension with temperature, for a solution of any number of components, in a change in which the composition is kept constant, is

$$\left(\frac{\partial \gamma}{\partial T}\right)_{\mu_i} = \frac{1}{T}\left\{h^\sigma - \frac{\theta^\sigma h^\beta}{\theta^\beta}\right\}. \tag{31}$$

h^σ is the heat absorbed and θ^σ the increase in volume when the area of the surface is increased isothermally and at constant pressure, reversibly, the components being taken from the liquid phase α; h^β and θ^β are the heat absorption and volume increase when one mole of the second phase β (liquid or vapour) is similarly formed from α. If $\theta^\sigma = 0$, i.e. if the increase in surface is unattended by any appreciable change in volume, (31) reduces to

$$\frac{\partial \gamma}{\partial T} = \frac{h^\sigma}{T},$$

in agreement with equation (7) of Chapter I.

Adsorption of solvent on salt solutions. The curious, very slight, lowering of the surface tension of water by very small concentrations of salts, discovered by Grinnell Jones and Ray, has very recently been confirmed, using a modification of the 'ring' method for measuring the tension, by M. Dole and J. A. Swartout.[2] In 1938, Langmuir[3] suggested that the effect was not a genuine lowering of surface tension, but was instrumental in origin; he calculated that there should be a film of liquid on the surface of glass or quartz, several hundred A. thick, for an appreciable distance above a meniscus in a capillary tube, and that this film (which reduces the effective radius of the capillary tube) is thick enough to make an appreciable difference to the surface tension, calculated on the assumption that the radius is that of the dry tube. He considers that this film is thinner with salt solutions than in pure water, so that the real radius of the tube was larger in the salt solutions than in the water, and the rise was smaller, without the tension being necessarily lower. Grinnell Jones and Frizzell[4] throw doubt on Langmuir's theory that the effect is purely instrumental; the thickness of the film depends on the ζ potential at the walls of the tube, which is not known accurately. They show that the lowering of tension is

[1] *Trans. Faraday Soc.* (1940), 930.
[2] *J.A.C.S.* (1940) 3039.
[3] *Science*, 88, 430 (1938).
[4] *J. Chem. Phys.* (1940), 986.

obtained even in the presence of concentrations of thorium salts which had been expected to reduce the ζ potential so far that the film thickness should be nearly the same as that of water.

Dole[1] offers a rather complex theory of the lowering of tension based on the assumed existence of particular spots on the air-water surface at which negative ions are adsorbed on water molecules possessing a special orientation, probably with the hydrogens inwards. These must, to fit the data, be present in the proportion of one oriented water molecule to about 25,000 ordinary molecules. The total lowering amounts to less than 0·0002 of the surface tension of water, so that its genuine existence may perhaps still need confirmation. If it does exist, it follows that ions are positively adsorbed in extremely dilute solutions, to some extent, and also that the form in which they are adsorbed has a smaller field of force than water molecules; normally ions have a larger field of force, as is shown by the high surface tension of fused salts.

Solutions of soaps and other long-chain colloidal electrolytes. K. S. G. Doss[2] ascribes the extremely slow adsorption of paraffin chain salts, and also of some dyestuffs of the benzopurpurin group, to the electrostatic repulsion of the ions diffusing up to the surface, by those already there. After a few ions have been adsorbed, additional ions approaching the surface have to overcome the potential barrier caused by the repulsion from the similar electric charges on the adsorbed ions before they can reach the position of stable adsorption, in which the hydrophobic parts of the ions are actually covering the surface. An ion with a considerable hydrophobic part in its constitution (which all ions strongly adsorbed at an air-water surface must have) will be in a 'trough' of potential energy when actually at the surface, but will have to cross an 'energy hump' before it reaches the surface if there are ions of similar sign already adsorbed there. Hence the diffusion from interior to surface requires an energy of activation, and if this is large enough the rate of diffusion to the surface will be slow. The explanation is ingenious, but it seems doubtful if the electrostatic potential barrier can be large enough to account for the very slow rates of lowering of surface tension sometimes observed. G. S. Hartley and J. W. Roe[3] point out that the potential is the well-known electrokinetic or ζ potential (Chap. VIII, § 8), and the figures available, unfortunately only for more concentrated solutions, would only account for a slowing of the rate of diffusion below the normal for these ions by about one-tenth of that actually observed. It is just possible, however, that higher ζ potentials, sufficient to account for the slow diffusion, would be found at the great dilutions at which this slow diffusion takes place.

It is often important, especially in preparing emulsions, to obtain the lowest possible interfacial tension between an aqueous solution and an oil. G. S. Hartley[4] points out that sodium or other monovalent salts of paraffin

[1] *J.A.C.S.* (1938), 904. [2] *Kolloid-Z.*, **84**, 138 (1938); **86**, 205 (1939).
[3] *Trans. Faraday Soc.* (1940), 105. [4] *Ibid.* (1941), 130.

chain salts, such as $C_{16}H_{33}O\ SO_3Na$, do not reduce the tension between a purely hydrocarbon oil and water below 1 or 2 dynes per cm. This is ascribed to the fact that these salts very easily form ionic micelles in solution; these micelles are aggregates of the ions with the water-soluble ends outwards and the hydrocarbon chains covered, and are very much more soluble than the single ions, in fact extremely soluble in water. Since these micelles are formed at low concentrations, the concentration of single ions in solution cannot increase sufficiently to produce a very great lowering of tension.

If, however, solutions of salts of similar constitution but with two paraffin chains each of about half the length of the single chain in the preceding case, such as

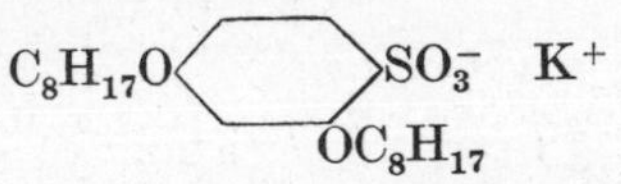

$$C_8H_{17}O\langle\ \ \rangle SO_3^- \quad K^+$$
$$OC_8H_{17}$$

are studied, very much lower interfacial tensions are observed, down to 0·05 dyne per cm. or less; this is probably because these ions pack much less tidily and easily into ionic micelles, so that the micelles are not formed until much higher concentrations, at which the concentration of single ions is sufficient to lower the interfacial tension very considerably. Under the names 'Aerosol' and 'Tergitol' substances of this type of constitution have come into prominence as very effective emulsifiers.

Small concentrations of di- and trivalent ions do, however, produce very low interfacial tensions with the simple paraffin chain salts;[1] and if substances such as cholesterol, which form complexes with the paraffin chain ions, are present in the oil, again very low tensions are possible. There is little doubt that either the polyvalent ion, or the other molecule of the complex, binds the paraffin chain ions together laterally in the interfacial film, so that more ions crowd into it for equal concentration of paraffin chain ion in the water, with a lower tension as a consequence of the greater crowding.

Adsorbed films between two immiscible liquids. The question of the meaning of the term p_H in the surface layer has been raised by Craxford, Gatty, and Teorell,[2] without, however, coming to any very clear decision. Danielli's estimate was a very rough one, based on the application of the Donnan equilibrium between the surface layer and the interior, and suffers from the difficulties always attending an attempt to consider concentrations in the surface layer in a similar way to concentrations in a bulk phase; the surface layer is not homogeneous. p_H is closely related to, and is determined by, the electrochemical potential (see Chap. VIII, pp. 304 ff.), and this depends on the electrostatic potential, which varies rapidly at different levels near to the surface; it appears possible that the only satisfactory definition of p_H in the surface may be one which varies rapidly at different depths. The question appears one which would repay

[1] C. Robinson, *Wetting and Detergency* (1937), 144.
[2] *Phil. Mag.*, **25**, 1061 (1938).

a thorough examination, especially in relation to theories of the constitution of the electrical double layer at surfaces.

Displacement of equilibria in adsorbed layers. In cases of cis-trans isomerism, usually one isomer is much more easily adsorbed than another, and sometimes one isomer can be effectively separated from the other by suitable choice of solvent and adsorbing surface.[1] Thus fumaric acid is much more strongly adsorbed than maleic, from aqueous solution, on to charcoal; *cis*-azobenzene is much the more strongly adsorbed from petroleum ether by alumina, while the *trans* form is far more adsorbed than the *cis*, from methyl alcohol, by charcoal.

The role of surface films in emulsification. Schulman and Cockbain[2] advance some new and important considerations on the stability and the inversion of emulsions. For stable oil in water (O/W) emulsions, they find that it is of great advantage to have present, in addition to a water-soluble emulsifying agent, a substance dissolved in the oil which interacts with the water-soluble emulsifying agent at the interface, forming a complex film containing both substances closely associated. They also find that, for O/W emulsions, the water-soluble emulsifier should be ionized, so that the interfacial film and consequently the droplets are electrically charged. The function of the charge is the same as in hydrophobic colloids, i.e. to cause repulsion between approaching droplets so that they do not easily collide and coalesce. In general, the same substances which form well-defined surface complexes at an air-water surface (see Chap. II, § 31) also stabilize emulsions best; thus sodium cetyl sulphate in the water, with cholesterol or elaidyl alcohol in the oil, give both complex films at the air-water surface and stable emulsions; cholesteryl esters, and the stereo-isomeric oleyl alcohol, do neither. The proportion between the amounts of water-soluble and oil-soluble agents should be that required to give a complete condensed interfacial film containing equal numbers of molecules of each substance, distributed over droplets at most 3 μ in diameter, and preferably smaller. An excess of the ionized water-soluble agent in the water phase does not impair the stability.

It is suggested that the principal function of the complex formation in the interfacial film is to bring this to the condensed state; a film composed of ions only would probably be gaseous, owing to the repulsion between the charged end groups. We have already seen evidence that condensed interfacial films stabilize emulsions better than less closely packed films; and further, more ions can be crowded into the interface if this is forcibly condensed by the van der Waals forces of lateral adhesion in the film than if the film is gaseous, so that the electric charge on the droplets becomes greater for the same area of surface. The formation of interfacial complexes lowers the interfacial tension,[3] which also assists the emulsification.

For inversion to water in oil (W/O) emulsions, the conditions appear

[1] Cf. Freundlich and W. Heller, *J.A.C.S.* (1939), 2228.

[2] *Trans. Faraday Soc.* (1940), 651, 661.

[3] A. E. Alexander and Schulman, *Trans. Faraday Soc.* (1940), 960.

to be (*a*) removal of the electric charges on the interfacial film, and (*b*) development of solidity, or at least high viscosity, in this film. Both these are favoured, with soaps as emulsifying agents, by di- or trivalent ions; but the monovalent thallous salts also produce W/O emulsions, a fact probably connected with the rather insoluble properties of thallous salts in general. With amines as emulsifying agents, di- and trivalent *anions* produce W/O emulsions. The polyvalent ions bind two or three long chains together laterally in the film, thus promoting rigidity. Their discharging effect facilitates the coalescence of the oil globules, and the tendency of the rigid films to pack together, face to face, as in Langmuir's multilayers, seems to assist the separation of the water into independent globules as the oil turns into a continuous phase. It is found that the water globules in W/O emulsions are usually distorted from a spherical shape owing to the solidity of the interfacial film.

CHAPTER V

Measurement of contact angles: hysteresis. Langmuir[1] suggests that the hysteresis of contact angles, especially with water, is due to the presence of a surface layer of molecules with one end hydrophilic and the other hydrophobic, which are overturned by the receding water. Normally such molecules (e.g. fatty acid) would be oriented with their polar ends towards the solid; the surface presented to an advancing liquid would therefore be hydrophobic. If, as the liquid recedes, these layers overturn, as would be quite natural, since the receding water would attract their polar groups, the surface left bare would be more hydrophilic than the original surface, so that the receding angle would be smaller. Hysteresis of contact angles certainly appears to be small, possibly zero, with water, when the surface of glass or quartz is really free from any trace of grease; and it is small also with hydrocarbon liquids, for which the work of adhesion is much the same for a hydrocarbon or a polar surface.

For the measurement of contact angles, by the reflection of light from the edge of a drop of liquid, Langmuir[2] describes a simply constructed instrument, said to give an accuracy of about one degree, which is amply sufficient for nearly all purposes.

The effect of roughness on the apparent contact angle of a solid surface has been given quantitative form by R. N. Wenzel.[3] If r, the 'roughness factor', is the ratio between the real and the apparent area of the surface, then

$$r(\gamma_S - \gamma_{SL}) = \gamma_L \cos\theta,$$

or

$$\cos\theta = \frac{r(\gamma_S - \gamma_{SL})}{\gamma_L}.$$

[1] *Science*, **87**, 493 (1938). [2] *J.A.C.S.* (1937), 2405.
[3] *Ind. Eng. Chem.*, **28**, 988 (1936).

The sign of $\cos\theta$ is therefore not changed by the roughness, but its magnitude, whether positive or negative, is increased, since r is necessarily greater than unity. Hence the roughness tends to magnify the amount by which the angle differs from 90°.

Transference of monolayers from water to solid surfaces. Multilayers. In 1920 Langmuir[1] dipped a clean glass plate into water covered by a monolayer of oleic acid, and found that an area of the monolayer equal to the area of the plate dipped was deposited on withdrawing the plate; this layer lubricated the surface and rendered it more or less hydrophobic. In 1934 Miss K. B. Blodgett, in Langmuir's laboratory,[2] found that any number of layers could be deposited successively by repeated dippings; and these 'multilayers', consisting of monolayers deposited one by one, have received considerable attention since that time.[3]

During deposition it is desirable to maintain the monolayer on the aqueous substratum under constant surface pressure; this is done by confining it with a long floating thread, behind which is placed a small quantity of a liquid spreading oil, which has a constant spreading pressure provided that there is excess liquid present as droplets on the surface. Oils used in this way are called 'piston oils'; convenient piston oils with their approximate spreading pressures are tricresyl phosphate (*c.* 10 dynes/cm.), castor oil (*c.* 16), ethyl myristate (*c.* 20·7), oleic acid (*c.* 29). The spreading pressures vary somewhat with temperature and with the purity of the oil; if the polar group in the oil molecule is acidic, the spreading pressure increases very much with increasing p_H; the above figures should not be taken as exact standards. Any desired spreading pressure less than that of the pure oil may be obtained by diluting the spreading oil with medicinal paraffin or some other non-spreading oil.[4]

The films may be transferred to the plate either on entering the water only, in which case it is termed an 'X'-film or 'X'-deposition, or on both entering and leaving ('Y'-deposition), or on leaving only ('Z'-deposition). Langmuir[5] and Bikerman[6] have pointed out that the deposition is dependent on the contact angle between the solid and the film-covered water surface. If the surface has the advancing and receding angles obtuse, 'X'-deposition only occurs; if the advancing angle is obtuse and the receding angle acute, 'Y'-deposition takes place; while 'Z'-deposition (which is rather uncommon) requires that both angles should be acute. This is because the water surface folds down naturally on to the solid, on entering only if the contact angle is obtuse, and on leaving only if the

[1] *Trans. Faraday Soc.*, **15**, 68.

[2] *J.A.C.S.* (1934), 495; (1935), 1007.

[3] Valuable reviews on multilayers may be found in Langmuir's Pilgrim Trust Lecture, *Proc. Roy. Soc.* A, **170**, 1 (1939); and Schulman, *Ann. Rep. Chem. Soc.* (1940), 103 ff.

[4] Adam, *Proc. Roy. Soc.* B, **122**, 134 (1937); A. Norris and T. W. J. Taylor, *J.C.S.* (1938), 1719.

[5] *Proc. Roy. Soc.* A, **170**, 22 (1939).

[6] *Ibid.* **170**, 130 (1939); *Trans. Faraday Soc.* (1940), 415.

angle is acute, as can easily be verified by a diagram. Since the hydrophobic end of the monolayer is uppermost, one would expect the polar groups in 'X'-deposited films to be outwards; in fact, however, these surfaces are not hydrophilic, but show almost the same contact angles to water as 'Y'-deposited films. It appears that the surface layer of molecules turns over soon after deposition. By increasing the surface pressure on the monolayer, a substance which deposits 'X' fashion at lower pressures may deposit 'Y' fashion, on both entering and leaving the water, because the higher surface pressure (or lower surface tension) lowers the contact angle for a given work of adhesion between solid and liquid.

The area of the monolayer which is removed from the water is equal to the apparent, not the real, area of the solid surface; the films appear to stretch across any small grooves or even holes in the solid; and if a fine wire gauze is dipped the area of the film deposited is equal to the size of the piece of gauze, not to the actual area of the wires forming it.

The composition of the films deposited,[1] in the case of fatty acids on water, is pure fatty acid if the solution is rather strongly acid, and soap, almost always the soap of a divalent metal (present in traces in the water), if the solution is fairly alkaline. At intermediate acidities the films consist of various proportions of acid and divalent soap; the presence of potassium and sodium salts also influences the composition of the films.

If such a mixed film, of soap and free acid, is treated with benzene or alcohol, the acid is dissolved out, but the film retains its original thickness within 1 per cent., even when the acid is as much as 60 per cent. of the original film. The voids in such 'skeleton' films may be filled by other liquids, and the refractive index of the film may be very greatly varied, by simple removal of the free acid, or by replacing it with other substances. By a suitable choice of refractive index and thickness of films deposited on glass the glass may be made non-reflecting, a great advantage for glazed instruments which may have to be read in a strong light. It is even possible to render the pores in a skeleton multilayer hydrophilic, by treatment with solutions of powerful wetting agents; water and aqueous solutions can thus be made to enter the film.

Very beautiful colour effects can be obtained, especially in polarized light, by coating a glass, or better a chromium plated, surface with different numbers of layers in different parts. The thickness of the films can be measured, by an interferometer or other optical means, using monochromatic light; the thickness of the unit films of the multilayer determined in this way agrees fairly well with the spacings determined by X-ray diffraction, perpendicular to the surface. If a sufficiently large number of films are deposited (there is no difficulty in depositing several thousand monolayers), the thickness may be measured by ordinary mechanical means; Astbury and others have even obtained a rough measurement with an ordinary screw micrometer.[2]

[1] Langmuir and V. J. Schaefer, *J.A.C.S.* (1936), 284.

[2] *Nature*, **142**, 33 (1938).

Electron[1] and X-ray[2] diffraction studies show that the films are crystalline, and very similar to the crystalline layers formed parallel to the surface, when long-chain aliphatic substances are melted and solidified on glass, after they have been deposited some time. Stenhagen finds that films of esters take time to become crystalline, this time decreasing, as with annealing processes in other forms of matter, with increasing temperature. The monolayers on water are not usually crystalline, so that one would expect only the X-ray or electron diffraction lines indicative of the spacing perpendicular to the surface, or along the length of the molecules, if these are not perpendicular, to appear until some rearrangement has occurred; but there is no doubt that, after some time, microcrystals appear, similar to crystals of the substances obtained in other ways. The microcrystals have not always exactly the same characteristics as any known crystalline form obtained in other ways; e.g. the crystals of stearic acid in the multilayer were shown by electron diffraction to be monoclinic, like other stearic acid crystals, but the angle β was not the same. Once crystallized, the microcrystals may extend as single crystals right through a multilayer of about 1,000 molecules thick.

Electron diffraction has the advantage over X-rays that it can reveal a good deal about the structure even of a monolayer on the surface. The *first* layers of barium stearate and stearic acid had the molecules approximately perpendicular to the glass, but there appeared to be no other regularity in arrangement. Two or more layers showed a hexagonal symmetry, the molecules remaining perpendicular, with barium stearate; with stearic acid the molecules were tilted, their long axes apparently lying in the plane formed by the normal to the surface and the direction of dipping.

The structure of the films seems to depend little on whether they are 'X' or 'Y' deposited; the pattern repeats itself perpendicular to the surface at every two layers, if the polar group is at, or very near, the end of the molecule; and at every layer, with esters in which the polar group is not very near the end of the molecule, just as in crystals formed by other means. This probably involves the turning over of the molecules in whole layers, a process which is not as astonishing as may seem at first sight, for if the film is first deposited with the polar groups remote from those of the next layer, any molecules which happen, in the course of thermal vibrations, to permit their polar end groups to approach near the end group of molecules in the next layer, will naturally remain inverted, and the overturning will take place molecule by molecule, not all at once.

Surface molecules with their polar groups buried are called 'endotropic', this is the normal stable position. Such surfaces have little reactivity or adsorptive power. Multilayer surfaces may be 'conditioned', the top

[1] L. H. Germer and K. H. Storks, *J. Chem. Phys.* (1938), 280.

[2] G. L. Clark and P. W. Leppla, *J.A.C.S.* (1936), 2199; Holley, *Physical Rev.*, **53**, 534 (1938); I. Fankuchen, *ibid.*, **53**, 909; E. Stenhagen, *Trans. Faraday Soc.* (1938), 1328; G. Knott, A. F. Wells, and J. H. Schulman, *Proc. Roy. Soc.* A, **176**, 534 (1940).

layer of molecules being probably turned over so as to become 'exotropic', with the polar groups outwards, by soaking in solutions of polyvalent metallic salts.[1] Such conditioned surfaces have a much greater adsorptive power, often rather specific, and very probably have the metallic ions incorporated in them, and a more open structure than an ordinary multi-layer surface. An unconditioned surface usually shows a large contact angle with water and a fairly large one even with oils; a surface conditioned with thorium, upon which a bile acid has been subsequently adsorbed, acquires zero contact angle with oils, while remaining strongly hydrophobic. Such a plate can adsorb hydrocarbon vapours, increasing in thickness; an unconditioned surface does not. These phenomena seem to indicate a considerable change in the structure of the multilayer, possibly extending far below the surface layer, and seem worthy of more detailed investigation.

While it appears true that, after some time, multilayers tend to crystallize in a manner similar to molten substances, many of their properties indicate that they can exist in much less stable states. The 'skeletonized' films have voids, amounting sometimes to about 50 per cent. of the volume, yet they retain their presumably sponge-like structure. Measurements of the surface potentials of multilayers give very varying results,[2] and the potentials change considerably with time; they appear to be mainly determined by ions entangled in the multilayers from the water, during deposition.

Multilayers of sterols,[3] chlorophyll,[4] and proteins[5] have also been built. Those of sterols show specific adsorptive powers for digitonin, according to the stereochemical configuration of the hydroxyl group; those of chlorophyll showed no fluorescence, although the quantity deposited was sufficient to give marked fluorescence in solution.

CHAPTER VII

Development of definite facets by oxidative attack of metals. Gwathmey and Benton have developed the technique of growing single crystals and cutting and polishing faces parallel to a natural crystal face.[6] The final polishing process consists in anodic treatment in a solution of phosphoric acid, and is claimed to produce a polished surface free from an amorphous or strained surface layer. When a spherical single crystal is superficially oxidized in air,[7] beautiful surface patterns develop, similar to those produced by etching reagents (p. 232); these consist of tiny facets, the principal ones being parallel to the (110) and (111) planes. These develop also in a hydrogen-oxygen mixture, and as they develop, so does

[1] Langmuir and Schaefer, *J.A.C.S.* (1937), 1406, 1762; Langmuir, *Science*, **87**, 493 (1938).
[2] Cf. R. W. Goranson and W. A. Zisman, *J. Chem. Phys.* (1939), 492.
[3] *J.A.C.S.* (1937), 1751.
[4] *Ibid.*, 2075.
[5] See the reviews cited on p. 399.
[6] *J. Physical Chem.* (1940), 35.
[7] *J. Chem. Physics* (1940), 431, 569.

the catalytic activity of the surface for combination of these gases increase. Ethylene-hydrogen mixtures develop neither these facets nor catalytic activity. The experiments so far reported are only preliminary, but their development seems likely to be of great interest. The action of oxygen on the copper surface rearranges the atoms to some considerable depth, to positions in which the chemical activity of the surface is much increased.

Existence of several types of surface with different specific catalytic properties. As mentioned on p. 33, Maxted, finding that certain poisons decrease the activity of platinum black in proportion to the amount of poison added, was inclined to doubt the conclusiveness of Vavon and Husson's proof that platinum black may possess several different types of surface, each capable of catalysing some type of hydrogenation. Russell and Loebenstein[1] find that nickel, deposited on quartz, is poisoned partially, probably by the deposition of carbon, when heated in methane, ethylene, or under certain conditions in a mixture of carbon dioxide and hydrogen. This treatment slows the rate of hydrogenation of carbon dioxide, at 315° C., to as little as one-third of the normal activity, which may be restored by heating in hydrogen, or, under different conditions, in carbon dioxide and hydrogen. The rate of hydrogenation of nitrous oxide is much less affected by these treatments, and the heating in hydrogen, which strongly activated the catalyst for hydrogenating carbon dioxide, in one instance actually slightly reduced the rate of hydrogenation of nitrous oxide. The poisoning effect of the carbon deposited was not proportional to the amount deposited, but the first portions decreased the activity very much more than later portions. It was tentatively suggested that an adsorbed layer of oxygen is formed during the hydrogenation of nitrous oxide, and that this oxygen-covered surface is the principal catalytic agent for hydrogenating nitrous oxide, but is a poison for the hydrogenation of carbon dioxide. The nickel can, however, perform such a great variety of functions that the phenomena are rather complicated, and the different reactions do not yet appear to have been nearly completely disentangled.

In an earlier paper[2] it is claimed that there is evidence for several different types of catalytic surface on copper used for hydrogenating ethylene. Oxygen is a poison for this reaction. If oxygen is admitted to an active copper catalyst, the hydrogenating power decreases linearly to zero, which does not afford evidence of heterogeneity. Poisoning by nitrous oxide produces little effect on the hydrogenating power until a certain amount of oxygen has been adsorbed, and then the catalytic activity is suppressed almost linearly. Partial removal of adsorbed oxygen by reduction in hydrogen makes it appear that small amounts of adsorbed oxygen have a much greater effect in suppressing hydrogenation than later portions; but it must be remembered that fresh catalytic surface may be formed during the reduction, so that the high activity of a surface

[1] *J.A.C.S.* (1940), 2573.

[2] Russell and Ghering, *J.A.C.S.* (1935), 2544.

from which most of the adsorbed oxygen has been removed may be actually greater than that of the surface before the oxygen was adsorbed.

H. S. Taylor[1] points out that a linear decrease in catalytic activity, with increasing amounts of poison, is not necessarily proof that the surface is homogeneous in all respects; it only shows that all parts of the surface adsorb this particular poison nearly equally.

A striking instance of the advantage of an unusual arrangement of atoms in a metal, for catalytic activity, is afforded by the 'Raney' nickel catalysts, formed by removing most of the aluminium from nickel-aluminium alloys. These have exceptional hydrogenating power. A. Taylor and J. Weiss[2] have shown, by X-ray studies, that provided more than about 5 per cent. of the aluminium remains in the alloy, the remaining metal, mostly nickel, retains some of the characteristics of the comparatively open spacing of the original alloy; it only collapses to the usual nickel structure when practically all the aluminium is removed. The high catalytic activity may be due either to a special spacing of the nickel atoms, or to a largely increased surface, possibly to both.

Metal films condensed in a high vacuum have, usually, a much lower catalytic activity than films condensed in a low pressure of an inert gas.[3] The films condensed in the gas had an oriented structure, with the (110) face parallel to the backing in the case of nickel, the (111) face in the case of iron. There was little, if any, definite orientation in the films condensed *in vacuo*. It has been suggested that the increased catalytic activity is, in part at least, due to the special spacing on the exposed crystal faces; but there may be other reasons, perhaps the presence of linear interfaces between the bare metal and the parts covered by adsorbed gas, or a larger real surface. The suggestion is interesting, however, and now that it is possible to make faces in selected crystal planes, to the practical exclusion of others, the study of the catalytic activity of special crystal faces does not seem beyond the bounds of possibility.

The mechanism of the catalytic ammonia synthesis. On p. 269 it was pointed out that studies of the exchange reactions between deuterium and hydrogen or ammonia proved that chemisorption of hydrogen occurs on the usual promoted iron catalysts, at room temperature or not far above. The hydrogen and deuterium are dissociated into atoms on the surface and are easily activated to replace each other. Nitrogen, however, is not nearly so easily dissociated and activated so that its atoms can exchange places. Joris and H. S. Taylor[4] have studied the exchange between molecules of the nitrogen isotopes of mass numbers 14 and 15,

$$^{15}N_2 + ^{14}N_2 = 2\,^{15}N^{14}N.$$

In the entire absence of hydrogen, equilibrium is reached very slowly,

[1] *12th Report on Catalysis* (John Wiley, 1940), 46.

[2] *Nature*, **141**, 1055 (1938).

[3] O. Beeck, A. Wheeler, and A. E. Smith, *Physical Rev.*, **55**, 601 (1939); *Proc. Roy. Soc.* A, **177**, 62 (1940).

[4] *J. Chem. Physics* (1939), 893.

many hours being required for even a slight conversion; the presence of hydrogen or some compound containing hydrogen greatly accelerates the exchange of isotopes. Here we find hydrogen acting as an assistant to the iron in its catalytic activity, a kind of gaseous 'promoter'.

Nitrogen, with its three valencies, can have each atom in its molecule separately linked to the iron substratum, by one or even two valency bonds, without the molecule being dissociated. If hydrogen is present and NH or NH_2 radicals are adsorbed, the attraction between the atoms in the nitrogen molecule will be much weakened or destroyed, so that each nitrogen atom is much more likely to be completely free from its original partner, and so be in a position either to enter into exchange reactions, or to form ammonia, than in the absence of another element capable of occupying one of the valencies. The velocity of decomposition or synthesis of ammonia is much greater than that of the exchange of nitrogen atoms. On tungsten the velocity is still slower, but hydrogen accelerates the reaction, as on iron.

The measurement of adsorption on solids. Several new techniques or refinements of older techniques have been described. H. M. Barrett and others[1] used a very delicate microbalance of quartz, mounted on a fine tungsten torsion wire, the adsorbent being contained in a light platinum pan. Changes of weight of the order 10^{-7} gramme could be measured. With this balance, powdered fused silica was found to adsorb very little water vapour, a pressure of 24 mm. being required to give a layer one molecule thick on the surface. A. King's sorption balance[2] has a container for the adsorbent mounted so as to float, hydrometer fashion, and any changes in weight are indicated by changes in the depth at which the hydrometer floats. With mercury as the floating liquid, a sensitivity of a few tenths of a milligramme is obtained; with oil the sensitivity is about 15 times as great. This instrument has the advantage that a large sample of the adsorbent can be used. The liquid floating the 'hydrometer' must, however, be maintained at an accurately constant temperature. An unusually delicate apparatus, measuring adsorption by the change in pressure in a gas space when the adsorption occurs, is due to Orr.[3]

Discontinuities in adsorption isotherms. Chambers and A. King[4] find discontinuities in the adsorption of carbon tetrachloride and water on charcoal, water on silica, water and ammonia on chabasite, and chloroform on chromic oxide. Sometimes several discontinuities were found during a pressure change of only 1 millimetre. Bangham and Mosallam[5] found, with carbon tetrachloride on mica, discontinuities, but at pressure intervals of many millimetres. These are probably of a different type, and it has been suggested that they correspond to the completion of molecular layers; but this is by no means certain yet. Barrer and Rideal[6] failed to find discontinuities in the adsorption of hydrogen on charcoal,

[1] *J.A.C.S.* (1940), 2839.
[2] *J.C.S.* (1939), 139; (1940), 160.
[3] *Proc. Roy. Soc.* A, **173,** 349 (1939).
[4] *J.C.S.* (1940), 156.
[5] *Proc. Roy. Soc.* A, **165,** 552 (1938).
[6] *Ibid.*, **149,** 247 (1935).

previously reported by other workers, and considered that these discontinuities disappeared if time was allowed for the attainment of equilibrium.

The cause of these discontinuities still seems obscure; the number of cases in which they have been found is too great for their attribution to experimental error, but it must be admitted that their detection does, at least in some cases, depend on the particular technique adopted in measuring the adsorption. A possible cause may be that cracks open up, suddenly exposing fresh areas for adsorption; if this is the explanation, the discontinuities would be scarcely likely to appear, at any rate at the same pressures, during gradual desorption of the gas.

Adsorption on mica and plane surfaces of salts. Much light has recently been thrown on the adsorption of non-polar gases and vapours on these surfaces by measurements extending from low pressures up to that at which condensation takes place.[1] Often, up to the point at which the first layer of molecules is complete, the curve of the amount adsorbed plotted vertically and pressure horizontally is concave downwards, roughly of the simple Langmuir form; though this is not always the case, oxygen on potassium chloride, for instance, giving a nearly linear curve, near the boiling-point. As the pressure is further increased, at first the adsorption (beyond the first layer) increases less rapidly than before, but as the condensation pressure is approached, the rate of increase of adsorption with pressure increases rapidly, finally extremely rapidly. In a few cases discontinuities, which may be connected with the completion of molecular layers, occur. Generally the amount which has to be adsorbed, after the completion of the first layer, indicates that bulk condensation takes place on these plane surfaces when not more than four or five layers are adsorbed.

After the first layer is complete, the heat of adsorption decreases, soon reaching a value not far different from the heat of condensation to bulk liquid. It seems likely that the field of force of the solid extends through very few molecular layers, so that after the first layer is complete, further condensation soon resembles bulk condensation fairly closely.

Adsorption on different forms of carbon. Study of the adsorption of oxygen and hydrogen on charcoals, graphite, and diamond[2] shows generally similar phenomena on all three allotropic forms of carbon; naturally the phenomena are more complicated on charcoal. Hydrogen and oxygen are held by van der Waals' adsorption at low temperatures, and by chemisorption at higher temperatures; the chemisorption appears to be slow, and the energy of activation, whether activation of the actual adsorption process or of diffusion to other parts of the surface, of hydrogen increases considerably on a graphite surface as the surface becomes more

[1] See especially Bangham and Mosallam, *Proc. Roy. Soc.* A, **165**, 552; **166**, 558 (1938); Orr, *ibid.*, **173**, 349 (1939). For mathematical theory, see Roberts and Orr, *Trans. Faraday Soc.* (1938), 1346.

[2] Barrer and Rideal, *Proc. Roy. Soc.* A, **149**, 231; Barrer, *ibid.*, **149**, 253 (1935); *J.C.S.* (1936), 1256, 1261.

completely covered. With diamond, the energy of activation for chemisorption of hydrogen varies little with progressive covering of the surface; this difference is interpreted as indicating a more homogeneous surface on diamond than on graphite. Hydrogen is probably held to the surface by a typical covalent C—H bond; and on charcoal a certain amount of methane is formed. Above 240° C. oxides of carbon are formed with oxygen on diamond, at first in small amounts, though rapidly; the amount increases with rising temperature. An adsorbed film of oxygen prevents, i.e. poisons, the adsorption of hydrogen.

CHAPTER VIII

Measurement of the ζ potential by means other than electrokinetic measurement. G. S. Hartley and J. W. Roe[1] point out that the ζ potential determines the distribution of ions near a surface in the same manner as the potential just outside an ion controls the ionic atmosphere in the Debye-Huckel theory of strong electrolytes. There is a simple relation between the concentration of an ion in the layer next to a surface and in the bulk solution at a distance from the surface and the ζ potential, so that if a means can be found of measuring the concentration of an ion in the surface and in the solution, it should be possible to estimate the ζ potential of that surface.

The work gained in bringing a hydrogen ion from the interior of a solution to the surface is $-\epsilon\zeta$. Hence, by the Boltzmann relation,

$$\frac{c_{\mathrm{H}'}^{\mathrm{surface}}}{c_{\mathrm{H}'}^{\mathrm{solution}}} = e^{-\epsilon\zeta/kT}, \tag{1}$$

$$-\log_{10} c_{\mathrm{H}'}^{\mathrm{surface}} = -\log_{10} c_{\mathrm{H}'}^{\mathrm{solution}} + \frac{\epsilon}{2{\cdot}303kT}\zeta.$$

$\frac{2{\cdot}303kT}{\epsilon}$ is, however, the well-known factor of electrochemistry, $\frac{2{\cdot}303RT}{\mathfrak{F}}$, 0·0591 at 25° C. Therefore, at 25° C.,

$$(p_{\mathrm{H}})_{\mathrm{surface}} = (p_{\mathrm{H}})_{\mathrm{solution}} + \frac{\zeta}{0{\cdot}0591}. \tag{1.1}$$

Indicators, if their ionizable groups are present almost exclusively at the surface, and if the colour and optical density of both forms are unaffected by this adsorption, may be used for determining the p_{H} at the surface. Using the triethanolamine salt of cetane sulphonic acid, the p_{H} at the surface of the micelles was found colorimetrically by diphenylazo-*o*-nitrophenol. *p*-nitrophenol was employed to find the p_{H} in the solution; curiously it was more difficult to find a suitable indicator for the bulk than for the surface p_{H}, since almost all indicators are more or less adsorbed at the surface of these paraffin chain salts. Preliminary experi-

[1] *Trans. Faraday Soc.* (1940), 101.

ments showed agreement to a few millivolts between the value of ζ deduced from equation (1.1) and from electrokinetic observations on cetane sulphonates. It is more difficult to see how the p_H could be measured at a surface which could not be repeated very many times, as with a colloidal solution, in a reasonable depth of water.

An attempt to find ζ potentials by measuring the effect of salt additions on the potential difference across an interface has been made by de Bruyn.[1] According to Stern's theory, the double layer in the water consists of a tightly adsorbed part, and a diffuse part, the diffuse part only contributing to the potential. Under conditions when the area of the surface and the adsorptive capacity are very large, addition of salt to the solution need not change any part of the total potential across the interface except that due to the diffuse part of the double layer. The change in potential difference across the interface then equals the change in the ζ potential, and the latter can be measured. Full details are not yet available.

Adsorption and oil-water potentials. Dean, Gatty, and Rideal[2] discuss the thermodynamics and the mechanism of the establishment of interfacial potential differences by the adsorption of ions, or by the adsorption or spreading of a film containing dipoles. They show that, *provided that one or more of the charged components can pass the phase boundary and come into equilibrium on both sides*, the adsorption of the interfacial film will not by itself change the phase boundary potential. For the electrochemical potentials of those charged components which can pass the boundary are equal, at equilibrium, in the two phases, i.e.

$$\bar{\mu}_i^\alpha = \mu_i^\alpha + z_i \mathfrak{F}\phi^\alpha = \mu_i^\beta + z_i \mathfrak{F}\phi^\beta = \bar{\mu}_i^\beta. \tag{2}$$

Unless there is appreciable alteration in the concentrations of ions, or electrons, on the two sides of the interface, so that the chemical potentials μ_i are changed, there will be no change in the potential difference $\phi^\alpha - \phi^\beta$ between α and β. If any change in interfacial potential occurs, after true equilibrium is reached, this must be due not to the dipole moment of the adsorbed film, but to a change in the ratio of the activities of at least one ion in the two phases; $\log a_i^\alpha/a_i^\beta$ must be appreciably altered as a result of the presence of that substance which is adsorbed, a_i being the activity of i. The amount adsorbed is rarely sufficient to make much difference to the concentration or activity in a bulk phase, except when the surface is of very large extent and the bulk phases small.

This does not invalidate the theory whereby potentials are set up by the passage of very small amounts of one charged component from one phase to another which, before the transfer, contained none of that charged component. In such a case the activity of that charged component is raised from zero to a finite, if small, quantity, and the chemical potential, and consequently the electrical potential difference, by (2), is altered by the passage of this small quantity across the interface.

[1] See Kruyt and Overbeek, *Trans. Faraday Soc.* (1940), 112.

[2] *Trans. Faraday Soc.* (1940), 161, 166, 173.

A *temporary* change in the phase boundary potential can, however, occur through adsorption or spreading of an insoluble monolayer. The orientation of the dipoles adsorbed is a very rapid process, but the passage of ions across the boundary, or in some cases the rearrangement of ions already present on the opposite side to that at which adsorption takes place, takes time, sometimes several minutes. Dean finds experimentally that spreading a protein film between various organic liquids and water, or treating an already spread albumen film with tannic acid, changes the interfacial potential by up to 40 millivolts, this change decaying to 1/*e*th of its maximum value in times varying from a second or two up to 30 minutes. There is a rough correlation between the duration of these temporary adsorption potentials and the electrical resistance of the organic liquid, i.e. with the permeability of this liquid to ions.

There are cases, however, including the very common one of an air-water surface, where no ions can possibly pass the boundary; thermodynamical equilibrium cannot therefore be set up between the water and air, and adsorption potentials (the surface potentials of Chapters II and III) are permanent. The usual method for measuring surface potentials with a radioactive air-electrode does not appreciably disturb the adsorption potentials; the gaseous ions are very few and are attracted into the water by image forces so that no double layer, compensating the double layer in the water due to the dipoles of the molecules in the surface film, can build up in the air.

CHAPTER IX

The mechanism of detachment of drops, and other rapidly changing surface phenomena. Hauser and others,[1] using a high-speed camera, show that the secondary small drop, formed when the long neck to which the upper part of a falling drop is drawn out breaks up, often consists of several droplets. The precise details vary with different liquids and are very complex. The oscillations of drops, or thin laminae of liquids, may be followed by high-speed cinematography, thus suggesting new methods of determining the dynamic surface tension; but so far few measurements are available.

A new dynamic method. Bond[2] caused two fine vertical jets of water, one moving up, the other down, to collide centrally, so that the water spreads out to a thin and nearly horizontal sheet. The surface tension can be calculated from the diameter of this sheet; the theory is naturally complicated. Puls[3] has applied the same method to mercury. The results on water appear accurate within 0·5 per cent., or better, and on mercury to agree with the best results available.

[1] *J. Physical Chem.* (1936), 973.
[2] *Proc. Physical Soc.*, **47**, 549 (1935).
[3] *Phil. Mag.*, **22**, 970 (1936).

SUBJECT INDEX

INDEX OF NAMES